INDUSTRIAL LOCOMOTIVES

including preserved and
minor railway locomotives

Now includes locomotive index

HANDBOOK
15EL

60th Anniversary   1949 to 2009

INDUSTRIAL RAILWAY SOCIETY
www.irsociety.co.uk

Published by the INDUSTRIAL RAILWAY SOCIETY
at 24 Dulverton Road, Melton Mowbray, Leicestershire, LE13 0SF

© INDUSTRIAL RAILWAY SOCIETY 2009

ISBN 978 1 901556 53 7   (hardbound)

ISBN 978 1 901556 54 4   (softbound)

British Library Cataloguing-in-Publication Data
A catalogue record for this book is available from the British Library

Visit the Society at   www.irsociety.co.uk

The content of this book is based on records created on behalf of the Industrial Railway Society by Eric Hackett, assisted by George Morton. These records have now been updated by Colin Billinghurst, assisted by Ian Bendall, John Beechey, Adrian Booth, Bob Darvill, Ted Knotwell and Mick Morgan.

The Society obtains information from a wide variety of sources, but primarily from reports of visits and other observations submitted by our readership, both members and non-members, plus some information kindly supplied by locomotive manufacturers, repairers, owners and operators. The publishers are extremely grateful for all this essential co-operation, without which production of our Handbooks would be impossible. All readers are encouraged to submit data, correctional, additional, or confirmatory, to the most seemingly appropriate Assistant Records Officer (see list on page 5) or by email to hist.records@irsociety.co.uk

Production co-ordinated by Ian Bendall
Final content draft prepared by Colin Billinghurst

The photographs are all from the collection of the late Malcolm Ainsworth. Malcolm was a member for many years and for several years was Hon. Visits Officer. Upon his death his collection was kindly donated to the Society and many of the photographs illustrated in this book were taken during Society visits, which Malcolm had organised on our behalf.
The photographs were prepared for publication by Dave Marden.

Distributed by IRS Publications, 24 Dulverton Road, Melton Mowbray, Leicestershire, LE13 0SF

Produced for the IRS by Print Rite, Witney, Oxon. 01993 881662.

CONTENTS

Cover Photographs

Front   Hunslet 60 tonne flameproof locomotive - Bluebird hauling 45 and 100 tonne Fuel Tanker wagons on hire at ExxonMobil Oil Refinery, Fawley on Southampton Water.

Rear   Hunslet Modernized 75 tonne Steelman Locomotive hauling Freightliner Heavy Haul Cement Wagons at Buxton Lime Industries, Tunstead Quarry.

The text of this book incorporates all amendments notified before 1st November 2008

INDUSTRIAL RAILWAY SOCIETY

This book has been produced by the INDUSTRIAL RAILWAY SOCIETY
which was founded in 1949 as the
Birmingham Locomotive Club, Industrial Locomotive Information Section

The Society caters for those interested in privately owned locomotives and railways. Members receive the INDUSTRIAL RAILWAY RECORD in addition to regular bulletins containing topical news and update amendments to Society-produced Handbooks. Access is available to a well stocked library and visits are arranged to industrial railways, etc.

If you are interested in industrial railways why not join the Society now.

Further details can be obtained by sending two first class stamps to
B. Mettam, 27 Glenfield Crescent, Newbold, Chesterfield, S41 8SF

or visit the Society website at **www.irsociety.co.uk**

INDUSTRIAL RAILWAY RECORD

This profusely illustrated magazine contains articles of lasting interest concerning a wide variety of industrial locomotives and railways of all gauges, at home and abroad. Accurate line drawings of locomotives and rolling stock, together with carefully prepared maps, are a regular feature.

The INDUSTRIAL RAILWAY RECORD is available to non-members by direct subscription. Enquiries regarding subscriptions and back numbers should be sent with two first class stamps to :
S.C. Robinson, 47 Waverley Gardens, London NW10 7EE

COUNTY HANDBOOK SERIES

Apart from "Handbook EL", the Society produces a range of volumes which record all known past and present locomotives in particular areas, with descriptions of the railways and the industries served. These Handbooks include a good range of maps, and a selection of photographs. Issues currently available (softback or hardback binding) are as follows. Prices include postage & packing.
London – 232 pages, 80 photographs and 24 maps
 £19.95 hardbound; £16.95 softbound
Mid & South Glamorgan – 384 pages with 95 photos and 37 maps
 £24.95 hardbound; £19.95 softbound
Herts & Middlesex – 408 pages with 65 photos and 37 maps
 £24.95 hardbound; £19.95 softbound
Buckinghamshire, Bedfordshire & Northamptonshire – 464 pages with 92 photos
 and 41 pages of maps - £24.95 hardbound; £19.95 softbound
Nottinghamshire – 432 pages with 95 photographs and 23 pages of maps –
 £24.95 hardbound; £19.95 softbound
Gwent ("Greater Monmouthshire" in fact) – 400 pages, 80 photographs, and
 24 pages of maps – £24.95 hardbound; £19.95 softbound

West Glamorgan, Dyfed & Powys North Staffordshire, South Staffordshire and North Wales are also available, please enquire for details, availability and prices.

The Railway Products of Baguley Drewry Ltd of Burton on Trent
This 372 page book (273mm by 210mm format) is the definitive history of this important builder. Hardbound with dust jacket and printed on high quality paper - **£29.99 (plus £5 postage)**

Orders to IRS Sales, 24 Dulverton Road, Melton Mowbray, LE13 0SF
Add 10% postage & packing if ordering a County Handbook.

FOREWORD to the 15th EDITION

This is the 15th in a line of EL (Existing Locomotive information as opposed to historical) Handbooks, which commenced publication in 1968. The lists include all known existing locomotives of 1ft 3in gauge and above, but excluding the Capital Stock of London Transport and the Train Operating Companies (ex British Railways). In addition, several significant monorail locomotives are also listed.

The lists are in accordance with our records for November 1st, 2008. We wish to stress that the majority of the information derives from the observations and researches of both members and other readers. We shall always rely on similar enthusiastic support to keep all the records up to date, so please send your observations (and your queries also) to whoever you judge to be the most appropriate Hon. Assistant Records Officer selected from the list below.

Or email our sorting office at hist.records@irsociety.co.uk

All relevant information received is subsequently distributed to members of the Industrial Railway Society by means of regular Bulletins, thus enabling the reader to keep this book up to date.

All historical matters

plus all matters UK Coal Industry
R.D. Darvill   (Asst. Hon. Records Officer),
119 Bath Street
Rugby
Warwickshire CV21 3JA

Current Observations
I.R. Bendall   (Asst. Hon. Records Officer)
46 Orson Drive
Wigston
Leicestershire LE18 2EJ

**Network Rail and related Contractors
(inc. former B.R. Departmental Stock)**
E.W. Knotwell   (Asst. Hon. Records Officer)
4 Fernbrook Drive
Harrow
Middlesex HA2 7EB

BR Locos used in Industry
A.J. Booth   (Asst. Hon. Records Officer)
13 Trinity Avenue
Bridlington
East Yorkshire YO15 2HD

Mining & Tunnelling Contractors Locos
J. Beechey   (Asst. Hon. Records Officer)
1669 Melton Road
East Goscote
Leicestershire   LE7 4YQ

**Ministry of Defence Locomotives
(Current and Historical)**
C. Billinghurst   (Asst. Hon. Records Officer)
70 Welch Road
Gosport
Hampshire PO12 4PZ

Preservation (Current & Historical)
M. Morgan   (Asst. Hon. Records Officer)
29 Groby Road
Ratby
Leicestershire   LE6 0LJ

Hon. Records Officer
R. Waywell
29 Caldbeck Close
Gunthorpe
Peterborough   PE4 7NE

Ireland–A. Waldron (Asst. Hon. Records Officer) 54 Middlebrook Drive, Lostock, Bolton. BL6 4RH

The Society also has the following contacts who collate information which is appropriate to the industrial railway scene but not normally documented in this volume –

Systems & Rolling Stock Records - David Monk-Steel, 15 Chelwood Walk, York YO26 4UH

Industrial Rail Cranes – David Monk-Steel (address above)

Industrial Railway Modelling – Jeff Sanders, 4 Unwin Place, Stevenage, Herts. SG2 9SX

INTRODUCTION

Within the main Country Sections of this book, information is presented in a similar format to that used in previous editions, with locomotives listed under owners' titles arranged alphabetically, within sub-groups of Industrial and Preservation Sites. Within these sub-groups, each location is sequenced alphabetically, using its main title, or surname if a person's name is included.

LOCATION HEADINGS include both National Grid References and postcodes where known, and details of missing grid references and/or postcodes will be most welcome.

Postcodes and Grid References are particularly useful for readers with Internet access, as either code can be requested at one of the free mapping sites (such as www.steetmap.co.uk or http://www.multimap.com) to obtain a printable map of the precise location of the railway site.

In general, we try to fix the Grid Reference/s to indicate the locomotive shed or stabling point, particularly at the larger sites.

DIVISION OF COUNTRIES. In recent years there have been a number of reorganisations of the Administrative Areas in England, Scotland and Wales, in some cases the traditional "geographic counties" having been re-mapped and divided to create small independent areas now administered by Unitary Authorities of one sort or another. In order to avoid fragmenting our listing data, in this edition we have amalgamated some listings under headings of their "most recent" larger-landmass titles (many of which are still in current use for certain administrative purposes).

In the case of Scotland, Wales and Northern Ireland, which have relatively few locomotive locations, we have listed the entries on a land area basis and have extended the location titles. The boundaries of the land areas have been selected to coincide with the coverage of books in our companion "Historic Handbook" series.

LOCOMOTIVES AT SCRAPYARDS purely for scrapping are not generally listed, unless they have been 'resident' for a year or more. Those at dealers' yards are, however, listed in order that readers can keep a full picture of their movements.

CONTRACTORS' LOCOMOTIVES can be found on sites in all parts of the country, working on sewer and tunnel schemes, etc. The locomotives of such firms are shown, in the usual way, in the list of the County in which the firm's plant depot (or main plant depot if more than one is in use) is situated. A list of such Contractors and Plant Hire specialists, and their relevant base counties, appears later in this Introduction, following the table listing Locomotive Builders.

HIRE FLEET OPERATORS. A small number of firms maintain a fleet of locomotives which are hired out to both Industrial Sites and Main-line Train Operating (TOC) Companies. The principal firms involved are listed on page 22. Within the listings of these fleet-owners, we detail their full fleet (in so far as we know it) under an entry only if they have an operational base. Such locos may also be listed at their current locations.

LOCATIONS THAT ARE CLOSED, but where locomotives are still present, are indicated either by "(Closed)" appearing beside their title or subtitle, or else in a line of text immediately beneath that title. When a location is still in operation but no longer uses rail traffic, although the locomotives remain onsite, this is indicated by "R.T.C." after the gauge concerned. The letters RTC are an abbreviation of the phrase "Rail Traffic Ceased".

TRACK GAUGE. The gauge(s) of the railway system(s) are given at the head of the locomotive list(s). At preservation sites and museums, etc, where several gauges differ by only a small fraction they are usually all listed under the nominal gauge of the majority.

SEQUENCE OF LOCOS WITHIN THE LISTS is generally in accordance with our basic formula of "list steam first, followed by non-steam", and, in each of these groups, "list ex-mainline locos first in main-line running number order, followed by non-mainline locos in builder/works number order". Permanent-way motorised trolleys, and other miscellaneous units, are usually relegated to the end of the lists. However, in some cases, the nature or details of the actual fleet dictates a different arrangement of listing.

LOCOMOTIVE NUMBER and NAME. The title of the locomotive - number, name or both - is given in the first two columns. A name unofficially bestowed and used by staff but not carried on the loco is indicated by quotes (inverted commas " "). Locomotives under renovation at preservation sites, etc, may not currently carry their intended title; nevertheless these are shown unless it is definitely known that the name will not be retained.

Ex British Railways / Train Operating Company / Leasing Company (ROSCO) locomotives are further identified by the inclusion of formerly carried numbers in brackets even if not carried now.

TYPE The type of locomotive is given in column three.

The Whyte system of wheel classification is used in the main, but when driving wheels are connected not by outside rods but by chains or other means (as in various 'Sentinel' steam locos and diesel locos) they are shown as 4w (four-wheeled), 6w (six-wheeled), or if only one axle is motorised it is shown as 2w-2.

Trapped Rail System locomotives are shown using wheel type "ad" (meaning "axles driven") – thus "3ad" indicates a loco which may have 3 or more axles, but only 3 are driven.

For ex British Railways / Train Operating Company / Leasing Company (ROSCO) diesel and electric locomotives, the usual development of the Continental notation is used.

The following abbreviations are used :-

CT	Crane Tank - a T type loco fitted with load lifting apparatus
F	Fireless steam locomotive
IST	Inverted Saddle Tank
PT	Pannier Tank - side tanks not fastened to the frame
ST	Saddle Tank
STT	Saddle Tank with Tender
T	side Tank or similar - a tank positioned externally and fastened to the frame
VB	Vertical Boilered locomotive
WT	Well Tank - a tank located between the frames under the boiler
BE	Battery powered Electric locomotive
BH	Battery powered electric locomotive - Hydraulic transmission
CE	Conduit powered Electric locomotive
D	Diesel locomotive - unknown transmission
DC	Diesel locomotive - Compressed air transmission
DE	Diesel locomotive - Electrical transmission
DH	Diesel locomotive - Hydraulic transmission
DM	Diesel locomotive - Mechanical transmission
F	(as a suffix, for example BEF, DMF) – Flameproof (see following paragraph)
FE	Flywheel Electric locomotive
GTE	Gas Turbine Electric locomotive
P	Petrol or Paraffin locomotive - unknown transmission
PE	Petrol or Paraffin locomotive - Electrical transmission
PH	Petrol or Paraffin locomotive - Hydraulic transmission
PM	Petrol or Paraffin locomotive - Mechanical transmission
R	Railcar - a vehicle primarily designed to carry passengers
RE	third Rail powered Electric locomotive
WE	overhead Wire powered Electric locomotive

FLAMEPROOF locomotives, usually battery but sometimes diesel powered, are denoted by the addition of the letter **F** to the wheel arrangement in column three.

CYLINDER POSITION is shown in column four for steam locomotives.

In each case, a prefix numeral (**3, 4, etc**) denotes more than the usual two cylinders.

IC	Inside cylinders
OC	Outside cylinders
VC	Vertical cylinders
G	Geared transmission - suffixed to IC, OC or VC

RACK DRIVE. Certain locomotives are fitted with rack-drive equipment to enable them to climb steep inclines; and were mainly developed for underground use in coal mines. The pattern of rack used was the "Abt" design. Locos that were built with (and are thought to still retain) this equipment are indicated by the word **RACK** in column four. However, due to contraction of the coal industry, such locos have often been transferred to sites where the rack equipment is no longer in use.

ROAD/RAIL. Certain locomotives are capable of working on either rail or road, many being of either Unilok or Unimog manufacture. These are indicated by **R/R** in column four.

STEAM OUTLINE. Non-steam locomotives, with a steam locomotive appearance added, are shown by **s/o** in column four.

MAKERS. The builder of the locomotive is shown in column five; the abbreviations used are listed on pages 10 to 21.

MAKERS NUMBER and DATE. The sixth column shows the works number, the next column the date which appears on the plate, or the date the loco was built if none appears on the plate.

DOUBTFUL INFORMATION. Information known to be doubtful is denoted as such by the wording, or printed in brackets with a question mark. Thus, Wkm (7573 ?) 1956 denotes that the loco is a Wickham built in 1956, and possibly of the works number 7573.

MISCELLANEOUS NOTES.

c	denotes circa, i.e. about the time of the date quoted
Dsm	indicates a "long-term" dismantled locomotive (as an aid to photographers, etc)
	Note: battery locos not carrying a battery are not regarded as Dsm
DsmT	used for motorised trollies which have been converted to engineless trailers
Pvd	denotes Preserved on site
reb	denotes the locomotive was rebuilt (by, and when, as per list)
	Note: "rebuilt" infers significant alteration to transmission or appearance; not a routine overhaul no matter how thorough that may have been
rep	indicates a major repair, and is ONLY detailed in the listings when a "repair plate" is (or was) affixed to the loco (and thus an aid to identification).
OOU	"Out Of Use" - indicates a locomotive which has, apparently permanently or at least for a significant period of time, ceased work

There are cases where all locomotives at a site are OOU but the railway, siding etc, is still in use, utilising a road tractor, cable-haulage or man-power for example.

Electric locomotives at steelworks and colliery sites are usually to be found working at Coke Ovens, the grid reference for the Ovens being shown in the usual place, when known.

HINTS ON RECORDING OBSERVATIONS

As already explained, the Society is largely reliant on the observations of enthusiasts to keep the records up to date, and we are always pleased to receive reports of visits, which should be sent to the Hon. Records Officer or his assistants. The following will, we hope, be of assistance to those sending in reports.

Report anything you see. With regard to locomotives this means reporting locos present, even if there is no change to the published list. Someone else may visit in the next six months and find a change, the date of which can then be narrowed down to this six months. In addition to locos, details of rolling stock, track layouts, and items of historical information gleaned, are all welcome and will be added to our "Historic Handbook" files. It is surprising how often these items are required later by other enthusiasts. There is nothing to beat a note made on the spot; a note now is far better than trying to get the information from the recollection of employees in five years time.

Care should always be taken to distinguish actual observation from personal inference. If you see a 4wDH with worksplate say S 10019 and numbered 19, all well and good; but if it does not carry a worksplate, that fact should be stated. You may infer the loco is S 10019 from the running number, or by reference to this Handbook. If you say 'number on bonnet', 'number on cabside' or 'loco assumed to be S 10019' as the case may be, we will know the position precisely, which is important when bonnets are exchanged or cabs rebuilt, for example. If a loco carries no identification, you will probably be able to guess its make from design features, and a note of livery may help. Also with diesel locomotives, a note should be made of the make of its engine, its type or model, and its serial number, if these can be obtained. "Anonymous" locos can often be positively identified, from our records, given such details.

A thorough search of all premises is worthwhile, as locos (particularly if OOU) are frequently hidden away - and how often have surprises turned up in this way. Further, if you search diligently and a loco is missing, it may be presumed to have gone and enquiries can be made, as to where it has gone or if it has been scrapped. Please try to ascertain such information from the staff. Similarly, in the case of new arrivals, exact dates of arrival should always be obtained if possible.

Firms' titles change from time to time, so please check from the office or board at the entrance. Subsidiary companies frequently display the title of a parent company, but we always use the name under which the company trades, i.e. the subsidiary where such exists.

It goes without saying that it is essential to obtain permission to enter premises to see locomotives, and this applies with equal force to 'preserved' locations other than public parks and museums. Established systems which operate trains or have 'Open Days' will usually permit inspection of locos by arrangement.

Locos shown as at private homes or farms are very often in storage or in the course of restoration and, as a rule, our members and readers are strongly advised to NOT, in any way possible, embarrass the owners by writing for permission to view, but rather to wait until the owners announce that their machines are available for inspection.

You may note that whilst we list details of all known existing locomotives, some appear under incomplete or imprecise heading titles. This is regrettable, but is entirely a direct consequence of a few individuals having ignored the advice given in the paragraph above.

Finally, please try to establish friendly relations with the firms visited, as we are only allowed access by their courtesy. Do not be a nuisance or hold up production, nor expose yourself to danger in any way, but show a healthy interest in the processes being carried out. In this way, not only you, but other enthusiasts also, will be welcome there at a later date.

BUILDERS and REBUILDERS of LOCOMOTIVES

A

A&O	Alldays & Onions Ltd, Birmingham
AB	Andrew Barclay, Sons & Co Ltd, Caledonia Works, Kilmarnock, Ayrshire
ABG	Andrew Barclay Locomotives, Graycar Industrial Estate, Barton-under-Needwood, Staffordshire.
	(A Division of LH Group Services Ltd)
ACCars	A.C.Cars Ltd, Thames Ditton, Surrey
Acton	Acton Works, Acton, Greater London
	London Transport Executive / London Underground Ltd (from /1987)
AE	Avonside Engine Co Ltd, Fishponds, Bristol
AEC	Associated Equipment Co Ltd, Southall, Middlesex
AEG	Allgemeine Elektrizitäts Gesellschaft, Berlin-Hennigsdorf, Germany
AEI	Associated Electrical Industries Ltd, Trafford Park, Greater Manchester
AFB	Société Anglo Franco-Belge des Ateliers de la Croyère, Seneffe et Godarville,
	Belgium
Afd	Ashford Works, Kent
	South Eastern & Chatham Railway / Southern Railway / British Railways
AH	A. Horlock & Co, North Fleet Iron Works, Kent
AK	Alan Keef Ltd, Cote Farm, Cote, near Bampton, Oxfordshire,
	then Lea Line, Ross-on-Wye, Herefordshire, from 11/1986
	(successor to SMH)
Albion	Albion Ltd, Scotstoun Works, Glasgow
Alco	American Locomotive Co, USA; and/or Montreal, Canada
Alco(C)	American Locomotive Co, Cooke Works, Paterson, New Jersey, USA
ALR	Abbey Light Railway, P.N.Lowe & Sons, Bridge Road, Kirkstall, Leeds
AP	Aveling & Porter Ltd, Invicta Works, Rochester, Kent
ARC	Amalgamated Roadstone Corporation Ltd, Stanton Harcourt Depot,
	near Witney, Oxfordshire
Arrol	Sir William Arrol & Co Ltd, Parkhead Crane Works, Glasgow
Artisair	Artisair Ltd, Moorwell Road, Yaddlethorpe, Scunthorpe, Lincolnshire.
AS&W	Allied Steel & Wire Ltd, Castle Works, Cardiff
ASEA	Allmänna Svenska Elektriska AB, Västerås, Sweden
Ashford	Ashford Plant Depot, Newtown Road, Ashford, Kent (B.R./Balfour Beatty/Network Rail)
Atlas	Atlas Loco & Mfg Co Ltd, Cleveland, Ohio, U.S.A.
AtW	Atkinson Walker Wagons Ltd, Frenchwood Works, Preston, Lancashire
AUG	Werk '23 August', Bucharest, Romania
AW	Sir W.G.Armstrong, Whitworth & Co (Engineers) Ltd, Newcastle-upon-Tyne

B

B&S	Bellis & Seekings Ltd, Birmingham
Bance	R. Bance & Co.Ltd, Cockrow Hill House, St. Mary's Road, Surbiton, Surrey
Barlow	H.N. Barlow, Southport, Lancashire
Barnes	A. Barnes & Co, Albion Works, Rhyl, North Wales
	(a subsidiary of Rhyl Amusements Ltd)
BateJ	John L. H. Bate, Reigate, West Sussex
Battison	Samuel Battison, c/o Tathams Ltd, Nottingham Road, Ilkeston, Derbyshire
BBC(S)	AG Brown Boveri & Cie, Baden, Aargau, Switzerland
BBC(G)	AG Brown Boveri & Cie, Mannheim, Germany
BBT	Brush Bagnall Traction Ltd, Loughborough, Leicestershire; and Stafford
B(C)	Peter Brotherhood, Engineers, Chippenham, Wiltshire
BD	Baguley-Drewry Ltd, Burton-on-Trent, Staffordshire
BE	Brush Electrical Engineering Co Ltd, Loughborough, Leicestershire
Berwyn	Berwyn Engineering, Thickwood, Chippenham, Wiltshire
BES	Beech Engineering Services, Unit 4, Wetmore Industrial Estate, Wharf Road,
	Burton-on-Trent, Staffordshire
BEV	British Electric Vehicles Ltd, Chapeltown, Southport, Lancashire
	("BEV" branded locos were later built by Wingrove & Rogers – see "WR")

Bg	E.E. Baguley Ltd, Burton-on-Trent, Staffordshire
BgC	Baguley Cars Ltd, Shobnall Road Works, Burton-on-Trent, Staffordshire
Bg/DC	built by Bg for DC; makers numbers identical
BGB	Becorit (Mining) Ltd, Grove Street, Mansfield Woodhouse, Nottingham, then Hallam Fields Road, Ilkeston, Derbyshire from /1984
BH	Black, Hawthorn & Co Ltd, Gateshead
BIS	War Department, Arncott Workshops, Bicester Depot, Oxfordshire and including Ministry of Defence, Bicester Depot Workshops
BL	W.J. Bassett Lowke Ltd, Northampton
BLW	Baldwin Locomotive Works, Philadelphia, Pennsylvania, USA
BM	Brown, Marshalls & Co Ltd, Adderley Park, Birmingham (in 1902 became part of what later became Metropolitan-Cammell Ltd)
BMR	Brecon Mountain Railway Co Ltd, Pant, Mid Glamorgan
BnM	Bord na Mona (Irish Turf Board) : Various of the larger sites (e.g. Bl, Bo, Dg & M) have built their own locos & railcars – see Section 4 (Ireland)
Bonnymount	Mr Taylor, Bonnymount Farm, Siston Common, Bristol
BoothE	E. Booth, Lappa Valley Railway, St. Newlyn East, near Newquay, Cornwall
BoothR	R. Booth, Isle of Man Railways, Douglas, Isle of Man
Borsig	A. Borsig GmbH, Berlin-Tegel, Germany
Bow	Bow Locomotive Works, North London Railway
Bowman	N.Bowman, Launceston Steam Railway, Cornwall
BP	Beyer, Peacock & Co Ltd, Gorton, Manchester
BPH	Beyer, Peacock (Hymek) Ltd, Gorton, Manchester
BRCW	Birmingham Railway Carriage & Wagon Co Ltd, Smethwick, West Midlands
BRE	British Rail Engineering Ltd
BRE(D)	British Rail Engineering Ltd, Derby Locomotive Works, Derby
BRE(S)	British Rail Engineering Ltd, Shildon Works, Co.Durham
Bredbury	Bredbury & Romiley Urban District Council, Cheshire [Greater Manchester]
BrownGM	G.M.Brown Ltd, Stanhopeburn, Stanhope, Co.Durham
BrownJ	Joe Brown, Farington Moss, Preston, Lancashire
Bruff	Bruff Rail Ltd, Suckley, Worcestershire
Brunning	H. Brunning (? of Crewe) – see Rhiw Valley Railway, Mid Wales
BT	Brush Electrical Machines Ltd, Traction Division, Falcon Works, Loughborough, Leicestershire
BTH	British Thomson-Houston Co Ltd, Rugby, Warwickshire
Bton	Brighton Works, Sussex – London, Brighton and South Coast Railway / Southern Railway / British Railways
BuryC&K	Bury, Curtis & Kennedy, Clarence Foundry, Love Lane, Liverpool
BV	Brook Victor Electric Vehicles Ltd, Burscough Bridge, Ormskirk, Lancashire
BVR	Bure Valley Railway Ltd, Aylsham, Norfolk
Byers	R.S. Byers Ltd, Houghton, Carlisle, Cumbria
Byworth	Byworth Engineering Ltd, Keighley, West Yorkshire

C

Cannon	Cannon, Dudley, West Midlands
Carland	Carland Engineering Ltd, Harold Wood, Essex
Carter	D.Carter, Tucking Mill Tramway, Midford, Somerset
CastleGKN	Castle Works (GKN Sankey Ltd), Hadley, Telford, Shropshire
Cdf	Cardiff West Yard Locomotive Works (Taff Vale Railway), Glamorgan
CE	Clayton Equipment Ltd, Burton-on-Trent, Staffordshire previously at Hatton, Derbyshire, where also traded as NEI Mining Equipment Ltd, and originally Clarke Chapman Ltd
Chance	Chance Manufacturing Co Inc, Wichita, Kansas, USA
Chaplin	Alexander Chaplin & Co Ltd, Cranstonhill Works, Glasgow
Chrz	Fabryka Lokomotywim "Feliksa Dzierzynskiego". Chrzanów, Poland
Civil	T.D.A. Civil, near Uttoxeter, Staffordshire
Clarkson	H. Clarkson & Son, York
ClayCross	Clay Cross Co Ltd, Spun Pipe Plant, Clay Cross Iron Works, Derbyshire
CM	Century Millwrights, Platts Eyot's Works, Sunbury-on-Thames, Surrey
Coalbrookdale	Coalbrookdale Co, Coalbrookdale Ironworks, Shropshire

Cockerill	Société pour L'Exploitation des Etablissements John Cockerill, Seraing, Belgium
ColebySim	Coleby-Simkins Engineering, Melton Mowbray, Leicestershire
Consett	Consett Iron Co Ltd, Consett Works, Co.Durham
Corpet	Corpet, Louvet & Compagnie, La Courneuve, Seine St.Denis, France
Couillet	Société Anonyme des Usines Métallurgiques du Hainaut, Couillet, Marcinelle, near Charleroi, Belgium
Cowlairs	Cowlairs Works, Glasgow
	North British Railway / London & North Eastern Railway / British Railways
CPM	C.P.M., Italy
CravenEA	E.A. Craven, North Shields, Northumberland
Cravens	Cravens Ltd, Darnall, Sheffield
Crewe	Crewe Works, Cheshire — London and North Western Railway / London, Midland & Scottish Railway / British Railways
CurwenD	D.A. Curwen, All Cannings, near Devizes, Wiltshire
CW	Cowlishaw Walker Engineering Co Ltd, Biddulph, Staffordshire

D

D	Dübs & Co, Glasgow Locomotive Works, Glasgow
Dar	Darlington Works, Co.Durham
	North Eastern Railway / London & North Eastern Railway / British Railways
Dar(PL)	Darlington Park Lane Plant Depot (British Rail), Co.Durham
Darlington	A1 Locomotive Trust, Hopetown Carriage Works, Darlington, Co. Durham
DB	Sir Arthur P. Heywood, Duffield Bank Works, Derbyshire
DC	Drewry Car Co Ltd, London (supply agents only)
DDak	Duro Dakovic, Industrije Lokomotive, Strojeva I Mostova, Slavonski Brod, Yugoslavia
Dec	Société Nouvelle des Etablissements Decauville Aîne, Petit Bourg, Corbeil, Essonne, France
DeDietrich	Société Lorraine des Anciens Établissements de Dietrich & Cie, France
Derby	Derby Locomotive Works
	Midland Railway / London, Midland & Scottish Railway / British Railways
DerbyC&W	Derby Carriage & Wagon Works, Litchurch Lane, Derby
	Midland Railway / London, Midland & Scottish Railway / British Railways
DeW	DeWinton & Co, Union Works, Caernarfon, North Wales
Diema	Diepholzer Maschinenfabrik (Fr.Schöttler GmbH), Diepholz, Germany
DK	Dick Kerr & Co Ltd, Preston, Lancashire (Britannia Works, Kilmarnock, Ayrshire until 1919)
DM	Davies & Metcalfe Ltd, Romiley, Stockport, Greater Manchester
Dodman	Alfred Dodman & Co, Highgate Works, Kings Lynn, Norfolk
Don	Doncaster Works, South Yorkshire
	Great Northern Railway / London & North Eastern Railway / British Railways
Donelli	F.L. Donelli SpA, Reggio, Italy
Donelon	J.F. Donelon Ltd, Horwich, Greater Manchester
DonM	British Rail, Marshgate Permanent Way Depot, Doncaster, South Yorkshire
Dorothea	Dorothea Restorations, Mevril Spring Works, New Road, Whaley Bridge, Derbyshire
Dotto	Dotto Trains, Castelfranco, Italy
Dowty	Dowty Group Ltd, Ashchurch, Gloucestershire
DP	Davey, Paxman & Co Ltd, Colchester, Essex
Dtz	Motorenfabrik Deutz AG / Humboldt-Deutz-Motoren AG / Klöckner-Humboldt-Deutz AG, Köln (Cologne), Germany
Dundalk	Dundalk Works, Great Northern Railway of Ireland
DunEW	Dundalk Engineering Works, Dundalk, Co. Louth, Republic of Ireland
	Locos built from parts supplied by Gleismac

EB	E. Borrows & Sons, St.Helens, Lancashire [Merseyside
EBW	E.B. Wilson & Co, Railway Foundry, Leeds
Eclipse	Eclipse Peat Co Ltd, Ashcott, Somerset
EE	English Electric Co Ltd, London
EEDK	English Electric Co Ltd, Dick Kerr Works, Preston, Lancashire
EES	English Electric Co Ltd, Stephenson Works, Darlington (successors to RSHD)
EEV	English Electric Co Ltd, Vulcan Works, Newton-le-Willows, Lancashire (successors to VF)
EK	Märstaverken, Eksjö, Sweden
ELC	East Lancashire Coachbuilders
Electro	Uzinele Electroputere, Craiova, Romania
Elh	Eastleigh Works, Hampshire
	London and South Western Railway / Southern Railway / British Railways
ENG/GEM	ENG/GEM, Wisbech, Cambridgeshire
ESCA	ESCA Engineering Ltd, 6 Wetheral Close, Hindley Industrial Estate, off Swan Lane, Hindley Green, Wigan, Greater Manchester
ESR	Exmoor Steam Railway, Devon
EVM	Elham Valley Museum, Peene Yard, Peene, Folkestone, Kent
EVRA	Ecclesbourne Valley Railway Association, Wirksworth, Derbyshire

Fairbourne	Fairbourne Railway Co, Fairbourne, Gwynedd, North Wales
Fairmont	Fairmont Railway Motors Ltd, Toronto, Ontario, Canada
FE	Falcon Engine Works, Loughborough, Leicestershire
Ferndale	K. Watson & k. Tingle, Ferndale Engineering, Canning Vale, Western Australia
FFP	Fire Fly Project, Great Western Preservations Ltd, Bristol (1987) and Didcot, Oxfordshire (from 1989)
FH	F.C. Hibberd & Co Ltd, Park Royal, London ("Planet" locomotives) later at Butterley Works, Ripley, Derbyshire
Fisons	Fisons Ltd, British Moss Works, Swinefleet, near Goole, East Yorkshire constructed from parts supplied by Diema
FJ	Fletcher Jennings & Co, Lowca Engine Works, Whitehaven, Cumbria
Flor	Wiener Lokomotivfabrik-AG, Wien-Floridsdorf, Austria
FMB	F.M.B. Engineering Co Ltd, Unit 10, Southlands, Latchford Lane, Oakhanger, near Bordon, Hampshire
Ford	Ford Motor Co Ltd, (? Dagenham, Essex)
FordTTC	Ford Motor Co Ltd, Thameside Technical Training Centre, Dagenham, Greater London
FosterRastrick	Foster, Rastrick & Co, Stourbridge, Worcestershire
FoxA	A. Fox
FRCo	Festiniog Railway Company, Boston Lodge Works, Porthmadog, North Wales
Frenze	Frenze Engineering, (Diss area), Norfolk
Freud	Stahlbahnwerke Freudenstein & Co, Berlin-Tempelhof, Germany
FRgroup4	Festiniog Railway, Group 4, Birmingham
Frichs	A/S Frichs Maskinfabrik & Kedelsmedie, Århus, Denmark
FRSociety	Festiniog Railway Society, North Staffs Group
Funkey	C.H. Funkey & Co (Pty) Ltd, Alberton, near Johannesburg, South Africa
FW	Fox, Walker & Co, Atlas Engine Works, Bristol

G&S	G.& S. Light Engineering Co Ltd, Stourbridge, Worcestershire
Gartell	Alan Gartell, Common Lane, Yenston, near Templecombe, Somerset
GB	Greenwood & Batley Ltd, Albion Ironworks, Armley, Leeds
GE	George England & Co Ltd, Hatcham Ironworks, London
GEC	General Electric Co Ltd, Witton, Birmingham
GECT	G.E.C.Traction Ltd, Vulcan Works, Newton-le-Willows, Lancashire
Geevor	Geevor Tin Mines Ltd, Pendeen, near St. Just, Cornwall

Geismar	Geismar (UK) Ltd, Salthouse Road, Brackmills Industrial Estate, Northampton and BP 327, 68006 Colmar, Alsace, France
G.Stephenson	George Stephenson, Hetton, Co.Durham
GH	Gibb & Hogg, Victoria Engine Works, Airdrie, North Lanarkshire
Ghd	Gateshead Works, Co.Durham North Eastern Railway / London & North Eastern Railway / British Railways
GIA	GIA Industria AB, Grangeberg, Sweden
GibbonsCL	C.L. Gibbons, c/o Bury Transport Museum, Bury Depot, Greater Manchester
Gleismac	Gleismac Italiana SpA, Viale Delia Stazione 3, 46030 Bigarello, Mantova, Italy
GM	General Motors Ltd, Electro-Motive Division, La Grange, Illinois, U.S.A.
Gmd	Gmeinder & Co GmbH, Mosbach, Germany
GMT	Gyro Mining Transport Ltd, Victoria Road, Barnsley, South Yorkshire, then Bramley Way, Hellaby Industrial Estate, Hellaby, near Rotherham, South Yorkshire from c/1987
GNS	Great Northern Steam Co Ltd, Unit 3, Forge Way, Cleveland Industrial Estate, Darlington, Co.Durham
Goold	J.R. Goold Engineering Ltd, Camerton, near Radstock, Somerset
Gorton	Gorton Works, Manchester Great Central Railway / London & North Eastern Railway / British Railways
Govan	Govan Workshops, Broomloan Road, Glasgow (Glasgow Corporation Transport Department, Underground Railway)
GR	Grant, Ritchie & Co, Townholme Engine Works, Kilmarnock, Ayrshire
GRC&W	Gloucester Railway Carriage & Wagon Co Ltd, Gloucester
Greaves	J.W. Greaves & Sons Ltd, Llechwedd Quarry, Blaenau Ffestiniog, North Wales
Greensburg	Greensburgh Machine Co, near Pittsburgh, Philidelphia, USA
Guest	Guest Engineering & Maintenance Co Ltd, Stourbridge, Worcestershire
GuinnessNL	Nigel L. Guinness, Cobham, Surrey
Gullivers	Gullivers Land, Milton Keynes, Bedfordshire

H

H	James & Fredk. Howard Ltd, Britannia Ironworks, Bedford
HAB	Hunslet-Barclay Ltd, Caledonia Works, Kilmarnock, Ayrshire
Hackworth	Timothy Hackworth, Soho Works, Shildon, Co.Durham
HallT	T.Hall, North Ings Farm Museum, Dorrington, near Ruskington, Lincolnshire
Hano	Hannoversche Maschinenbau-AG (vormals Georg Egestorff), Hannover-Linden, Germany
Harbin	Harbin Forest Machinery Factory, Harbin, Heilongjiang Province, China
HardyK	K. Hardy, Brookhouse, Badgeworth, near Cheltenham, Gloucestershire
Harsco	Harsco Track Technologies, Unit 1, Chewton Street, Eastwood, Nottinghamshire. (successors to Permaquip).
Hart	Sächsische Maschinenfabrik, vormals Richard Hartmann AG, Chemnitz, Germany
HartlepoolBSC	Hartlepool Works (British Steel Corporation), North Teesside
Haydock	Haydock Foundry Co Ltd, Haydock, Lancashire
HaylockJ	J. Haylock
Hayne	N. Hayne, Sheppards Tea Rooms & Boat House, near Saltford, Somerset, later Blaise Castle, Henbury, Bristol [Gloucestershire]
Haytor	M.P. Haytor & Son, Frensham, Surrey
HB	Hudswell Badger Ltd, Railway Foundry, Hunslet, Leeds
HC	Hudswell, Clarke & Co Ltd, Railway Foundry, Hunslet, Leeds
HE	Hunslet Engine Co Ltd, Hunslet, Leeds
Heath	Robert Heath & Sons Ltd, Norton Ironworks, Stoke-on-Trent
Hedley	William Hedley, Wylam Colliery, Northumberland
Hen	Henschel & Sohn GmbH, Kassel, Germany
Herschell	Allan Herschell, North Tonawanda, New York, USA
H(L)	Hawthorns & Co, Leith Engine Works, Edinburgh
HL	R.& W.Hawthorn, Leslie & Co Ltd, Forth Bank Works, Newcastle-upon-Tyne
HLH	Hunslet Locomotive Hire Ltd, Station Road, Killamarsh, Derbyshire
HLT	Hughes Locomotive & Tramway Engine Works Ltd, Loughborough, Leicestershire
HopleyCP	

Hor	Horwich Works, Lancashire — Lancashire and Yorkshire Railway / London, Midland & Scottish Railway / British Railways
House	B. House
HPET	H.P.E.Tredegar Ltd, Tafarnaubach Industrial Estate, near Tredegar, Gwent
HSE	Harry Steer Engineering, Breaston, near Derby
HT	Hunslet Taylor Consolidate (Pty) Ltd, Germiston, Transvaal, South Africa
HU	Robert Hudson Ltd, Leeds
HuntTG	T.G. Hunt, Oldbury, West Midlands
Hutchings	R. Hutchings
HW	Head, Wrightson & Co, Teesdale Ironworks, Thornaby-on-Tees, North Yorkshire
Hy-rail	This is a trademark of Harsco Track Technologies / Permaquip (see- HTT / Perm)

I

Inchicore	Inchicore Works, Dublin — Great Southern & Western Railway / Great Southern Railways / Córas Iompair Éireann / Iarnród Éireann
Iso	Iso Speedic Co Ltd, Fabrications & Electric Vehicles, Charles Street, Warwick
Iveco	
IZU	Instant Zip-Up, Newport, Shropshire

J

Jaco	Jaco Engineering Co Ltd, Edwards Road, Birmingham
Jaywick	Jaywick Light Railway, near Clacton, Essex
Jesty	Bedford & Jesty Ltd, Doddings Farm, Bere Regis, Dorset
Jenbach	Jenbachwerke A G, Jenbach, Austria.
JF	John Fowler & Co (Leeds) Ltd, Hunslet, Leeds
JMR	J.M.R.(Sales) Ltd, 173 Liverpool Road South, Birkdale, Southport, Lancashire
Jung	Arn.Jung Lokomotivfabrik GmbH, Jungenthal, near Kirchen-an-der-Sieg, Germany

K

K	Kitson & Co, Airedale Foundry, Leeds
KC	Kent Construction & Engineering Co Ltd, Ashford, Kent
Kearsley	Kearsley Power Station (Central Electricity Generating Board), Radcliffe, Greater Manchester
Kennan	Thos Kennan & Son, Dublin
Kershaw	
Kew	Kew Bridge Steam Museum, Kew Bridge Museum Steam Railway, Green Dragon Lane, Brentford, London
Kierstead	Kierstead Systems & Controls Ltd, Ketley Bank Hall, Telford, Shropshire
Kilmarnock	Kilmarnock Regional Civil Engineers Workshops (British Rail, Scottish Region) Kilmarnock, Ayrshire (conversions only)
Kitching	A.Kitching, Hope Town Foundry, Darlington, Co.Durham
KM	Krauss Maffei AG, München (Munich), Germany
Knotwell	M. Knotwell
Krauss	Lokomotivfabrik Krauss & Co
KraussL	Lokomotivfabrik Krauss & Co, Linz, Austria
KraussM	Lokomotivfabrik Krauss & Co, Marsfeld Works, München (Munich), Germany
KraussS	Lokomotivfabrik Krauss & Co, Sendling Works, München (Munich), Germany
Krupp	Friedrich Krupp, Maschinenfabriken Essen, Abt. Lokomotivbau, Essen, Germany
KS	Kerr, Stuart & Co Ltd, California Works, Stoke-on-Trent, Staffordshire

L

L	R.A.Lister & Co Ltd, Dursley, Gloucestershire
LaMeuse	Société Anonyme des Ateliers de Construction de la Meuse, Sclessin, Liège, Belgium
Lake&Elliot	Lake & Elliot Ltd, Braintree, Essex
Lancing	Lancing Carriage Works (Southern Railway / British Railways), Sussex
LancTan	Lancashire Tanning Co Ltd, Littleborough, Lancashire
Landrover	Landrover Ltd, Solihull, West Midlands
Lawson	C. Lawson, 11 Okeley Lane, Highfield Estate, Tring, Hertfordshire
LB	Lister Blackstone Traction Ltd, Dursley, Gloucestershire (successor to L)

LBNGRS	Leighton Buzzard Narrow Gauge Railway Society, Stonehenge Workshops, Leighton Buzzard, Bedfordshire
Leake	J. Leake, Lytchett Matravers, Dorset
LemonB	J.Lemon-Burton, Paynesfield, Albourne Green, West Sussex, and Shelmerdine & Mulley Ltd, Edgeware Road, Cricklewood, London NW2
Lewin	Stephen Lewin, Dorset Foundry, Poole, Dorset
Leyland	Leyland Vehicles Ltd, Workington, Cumbria
LHGroup	L.H.Group Services Ltd, Barton-under-Needwood, Staffordshire
Lima	Lima Locomotive Works Inc., Lima, Ohio, U.S.A.
Lind	James Lind & Sons
LJ	Lester Jones, Hobart, Tasmania.
LlanwernBSC	Llanwern Works (British Steel Corporation), Newport, Gwent
LMM	Logan Mining & Machinery Co Ltd, Dundee
LO	Lokomo Oy, Tampere, Finland
LocoEnt	Locomotion Enterprises (1975) Ltd, Bowes Railway, Springwell, Gateshead, Co.Durham
Locospoor	Locospoor, The Hague, Holland
Longhedge	Longhedge Works, London — South Eastern & Chatham Railway
Longleat	Longleat Light Railway, Longleat, Warminster, Wiltshire

M

M&P	Mather & Platt Ltd, Park Works, Manchester
Mace	C.Mace, The Woodland Railway, Kent
Maffei	J.A. Maffei AG, Locomotiv & Maschinenfabrik, München (Munich), Germany
MaK	Maschinenbau Kiel GmbH, Kiel-Friedrichsort, Germany
MaLoWa	MaLoWa Bahnwerkstatt GmbH, Klostermansfeld, Germany
Massey	G.D. Massey, 57 Silver Street, Thorverton, Exeter, Devon
Matisa	Matisa Material Industriel SA, Arc-En-Ciel 2, Crissier, Lausanne, Switzerland
MatisaSPA	Matisa SpA, S.Palomba, Rome, Italy
Maxitrack	Maxitrack, "Rothiemay", Offham Road, West Malling, Kent
McGarigle	P.McGarigle, Niagara Falls, near Buffalo, New York, USA ("Cagney" locos)
MER	Manx Electric Railway, Derby Castle Works, Douglas, Isle of Man
Mercia	Mercia Fabrications Ltd, Steel Fabrications, Units K1 & K3, Dudley Central Trading Estate, Shaw Road, Dudley, West Midlands
Mercury	Mercury Truck & Tractor Co Ltd, Gloucester
Meridian	Meridian (Motioneering) Ltd, Bradley Way, Hellaby Industrial Estate, Hellaby, near Rotherham, South Yorkshire
Metalair	Metalair Ltd, Wokingham, Berkshire
MetallbauE	Metallbau Emmein GmbH, Eichenstrasse 58, 49733, Germany
MetAmal	Metropolitan Amalgamated Railway Carriage & Wagon Co Ltd (until 6/1912)
MetC&W	Metropolitan Carriage, Wagon & Finance Co Ltd (6/1912 to 12/1928)
MetCam	Metropolitan-Cammell Carriage, Wagon & Finance Co Ltd (1/1929 to 10/1934) Metropolitan-Cammell Carriage & Wagon Co Ltd (1/1935 to 12/1964) Metropolitan-Cammell Ltd (from 1/1965) — all located in Birmingham
MH	Muir-Hill (Engineers) Ltd, Trafford Park, Manchester
Middleton	Middleton Railway Trust, Hunslet, Leeds, West Yorkshire
Minilok	allrad-Rangiertecknik GmbH, D-5628 Heiligenhaus Bez, Dusseldorf, Germany Note that the firm spells their name with a small 'a'
Minirail	Minirail Ltd, Frampton Cotterell, Bristol
Mkm	Markham & Co Ltd, Chesterfield, Derbyshire
Moës	S.A. Moteurs Moës, Waremme, Belgium
MoorsValley	Moors Valley Railway, Moors Valley Country Park, Horton Road, Ashley Heath, Ringwood, Hampshire
MorrisRP	R.P. Morris, 193 Main Road, Longfield, Kent
Morse	R.H. Morse, Potter Heigham, Norfolk
MossAJ	A.J. Moss, 97 Martin Lane Ends, Scarisbrick, Lancashire
Motala	AB Motala Verkstad, Motala, Sweden
Moyse	Locotracteurs Gaston Moyse, La Courneuve, Seine St.Denis, France
MR	Motor Rail & Tramcar Co Ltd / Motor Rail Ltd, Simplex Works, Bedford

MSI	The Museum of Science & Industry in Manchester, Liverpool Road, Castlefield, Manchester
MV	Metropolitan-Vickers Electrical Co Ltd, Trafford Park, Manchester
MW	Manning, Wardle & Co Ltd, Boyne Engine Works, Hunslet, Leeds

N

N	Neilson & Co, Hyde Park Works, Springburn, Glasgow
NB	North British Locomotive Co Ltd, Glasgow
NBH	North British Locomotive Co Ltd, Hyde Park Works, Glasgow
NBQ	North British Locomotive Co Ltd, Queens Park Works, Glasgow
NCC	Northern Counties Committee (of London, Midland & Scottish Rly etc) York Road Works, Belfast, Northern Ireland
NDLW	North Dorset Locomotive Works
Neasden	Neasden Works (Metropolitan Railway), London
Newag	Newag, Ripshorster Strabe, Oberhausen, Germany
Niteq	Niteq BV, Overspoor 21, 1688 J.G. Nibbexwould, Netherlands. http://www.niteq.nl/uk/.
NMW	National Museum of Wales, Industrial & Maritime Museum, Butetown, Cardiff, South Glamorgan
NNM	Noord Nederlandsche Machinefabriek BV, Winschoten, Holland
Nohab	Nydquist & Holm AB, Trollhättan, Sweden
NR	Neilson Reid & Co, Glasgow
NW	Nasmyth, Wilson & Co Ltd, Bridgewater Foundry, Patricroft, Manchester

O

Oerlikon	Maschinenfabrik Oerlikon, Zurich, Switzerland
OK	Orenstein & Koppel AG, Berlin-Drewitz and Abt.Montania, Nordhausen, Germany then, from 1945 : – Orenstein-Koppel und Lübecker Maschinenbau AG, Dortmund-Dorstfeld, Germany
OldburyC&W	Oldbury Carriage & Wagon Co Ltd, Birmingham
OwenGD	G.D. Owen, North Wales Tramway Museum, Tal-y-Cafn, North Wales

P

P	Peckett & Sons Ltd, Atlas Locomotive Works, St.George, Bristol
Parry	J.P.M.Parry & Associates Ltd, Corngreaves Trading Estate, Cradley Heath, West Midlands
Pendre	Pendre Works (Talyllyn Railway Co), Tywyn, Gwynedd, North Wales
Perm	The Permanent Way Equipment Co Ltd, Pweco Works, Lillington Road North, Bulwell, Nottingham — later at 1 Giltway, Giltbrook, Nottingham
Plasser	Plasser Railway Machinery (GB) Ltd, Drayton Green Road, West Ealing, London
PortTalbotBSC	Port Talbot Works (British Steel), Port Talbot, West Glamorgan
Potter	D.C. Potter, Yaxham Park, Yaxham, near Dereham, Norfolk
Powell	Alan Powell, Norwich, Norfolk
PPM	Parry People Movers Ltd, Corngreaves Trading Estate, Overend Road, Cradley Heath, West Midlands
Prestige	Prestige Engineering, Abbotskerwell, Newton Abbot, Devon
PRoyal	Park Royal Vehicles, Park Royal, London
Pritchard	William Pritchard, c/o Manchester, Bury, Rochdale & Oldham Steam Tramway, Oldham, Lancashire
PSteel	Pressed Steel Ltd, Linwood, Paisley, Renfrewshire
PVRA	Plym Valley Railway Association, Marsh Mills, Plympton, Devon
PWR	Pikrose & Co Ltd, Wingrove & Rogers Division, Delta Road, Audenshaw, Greater Manchester (successors to WR)

R

Ravenglass	Ravenglass & Eskdale Railway Co Ltd, Ravenglass, Cumbria
Red(F)	Redland Bricks Ltd, Funton Works, near Sittingbourne, Kent
Red(T)	Redland Bricks Ltd, Baltic Road, Tonbridge, Kent
Redstone	Mr Redstone, Penmaenmawr, North Wales
RegentSt	Regent Street Polytechnic, London

Renault	Régie Nationale des Usines Renault, Division Matériel Ferroviaire, Choisy-le-Roi, near Paris, France (from 1945)
	earlier:- SA de Usines Renault, Billancourt, near Paris
Resco	Resco (Railways) Ltd, Bilton Road, Manor Road Industrial Estate, Erith, Greater London
Resita	Uzinele de Fier si Domeniile din Resita Societate Anonima Resita, Resita, Romania.
	(later: Combinatul Metalurgic)
RFSD	R.F.S. Engineering Ltd, Doncaster Works, Hexthorpe Road, Doncaster
RFSK	R.F.S. Engineering Ltd, Kilnhurst Works, Hooton Road, Kilnhurst, South Yorkshire (successors to TH)
RH	Ruston & Hornsby Ltd, Lincoln
RHDR	Romney Hythe & Dymchurch Railway, New Romney, Kent
Rhiw	Rhiw Valley Light Railway (J.Woodruffe), Lower House, Manafon, near Welshpool, Powys, Mid Wales
Rhiwbach	Rhiwbach Quarries Ltd, Rhiwbach Slate Quarry, North Wales
Richard	Establishments B Richard, Saint – Denis – de l' Hotel, Loire, France
Riley	Ian V.Riley Engineering, Arbour Locomotive Works, Arbour Lane, Kirkby, Merseyside — later Bury Car Sheds, Bury, Greater Manchester
Riordan	Riordan Engineering Ltd, Surbiton, Surrey
RM	Road Machines (Drayton) Ltd, West Drayton, Middlesex
	later at Iver, Buckinghamshire
Roanoke	Roanoke, Grange Hill Industrial Estate, Bratton Fleming, Devon
Robel	Robel & Co, Maschinenfabrik, Munchen, Germany
Rosewall	K. Rosewall, Cross Elms Nursery, Bristol
RP	Ruston, Proctor & Co Ltd, Lincoln
RR	Rolls Royce Ltd, Sentinel Works, Harlescott, Shrewsbury, Shropshire (successors to Sentinel)
R&R	Ransomes & Rapier Ltd, Riverside Works, Ipswich, Suffolk
RS	Robert Stephenson & Co Ltd, Forth Street, Newcastle-upon-Tyne and Darlington, Co.Durham
RSH	Robert Stephenson & Hawthorns Ltd
RSHD	Robert Stephenson & Hawthorns Ltd, Darlington Works, Co.Durham
RSHD/WB	built by RSHD but ordered by WB
RSHN	Robert Stephenson & Hawthorns Ltd, Newcastle-upon-Tyne Works (successors to HL)
RSM	Royal Scottish Museum, Chambers Street, Edinburgh
RT&Co(C)	Richard, Thomas & Co Ltd, Crowle Brickworks, Lincolnshire (loco constructed from parts supplied by FH)
Ruhrthaler	Ruhrthaler Maschinenfabrik Schwarz & Dyckerhoff AG, Mülheim/Ruhr, Germany
RWH	R.& W.Hawthorn & Co, Forth Bank Works, Newcastle-upon-Tyne (later HL)

S

S	Sentinel (Shrewsbury) Ltd, Harlescott, Shrewsbury, Shropshire.
	(Diesel locomotives numbered between 10001 and 10183 were actually designed and built by Rolls Royce Ltd, but were fitted with Sentinel worksplates)
Sabero	Huileras de Sabero y Anexas SA, Sabero, Spain
SAFOP	SAFOP s.p.a. Corso Lino Zanussi 55, 33080, Porcia, Italy
Sara	Sara & Burgess, Penryn, Cornwall
Saxby	Frank Saxby & Co, Guildford Works, Surrey
Scarrott	D.J. Scarrott, Kingsteignton, Newton Abbot, Devon
Schalke	Schalke Eisenhette Maschinenfabrik GmbH, Magdeburger Strasse 37, Gelsenkirchen-Schalke, West Germany
Schichau	F. Schichau, Maschinen- und Lokomotivfabrik, Elbing, Germany (now Elbtag, Poland)
Schöma	Christoph Schöttler Maschinenfabrik GmbH, Diepholz, Germany
Schw	L. Schwartzkopff, Berlin, Germany (later Berliner Maschinenbau-AG — see BMAG)
ScienceMus	Science Museum, South Kensington, London.
ScottP	Peter Scott, Hillsborough, Northern Ireland
Scul	Sculfort, Zac des fonds St Jaques, Feignies, France

SCW	I.C.I. Ltd, South Central Workshops, Tunstead, Derbyshire
Sdn	Swindon Works, Wiltshire — Great Western Railway / British Railways
SdnCol	Swindon College, Department of Engineering, North Star Avenue, Swindon
SDSI(S)	South Durham Steel & Iron Co Ltd, Stockton Works, Co.Durham
Selhurst	Selhurst Maintenance Depot, Greater London — British Rail, Southern Region
SET	Stored Energy Technology, Litchurch Lane, Derby
SGLR	Steeple Grange Light Railway, Steeplehouse Junction, Wirksworth, Derbyshire
S&H	Strachan & Henshaw Ltd, Ashton, Bristol
Shackerstone	Shackerstone Station (The Battlefield Line), Leicestershire
Sharon	Sharon Engineering Ltd, Leek, Staffordshire
—	Shelmerdine & Mulley Ltd, Edgeware Road, Cricklewood, London NW2 (see code "LemonB")
ShepherdFG	F.G. Shepherd, Flow Edge Colliery, Middle Fell, Alston, Cumbria
Siemens	Siemens Bros Ltd, London — possibly agents for :-
S&H(B)	Siemens & Halske, Berlin, Germany (until 1903)
SSW	Siemens-Schuckert-Werke, Berlin, Germany (from 1903)
SIG	Schweizerische Industriegesellschaft, Neuhausen am Rheinfall, Switzerland
SkinnerD	D. Skinner, 660 Streetsbrook Road, Solihull, West Midlands
SL	Severn-Lamb UK Ltd, Western Road, Stratford-Upon-Avon, Warwickshire then Alcester, Warwickshire.
SLM	Schweizerische Lokomotiv- und Maschinenfabrik, Winterthur, Switzerland
SMH	Simplex Mechanical Handling Ltd, Elstow Road, Bedford (successor to MR)
SmithEL	E.L. Smith, Garsington, Oxfordshire
SmithN	N. Smith, Heatherslaw Light Railway, Heatherslaw Mill, near Coldstream, Northumberland
SmithP	Smith, Pengam, South Glamorgan
SMR	Saltburn Miniature Railway, Valley Gardens, Saltburn, North Yorkshire
SouthCrofty	South Crofty Ltd, Pool, near Camborne, Cornwall
SPA	Specialist Plant Associates Ltd, 23 Podington Airfield, Hinwick, Bedfordshire
Spence	Wm.Spence, Cork Street Foundry, Dublin
SPL	Science Projects Ltd, (Constructors), Hammersmith, London
Spondon	Spondon Power Station, Derbyshire Derbyshire & Nottinghamshire Electric Power Co Ltd
SRS	Swedish Rail Systems Euroc, PO Box 1031, S-171 20 Solna, Sweden
SS	Sharp, Stewart & Co Ltd, Atlas Works, Manchester (until 1888) then Atlas Works, Glasgow
StanhopeT	T.Stanhope, Arthington Station, near Leeds, West Yorkshire
Steamtown	Steamtown Railway Museum, Warton Road, Carnforth, Lancashire
StewartWP	W.P.Stewart, Washington Sheet Metal Works, Industrial Road, Hertburn Industrial Estate, Washington, Co.Durham
Stoke	Stoke Works, Stoke-on-Trent (North Staffordshire Railway)
StokesMJ	M.J. Stokes, Little West Garden Railway, Southerndown, Mid Glamorgan
Str	Stratford Works, London Great Eastern Railway / London & North Eastern Railway / British Railways
StrawberryHill	Strawberry Hill Depot, South London (British Rail)
StRollox	St.Rollox Works, Glasgow Caledonian Railway / London, Midland & Scottish Railway / British Railways
STRPS	South Tynedale Railway Preservation Society, Alston Station, Cumbria
Strüver	Ad.Strüver AG, Hamburg, Germany
Swanhaven	Swanhaven, Hull, East Yorkshire
SwingStage	Swing Stage, Canada
Syl	Sylvester Steel Co, Lindsay, Ontario, Canada

Tambling	N.J. Tambling, Lappa Valley Railway, St. Newlyn East, near Newquay, Cornwall
TaylorB	B.Taylor, 7 Abbey Road, Shepley, Huddersfield, West Yorkshire
TaylorJ	J. Taylor, The Ford, Woolhope, Herefordshire
TG	T. Green & Son Ltd, Leeds
TH	Thomas Hill (Rotherham) Ltd, Vanguard Works, Kilnhurst, South Yorkshire
Thakeham	Thakeham Tiles Ltd, Thakeham, Sussex
Thursley	The Thursley Railway, Hampshire
TK	Oy Tampella Ab, Tampere, Finland
TMA	TMA Automation Ltd, Feeds Automated Systems, Jubilee Works, Tyburn Road, Erdington, Birmingham
Todd Kitson & Laird	Todd, Kitson & Laird, Leeds
Trackmobile	Trackmobile Ltd, La Grange, Georgia, USA
TS&S	Track Supplies & Services Ltd, Old Wolverton Road, Old Wolverton, Milton Keynes, Buckinghamshire
TU	Task Undertakings Ltd, Birmingham
Tunn	Tunnequip Ltd, Nowhurst Lane, Broadbridge Heath, Horsham, West Sussex
TurnerT	T. Turner, Long Eaton, Derbyshire
TyseleyLW	Tyseley Locomotive Works (Standard Gauge Steam Trust), Warwick Road, Tyseley, Birmingham

UCA	UCA, Antwerp, Belgium
UK Loco	UK Loco Ltd, Unit 1, The Heath Works, Main Road, Cropthorne, Worcestershire
Unilok	Unilok locos, but whether "(G)" or "(H)" as yet unrecorded.
Unilok(G)	Unilokomotive Ltd, International Division, Mervue Industrial Estate, Galway, Co.Galway, Republic of Ireland
Unilok(H)	Hugo Aeckerle & Co, Hamburg, Germany
Unimog	Unimog road/rail locos — Mercedes Benz AG, Stuttgart, Germany

Vanstone	D. Vanstone, Pixieland Mini-Zoo, Kilkhampton, near Bude, Cornwall
VE	Victor Electrics Ltd, Burscough Bridge, Lancashire
VER	Volks Electric Railway (Magnus Volk), Madeira Drive, Brighton, Sussex
VF	Vulcan Foundry Ltd, Newton-le-Willows, Lancashire
VIW	Vulcan Iron Works, Wilkes-Barre, Pennsylvania, U.S.A.
VL	Vickers Ltd, Barrow-in-Furness, Cumbria
Vollert	Hermann Vollert GmbH & Co KG, Maschinenfabrik, 7102 Weinsberg/Wurtt, Germany

WalkerG	G. Walker, Lakeside Miniature Railway, Marine Lake, Southport, Merseyside
WalkerS	Samuel Walker
Waterfield	James Waterfield, Boston, Lincolnshire
WB	W.G.Bagnall Ltd, Castle Engine Works, Stafford
Wbton	Wilbrighton Wagon Works, Shropshire
WCI	Wigan Coal & Iron Co Ltd, Kirkless, Wigan, Lancashire
WeaverP	P. Weaver, New Farm, Lacock, near Corsham, Wiltshire
Werk	Werkspoor NV, Utrecht, Holland
WhC	Whiting Corporation, Harvey, Illinois, U.S.A.
WHR(GF)	Welsh Highland Light Railway (1964) Ltd, Gelert's Farm Works, Porthmadog, North Wales
WilliamsWJ	W.J. Williams, Blaenau Ffestiniog, North Wales
Wilmott	Wilmott Bros (Plant Services) Ltd, Ilkeston, Derbyshire
WilsonAJ	A.J. Wilson, 6 Trentdale Road, Carlton, Nottingham
Wilton(ICI)	Wilton Works (Imperial Chemical Industries Ltd), Middlesbrough, North Yorkshire
Windhoff	Rheiner Maschinenfabrik Windhoff AG, Rheine, Germany

Winson	Winson Engineering, Porthmadog (later Penrhyndeudraeth), North Wales and at Daventry, Northamptonshire
WkB	Walker Bros (Wigan) Ltd, Wigan, Lancashire
Wkm	D.Wickham & Co Ltd, Ware, Hertfordshire
WkmR	Wickham Rail, Bush Bank, Suckley, Worcestershire (successors to Bruff & Wkm)
WLLR	West Lancashire Light Railway, Hesketh Bank, near Preston, Lancashire
W&LLR	Welshpool & Llanfair Light Railway Preservation Co Ltd, Llanfair Caereinion, Powys, Mid Wales
WMD	Waggon & Maschinenbau GmbH, Donauwörth, Germany
Wolverton	Wolverton Works, Buckinghamshire — British Rail Engineering Ltd
Woodings	Woodings Railcar Ltd, Alexandria, Ontario, Canada
Woolwich	Woolwich Arsenal, London
WR	Wingrove & Rogers Ltd, Kirkby, Liverpool (successors to BEV)

Y

YE	Yorkshire Engine Co Ltd, Meadow Hall Works, Sheffield
YEC	Yorkshire Engine Company Ltd, Unit 7, Meadow Bank Industrial Estate, Harrison Street, Rotherham, South Yorkshire; *and later at* Unit A3, Templeborough Enterprise Park, Bowbridge Close, Rotherham, South Yorkshire
York(BRE)	York Works (British Rail Engineering Ltd), North Yorkshire
Young&Co	J. Young & Co, Leeds

Z

| Zephir | Zephir S.p.a., via Salvador Allende 85, 41100 Modena, Italy |

9

| 9E | Nine Elms Works, London — London & South Western Railway |

CONTRACTORS

Listed below are the Civil Engineering Contractors / Plant Hire specialists who own locos for use on tunnelling and sewer contracts, etc. The locos are to be found in all parts of the Country but the details of the loco fleets are listed under the firm's main depot in the County shown below.

TITLE OF FIRM	COUNTY
Amalgamated Construction	South Yorkshire
Amec Construction	Staffordshire
Byzac Contractors Ltd	Lancashire
D.C.T. Civil Engineering	Greater Manchester
V.J. Doneghan (Plant) Ltd	Greater Manchester
Grant Rail Ltd	Lincolnshire
McNicholas Construction Co Ltd	Hertfordshire
J.Murphy & Sons Ltd	Greater London
Edmund Nuttall Ltd	Greater London
South Western Mining & Tunnelling Ltd	Cornwall
Specialist Plant Associates Ltd	Bedfordshire
Thyssen (Great Britain) Ltd	West Yorkshire
A.E.Yates Ltd	Greater Manchester

HIRE FLEET OPERATORS

A number of companies are particularly active in the loco hire business, maintaining a fleet of locomotives for hire or sale. Such locos are hired out to industrial users and main-line "TOC" (Train Operating Companies). As such the locos can be seen all over the country, frequently on short-term loan. Hire Fleet Operators are listed in this book in the county of their principal or headquarters address, together with known details of their current fleet. In several cases, however, few or no locomotives are stabled at the addresses given.

Alan Keef Ltd (narrow gauge locos)	Herefordshire
Harry Needle Railroad Co Ltd, St.Helens	Merseyside
John Payne	Warwickshire
L H Group Services Ltd,	Staffordshire
Mike Darnall, Newton Heath	Greater Manchester
RMS Locotec Ltd, Dewsbury	West Yorkshire
Staffordshire Locomotive, Lichfield	Staffordshire
Wabtec Rail Ltd, Doncaster	South Yorkshire
WB Power Services Ltd, Ilkeston	Derbyshire

SECTION 1 — ENGLAND

‡   "Tyne & Wear" has been replaced by a number of Unitary Authorities. Rather than fragment our listings, we have amalgamated locations south of the River Tyne into the County Durham listing, and locations north of the river into the Northumberland listing.

BEDFORDSHIRE

INDUSTRIAL SITES

SPECIALIST PLANT ASSOCIATES LTD,
PLANT DEPOT, 23 PODINGTON AIRFIELD, HINWICK, WELLINGBOROUGH
Locos present in yard between use on contracts   SP 948608

Gauge 2ft 6in

03418		4wDH		CE	B1563Q	1978	
	SPS 419	4wDH		CE			

Gauge 750mm

2B		4wBE		CE	B4057B	1994	

Gauge 2ft 0in

2.4.70		4wBE		CE	B4010A	1994	
3.4.60		4wBE		CE	B4010B	1994	

Gauge 2ft 0in / 1ft 6in

–		4wBE		CE	B3686A	1990	
–		4wBE		CE	B3686B	1990	
	RR51 7001	4wBE		CE	B3686C	1990	
			reb	CE	B4075.1	1995	
	RR51 7002	4wBE		CE	B3686D	1990	
			reb	CE	B4075.2	1995	
JM 83	SP 83	4wBE		CE	5942A	1972	
JM 84		4wBE		CE	5942B	1972	
SP 203		4wBE		CE	B0182C	1974	
JM 88		4wBE		CE	B0402A	1974	
(JM) 90		4wBE		CE	B0402C	1974	
–		4wBE		CE	B0943	1976	
02		4wBE		CE	B0997A	1977	
			reb	CE	B3903	1992	
SP 204		4wBE		CE	B1808	1978	
			reb	CE	B3214A	1985	
			reb	CE	B3825	1992	
SP 36		4wBE		CE			
SP 86		4wBE		CE			
			reb	SPA		1995	
SP 03 364		4wBE		CE			

Gauge 1ft 10in

		4wBE		CE	B2247A	1980	+
050		4wBE		CE	B3077A	1983	+
		4wBE		CE			
		4wBE		CE			

SP80	CONTEX 2	4wBE	CE	5940B	1972
SP 202		4wBE	CE	B0176A	1974

+ identity assumed

PRESERVATION SITES

BEDFORDSHIRE STEAM ENGINE PRESERVATION SOCIETY, CLIFTON
Gauge 2ft 0in

–	0-6-0T	OC	Dec	1735	1919

GREAT WOBURN RAILWAY, PETER SCOTT WOBURN SAFARI PARK, WOBURN
Gauge 1ft 8in SP 962343

LADY ALEXANDRA	0-4-0DH	s/o	AK	70	2004

LEIGHTON BUZZARD NARROW GAUGE RAILWAY SOCIETY
Locos are kept at :-

Pages Park Shed SP 929242
Stonehenge Workshop SP 941275

Gauge 2ft 6in

WD 767139	2w-2PMR		Wkm	3282	1943

Gauge 2ft 0in

4	DOLL	0-6-0T	OC	AB	1641	1919	
	SEZELA No.4	0-4-0T	OC	AE	1738	1915	
No.3	RISHRA	0-4-0T	OC	BgC	2007	1921	
16	LION	4-6-0T	OC	BLW	44656	1917	
1	CHALONER	0-4-0VBT	VC	DeW		1877	
73	"BERLIN"	0-4-0WT	OC	Freud	73	1901	
			reb	ARC		c1983	
	PETER PAN	0-4-0ST	OC	KS	4256	1922	
No.113	PIXIE "2"	0-4-0ST	OC	KS	4260	1922	
No.11	P.C.ALLEN	0-4-0WT	OC	OK	5834	1912	
	PEDEMOURA	0-6-0WT	OC	OK	10808	1924	
"5"	ELF	0-6-0WT	OC	OK	12740	1936	
–		0-4-0WT	OC	OK	2544	1907	
4	PETER WOOD	4wDH		HE	9347	1994	
No.5		4wDM		MR	5608	1931	b
No.6	MABEL 1	4wDM		MR	5875	1935	b
"7"	8986 FALCON	4wDM		OK	8986	1938	
No.8		2w-2DMR		Bg	3539	1959	
			reb	AK		1988	f
8	"GOLLUM"	4wDM		RH	217999	1942	
"9"	"MADGE"	4wDM		OK	7600	1938	
10	21 HAYDN TAYLOR	4wDM		MR	7956	1945	

12	CARBON	4wPM	MR	6012	1930	
13	ARKLE	4wDM	MR	7108	1936	
"14"		4wDM	HE	3646	1946	
"15"		4wDM	FH	2514	1941	
"16"		4wDM	L	11221	1939	
No.17	DAMREDUB	4wDM	MR	7036	1936	
"18"	FËANOR	4wDM	MR	11003	1956	
"19"		4wDM	MR	11298	1965	
"20"	60S317 "VILYA"	4wDM	MR	60S317	1966	
No.21	FESTOON	4wPM	MR	4570	1929	
"22"	"FINGOLFIN"	4wDM	LBNGRS	1	1989	c
23		4wDM	RH	164346	1932	
24		4wDM	MR	11297	1965	
24		4wDM	MR	4805	1934	Dsm
"25"		4wDM	MR	7214	1938	
"26"	YIMKIN	4wDM	RH	203026	1942	e
27	POPPY	4wDH	RH	408430	1957	
28	R.A.F. STANBRIDGE	4wDM	RH	200516	1940	d
29	CREEPY YARD No. P 19774	4wDM	HE	6008	1963	
No.30	MANIFOLD MAGGIE	4wDM	MR	8695	1941	
31	No.37658 THORIN OAKENSHIELD	4wPM	L	4228	1931	
"32"		4wDM	RH	172892	1934	
33		4wDM	FH	3582	1954	Dsm
No.34	RED RUM	4wDM	MR	7105	1936	
"35"	9303/507	0-4-0DM	HE	6619	1966	
"36"	"CARAVAN"	4wDM	MR	7129	1936	
"37"		4wDM	RH	172901	1935	
No.38	HARRY BARNETT	4wDM	L	37170	1951	
LM 39	T.W.LEWIS	4wDM	RH		1954	a
"40"	TRENT	4wDM	RH	283507	1949	
41	LOD/758054 SOMME	4wDM	HE	2536	1941	
"42"	"SARAH"	4wDM	RH	223692	1943	
43		4wDM	MR	10409	1954	
44		4wDM	MR	7933	1941	
"45"		4wDM	MR	21615	1957	
"46"		4wDM	RH	209430	1942	
"47"		4wDM	HU	38384	1930	
"48"		4wDM	HE	4351	1952	
No.80	BEAUDESERT	4wDH	SMH	101T018	1979	
		reb	AK	59R	1999	
No.131		4wDM	MR	5613	1931	Dsm
No.1568		4wPM	FH	1568	1927	
WD2182	No. LR 10227	4wPM	MR	461	1917	
2275	3098 No. L.R.10756	4wPM	MR	1377	1918	
R8		4wDM	MR	5612	1931	Dsm
LOD	758009	4wDM	MR	8641	1941	
LOD	758220	4wDM	MR	8745	1942	
	BLUEBELL	4wDM	FH		1943	g
	"REDLANDS"	4wDM	MR	5603	1931	Dsm

–	4wDM		MR	8731	1941	Dsm
–	4wDM		MR			Dsm
–	4wDM		RH	187105	1937	
–	4wDM		RH	218016	1943	Dsm
RTT/ 767182	2w-2PMR		Wkm	2522	1938	

Gauge 1ft 10¾in

ELIDIR	0-4-0T	OC	AE	2071	1933	

a	either RH 375315 or RH 375316
b	converted into a brake van
c	built from parts of RH 425798/1958 & RH 444207/1961
d	carries plate RH 200513
e	nameplate is in Arabic
f	rebuilt from 4ft 8½in gauge 2w-2DMR, now an unpowered coach
g	either FH 2631 or FH 2834

THE LIGHT RAILWAY ASSOCIATION, STEVINGTON & TURVEY LIGHT RAILWAY, TURVEY

Gauge 2ft 0in

TL 967524

	CATFISH	4wDM	Diema	1600	1953	
	–	4wPM	FH	1767	1931	Dsm
No.15	OLDE	4wDM	HE	2176	1940	
	–	4wDM	MR	5877	1935	
	–	4wDM	MR	7128	1936	Dsm
No.1	PAUL COOPER	4wDM	MR	9655	1951	
	–	4wDM	OK	3685	1929	
11	NEEDHAM	4wDM	OK	6504	1936	
	–	4wDM	OK	7728	1937	Dsm
No.7	COLLINGWOOD	4wDM	RH	373359	1954	

Gauge 1ft 6in

1514	0-4-0BE	WR			+

+	currently under renovation elsewhere

Mrs. MACKINNON

Gauge 1ft 8in

–	4wDM	OK	6703	1936	Pvd

Loco believed to be preserved by a member of the family at an unknown location.

RAY MASLEN & FRIENDS, PRIVATE RAILWAY, ARLESEY

Gauge 2ft 0in

CLARABEL	4wDMF	HE	4758	1954	
–	4wDM	L	37911	1952	
–	4wDM	RH	441951	1960	
RTT 767187	2w-2PM	Wkm	2559	1939	Dsm
RTT/767094	2w-2PM	Wkm	3033	1941	Dsm

WHIPSNADE WILD ANIMAL PARK LTD,
GREAT WHIPSNADE RAILWAY, WHIPSNADE ZOO
Gauge 2ft 6in TL 004172

No.2	EXCELSIOR	0-4-2ST	OC	KS	1049	1908	
No.4	SUPERIOR	0-6-2T	OC	KS	4034	1920	
3		4wDH		BD	3780	1983	
	VICTOR	0-6-0DM		JF	4160004	1951	
9	HECTOR	0-6-0DM		JF	4160005	1951	
	HERCULES	0-6-0DH		AUG	24376	1981	

BERKSHIRE

PRESERVATION SITES

D. BUCK, near WINDSOR
Gauge 1524mm

1016	4-6-2	OC	TK	946	1955	

Gauge 4ft 8½in — locos are kept at a private site.

	HORNPIPE	0-4-0ST	OC	P	1756	1928	
334\G102	SIR VINCENT	4wWT	G	AP	8800	1917	
	"TRACKRAT"	2-2wDHR	Group Engineering				
					RAT2001	c1998	

Mrs. MARY KEELY, KNOWL HILL
Gauge 1ft 3in SU 826803

–	4-4-0	OC	T S Thurston	incomplete loco OOU	

LEGOLAND, WINDSOR
Gauge 2ft 0in SU 939746

	AMEY	4wDM		MR	7902	1939
	THE IRON BADGER	4-4-0DH	s/o	SL	663	1995

PETER SMITH, NEWBURY
Gauge 1ft 11½in

	(GELLI)	0-4-0VBT	VC	DeW		1893	Dsm
	SUZANNE	4wDM		LB	55730	1968	

NICK WILLIAMS, Private Railway, READING
Gauge 2ft 0in

9	JACK	0-4-0T	OC	AB	1871	1925	

2	SEZELA No.2		0-4-0T	OC	AE	1720	1915	
6	SEZELA No.6		0-4-0T	OC	AE	1928	1923	
–			4wDM		FH	2163	1938	
	LR 2478		4wPM		MR	1757	1918	
–			4wDM		MR	7512	1938	
–			4wDM		MR	11264	1964	
–			4wDM		RH	277265	1949	
–			4wDM		RH	296091	1949	
–			0-4-0BE		WR	N7661	1974	
	RTT 767186		2w-2PM		Wkm	2558	1939	Dsm

WINDSOR STATION LTD, WINDSOR & ETON CENTRAL STATION

Gauge 4ft 8½in — non-working replica of Sdn 1401 / 1894 SU 969773

3041	THE QUEEN	4-2-2	Steamtown	1983

BRISTOL

INDUSTRIAL SITES

COUNTY OF AVON FIRE BRIGADE, AVONMOUTH FIRE STATION (Bristol)
and YATE FIRE STATION (Gloucestershire)
Gauge 4ft 8½in ST 517784, 714826

	E669 JOU	4wDM	R/R	Perm		1996
	N842 HFB	4wDM	R/R	Renault		1995
–		2w-2PMR		Bance	137	2004

R.& A. GUNN, BRISTOL
Gauge 1ft 10in — loco in storage.

–	4wBE	WR	2489	1943

PRESERVATION SITES

BRISTOL INDUSTRIAL MUSEUM,
BRISTOL HARBOUR RAILWAY, PRINCES WHARF, CITY DOCK, BRISTOL
Gauge 4ft 8½in ST 585722

No.34	PORTBURY	0-6-0ST	OC	AE	1764	1917
3		0-6-0ST	OC	FW	242	1874
	HENBURY	0-6-0ST	OC	P	1940	1937
–		0-4-0DM		RH	418792	1959

JOE NEMETH ENGINEERING LTD, WASHINGPOOL FARM, MAIN ROAD, EASTER COMPTON, BRISTOL
Visitors welcome by appointment only.
Gauge 600mm   www.joenemethengineeringltd.com

3175		0-4-0WT	OC	Jung	3175	1921

BUCKINGHAMSHIRE

INDUSTRIAL SITES

ALSTOM RAILCARE, WOLVERTON WORKS, STRATFORD ROAD, WOLVERTON
Gauge 4ft 8½in   SP 812413

(D3796)	08629	0-6-0DE	Derby	1959
D3816	(08649)	0-6-0DE	Hor	1959
	TITCHIE	4wDM	SMH 103GA078	1978

PRESERVATION SITES

GULLIVERS LAND, MILTON KEYNES
Gauge 1ft 3in

No.2	0-6-0+6wDE s/o	Gullivers	1999

LAVENDON NARROW GAUGE RAILWAY, HAROLD ROAD, LAVENDON.
Gauge 3ft 0in   SP 922537

–	4wBE	GB	

MILTON KEYNES CENTRAL STATION, MILTON KEYNES
Gauge 4ft 8½in — non working replica   SP 842381

1009	WOLVERTON	2-2-2	IC	Mercia	1991

QUAINTON RAILWAY SOCIETY LTD, BUCKINGHAMSHIRE RAILWAY CENTRE, QUAINTON ROAD STATION, nr AYLESBURY
Gauge 4ft 8½in   SP 736189, 739190

5080	DEFIANT	4-6-0	4C	Sdn	1939
6989	WIGHTWICK HALL	4-6-0	OC	Sdn	1948

No.	Name	Type	Cyl	Builder	Works No.	Date	Note
7200		2-8-2T	OC	Sdn		1934	
9466		0-6-0PT	IC	RSHN	7617	1952	
41298		2-6-2T	OC	Crewe		1951	
46447		2-6-0	OC	Crewe		1950	
	SWANSCOMBE	0-4-0ST	OC	AB	699	1891	
–		0-4-0F	OC	AB	1477	1916	
	LAPORTE	0-4-0F	OC	AB	2243	1948	
		4wWT	G	AP	807	1872	
No.1	SIR THOMAS	0-6-0T	OC	HC	1334	1918	
	MILLOM	0-4-0ST	OC	HC	1742	1946	
	ARTHUR	0-6-0ST	IC	HE	3782	1953	
	JUNO	0-6-0ST	IC	HE	3850	1958	
N.C.B.66		0-6-0ST	IC	HE	3890	1964	a
–		0-4-0ST	OC	HL	3717	1928	
No.1	COVENTRY No.1	0-6-0T	IC	NBH	24564	1939	
1		0-4-4T	IC	Neasden	3	1898	
–		0-4-0T	OC	P	1900	1936	
2087	LT 55 GIBRALTAR	0-4-0ST	OC	P	2087	1948	
	ROKEBY	0-4-0ST	OC	P	2105	1950	+
	L.N.E.R.40	4wVBT	VCG	S	6515	1926	
11		4wVBT	VCG	S	9366	1945	
5208		2w-2-2-2w-4-4 12CGR		S	9418	1950	
7	SUSAN	4wVBT	VCG	S	9537	1952	
–		0-4-0ST	OC	WB	2469	1932	
	CHISLET	0-6-0ST	OC	YE	2498	1951	
D2298		0-6-0DM		_(RSHD	8157	1960	
				(DC	2679	1960	
T1		4wDM		FH	2102	1937	
	WALRUS	0-4-0DM		FH	3271	1949	
–		4wDM		FH	3765	1955	
	ESSO	0-4-0DM		HE	2067	1940	
	OSRAM	0-4-0DM		JF	20067	1933	
	REDLAND	4wDM		KS	4428	1930	
–		0-4-0DE		RH	425477	1959	
			reb	Resco		1979	
1139	HILSEA	4wDM		RH	463153	1961	
M51886		2-2w-2w-2DMR		DerbyC&W		1960	
M51899	AYLESBURY COLLEGE	2-2w-2w-2DMR		DerbyC&W		1960	
53028		2w-2-2-2wRER		BRCW		1938	
54233		2w-2-2-2wRER		GRC&W		1939/40	
			reb	Acton		1941	
ARMY 9040		2w-2PMR		Wkm	6963	1955	
RLC 009037		2w-2PMR		Wkm	8197	1958	
	(TP53P)	2w-2PMR		Wkm	8263	1959	

+ actually built in 1948 but plates dated as shown
a currently at South Coast Steam Co Ltd, Dorset

Gauge 3ft 6in

No.	Name	Type	Cyl	Builder	Works No.	Date
3405	JANICE	4-8-4	OC	NBH	27291	1953

Gauge 2ft 0in

803	2w-2-2-2wRE	EEDK	803	1931	+

+ built 1931 but originally carried plates dated 1930

SIR WILLIAM McALPINE Bt, THE FAWLEY HILL RAILWAY, FAWLEY HILL, FAWLEY GREEN, near HENLEY-on-THAMES
Gauge 4ft 8½in   SU 755861

SIR ROBERT McALPINE & SONS (LONDON) LIMITED No.31

		0-6-0ST	IC	HC	1026	1913
D2120 (03120)		0-6-0DM		Sdn		1959
(ARMY 9112)		4wPMR		Bg	3538	1959
–		4wDM		FH	3817	1956
ERNIE		4wDM		FH	3894	1958
			reb	AB	6930	1988
"SIR WILLIAM"		4wDM		RH	294266	1951

SIR JEREMY SULLIVAN, WOTTON LIGHT RAILWAY, near AYLESBURY
Gauge 1ft 3in

SANDY	0-6-0T	OC	ESR	301	1996
PAM	0-4-0DH		AK	52	1996
POMPEY	4w-4wDH		AK	64	2001

CAMBRIDGESHIRE

INDUSTRIAL SITES

EUROPEAN METAL RECYCLING LTD, MAYER PARRY RECYCLING, 111 FORDHAM ROAD, SNAILWELL, NEWMARKET
Gauge 4ft 8½in   TL 638678

ARMY 410	0-4-0DH		NBQ	27645	1958
468048	0-6-0DH		RH	468048	1963

NETWORK RAIL, WHITEMOOR YARD, MARCH
Gauge 4ft 8½in   TF 415985

(D3924)	08756	H 039	0-6-0DE	Hor		1961
(D4115)	08885	H 042	0-6-0DE	Hor		1962

Shunting carried out by Contractor – currently R.M.S. Locotec Ltd, Wakefield, West Yorkshire.

THE POTTER GROUP LTD - ELY, RAIL DISTRIBUTION CENTRE, QUEEN ADELAIDE, ELY

Gauge 4ft 8½in   TL 563810

–		0-6-0DH		TH	150C	1965
	a rebuild of	0-6-0VBT	VCG	S		
03038		4wDM	R/R	Unimog		
				424121 10 083216		1982

RUGBY CEMENT, BARRINGTON CEMENT WORKS
(Part of Cemex UK Ltd)

Gauge 4ft 8½in   TL 396504

–	6wDE	GECT	5578	1980	
7	4wDH	S	10040	1960	
No.8	4wDH	TH	178V	1967	Pvd

PRESERVATION SITES

R. BLACKMORE, MILL GREEN FARM, HORSEHEATH

Gauge 600mm   TL 624452

R/4 'JANE'		4wDM	MR	8565	1940
RTT/767178		2w-2PM	Wkm	3170	c1943

Gauge 2ft 0in

RTT/767095		2w-2PM	Wkm	3414	1943
	rebuilt as	2w-2DM			1992

C. CROSS, 4 PACIFIC CLOSE, MARCH

Gauge 4ft 8½in   TF 415975

40/234 N	2w-2PMR	Wkm	9523	1963

Mr. DRAGE, NEW BUILDINGS FARM, HEYDON, near ROYSTON

Gauge 4ft 8½in   TL 419409

–		0-4-0ST	OC	AB	1219	1910
11 13 NEWCASTLE	0-6-0ST	IC	MW	1532	1901
960236		2w-2PMR	Wkm	1519	1934

IMPERIAL WAR MUSEUM, DUXFORD AERODROME

Gauge 2ft 0in   TL 461462, 456456

–	4wPM	MR	1364	1918
–	4wPM	MR	3849	1927

NENE VALLEY RAILWAY LTD

Locos are kept at :-

Peterborough Nene Valley TL 188982
Wansford Steam Centre TL 093979

Gauge 4ft 8½in

(61306)	No.1306 MAYFLOWER	4-6-0	OC	NBQ	26207	1948	
73050	CITY OF PETERBOROUGH	4-6-0	OC	Derby		1954	
No. 5485		0-8-0T	OC	Chrz	5485	1961	
No.15		0-6-0ST	IC	AB	2183	1945	
–		0-4-0VBT	OC	Cockerill	1626	1890	
Ty2-7173	30D43 873	2-10-0	OC	Flor	16626	1943	
Nr.656		0-6-0T	OC	Frichs	360	1949	
	RHOS	0-6-0ST	OC	HC	1308	1918	
	DEREK CROUCH	0-6-0ST	IC	HC	1539	1924	
1	THOMAS	0-6-0T	OC	HC	1800	1947	
	JACKS GREEN	0-6-0ST	IC	HE	1953	1939	
75006		0-6-0ST	IC	HE	2855	1943	
	230 D 116	4-6-0	4CC	Hen	10745	1911	
64.305		2-6-2T	OC	Krupp	1308	1934	
1178		2-6-2T	OC	Motala	516	1914	
S.V.B.J. 101		4-6-0	OC	Nohab	2082	1944	
D306	(40106) ATLANTIC CONVEYOR						
		1Co-Co1DE		_(EE	2726	1960	
				(RSHD	8136	1960	
(D)1971	47270 SWIFT	Co-CoDE		Crewe		1965	
(D5801)	31271 STRATFORD 1840 – 2001						
		A1A-A1ADE		BT	302	1961	
(D6776	37076) 37518	Co-CoDE		_(EE	3068	1962	
				(RSHD	8322	1962	
D9516		0-6-0DH		Sdn		1964	
(D9518)	9312/95 NCB No.7	0-6-0DH		Sdn		1964	
D9520	45	0-6-0DH		Sdn		1964	
D9523		0-6-0DH		Sdn		1964	
01566	D9504	0-6-0DH		Sdn		1964	a
W 51347		2-2w-2w-2DMR		PSteel		1960	
W 51401		2-2w-2w-2DMR		PSteel		1960	
–		0-4-0DH		EEV	D1123	1966	
–		4wDM		FH	2896	1944	OOU
–		0-4-0DM		RH	304469	1951	
	BARABEL	0-4-0DH		RR	10202	1964	
DL83		0-6-0DH		RR	10271	1967	
NCB No.11	BIRCH COPPICE	4wDH		TH	134C	1964	
	a rebuild of	4wVBT	VCG	S	9578	1954	
–		0-4-0DE		YE	2654	1957	
–		0-6-0DE		YE	2670	1958	
	DR 98500	4wDHR		Plasser	52788	1985	
	NVR 1612	2w-2PMR		Wkm		1944	
5		2-2wPMR		Bance			

a   currently on loan to Aggregate Industries UK Ltd, Bardon Hill Quarry, Leicestershire

C.J.& A.M. PEARMAN, 4 TANGLEWOOD, ALCONBURY WESTON, HUNTINGDON
Gauge 1ft 11½in

–	4wPM	MR	2059	1920	

RAILWORLD, (MUSEUM OF WORLD RAILWAYS), WOODSTON, PETERBOROUGH
Gauge 4ft 8½in   TL 188982

No.996	4-6-2	4C	Frichs	415	1950
804 X-411	Bo-BoDE		Alco	77778	1950

Gauge 2ft 6in

5 LBC 1 NUTTY	4wVBT	ICG	S	7701	1929	+

+   stored off site

SHEPRETH WILDLIFE PARK, WILLERSMILL ROAD, SHEPRETH
Gauge 400mm   TL 393481

–	4-6wRE	s/o	UK Loco		2007

S. THOMASON, PRIVATE LOCATION, HUNTINGDON
Gauge 2ft 6in

–	4wBE	WR	3557	1946

Gauge 750mm

10	4wDM	Moes

Gauge 600mm

12	4wDM	Moes

ROGER WOLFERSTAN, 238, HIGH STREET, CHESTERTON
Gauge 2ft 0in

–	4wDM	LB	54684	1965

CHESHIRE

INDUSTRIAL SITES

BOMBARDIER TRANSPORTATION INC. OF CANADA, CREWE WORKS
Gauge 4ft 8½in   SJ 691561

D4173	(08943) PET II	0-6-0DE		Dar		1962
18	TINY II	0-4-0DH		YE	2676	1959
		4wDH	R/R	NNM	77501	1980

CROGHAN HILL HORTICULTURE LTD,
WILMSLOW PEAT FARM, LINDOW MOSS, MOOR LANE, WILMSLOW
Gauge 2ft 0in   R.T.C.   SJ 823803

–	4wDM	AK	No.4	1979	OOU
–	4wDH	LB	50888	1959	OOU
–	4wDM	LB	52528	1961	Dsm

THE O'CONNOR GROUP, WIDNES INTERMODAL RAIL DEPOT, WIDNES
Gauge 4ft 8½in   SJ 503846

7189	GAFFER	0-6-0DH	HE	7189	1970

PRESERVATION SITES

BROOKSIDE GARDEN CENTRE LTD, LONDON ROAD NORTH, POYNTON
Gauge 4ft 8½in   SJ 925853

KATIE	0-4-0ST	OC	AB	2226	1946

CREWE HERITAGE TRUST, CREWE HERITAGE CENTRE, CREWE
Gauge 4ft 8½in   ST 708553

5553		2-6-2T	OC	Sdn		1928	+
6634		0-6-2T	IC	Sdn		1928	
7027	THORNBURY CASTLE	4-6-0	4C	Sdn		1949	
60009	UNION OF SOUTH AFRICA						
		4-6-2	3C	Don	1853	1937	
70000	BRITANNIA	4-6-2	OC	Crewe		1951	
92134		2-10-0	OC	Crewe		1957	
(D172)	46035 (97403) IXION	1-Co-Co-1DE		Derby		1962	
(D1770	47175) 47575	Co-CoDE		BT	532	1964	
D2073	(03073)	0-6-0DM		Don		1959	
(D3998)	08830	0-6-0DE		Derby		1960	

M 49002		Bo-BoWE	Derby		1977	
87035		Bo-BoWE	Crewe		1974	

+   loco is based here but will be loaned out to other locations

DUKE OF WESTMINSTER, EATON HALL RAILWAY, EATON HALL, ECCLESTON, near CHESTER
Gauge 1ft 3in — private location with no public access.   SJ 386612

KATIE	0-4-0T	OC	Thursley / FMB	1994

GULLIVERS WORLD, LOST WORLD RAIL ROAD, SHACKLETON CLOSE, WARRINGTON
Gauge 1ft 3in   SJ 590900

1		0-6-0+6wDE	s/o	Meridian	1989
INVICTA		4wPH		Maxitrack	1989

NEVILLE JONES, CHESTER AREA
Gauge 2ft 6in

50	0-6-0DH	HB	D1419	1971

L.N.W.R. LTD, CREWE CARRIAGE WORKS, CREWE
Gauge 4ft 8½in

(D408)	50008 THUNDERER	Co-CoDE	_(EE	3778	1967
			(EEV	D1149	1967
(D431)	50031 HOOD	Co-CoDE	_(EE	3801	1968
			(EEV	D1172	1968
(D3978)	08810	0-6-0DE	Derby		1960
(D4036)	08868	0-6-0DE	Dar		1960

TESCO STORES LTD, VERNON WAY, CREWE
Gauge 4ft 8½in   SJ 707554

ELIZABETH	0-4-0ST	OC	AE	1865	1922	+

+   works number carried is shown as 1868 in error

WRENBURY STATION
Gauge 4ft 8½in

(D3290 08220)	0-6-0DE	Derby		1956

CORNWALL

INDUSTRIAL SITES

DRILLSERVE, PLANT YARD, ROSCROGGAN, near CAMBORNE
Locomotives for resale are occasionally present.   SW 648418
Gauge 750mm

–	4wDH?		GIA	55134	1966

IMERYS CLAY COMPANY
Blackpool Driers, Burngullow
Gauge 4ft 8½in   SW 985525

(D3390 08320) P400D SUSAN	0-6-0DE	Derby		1957

Crugwallins Sidings
Gauge 4ft 8½in   SW 978525

P403D DENISE	4wDH	S	10029	1960

Drinnick Mill
Gauge 4ft 8½in

P404D G924 ACV ELAINE	4wDM	R/R	Trackmobile GN960300689		1989

Rocks Works, near Bugle
Gauge 4ft 8½in   SX 025586

(D3513 08398) 402D ANNABEL	0-6-0DE	Derby		1958

SOUTH WESTERN MINING & TUNNELLING LTD, PLANT DEPOT, COTTONWOOD, NANSTALLON, BODMIN
Gauge 2ft 0in   SX 021677

–	0-4-0BE	WR	G7174	1967

T. WARE, SCRAP DEALER, CARHARRACK, near ST.DAY
Gauge 4ft 8½in   SW 741417

TO 9362	4wDM	RH	349041	1953	OOU

PRESERVATION SITES

BODMIN & WENFORD RAILWAY plc

Locos are kept at :-

Bodmin General Station	SX 074664
Bodmin Parkway	SX 110640
Bodmin Walker Lines Sidings	SX 060660
Boscarne Junction	SX 044675
Fitzgerald Lighting	SX 079655

Gauge 4ft 8½in

4247		2-8-0T	OC	Sdn	2637	1916
4612		0-6-0PT	IC	Sdn		1942
5552		2-6-2T	OC	Sdn		1928
6435		0-6-0PT	IC	Sdn		1937
(30120)	120	4-4-0	IC	9E	572	1899
30587		2-4-0WT	OC	BP	1412	1874
30585		2-4-0WT	OC	BP	1414	1874
	JUDY	0-4-0ST	OC	WB	2572	1937
–		0-6-0ST	IC	WB	2766	1944
19		0-4-0ST	OC	WB	2962	1950
	ALFRED	0-4-0ST	OC	WB	3058	1953
–		0-4-0F	OC	WB	3121	1957
(D442)	50042 TRIUMPH	Co-CoDE		_(EE	3812	1968
				(EEV	D1183	1968
(D1787)	47306	Co-CoDE		BT	549	1964
D3452		0-6-0DE		Dar		1957
(D3559)	08444	0-6-0DE		Derby		1958
(D6527)	33110	Bo-BoDE		BRCW	DEL119	1960
(D8197)	20197	Bo-BoDE		_(EE	3678	1966
				(EEV	D1073	1966
(D6842)	37142	Co-CoDE		_(EE	3317	1963
				(EEV	D816	1963
50980	LO 275	2-2w-2w-2DMR		DerbyC&W		1959
51947		2-2w-2w-2DMR		DerbyC&W		1961
W52054	LO 618	2-2w-2w-2DMR		DerbyC&W		1960
	PETER	0-4-0DM		JF	22928	1940
NDS 3		4wDM		RH	443642	1960

CORNWALL COUNTY COUNCIL,
GEEVOR TIN MINES MUSEUM, PENDEEN, near ST.JUST

Two of the un-numbered CE locos are numbered 2 and 8, but which works numbers these pair with is unknown.

Gauge 1ft 6in
SW 375346

3	4wBE	CE	5739	1970
–	4wBE	CE	B1501	1977
–	4wBE	CE	B0189A	1978
–	4wBE	CE	B0189B	1978
13	4wBE	CE	B1851A	1978
15	4wBE	CE	B3132A	1984

B3606A		4wBE	CE	B3606A	1989	
–		4wBE	CE	B3606C	1989	
–		4wBE	CE	B3606D	1989	
1		0-4-0BE	Geevor			
2		0-4-0BE	Geevor			
4		0-4-0BE	Geevor			Pvd
11		0-4-0BE	Geevor			
13		0-4-0BE	Geevor			
15		0-4-0BE	Geevor			
19		0-4-0BE	Geevor			
–		0-4-0BE	Geevor			
–		0-4-0BE	Geevor			
–		0-4-0BE	Geevor			
–		4wBE	WR			

The Geevor-built locos are based on, and use parts of, WR or CE locos.

J. EVANS, CALLINGTON
Gauge 2ft 0in

SYBIL	0-4-0ST	OC	WB	1760	1906	+

+   currently under restoration elsewhere

HELSTON DIESEL GROUP, TREVARNO
Gauge 4ft 8½in   **www.helstondieselgroup.co.uk**

D2959	SHIRE LODGE	0-4-0DM	RH	327974	1954
D2960	IVOR	0-4-0DM	RH	395305	1956
(50413)		2-2w-2w-2DMR	PRoyal	B38848	1958

LAPPA VALLEY STEAM RAILWAY & COUNTRY LEISURE PARK, BENNY HALT, ST.NEWLYN EAST, near NEWQUAY
Gauge 1ft 3in   SW 838574, 839564

No.2	MUFFIN		0-6-0	OC	Berwyn		1967
				reb	Tambling		1991
No.1	ZEBEDEE		0-6-2T	OC	SL	7434	1974
		rebuilt as	0-6-4T	OC	Tambling		1990
4	POOH		4wDM		L	20698	1942
3	GLADIATOR		4w-4DH		Minirail		c1960
	(DOUGAL)		4w-4PM		BoothE		1975	+ DsmT

+   unpowered flat wagon

LAUNCESTON STEAM RAILWAY CO, LAUNCESTON
Gauge 600mm   SX 328850

LILIAN	0-4-0ST	OC	HE	317	1883
VELINHELI	0-4-0ST	OC	HE	409	1886
COVERTCOAT	0-4-0ST	OC	HE	679	1898

	DOROTHEA		0-4-0ST	OC	HE	763	1901	
89			4wVBT	VC	Bowman		2004	
38			2w-2-2-2wRE		EEDK	761	1930	
42			2w-2-2-2wRE		EEDK	806	1930	
–			4wDM		FH	1896	1935	Dsm
2			4wDM		MR	5646	1933	
–			2w-2BER		Bowman		c1986	
		reb	4wBE		Bowman		(date unknown)	
			4w-4DER		Bowman		2003	
2			4wPER		Bowman		2003	
		reb	4wDER		Bowman		2004	

MOSELEY N.G. INDUSTRIAL TRAMWAY & MUSEUM, TUMBLY DOWN FARM, TOLGUS MOUNT, REDRUTH
Gauge 2ft 0in   SW 686428

	THE LADY D	4wDM		MR	8934	1944	
AD40	LOD 758366	4wDM		RH	202000	1940	
	SMELTER	4wDM	s/o	RH	229647	1943	
–		4wBE		GB	2345	1951	
	"CATHODE"	4wBE		GB	2960	1959	
	ANODE	4wBE		GB	420172	1969	
1298		0-4-0BE		WR	1298	1938	
20	DIODE	0-4-0BE		WR	L1021	1983	

M.P.S. METAL PROTECTION SERVICES, GREAT WESTERN RAILWAY YARD, near TRURO
Gauge 4ft 8½in   SW 721492

YARD No.5200	4wDM		FH	3776	1956

NATIONAL TRUST, LEVANT MINE
Gauge 1ft 6in   SW 368346

–	4wBE		CE	B3606B	1989

PARADISE RAILWAY, BIRD PARADISE, PARADISE PARK, HAYLE
Gauge 1ft 3in   SW 555365

No.3 ZEBEDEE	4wDM		L	10180	1938

PHOENIX LIGHT RAILWAY TRUST, EAST CORNWALL DEPOT
Gauge 2ft 0in

–	0-4-0DM	s/o	Bg	3235	1947
–	4wDM		L	11410	1939
SIMON	4wDM		MR	7126	1936
–	4wDM		RH	186318	1937

ROBINSON'S SHAFT, FORMER SOUTH CROFTY MINE, POOL, near CAMBORNE
Gauge 1ft 10in

–	4wBE	CE		Dsm

ROSEVALE MINING HISTORICAL SOCIETY, ZENNOR
Gauge 2ft 0in   SW 458380

–	0-4-0BE	WR		
		reb SouthCrofty		

RTZ MINING & EXPLORATION LTD,
DELABOLE SLATE, PENGELLY ROAD, DELABOLE, CAMELFORD
Gauge 1ft 11in   SX 074836

No.2	4wDM	MR	3739	1925

JOHN SPENCELEY, TREVAYLOR FARM
Gauge 2ft 0in Locos stored at private location with no public access

–	0-4-0VBT	VC	Roanoke	2004
(LOD/758221)	4wDM	MR	8886	1944

THE SPIRIT OF THE WEST AMERICAN THEME PARK,
RETALLACK, near ST COLUMB MAJOR
Gauge 1524mm   SW 936658

1103	2-8-0	OC	LO	141	1943

ST. AUSTELL CHINA CLAY MUSEUM LTD,
CHINA CLAY COUNTRY PARK, MINING & HERITAGE CENTRE,
WHEAL MARTIN, CARTHEW, near ST. AUSTELL
Gauge 4ft 6in   SX 004555

LEE MOOR No.1	0-4-0ST	OC	P	783	1899

Gauge 2ft 6in

–	4wDM	RH	244558	1946

THE TREVITHICK SOCIETY – THE CARN BREA MINING SOCIETY – THE FRIENDS OF KING EDWARD MINE
King Edward Mine, Troon, near Camborne
Gauge 1ft 10in   SW 664389

60	4wBE	SouthCrofty	1992

Redruth Community Centre, Chapel Street, Redruth
Gauge 1ft 10in   SW 696423

(66)	4wBE	SouthCrofty	1996

CUMBRIA

INDUSTRIAL SITES

AYLE COLLIERY CO LTD, AYLE EAST DRIFT, ALSTON

Gauge 2ft 6in — Surface   NY 728498

15/PLB6	152183	No.5261	4wBEF	CE	5074	1965	
15PLB15	15/19	No.5097	4wBEF	CE	5097	1966	
	15/27	No.B0909B	4wBEF	CE	B0909B	1976	
	6/41		0-4-0BE	WR	6133	1959	Dsm
	6/43		4wBE	WR	6297	1960	Dsm
	6/44		0-4-0BE	WR	6595	1962	Dsm
	6/44		0-4-0BE	WR	C6710	1963	Dsm
	6/46		0-4-0BE	WR	6593	1962	Dsm

Gauge 2ft 0in — Surface & Underground

–		4wBE	CE	5667	1969	
–		4wBE	CE	5667	1969	Dsm
–		4wBE	CE	5667	1969	
1520		4wBEF	CE	B0445	1975	
–		4wBEF	GB	2382	1953	Dsm
–		4wDMF	HE	3496	1947	Dsm
–		4wDMF	HE	4569	1956	OOU
–		0-4-0DMF	HE	4991	1955	OOU
	rebuilt as	4wDMF	‡		1977	
–		0-4-0DM	HE	5222	1958	
LE/12/75	P17271	4wBE	WR	E6807	1965	

‡ rebuilt by Ayle Colliery Co Ltd

Gauge 1ft 7½in — Surface

–		0-4-0BE	WR	D6754	1964	Dsm

Gauge 1ft 6in — Surface

4		4wBE	CE	5712	1969	
16 82		4wBE	CE	B3132B	1984	

A.W. BLAKE LTD, (AGRICULTURAL ENGINEERS), SWATHWAITE HEAD, IVEGILL, CARLISLE

Gauge 2ft 0in   NY 421436

3	WEDHOLME	4wDM	MR	8885	1944	OOU
11140		4wDM	MR	8905	1944	OOU
–		4wDM	MR	+		OOU

+ either MR 7463/1939 or MR 9231/1947[see p.47]

BRITISH NUCLEAR FUELS plc, WINDSCALE FACTORY, SELLAFIELD

Gauge 4ft 8½in
NY 025034

B.N.F.L.1	PB 1056.860	0-4-0DH		HE	7426	1982
			reb	HAB	6480	1997
B.N.F.L.2	PB 1056.860	0-4-0DH		HE	7427	1982
B.N.F.L.4	PB 1056.860	0-6-0DH		HE	9000	1983
			reb	HE	9288	1987
			reb	YEC	L117	1992
B.N.F.L.3		0-4-0DH		HE	7406	1977
			reb	HE	9200	1983
			reb	HAB	6478	1997
B.N.F.L.2		0-6-0DH		S	10111	1963
			reb	TH		1987
			reb	HAB	6479	1997
(No. 5)	4	0-4-0DH		HE	6975	1968
No.6	H0344	4wDH	R/R	_(Minilok	158	1991
				(YEC	L105	1992

CORUS, SECTIONS, PLATES & COMMERCIAL STEELS, SHAPFELL LIMESTONE QUARRIES, SHAP, PENRITH

Gauge 4ft 8½in
NY 571134

278		6wDE	GECT	5468	1977
272	GROSMONT	6wDE	GECT	5470	1978

CORUS TRACK PRODUCTS, MOSS BAY WORKS, DERWENT HOWE, WORKINGTON

Gauge 4ft 8½in
(Closed) NX 988269

No.403	0-6-0DH	HE	7543	1978
No.404	0-6-0DH	HE	8978	1979

CUMBRIA COUNTY COUNCIL, PRINCE OF WALES DOCK, THE PORT OF WORKINGTON

Gauge 4ft 8½in
NX 993294

No.211		0-4-0DE	YE	2628	1956
No.212		0-4-0DE	YE	2684	1958
1		0-6-0DH	HE	8976	1979
	reb		HE	9306	
	reb		HE	6706	2000
2		0-6-0DH	HE	8977	1980
	reb		HE	9307	1992
	reb		HE	6707	2000

DIRECT RAIL SERVICES, KINGMOOR DEPOT, CARLISLE

Gauge 4ft 8½in

Locomotives from British Nuclear Fuels plc, Sellafield occasionally present for repair/overhaul.

EGREMONT MINING CO LTD, FLORENCE IRON ORE MINE, EGREMONT

Gauge 2ft 6in — Underground   NY 018103

7		4wBE	WR	6218	1961	
–		4wBE	WR	C6694	1963	

THE BUTTERMERE AND WESTMORLAND GREEN SLATE CO LTD
HONISTER SLATE QUARRY, BORROWDALE

Gauge 2ft 0in   NY 225136

3236	0-4-0DM	s/o	Bg	3236	1947	Pvd
–	0-4-0BE		WR			
–	4wBE		PWR			
				AO.296V.03	1992	

MINISTRY OF DEFENCE, DEFENCE MUNITIONS,
LONGTOWN DEPOT, near CARLISLE

See Section 6 for full details.

F.G.SHEPHERD, FLOW EDGE SCRAP YARD, MIDDLE FELL, ALSTON

Gauge 2ft 0in   NY 734442

–	4wBEF	CE	B3084	1984	

Loco stored at unknown location

STOBART RAIL, BLACKDYKE ROAD, KINGSTOWN, CARLISLE

Roadrail vehicles are present in this yard between use on contracts.

Gauge 4ft 8½in   www.stobartrail.co.uk

WO 31	4wDM	R/R	Unimog	160572

UNITED KINGDOM ATOMIC ENERGY AUTHORITY,
"PILE No.2", BUILDING B12, WINDSCALE

Gauge 2ft 5½in   NY 030043

PV 7	2w-2BE	WR	

WILLIAM SINCLAIR HORTICULTURE LTD,
BOLTON FELL MILL, near HETHERSGILL

Gauge 2ft 0in   NY 487699

–		4wDM	LB	51651	1960	OOU
	LYNE	4wDM	MR	7037	1936	
	LIDDEL	4wDM	MR	7188	1937	
SO 39		4wDM	MR	7190	1937	OOU
	BECKY	4wDM	MR	7215	1938	OOU
	ESK	4wDM	MR	7498	1940	
	IRTHING	4wDM	MR	8655	1941	

GELT		4wDM	MR	8696	1941	
SARK		4wDM	MR	8825	1943	
EDEN		4wDM	MR	20058	1949	
87025	L201N	4wDM	MR	22238	1965	OOU
87032	L202N	4wDM	MR	40S412	1973	
–		4wDM	RH	283513	1949	
	rebuilt as	4wDH	AK	20R	1986	OOU
–		4wDM	AK	No.5	1979	OOU
–		4wDM	AK	26	1988	OOU

PRESERVATION SITES

APPLEBY HERITAGE CENTRE, APPLEBY STATION
Gauge 4ft 8½in

4979	WOOTTON HALL	4-6-0	OC	Sdn		1930

BLENNERHASSETT WATERMILL, near ASPATRIA
Gauge 2ft 0in   NY 184419

–	4wDM	FH	3756	1955	
–	4wDM	RH	273525	1949	
–	0-4-0BE	WR	(4149	1949?)	
	reb	ShepherdFG			

Gauge 1ft 10in

No.1	4wBE	s/o	ShepherdFG	c1973	
	reb	‡		1988	

‡   rebuilt by S.Frogley, Nent Valley Rly.

EDEN VALLEY RAILWAY TRUST, WARCOP STATION
Gauge 4ft 8½in   NY 753156

(D6950)	37250		Co-CoDE	_(EE	3507	1964
				(EEV	D938	1964
	DARLINGTON		0-6-0DH	RSH/WB	8343	1962
21			0-4-0DH	JF	4220045	1967
205009	60108		4-4wDER	Afd/Elh		1957
2315	61798		4w-4wRER	Afd/Elh		1961
2315	61799		4w-4wRER	Afd/Elh		1961
2311	61804		4w-4wRER	Afd/Elh		1961
2311	61805		4w-4wRER	Afd/Elh		1961
(68003)	(9003)		4w-4RE/BER	Afd/Elh		1960
S68005	(9005)	931 095	4w-4RE/BER	Afd/Elh		1960
68045			2w-2PMR	Wkm	730	1932	DsmT
DE 320468	(DB 965050)		2w-2PMR	Wkm	7565	1956

ENGLISH NATURE, FORMER SCOTTS CUMBRIA WORKS SITE, KIRKBRIDE, WIGTON
Gauge 2ft 0in

		4wDM	MR		+	a

+ either MR 9231/1947 or MR 7463/1939 [see p. 43]
a currently away for restoration

THE ESKDALE (CUMBRIA) TRUST, RAILWAY MUSEUM, RAVENGLASS
Gauge 1ft 3in SD 086967

		SYNOLDA	4-4-2	OC	BL	30	1912	
		ELLA	0-6-0T	OC	DB	2	1881	+
	1	SCOOTER	2-2wPMR		Ravenglass		1971	

+ side frames only

HAIG COLLIERY MINING MUSEUM, WHITEHAVEN
Gauge 4ft 8½in NX 967176

	ASKHAM HALL		0-4-0ST	OC	AE	1772	1917
ND 3815			0-4-0DM		HE	2389	1941
ARMY 244	88 EQ		0-4-0DH		TH	130c	1963
		a reb of	0-4-0DH		JF	22971	1942
(227)			0-4-0DM		_(VF	5262	1945
					(DC	2181	1945

Gauge 2ft 6in

		0-4-0BE	WR	(5931	1958 ?)

KESWICK MINING MUSEUM, OTLEY HOUSE, OTLEY ROAD, KESWICK
Gauge 2ft 0in NY 264237

8	4wBE	WR	(P7624 1975)?	Pvd

LAKESIDE & HAVERTHWAITE RAILWAY CO LTD, HAVERTHWAITE
Gauge 4ft 8½in www.lakesiderailway.co.uk SD 349843

		5643	0-6-2T	IC	Sdn		1925
		42073	2-6-4T	OC	Bton		1950
		No.10	0-6-0T	OC	AB	1245	1911
		–	0-6-0F	OC	AB	1550	1917
	1	DAVID	0-4-0ST	OC	AB	2333	1953
	11	REPULSE	0-6-0ST	IC	HE	3698	1950
		CUMBRIA					
		FURNESS RAILWAY 150	0-6-0ST	IC	HE	3794	1953
		No.20	0-4-0ST	IC	SS	1448	1863
		rebuilt as	0-4-0	IC			1998
		PRINCESS	0-6-0ST	OC	WB	2682	1942
	2996	VICTOR	0-6-0ST	OC	WB	2996	1951

D2072	(03072)		0-6-0DM	Don		1959
D2117			0-6-0DM	Sdn		1959
D5301	(26001)		Bo-BoDE	BRCW	DEL46	1958
(D8314)	20214 AUSTIN MAHAR		Bo-BoDE	_(EE	3695	1967
				(EEV	D1090	1967
7120	AD601		0-6-0DE	Derby		1945
No.2	FLUFF		0-4-0DM	JF	21999	1937
	"RACHEL"		4wPM	MR	2098	1924
M52071			2-2w-2w-2DMR	BRCW		1962
M52077			2-2w-2w-2DMR	BRCW		1961

H. POTTS, APPLEBY
Gauge 2ft 0in

5		4wBE	WR	

RAVENGLASS & ESKDALE RAILWAY CO LTD, RAVENGLASS
Gauge 1ft 3¼in   www.ravenglass-railway.co.uk   SD 086967, NY 137000

	RIVER MITE	2-8-2	OC	Clarkson	4669	1966	
No.3	RIVER IRT	0-8-2	OC	DB	3	1894	
			reb	Ravenglass		1927	
	KATIE	0-4-0T	OC	DB	4	1896	b
6	RIVER ESK	2-8-2	OC	DP	21104	1923	
	THE FLOWER OF THE FOREST	2w-2VBT	VCG	Ravenglass	5	1985	
No.10	NORTHERN ROCK	2-6-2	OC	Ravenglass	10	1976	
No.1	BLACOLVESLEY	4-4-4PM	s/o	BL		1909	
–		4wBE		GB	2782	1957	
I.C.L.9	CYRIL	4wDM		L	4404	1932	
			reb	Ravenglass		1986	
–		4wDM		L	40009	1954	a DsmT
21	LES	4wDM		LB	51721	1960	
	QUARRYMAN	4wPM		MH	2	1926	
I.C.L.No.1		4-4wPM		Ravenglass		1925	
	PERKINS	4w-4DM		Ravenglass		1933	
	a rebuild of	4wPM		MH	NG39A	1929	
	LADY WAKEFIELD	4w-4wDH		Ravenglass		1980	
	ANITA	4wDM		RH	277273	1949	c
I.C.L. No.11	DOUGLAS FERRIERA	4w-4wDH		TMA	28800	2005	
	SHELAGH OF ESKDALE	4-6-4DH		SL		1969	

a converted to a flat wagon
b currently away for restoration
c in use as a flail mower

SOUTH TYNEDALE RAILWAY PRESERVATION SOCIETY, ALSTON STATION
Gauge 2ft 0in   NY 717467

	BARBER	0-6-2ST	OC	TG	441	1908
10	NAKLO	0-6-0WTT	OC	Chrz	3459	1957
UVE No.1		0-4-2T	OC	HE	1859	1937
6	THOMAS EDMONDSON	0-4-0WTT	OC	Hen	16047	1918

	HELEN KATHRYN	0-4-0WT	OC	Hen	28035	1948		
	SACCHARINE	0-4-2T	OC	JF	13355	1912		
NG 25		4wBE		BD	3704	1973		
			reb	AB	6526	1987		
2519	2103/35	4wBEF		_(EE	2519	1958		
				(Bg	3500	1958	a	Dsm
4	NAWORTH	0-6-0DMF		HC	DM819	1952		
–		0-6-0DMF		HC	DM1169	1960		Dsm
1247	OLD RUSTY	0-6-0DMF		HC	DM1247	1961		
9		0-4-0DMF		HE	4109	1952		
			reb	STRPS		1992		
–		0-4-0DMF		HE	4110	1953		
11	CUMBRIA	4wDM		HE	6646	1967		
20		4wDM		MR	5880	1935	b	Dsm
P.W.No.1	DB 965082	2w-2DMR		Wkm	7597	1957		

a   chassis used as a frame for a mobile crane
b   frame only.

STAINMORE RAILWAY COMPANY, KIRKBY STEPHEN EAST STATION
Gauge 4ft 8½in   NY 769075

	F.C. TINGEY	0-4-0ST	OC	P	2084	1948	
(D1909	47820) 47785	Co-CoDE		BT	671	1965	
(D5669)	31410	A1A-A1ADE		BT	269	1960	
(D6846)	37146	Co-CoDE		_(EE	3321	1963	
				(VF	D820	1963	
(D6869	37169) 37674	Co-CoDE		-(EE	3347	1963	
				(VF	D833	1963	
(D8169)	(20169)	Bo-BoDE		_(EE	3640	1966	
				(EEV	D1039	1966	
–		4wDH		FH	3958	1961	
No.305		0-4-0DH		YE	2952	1965	

THRELKELD QUARRY & MINING MUSEUM, THRELKELD QUARRY, near KESWICK

NY 318215, 327245
Locos are also kept at Bramcrag Quarry   NY 320222
                    Hilltop Quarry.   NY 321231

Gauge 3ft 2¼in

–		4wDM	RH	320573	1951	Dsm

Gauge 2ft 6in

–		4wBE	BV	608	1971	
46		4wBE	BV	609	1971	
48		4wBE	BV	610	1971	
–		0-4-0DM	HE	2248	1940	Dsm
(YARD No.P9261)		0-4-0DM	HE	2254	1940	OOU
–		0-4-0DM	HE	2267	1940	Dsm

8		4wDH		HE	8830	1979
10		4wDH		HE	8966	1980
11		4wDH		HE	8968	1980

Gauge 2ft 0in

	SIRTOM	0-4-0ST	OC	WB	2135	1925	
	ALD HAGUE	4wPM		FH	3465	1954	
–		0-4-0DMF		HC	DM752	1949	OOU
–		0-4-0DMF		HE	3149	1945	OOU
–		4wDM		HE	3595	1948	
8		4wPM		KC		c1926	
–		4wDM		LB	52885	1962	
89		4wPM		MR	4565	1928	
3	K 11143	4wDM		MR	7191	1937	Dsm
–		4wDM		MR	7522	1948	
–		4wDM		MR	8627	1941	
1	K 11039	4wDM		MR	8698	1941	Dsm
–		4wDM		MR	8860	1944	
–		4wDM		MR	8937	1944	
–		4wDM		MR	9846	1952	
–		4wDM		MR	40S383	1971	
–		4wDM		RH	217993	1943	Dsm
R6	ND 6456	4wDM		RH	221626	1943	
–		4wDM		RH	223744	1944	Dsm
	ND 6440	4wDM		RH	242918	1947	
001		4wDM		RH	444208	1961	
–		4wDMF		RH	497760	1963	
	MAVIS	4wDM		RH	7002/0967/6	1967	
–		4wBE		CE	B0475	1975	OOU
–		4wBE		CE	B0495	1975	
7		4wBE		CE	B1854	1979	
2		4wBE		WR			
7		4wBE		WR			
–		4wBE		WR			+
–	LLECHWEDD	4wBE		WR			+
	"BREDBURY"	2w-2PM		Bredbury		c1954	

+   possibly one of C6765 1963 or C6766 1963, [see also p.275]

DERBYSHIRE

INDUSTRIAL SITES

ACORDIS- ACETATE PRODUCTS LTD, SPONDON WORKS

Gauge 4ft 8½in   RTC   SK 405347

–	0-4-0DH	RH	518190	1965	OOU	

BOMBARDIER TRANSPORTATION INC. of CANADA, LITCHURCH LANE, DERBY

Gauge 9ft 10in   SK 364345

(TRAVERSER No.4)	0-4-0WE	DerbyC&W	1985	

Gauge 4ft 8½in

D3769 (08602) AZ 004	0-6-0DE	Derby		1959	
(D4014 08846) 003	0-6-0DE	Hor		1961	
L.J. BREEZE	6wDH	RR	10275	1969	
3335	0-4-0WE	DerbyC&W		1935	OOU

CEMEX NORTH EAST,
DOVE HOLES QUARRY, DALE ROAD, DOVE HOLES, BUXTON

Gauge 4ft 8½in   SK 088773

–	0-6-0DH	S	10107	1963	+
–	0-6-0DH	S	10186	1964	
	reb	HAB	6459	1989	

+   loco carries plate "UNIT No.10216"

W.H. DAVIS & SONS (1984) LTD, LANGWITH JUNCTION

Gauge 4ft 8½in   SK 529683

4332	4wDM	RH	321732	1952

DOROTHEA RESTORATIONS, OLD GASWORKS, NEW ROAD, WHALEY BRIDGE

Locomotives occasionally present for restoration or overhaul.   SK 014804

LAFARGE CEMENT UK, HOPE CEMENT WORKS, HOPE

Gauge 4ft 8½in   SK 167823

(D8168) 20168	Bo-BoDE	_(EE	3639	1966	
SIR GEORGE EARLE		(EEV	D1038	1966	+
30	0-6-0DH	AB	616	1977	+
01570 BLUE JOHN	B-B DH	HAB	773	1990	
PEVERIL	0-6-0DH	S	10087	1963	
	reb	AB	6140	1989	

DERWENT		0-6-0DH		S	10156	1963	
			reb	AB	6004	1988	
62		6wDH		TH	316V	1987	+

+   on hire from Harry Needle Railroad Co Ltd

LEANDER ARCHITECTURAL, FLETCHER FOUNDRY, HALLSTEAD CLOSE, DOVE HOLES, near BUXTON

Locomotives occasionally present for restoration or overhaul.

Gauge 2ft 0in   [visitors welcome – but first phone T. McAvoy on 01298 814941]   SK 076784

	PHEONIX	0-4-0ST	OC	Ferndale	21	2001	a
–		0-6-0T	OC	KS	3014	1916	
51	No.646	0-4-0PM		BgC	646	1918	
23		4wDM		L	52031	1960	+
–		4wDM		LB	53225	1962	
–		4wDM		RH	264252	1952	OOU
6		4wBE		WR	7967	1978	

+   plate reads 25031.
a   carries worksplate H.K. Porter 18635 1896

MOORSIDE MINING CO LTD, PLANT YARD, ROTHERSIDE ROAD, ECKINGTON

Plant depot with locos for resale occasionally present.   SK 436800

Gauge 2ft 0in

24		4wBEF		CE	B0427	1975
			reb	CE	B2926	1982
No.5	B3167	4wBEF		CE	B3167	1985

RAIL VEHICLE ENGINEERING LTD, LONDON ROAD, DERBY

Locomotives for repair usually present.   SK 364349

Gauge 4ft 8½in

(D3236) 08168	0-6-0DE		Dar	1956	a

a   currently at The Bluebell Railway, East Sussex

SAINT-GOBAIN PIPELINES plc, STANTON WORKS, STANTON BY DALE, ILKESTON

Gauge 4ft 8½in   RTC   SK 473389

63	689/172 RON	0-4-0DH		TH	227V	1970	OOU

TARMAC BUXTON LIME & CEMENT, TUNSTEAD QUARRY, GREAT ROCKS, TUNSTEAD

(including Lime Group Workshops & Stores)

Gauge 4ft 8½in   SK 101743, 097755

SCW/1/29	DOVEDALE	0-6-0DH		RR	10284	1969
			reb	TH		1974
SCW/1/04	CHEEDALE	4wDH		TH	284V	1979

SCW/1/05	HARRY TOWNLEY	4wDH	TH	289V	1980
	LIZY IZABELLA	0-6-0DH	TH	V325	1987
	HIGH PEAK	6w-6wDH	Vollert		2003

WALKER & PARTNERS LTD, INKERSALL ROAD ESTATE, STEPHENSON ROAD, STAVELEY, CHESTERFIELD   www.walkerandpartners.co.uk

Dealers yard, with locos for resale occasionally present.   SK 436743

Gauge 2ft 0in

1524	2143	4wBEF	CE	B3611	1989
2474	PL No. 2207/458	4wBEF	_(EE	2474	1958
			(RSHN	7942	1958
2527	PL No. 9303/25	4wBEF	_(EE	2527	1957
			(RSHN	8046	1957

SAM WARD, STATION ROAD, KILLAMARSH

Gauge 2ft 0in   SK 448810

| – | | 4wDM | HE | 6013 | 1961 |

WB POWER SERVICES LTD,
Diesel Engine and Locomotive Specialists,
MANNERS INDUSTRIAL ESTATE, MANNERS AVENUE, ILKESTON   SK 458425

This is understood to be a complete FLEET LIST of the locos owned by (or in the care of) this company, which operates from the above address. Some locos are for hire or resale, and may be in use or stored at a number of locations.

Locos under repair are occasionally present.

Gauge 4ft 8½in

44	MITCHELL		0-6-0DH		HE	7396	1974	c
			reb		Wilmott		2000	
	ANDREW		4wDH		TH	164V	1966	a
	JOANNA		4wDH		TH	177C	1967	
		a rebuild of	4wVBT	VCG	S	9401	1950	b
390	AMESBURY		0-6-0DE		YE	2756	1959	b

a   currently at Marcroft Engineering, Staffordshire
b   currently on loan to Telford Horsehay Trust, Horsehay, Telford, Shropshire
c   currently at Conoco Ltd, South Killingholme, Lincolnshire

PRESERVATION SITES

BARROW HILL ENGINE SHED SOCIETY,
BARROW HILL ROUNDHOUSE RAILWAY CENTRE, CAMPBELL DRIVE, BARROW HILL, STAVELEY

Gauge 4ft 8½in   SK 414755

41708		0-6-0T	IC	Derby		1880	
45593	KOLHAPUR	4-6-0	3C	NBQ	24151	1935	
60532	BLUE PETER	4-6-2	3C	Don	2023	1948	
61264		4-6-0	OC	NBQ	26165	1947	
(62660)	No.506 BUTLER HENDERSON						
		4-4-0	IC	Gorton		1920	
	HENRY	0-4-0ST	OC	HL	2491	1901	
	"THE WELSHMAN"	0-6-0ST	IC	MW	1207	1890	
–		0-6-0ST	IC	P	2000	1942	
"9"		0-6-0ST	OC	YE	2521	1952	
56006		Co-CoDE		Electro		1977	
58001		Co-CoDE		Don		1982	
(D86)	45105	1Co-Co1DE		Crewe		1961	
(D100)	45060						
	SHERWOOD FORESTER	1Co-Co1DE		Crewe		1961	
(D213)	40013 ANDANIA	1Co-Co1DE		_(EE	2669	1959	
				(VF	D430	1959	
(D1969)	47791	Co-CoDE		Crewe		1965	
(D2066)	03066	0-6-0DM		Don		1959	
D2302		0-6-0DM		_(RSHD	8161	1960	
				(DC	2683	1960	+
D2324		0-6-0DM		_(RSHD	8183	1961	
				(DC	2705	1961	+
(D2996	07012)	0-6-0DE		RH	480697	1962	
(D3607)	08492	0-6-0DE		Hor		1959	+
(D3862)	08695	0-6-0DE		Hor		1959	+
D4092		0-6-0DE		Dar		1962	+
D5300	(26007)	Bo-BoDE		BRCW	DEL45	1958	
(D5311)	26011	Bo-BoDE		BRCW	DEL56	1959	
(D6521)	33108	Bo-BoDE		BRCW	DEL113	1960	
(D6553)	33035	Bo-BoDE		BRCW	DEL145	1961	
(D6859	37159) 37372	Co-CoDE		_(EE	3337	1963	
				(EES	8390	1963	
(D6901)	37201	Co-CoDE		_(EE	3379	1963	
				(EEV	D845	1963	+
(D6917)	37217	Co-CoDE		_(EE	3395	1963	
				(EEV	D861	1963	+
(D6975)	37275	Co-CoDE		_(EE	3535	1965	
				(EEV	D964	1965	
(D8041 20041) 20901		Bo-BoDE		_(EE	2763	1959	
				(VF	D488	1959	+
(D8092)	20092	Bo-BoDE		_(EE	2998	1961	
				(RSHD	8250	1961	+
(D8096)	20096	Bo-BoDE		_(EE	3002	1961	
				(RSHD	8254	1961	+

(D8101	20101)	20904	Bo-BoDE	_(EE	3007	1961
				(RSHD	8259	1961 +
(D8105	20105)	2016 36	Bo-BoDE	_(EE	3011	1961
				(RSHD	8263	1961 +
(D8107	20107)		Bo-BoDE	_(EE	3013	1961
				(RSHD	8265	1961
(D8119)	20119		Bo-BoDE	_(EE	3025	1962
				(RSHD	8277	1962 +
(D8121)	20121		Bo-BoDE	_(EE	3027	1962
				(RSHD	8279	1962
(D8132)	20132		Bo-BoDE	_(EE	3603	1966
				(EEV	D1002	1966 +
(D8325	20225)	20905	Bo-BoDE	_(EE	3706	1967
				(EEV	D1101	1967 +
18000			A1A-A1A GTE	_(BBC(S)	4559	1949
				(SLM	3977	1949
E3003	(81002)		Bo-BoWE	_(BRCW		1960
				(BTH	1085	1960
E3035	(83012)		Bo-BoWE	_(EE	2941	1960
				(VF	E277	1960
(E3036)	84001		Bo-BoWE	NB	27793	1960
(E3054)	82008		Bo-BoWE	_(BP	7892	1961
				(AEI/MV	1029	1961
(E3061)	(85006)	85101 101 DONCASTER PLANT 150 1853 - 2003				
			Bo-BoWE	Don		1961
89001			Co-CoWE	(Crewe		1986
				(BT	875	1986
46	20/110/706		0-6-0DH	AB	612	1976
No.613	20 110 709		0-6-0DH	AB	613	1977
			reb	AB		1986
10			0-6-0DH	EEV	D1228	1967 +
X7215	KEMIRA 1		0-6-0DH	GECT	5380	1972 +
No.7	31		0-6-0DH	HE	6973	1969 +
(11)	"VALIANT"		0-6-0DH	RR	10213	1964
			reb	TH		1988 +
7			0-6-0DH	RR	10279	1968 +
	HARRY		0-4-0DM	_(RSHN	7922	1957
				(DC	2589	1957
9			0-6-0DH	TH	237V	1971 +

+   property of Harry Needle Railroad Co Ltd, Merseyside

CRICH TRAMWAY VILLAGE, CRICH, near MATLOCK
Gauge 4ft 8½in
SK 345549

47		0-4-0VBTram	BP	2464	1885	
–		0-4-0VBTram	BP	2734	1886	c Dsm
–		4wWE	EEDK	717	1927	
	RUPERT	4wDM	RH	223741	1944	a
	G.M.J.	4wDM	RH	326058	1952	b

a   rebuilt in 1963 from 600mm gauge
b   rebuilt in 1969 from 3ft 3in gauge
c   currently stored at Clay Cross store

Gauge 1ft 2½in

46		0-4-0VBTram	OC	Pritchard	1941

DELTIC PRESERVATION SOCIETY, BARROW HILL ROUNDHOUSE RAILWAY CENTRE, CAMPBELL DRIVE, BARROW HILL, STAVELEY

Gauge 4ft 8½in   SK 413755

(D9000)	55022	ROYAL SCOTS GREY				
		Co-CoDE	_(EE	2905	1960	
			(VF	D557	1960	
D9009	(55009)	ALYCIDON	Co-CoDE	_(EE	2914	1960
			(VF	D566	1960	
9015	(55015)	TULYAR	Co-CoDE	_(EE	2920	1960
			(VF	D572	1960	
(D9019)	55019	ROYAL HIGHLAND FUSILIER				
		Co-CoDE	_(EE	2924	1960	
			(VF	D576	1960	

S. DENTITH, ASHBOURNE

Locomotive stored at a private location
Gauge 2ft 0in

_		4wDM	L	10994	1939	Dsm

TERRY GIBSON, DERBY

Gauge 1ft 3in

	KING GEORGE	4-4-2	OC	BL	22	1915
6100	ROYAL SCOT	4-6-0	OC	Carland [6100]		1950

GULLIVERS KINGDOM LTD, MATLOCK BATH

Gauge 1ft 9½in   SK 289578

	HILLARY	4w-4RE	s/o	Sharon	1988

MIKE HART, PRIVATE STORAGE SITE

Gauge 4ft 8½in

9120		4wDMR	BD	3709	1975

LITTLE MILL INN, ROWARTH, near NEW MILLS

Gauge 4ft 8½in   SK 011890

(3051 CAR No.289)		4w-4wRER	MetCam	289	1932

MARKEATON PARK LIGHT RAILWAY, MARKEATON PARK, DERBY

Gauge 1ft 3in   SK 334372

	MARKEATON LADY	0-4-2T	OC	ESR	300	1996
D5905	CITY OF DERBY	4w-4wDM		BrownJ		1995

MIDLAND RAILWAY – BUTTERLEY (MIDLAND RAILWAY TRUST LTD)

Locomotives are kept at :-

Butterley SK 403520
Swanwick Junction SK 412519
Hammersmith SK 397519
Princess Royal Class Locomotive Trust Depot, Swanwick Junction SK 410520

Gauge 4ft 8½in

158A		2-4-0	IC	Derby		1866	
44027		0-6-0	IC	Derby		1924	
44932		4-6-0	OC	Hor		1945	
45491		4-6-0	OC	Derby		1943	
46203							
	PRINCESS MARGARET ROSE	4-6-2	4C	Crewe	253	1935	
(46233)	6233						
	DUCHESS OF SUTHERLAND	4-6-2	4C	Crewe		1938	
(47327)	16410	0-6-0T	IC	NBH	23406	1926	
47357		0-6-0T	IC	NBQ	23436	1926	
			reb	Derby		1973	
(47445)		0-6-0T	IC	HE	1529	1927	Dsm
(47564)		0-6-0T	IC	HE	1580	1928	Dsm
53809	(13809)	2-8-0	OC	RS	3895	1925	
73129		4-6-0	OC	Derby		1956	
80080		2-6-4T	OC	Bton		1954	
92219		2-10-0	OC	Sdn		1960	
	"STANTON No.24"	0-4-0CT	OC	AB	1875	1925	
No.2	PN 8292	0-4-0F	OC	AB	2008	1935	
	"GLADYS"	0-4-0ST	OC	Mkm	109	1894	
19	OSWALD	0-4-0ST	OC	NW	454	1894	
1163	WHITEHEAD	0-4-0ST	OC	P	1163	1908	a
	VICTORY	0-4-0ST	OC	P	1547	1919	
1	LYTHAM ST.ANNE'S	0-4-0ST	OC	P	2111	1949	
	GEORGE	0-4-0ST	OC	RSHN	7214	1945	
63	CORBY	0-6-0ST	IC	RSHN	7761	1954	

CASTLE DONINGTON POWER STATION

No.1		0-4-0ST	OC	RSHN	7817	1954
–		4wVBT	VCG	S	9370	1947

(D4)	44004 GREAT GABLE	1Co-Co1DE		Derby		1959
(D40)	45133	1Co-Co1DE		Derby		1961
(D53)	45041					
	ROYAL TANK REGIMENT	1Co-Co1DE		Crewe		1962
D120	(45108)	1Co-Co1DE		Crewe		1961
D182	(46045) (97404)	1Co-Co1DE		Derby		1962
D212	(40012) AUREOL	1Co-Co1DE		_(EE	2668	1959
				(VF	D429	1959
(D407)	50007	Co-CoDE		_(EE	3777	1967
	SIR EDWARD ELGAR			(EEV	D1148	1967

57 - Derbyshire

D1048	WESTERN LADY	C-C DH	Crewe		1962	
(D1500)	47401 NORTH EASTERN	Co-CoDE	BT	342	1962	
D1516	(47417)	Co-CoDE	BT	358	1963	
(D1619	47564) 47761	Co-CoDE	Crewe		1964	
D2138		0-6-0DM	Sdn		1960	
D2858		0-4-0DH	YE	2817	1960	
(D3401)	08331	0-6-0DE	Derby		1957	
(D3757)	08590	0-6-0DE	Crewe		1959	
(D5522)	31418 BOADICEA	A1A-A1A DE	BT	121	1959	
(D6530)	33018	Bo-BoDE	BRCW	DEL122	1960	
(D6564)	33046	Bo-BoDE	BRCW	DEL 156	1961	
D6586	(33201)	Bo-Bo DE	BRCW	DEL157	1962	
(D6890)	37190 DALZELL	Co-Co DE	_(EE	3368	1963	
			(EES	8411	1963	
(D)7671	(25321)	Bo-BoDE	Derby		1967	
D8001	(20001)	Bo-BoDE	_(EE	2348	1957	
			(VF	D376	1957	b
(D8305)	20205	Bo-BoDE	_(EE	3686	1967	
			(EEV	D1081	1967	
(D8327)	20227	Bo-BoDE	_(EE	3685	1967	
	SIR JOHN BETJEMAN		(EEV	D1080	1967	
12077		0-6-0DE	Derby		1950	
E27000	No.1502 ELECTRA	Co-CoWE	Gorton	1065	1953	
(No.2)		0-4-0DM	AB	416	1957	
	rebuilt	0-4-0DH	AB		1980	
–		0-4-0DH	AB	441	1959	
EMFOUR 9	ALBERT	0-6-0DM	HC	D1114	1958	
No.20		0-6-0DM	HC	D1121	1958	
No.77	"ANDY"	0-4-0DM	JF	16038	1923	
–		2-2wDM	Mercury	5337	1927	
"RS 12"		4wDM	MR	460	1918	
"RS 9"		4wDM	MR	2024	1920	
–		0-4-0DE	RH	384139	1955	
AD 9118		4wDMR	BD	3707	1975	
E50019		2-2w-2w-2DMR	DerbyC&W		1957	
(50164)	53164	2-2w-2w-2DMR	MetCam		1956	
(50170)	53170	2-2w-2w-2DMR	MetCam		1957	
(50253)	53253	2-2w-2w-2DMR	MetCam		1957	
(E51118)		2-2w-2w-2DMR	GRC&W		1957	
51341		2-2w-2w-2DMR	PSteel		1960	
51353		2-2w-2w-2DMR	PSteel		1960	
51395		2-2w-2w-2DMR	PSteel		1960	
51398		2-2w-2w-2DMR	PSteel		1960	
(51567)	977854 LO 911	2-2w-2w-2DMR	DerbyC&W		1959	
M51591	(M55966)	2-2w-2w-2DHR	DerbyC&W		1959	
(51937)	977806 LO 905	2-2w-2w-2DMR	DerbyC&W		1960	
55929	(977775)	2-2w-2w-2DMR	DerbyC&W		1956	
(M 51610)	M 55967	2-2w-2w-2DHR	DerbyC&W		1959	
(M51625)	M55976	2-2w-2w-2DHR	DerbyC&W		1959	
79018	(DB975007)	2-2w-2w-2DMR	DerbyC&W		1954	

141 113 55513		4wDHR		_(BRE(D)				
				(Leyland			1984	
			reb	AB		761	1989	
141 113 55533		4wDHR		_(BRE(D)				
				(Leyland			1984	
			reb	AB		760	1989	
(DX) 68801		4wDHR		Perm		002	1985	
(DX) 68803 RTU 8803		4wDHR		Perm		004	1985	
PWM 3949		2w-2PMR		Wkm		6934	1955	DsmT
DX 68062 (TR34 DB 965566 PT52P)		2w-2PMR		Wkm		8272	1959	
RT 1		4w-4wDHR		Balfour Beatty			c1993	

a   based here, but visits other locations
b   currently on loan to Wyvernrail plc, Wirksworth

Gauge 2ft 0in — Golden Valley Light Railway   SK 412519, 414519

"PEARL 2"	0-4-2IST	OC	Civil	No.1	1997		
2	0-4-0WT	OC	OK	7529	1914		
D3753	4wDH		BD	3753	1980		
–	4wDM		Dtz	10248	1931		
–	0-6-0DMF		HC	DM1117	1957		
NG 34	4wDH		HE	7009	1971		
–	4wDM		HE	7178	1971		
–	4wDM		L	3742	1931		
		reb	FMB		1993		
–	4wDM		LB	53726	1963		
LOD 758228 No.4	4wDM		MR	8667	1941		
T2 PIONEER	4wDM		MR	8739	1942		
LOD 758028 LO 3009	4wDM		MR	8855	1943		
HOLWELL CASTLE	4wDM		MR	11177	1961		
15	4wDM		MR	11246	1963		
CAMPBELL BRICKWORKS No.1	4wDM		MR	60S364	1968		
–	4wDM		OK	5125	1933		
LOD 758263 AD 41 LYDDIA	4wDM		RH	191646	1938		
BERRY HILL	4wDM		RH	222068	1943		
–	4wDMF		RH	480678	1961	Dsm	
L203N U84	4wDM		RH	7002/0567/6	1967		
–	4wDM		SMH	40SD529	1984		
ELLISON	4wDH		SMH	101T020	1979		
NG 24	4wBE		BD	3703	1973		
		reb	AB		1986		
19 "BABY JANE"	0-4-0BE		WR				

Gauge 1ft 9in

6201 PRINCESS ELISABETH	4-6-2DH	s/o	HC	D611	1938	
6203 PRINCESS MARGARET ROSE						
	4-6-2DH	s/o	HC	D612	1938	

NATIONAL STONE CENTRE, PORTER LANE, WIRKSWORTH
Gauge 4ft 8½in   SK 286553

–		0-4-0DH		SCW		1960
	a rebuild of	0-4-0ST	OC	AE	1913	1923

PEAK DISTRICT MINES HISTORICAL SOCIETY
Cliff Quarry, National Tramway Museum, Wake Bridge Station, Crich
Gauge 2ft 0in   SK 342554

4	4wBE		WR	3492	1946

Peak District Mining Museum, Temple Mine, Temple Road, Matlock Bath
Gauge 1ft 5in   SK 293583

–	4wBE		GB	1445	1936

PEAK RAIL plc
Locos are kept at :-   Darley Dale   SK 274626
                                                        Rowsley South SK 262640

Gauge 4ft 8½in

48624		2-8-0	OC	Afd		1943	
68006		0-6-0ST	IC	HE	3192	1944	
			reb	HE	3888	1964	b
150 ROYAL PIONEER		0-6-0ST	IC	RSHN	7136	1944	
			reb	HE	3892	1969	
7597 ZEBEDEE		0-6-0T	OC	RSHN	7597	1949	
VULCAN		0-4-0ST	OC	VF	3272	1918	
68012 THE DUKE		0-6-0ST	IC	WB	2746	1944	
D8 (44008) PENYGHENT		1Co-Co1DE		Derby		1959	
(D429) 50029 RENOWN		Co-CoDE		_(EE	3799	1968	
				(EEV	D1170	1968	
(D430) 50030 REPULSE		Co-CoDE		_(EE	3800	1968	
				(EEV	D1171	1968	
(D1606 47029) 47635 JIMMY MILNE							
		Co-CoDE		Crewe		1964	
(D2027 03027)		0-6-0DM		Sdn		1958	
(D2037) 03037		0-6-0DM		Sdn		1959	+
(D2099) 03099		0-6-0DM		Don		1960	
(D2113) (03113)		0-6-0DM		Don		1960	
D2118		0-6-0DM		Sdn		1959	+
(D2139)		0-6-0DM		Sdn		1960	+
D2199		0-6-0DM		Sdn		1961	b
(D2229)		0-6-0DM		_(VF	D278	1955	
				(DC	2552	1955	
D2272 2272 ALFIE		0-6-0DM		_(RSHD	7914	1958	+
				(DC	2616	1958	
D2284		0-6-0DM		_(RSHD	8102	1960	
				(DC	2661	1960	

D2337	DOROTHY	0-6-0DM		_(RSHD	8196	1961	
				(DC	2718	1961	
(D2420	97804) 06003	0-4-0DM		AB	435	1959	+
(D2587)		0-6-0DM		HE	5636	1959	+
			reb	HE	7180	1969	
D2854		0-4-0DH		YE	2813	1960	+
(D2866)		0-4-0DH		YE	2849	1961	
D2868		0-4-0DH		YE	2851	1961	+
D2953		0-4-0DM		AB	395	1955	
(D2997	07013)	0-6-0DE		RH	480698	1962	
(D3023)	08016	0-6-0DE		Derby		1953	
(D5800)	31270	A1A-A1ADE		BT	301	1961	
(D6852)	37152	Co-CoDE		_(EE	3327	1963	
				(EEV	D826	1963	
(D6888)	37188	Co-CoDE		_(EE	3366	1963	
				(EES	8409	1963	+
D9016	(55016) GORDON HIGHLANDER						
		Co-CoDE		_(EE	2921	1960	
				(VF	D573	1960	
D9500	(9312/92 No.1)	0-6-0DH		Sdn		1964	
D9502		0-6-0DH		Sdn		1964	+
D9525		0-6-0DH		Sdn		1965	+
12061		0-6-0DE		Derby		1949	
(PWM 654)	97654	0-6-0DE		RH	431761	1951	
64		0-6-0DE		BT	803	1978	
	M.S.C.ENGINEERS E1						
	CASTLEFIELD	0-6-0DM		HC	D1199	1960	
107		0-6-0DH		NBQ	27932	1959	Dsm
	(CYNTHIA)	4wDM		RH	412431	1957	
	"BIGGA"	0-4-0DH		TH	102C	1960	
	a rebuild of	0-4-0DM		JF	4200019	1947	
–		4wDH		TH	265V	1976	a
B.S.C.2		0-4-0DE		YE	2480	1950	
H 051		0-6-0DH		YE	2940	1965	
(DB 6	TR6) (A30)	2w-2PMR		Wkm	6901	1954	
	rebuilt as	2w-2DHR					
	"TONY"	4wDMR		Wkm	9688	1965	

+   property of Harry Needle Railroad Co Ltd, Merseyside
a   property of Andrew Briddon; based here between hirings
b   property of R.M.S. Locotec Ltd, West Yorkshire

Gauge 2ft 0in — Derbyshire Dales Narrow Gauge Railway, Rowsley South

–		4wDHF		HE	8917	1980
–		4wDM		MR	435	1917
			reb	MR	3663	1924
87009		4wDM		MR	4572	1929
–		4wDM		MR	5853	1934
22		4wDM		MR	8756	1942
–		4wDM		MR	22070	1960
85049		4wDM		RH	393325	1952
85051		4wDM		RH	404967	1957
–		4wDM		RH	487963	1963

PHIL ROWE
Gauge 750mm

Loco stored at unknown location

		0-6-0WT	OC	Chrz	2959	1951	
—		0-6-0WT	OC	Chrz	2959	1951	

STEEPLE GRANGE LIGHT RAILWAY,
STEEPLEHOUSE JUNCTION, WIRKSWORTH
Gauge 2ft 0in   SK 288554

No.1881		4wPM		FH	1881	1934	
—		4wPM		FH	3424	1949	a
—		4wDM		L	37366	1951	a
	SPONDON	4wBE		Spondon		1926	a

Gauge 1ft 6in

—		4wVBT	VC	Jaywick		1939	a Dsm
ZM32	11 HORWICH	4wDM		RH	416214	1957	
551		4wBE		BEV	551	1924	
	LIZZIE	4wDM		ClayCross		1973	+
—		4wDM		FH	4008	1963	Dsm
6		4wBE		GB	2493	1946	
No.3		4wBE		GB	6061	1961	
L 10		4wBE		CE	5431	1968	
L 16	PEGGY	4wBE		CE	B0109B	1973	
14	LADY MARJORIE	4wBE		CE	B0922B	1975	
3		4wBE		Greensburg			
4		4wBE		Greensburg			
2	HUDSON	2-2wPM		SGLR		1988	

+   constructed from parts supplied by Listers
a   currently under renovation elsewhere

UNICON PROPERTIES LTD, CANAL STREET, WHALEY BRIDGE
Locomotives occasionally present for restoration/overhaul, etc.   SK 013818

WYVERNRAIL plc, ECCLESBOURNE VALLEY RAILWAY,
WIRKSWORTH STATION, COLDWELL STREET, WIRKSWORTH
Gauge 4ft 8½in   SK 289541

—		0-4-0ST	OC	AB	2217	1947	
No.3		0-4-0ST	OC	AB	2360	1954	
—		0-6-0T	OC	HC	1884	1955	
(D2084)	03084 HELEN-LOUISE	0-6-0DM		Don		1959	
D2158	(03158) MARGARET-ANN	0-6-0DM		Sdn		1960	
D2971	KIRTLEY	0-4-0DM		RH	313394	1952	
(D5814)	31414 (31514)	A1A-A1ADE		BT	315	1961	
D8001	(20001)	Bo-BoDE		_(EE	2348	1957	
				(VF	D376	1957	
7	JANA	0-6-0DH		EEV	D1201	1967	

–		0-6-0DH	EEV	D1230	1969
	CLAIRE	0-4-0DH	HC	D1388	1970
11520		0-4-0DM	RH	319284	1952
	SIR PETER AND LADY HILTON				
		0-4-0DE	RH	402803	1956
GR 5088	LRH 08301	0-4-0DE	RH	420137	1958
–		4wDH	RR	10194	1964
51073		2-2w-2w-2DMR	GRC&W		1959
51188		2-2w-2w-2DMR	MetCam		1958
W51360	T302	2-2w-2w-2DMR	PSteel		1960
51505		2-2w-2w-2DMR	MetCam		1959
M55006	L106	2-2w-2w-2DMR	GRC&W		1958
(975 010)	M 79900	2-2w-2w-2DMR	DerbyC&W		1956
	L263 MNU	4wDMR R/R	Perm		1993
	MURIEL	2w-2DER	EVRA		2000

Gauge 2ft 0in

–	4wDM	L	26288	1944

DEVON

INDUSTRIAL SITES

AGGREGATE INDUSTRIES UK LTD, MELDON QUARRY, near OKEHAMPTON
Gauge 4ft 8½in   SX 568927

(D4167)	08937 BLUEBELL MEL	0-6-0DE	Dar		1962
MSC 0256	FLYING FALCON	0-4-0DH	JF	4220016	1962

BABCOCK MARINE, DEVONPORT ROYAL DOCKYARD, DEVONPORT
Gauge 4ft 8½in   SX 449558

RTU 1	DENNIS	4wDM	CE	B4314A	2000
RTU 2	HENRY	4wDM	CE	B4314B	2000

MINISTRY OF DEFENCE, OKEHAMPTON RANGES TARGET RAILWAY, OKEHAMPTON
Gauge 2ft 6in   SX 586932

RTT/767138 CAPTAIN	2w-2PM	Wkm	3284	1943	

Gauge 600mm

RTT/767149 PRESIDENT	2w-2PM	Wkm	3151	1943	OOU
RTT/767163	2w-2PM	Wkm	3236	1943	OOU

MINISTRY OF DEFENCE, NAVY DEPARTMENT, ROYAL NAVAL ARMAMENT DEPOT, ERNESETTLE, DEVON

See Section 6 for full details.

R.M.S. LOCOTEC LTD, MELDON QUARRY, near OKEHAMPTON

Gauge 4ft 8½in   SX 568927

PE 9803		2-2wDMR	Robel	56.27-10-AG38	1983	
(DX 68086)	SM 02	2w-2DMR	Wkm	10841	1975	
	SM 01	2w-2DMR	Wkm	10842	1975	Dsm
		2w-2PMR	Wkm			

PRESERVATION SITES

BICTON WOODLAND RAILWAY, BICTON PARK BOTANICAL GARDENS, EAST BUDLEIGH

Gauge 1ft 6in   www.bictongardens.co.uk   SY 074862

	SIR WALTER RALEIGH	0-4-0DH	s/o	AK	61	2000
	CLINTON	4wDM		HE	2290	1941
B.W.R. 2	BICTON	4wDM		RH	213839	1942
		reb	s/o	AK	75R	2007

BIDEFORD HERITAGE RAILWAY CENTRE, BIDEFORD STATION

Gauge 4ft 8½in   SS 457262

| | KINGSLEY | 4wDM | FH | 3832 | 1957 |

C. BURGES, EXETER & TEIGN VALLEY RAILWAY,
G.W.R.(CHRISTOW), SHELDON LANE, DODDISCOMBSLEIGH, EXETER

Gauge 4ft 8½in   SX 839868

	PERSEUS	0-4-0DM	_(VF	D98	1949
			(DC	2269	1949
DR 90011		4wDMR	Matisa	PV620	1967
	2831	2w-2PMR	Wkm	5009	1949

Gauge 2ft 0in

| S26 | 25 | 0-4-0BE | WR | D6886 | 1964 |
| | – | 0-4-0BE | WR | | |

'BYGONES' VICTORIAN EXHIBITION STREET AND RAILWAY MUSEUM,
FORE STREET, ST.MARYCHURCH, TORQUAY

Gauge 4ft 8½in   SX 922658

| | No.5 PATRICIA | 0-4-0ST | OC | HC | 1632 | 1929 |

COMBE MARTIN WILDLIFE AND DINOSAUR PARK, COMBE MARTIN, near ILFRACOMBE

Gauge 1ft 3in   SS 600452

–		2-8-0PH	s/o	SL		70.5.87	1987

COUNTRY LIFE MUSEUM, SANDY BAY HOLIDAY CENTRE, near EXMOUTH

Gauge 1ft 6in   SY 035808

–		4-2-2	OC	RegentSt	1898
	SIR FRANCIS DRAKE	4-6-0	OC	Scarrott	1988

DARTMOOR RAIL LTD, MELDON QUARRY, near OKEHAMPTON

Gauge 4ft 8½in   SX 568927

–		0-6-0T	OC	HC	1864	1952	Dsm
205028	60146	4w-4wDER		Afd/Elh		1962	
205032	60150	4w-4wDER		Afd/Elh		1962	
S61743		4w-4wRER		Afd/Elh		1960	
98303		4wDMR		Geismar			
					G.780.004	1985	

DEVON RAILWAY CENTRE, BICKLEIGH MILL, CADLEIGH STATION, TIVERTON

Gauge 4ft 8½in   www.devonrailwaycentre.co.uk   SS 938076

"BORIS"	0-4-0DM		Bg	3357	1952

Gauge 3ft 0in

105H006	4wDH		MR	105H006	1969

Gauge 2ft 9in

CLAUDE	4wDM		RH	435398	1959

Gauge 2ft 0in

No.14		0-4-0WT	OC	OK	5744	1912
–		4wPM		FH	1747	1931
–		4wDM		FH	2025	1937
2201		4wDM		FH	2201	1939
6299		4wPM		L	6299	1935
–		4wDM		L	34025	1949
	IVOR	4wDM		MR	8877	1944
–		4wDM		MR	20073	1950
649	SIR TOM	4wDM		MR	40S273	1966
	HORATIO	4wDM	s/o	RH	217967	1942
–		4wDM		RH	235711	1945
–		4wDM		RH	418770	1957
1300	S14	0-4-0BE		WR		c1950

EXMOOR STEAM RAILWAY, CAPE OF GOOD HOPE FARM, BRATTON FLEMING

Locomotives under construction and repair are usually present.   SS 662383

Gauge 2ft 0in

77	2-6-2+2-6-2T	4C	Hano	10629	1928
109	2-6-2+2-6-2T	4C	BP	6919	1939
115	2-6-2+2-6-2T	4C	BP	6925	1937
130	2-6-2+2-6-2T	4C	BP	7431	1951
135	2-8-2	OC	AFB	2685	1952
–	4wDH		HE	9333	1994
–	4wDH		HE	9336	1994
LOD 758035	4wDM		MR	8856	1944

C. GROVE, BERE FERRERS STATION

Gauge 4ft 8½in   SX 452635

HILDA	0-4-0ST	OC	P	1963	1938
ND 6438 ARMY S4 VORTIGERN	0-4-0DM		HE	2642	1941
EARL OF MOUNT EDGECUMBE	0-4-0DM		HE	3133	1944
–	0-4-0DM		HE	3395	1946

LYNTON & BARNSTAPLE RAILWAY ASSOCIATION

The Milky Way Railway, The Milky Way & The North Devon Bird of Prey Centre, Downland Farm, near Clovelly

Gauge 2ft 0in   SS 327229

–	4w-4wDH	SL	23	1973

LYNTON & BARNSTAPLE RAILWAY TRUST

Woody Bay Station, near Parracombe

Gauge 2ft 0in   www.lynton-rail.co.uk   SS 682464

No.1643	BRONLLWYD	0-6-0WT	OC	HC	1643	1930	
	SID	0-4-0WT	OC	Maffei	4127	1925	
–		0-6-0DM		Bg/DC	2393	1952	a
9	RS0009	0-6-0DM		Bg/DC	2395	1952	a
P6496	DH 294	4wDH		HE	6652	1965	
	HEDDON HALL	4wDH		HE	6660	1965	
	TITCH	4wDM		MR	8729	1941	

a   currently in store at a private location

G.D. MASSEY, 57 SILVER STREET, THORVERTON, EXETER

Gauge 2ft 0in   SS 932018

–	4wBER	Massey		1967
–	2w-2PM	Massey		1994

THE MORWELLHAM & TAMAR VALLEY.TRUST, MORWELLHAM QUAY, near TAVISTOCK

Gauge 2ft 0in SX 448699

1	GEORGE	4wBE	WR	H7197	1968	
2	BERTHA	4wBE	WR	6298	1960	
5494 3	CHARLOTTE	4wBE	WR	G7124	1967	
4	LUDO	4wBE	WR	6769	1964	
5	WILLIAM	4wBE	WR	C6770	1964	
6	MARY	4wBE	WR	5665	1957	
No.7	HAREWOOD	4wBE	WR	D6800	1964	
8		4wBE	WR			Dsm

DART VALLEY RAILWAY plc, PAIGNTON & DARTMOUTH STEAM RAILWAY

Locos are kept at :-
Churston SX 896564
Kingswear SX 884515
Park Siding, Paignton SX 889606

Gauge 4ft 8½in www.paignton-steamrailway.co.uk

4277		2-8-0T	OC	Sdn	2857	1920
4555	WARRIOR	2-6-2T	OC	Sdn		1924
4588	TROJAN	2-6-2T	OC	Sdn		1927
5239	GOLIATH	2-8-0T	OC	Sdn		1924
7827	LYDHAM MANOR	4-6-0	OC	Sdn		1950
75014		4-6-0	OC	Sdn		1951
D2192	TITAN	0-6-0DM		Sdn		1961
D3014	SAMSON	0-6-0DE		Derby		1952
D7535	(25185) HERCULES	Bo-BoDE		Derby		1965
(DB 966030)	CE 68200	2w-2DMR		Plasser	419	1975

PLYM VALLEY RAILWAY ASSOCIATION, MARSH MILLS, PLYMPTON

Gauge 4ft 8½in SX 520571

	ALBERT	0-4-0ST	OC	AB	2248	1948	a
	BYFIELD	0-6-0ST	OC	WB	2655	1942	
(D2046)		0-6-0DM		Don		1958	
			reb	HE	6644	1967	
(D3002 11 DULCOTE) 13002		0-6-0DE		Derby		1952	
(D6907) 37207		Co-CoDE		_(EE	3385	1963	
				(EEV	D851	1963	
W51365	T304	2-2w-2w-2DMR		PSteel		1960	
W51407	T304	2-2w-2w-2DMR		PSteel		1960	
–		4wDM		FH	3281	1948	
–		4wDH		TH	125V	1963	
	B445 WPO	4wDMR	R/R	Bruff	502	c1984	
–		2w-2PMR		Wkm	3366	1943	Dsm
–		2w-2PMR		Wkm	4154	1949	Dsm
–		2w-2PMR		Wkm	4992	1949	
			reb	PVRA		1989	DsmT
–		2w-2PMR		Wkm	5002	1949	
			reb	PVRA		1989	DsmT

a currently at South Coast Steam Ltd, Portland, Dorset for restoration

W.L.A. PRYOR, LYNTON RAILWAY STATION, STATION HILL, LYNTON

Gauge 2ft 0in   SS 719488

No.3	BRUNEL	42	4wDM		RH	179880	1936

ROANOKE ENGINEERING, UNIT 2a, GRANGE HILL INDUSTRIAL ESTATE, BRATTON FLEMING, BARNSTAPLE

Gauge 1ft 11½in   www.roanoke.co.uk   SS 649379

"GERTRUDE"	0-6-0T	OC	AB	1578	1918

SOUTH DEVON RAILWAY TRUST, THE PRIMROSE LINE

Locos are kept at :-

Buckfastleigh SX 747663
Staverton Bridge SX 785638

Gauge 7ft 0¼in   www.southdevonrailway.org

151	TINY	0-4-0VBWT	VCG	Sara		1868

Gauge 4ft 8½in

1369		0-6-0PT	OC	Sdn		1934
1420		0-4-2T	IC	Sdn		1933
2873		2-8-0	OC	Sdn	2779	1918
3205		0-6-0	IC	Sdn		1946
3803		2-8-0	OC	Sdn		1939
4920	DUMBLETON HALL	4-6-0	OC	Sdn		1929
5526		2-6-2T	OC	Sdn		1928
WD 132	SAPPER	0-6-0ST	IC	HE	3163	1944
			reb	HE	3885	1964
68011	ERROL LONSDALE	0-6-0ST	IC	HE	3796	1953
	GLENDOWER	0-6-0ST	IC	HE	3810	1954
–		0-6-0ST	IC	K	5474	1934
1	ASHLEY	0-4-0ST	OC	P	2031	1942
(D402)	50002 SUPERB	Co-CoDE		_(EE	3771	1967
				(EEV	D1142	1967
D2246	(11216)	0-6-0DM		_(RSHN	7865	1956
				(DC	2578	1956
D3666	(09002)	0-6-0DE		Dar		1959
(D5526)	31108	A1A-A1A DE		BT	125	1959
(D6501)	33002	Bo-BoDE		BRCW	DEL93	1960
(D6737	37037) 37321 LOCH TREIG					
		Co-CoDE		_(EE	2900	1961
				(VF	D616	1961
(D7612)	(25262) 25901	Bo-BoDE		Derby		1966
D8110	(20110) RIVER DART	Bo-BoDE		_(EE	3016	1962
				(RSHD	8268	1962
(D8118)	20118 SALTBURN-BY-THE-SEA					
		Bo-BoDE		_(EE	3024	1962
				(RSHD	8276	1962
M51592		2-2w-2w-2DHR		DerbyC&W		1959
(M)51604		2-2w-2w-2DHR		DerbyC&W		1959
55000	122 100	2-2w-2w-2DMR		GRC&W		1958

–		0-4-0DM	JF	4210141	1958	
–		0-4-0DH	RH	418793	1957	
LO 52		0-6-0DE	YE	2745	1960	
–		2w-2PMR	Wkm	946	1933	DsmT
–		2w-2PMR	Wkm	4146	1947	
–		2w-2PMR	Wkm	4149	1947	DsmT
PWM 3767	ADRIAN	2w-2PMR	Wkm	6646	1953	
PWM 3773		2w-2PMR	Wkm	6652	1953	
–		2w-2PMR	Wkm	8198	1958	
	THE ADDICK	2w-2PMR	Wkm	11717	1976	

Gauge 4ft 6in

LEE MOOR No.2	0-4-0ST	OC	P	784	1899

P. SPENCER, BRIXHAM
Gauge 1ft 3in Stored at a private location

3205	EARL OF DEVON	4-4-0	IC	Prestige		2001

TARKA VALLEY RAILWAY GROUP, TORRINGTON STATION
Gauge 4ft 8½in   SS 479198

No.1	PROGRESS	0-4-0DH	JF	4000001	1945

TIVERTON MUSEUM SOCIETY,
TIVERTON MUSEUM, ST.ANDREW STREET, TIVERTON
Gauge 4ft 8½in   SS 955124

1442	0-4-2T	IC	Sdn		1935

MARTIN TURNER,
c/o BRIGHTLYCOTT COTTAGE, SHIRWELL ROAD, BARNSTAPLE
Gauge 4ft 8½in   SS 571354

–	4wDM	FH	2893	1944

UNKNOWN OWNER, UNKNOWN LOCATION
Gauge 2ft 0in

–	4wDH	HLH	001	1996

DORSET

INDUSTRIAL SITES

ALASKA ENVIRONMENTAL CONTRACTING LTD,
STOKEFORD FARM, EASTOKE, WAREHAM
Gauge 2ft 0in   SY 873872

	PORT OF POOLE	4wDM	MR	8614	1941

MINISTRY OF DEFENCE, LULWORTH RANGES, EAST LULWORTH
See Section 6 for full details.

POOLE HARBOUR COMMISSIONERS, NEW QUAY, LOWER HAMWORTHY
Gauge 4ft 8½in   SZ 009901

		4wDH		TH	173V	1966
–			reb	YEC	L116	1993

SOUTH COAST STEAM CO LTD, UNIT 9, TRADECROFT INDUSTRIAL ESTATE,
PORTLAND
Locomotives usually present for maintenance, repair and /or restoration   SY 685723

Gauge 4ft 8½in

3278		2-8-0	OC	Alco	71533	1944
35018	BRITISH INDIA LINE	4-6-2	3C	Elh		1945
	ALBERT	0-4-0ST	OC	AB	2248	1948
47160	CUNARDER	0-6-0T	OC	HE	1690	1931
N.C.B.66		0-6-0ST	IC	HE	3890	1964
7715	(L99)	0-6-0PT	IC	KS	4450	1930
–		4wDH		RR	10252	1966

VITACRESS SALADS LTD, WATERCRESS GROWERS,
DODDINGS FARM, BERE REGIS
Gauge 1ft 6in   SY 852934

	VITACRESS	4wPH	Jesty		1948

PRESERVATION SITES

AVON CAUSEWAY HOTEL, HURN, near BOURNEMOUTH
Gauge 4ft 8½in   SZ 136976

–	0-4-0DM	JF	22871	1939

R. BROWN, MOTCOMBE, near SHAFTSBURY

Gauge 4ft 8½in   ST 846267

| 1018 | | 4w-4wRER | | MetCam | | 1959 |
| 1304 | | 2w-2-2-2wRER | | MetCam | | 1961 |

JEFF LEAKE, 154 WAREHAM ROAD, LYTCHETT MATRAVERS

Gauge 1ft 3in

–		4w-4BER		Leake		1992
–		0-4-0BE		Leake		1992
–		0-4-0DM	s/o	Leake		1992

MICKY FINN RAILWAY, near POOLE

Gauge 2ft 0in

| 8 | | 4wDM | | L | 28039 | 1945 |
| – | | 4wDM | | MR | 26007 | 1964 |

MOORS VALLEY RAILWAY, MOORS VALLEY COUNTRY PARK, HORTON ROAD, ASHLEY HEATH, RINGWOOD

Gauge 1ft 3in   SZ 104061

| KATIE | | 0-4-0T | OC | FMB | 002 | 1997 |
| | rebuilt as | 0-4-2T | OC | HaylockJ | | |

NORTH DORSET RAILWAY TRUST, SHILLINGSTONE STATION

Gauge 4ft 8½in   ST 825116

| 92207 | MORNING STAR | 2-10-0 | OC | Sdn | | 1959 |
| – | | 4wDM | | RH | 466629 | 1962 |

SWANAGE RAILWAY SOCIETY

Locos are kept at :-

Swanage Station SZ 026789
Swanage Shed SZ 028789
Herston Railway Works SZ 018793

Gauge 4ft 8½in

5786		0-6-0PT	IC	Sdn		1930
30053		0-4-4T	IC	9E		1905
34010	SIDMOUTH	4-6-2	3C	Bton		1945
34028	EDDYSTONE	4-6-2	3C	Bton		1946
34070	MANSTON	4-6-2	3C	Bton		1947
34072	257 SQUADRON	4-6-2	3C	Bton		1948
80078		2-6-4T	OC	Bton		1954
80104		2-6-4T	OC	Bton		1955
–		0-4-0ST	OC	P	1611	1923
(D3551)	08436	0-6-0DE		Derby		1958
D3591	(08476)	0-6-0DE		Crewe		1958

D6515	(33012)	STAN SYMES	Bo-BoDE		BRCW	DEL107	1960
(D6528)	33111		Bo-BoDE		BRCW	DEL120	1960
(D6552)	33034		Bo-BoDE		BRCW	DEL144	1961
(D8188)	20188	RIVER YEO	Bo-BoDE		_(EE	3669	1966
					(EEV	D1064	1966
W51346			2-2w-2w-2DMR		PSteel		1960
W51388			2-2w-2w-2DMR		PSteel		1960
51933			2-2w-2w-2DMR		DerbyC&W		1960
2054	BERYL		4wPM		FH	2054	1938
	MAY		0-4-0DM		JF	4210132	1957
	SWANWORTH		4wDM		RH	518494	1967

Purbeck Mineral & Mining Group, Corfe Castle
Gauge 2ft 8in

	(SECUNDUS)	0-6-0WT	OC	B&S		1874

Gauge 2ft 0in

	SNAPPER	4wDM		RH	283871	1950

P.C. VALLINS, near BLANDFORD
Gauge 2ft 0in   Private Location

–		4wDM		L	9256	1937
20		4wPM		L	18557	1942
–		4wDM		LB	51917	1960

COUNTY DURHAM

OUR DEFINITION OF "COUNTY DURHAM" NOW INCLUDES THOSE LOCATIONS WHICH WERE SITUATED WITHIN THE PART, OF THE FORMER COUNTY OF TYNE & WEAR, WHICH IS SOUTH OF THE RIVER TYNE AND NOW COMPRISES OF A NUMBER OF UNITARY AUTHORITIES

INDUSTRIAL SITES

BRITISH ENERGY, NUCLEAR ELECTRIC DIVISION, HARTLEPOOL POWER STATION, SEATON CAREW

Gauge 4ft 8½in   NZ 532270

H 058		4wDH	RR	10280	1968	+

+   on hire from R.M.S. Locotec Ltd, Wakefield, West Yorkshire

CORUS, TUBES AND PIPES, NORTH EAST PIPE MILLS, HARTLEPOOL MILL, BRENDA ROAD, HARTLEPOOL

Gauge 4ft 8½in   NZ 505276, 505278

425		6wDE	GECT	5425	1977	OOU
264	PORT MULGRAVE	6wDE	GECT	5461	1977	OOU

42 Inch Mill   Shunted by contractor - Astontrack (Sub – Ed Murray & Sons)

Gauge 4ft 8½in

1	4wDE	Moyse	1464	1979
2	4wDE	Moyse	1364	1976

GREAT NORTHERN STEAM CO LTD
UNIT 3, FORGE WAY, CLEVELAND INDUSTRIAL ESTATE, DARLINGTON

New miniature locos under construction occasionally present.   NZ 296157

KOMATSU UK LTD, BIRTLEY

New road/rail vehicles under construction usually present.

ED MURRAY & SONS LTD, CASEBOURNE ROAD, LONGHILL INDUSTRIAL ESTATE, HARTLEPOOL

Gauge 4ft 8½in

–	0-4-0DH	HE	7425	1981	
MURR 1	4wDE	Moyse	1364	1976	a
MURR 2	4wDE	Moyse	1464	1979	a
(2) 3	4wDE	Moyse	1365	1976	Dsm
DH26	4wDH	RR	10229	1965	

a   currently at Astontrack (sub of Ed Murray & Sons Ltd), Corus 42 Inch Mill, Hartlepool

PORT OF SUNDERLAND AUTHORITY, SOUTH DOCKS, SUNDERLAND
Gauge 4ft 8½in   RTC   NZ 410573, 411578

21	0-4-0DE	RH	395294	1956	OOU
P.S.A. No.22	0-4-0DE	RH	416210	1957	OOU

SHERBURN STONE CO LTD, BROADWOOD QUARRY, FROSTERLEY, STANHOPE
Gauge 3ft 0in

20/110/738	4wDHF	CE	B0190	1974	
	reb	CE	B2293	1983	OOU

Gauge 2ft 0in

3	4wBE	WR	Dsm
–	0-4-0BE	WR	Dsm

TYNE & WEAR FIRE & RESCUE SERVICE, BARMSTON MERE TRAINING CENTRE, NISSAN WAY, WASHINGTON
Gauge 4ft 8½in

3721	4w-4wRER	MetCam	1983	OOU

Used as a static training aid.

T.J. THOMSON & SON LTD
Millfield Scrap Works, Stockton
Apart from the locos listed, other locos for scrap are occasionally present.   NZ 438193

Gauge 4ft 8½in

J.W.H.	0-4-0DH	AB	558	1970	OOU
ZZ 267	0-6-0DH	EEV	4003	1971	
60 689/170 LBH 47 KEN	0-4-0DH	RR	10253	1967	
01568 HELEN	4wDH	TH	264V	1976	
01567 ELIZABETH	4wDH	TH	276V	1977	
25	4wDH	TH	279V	1978	OOU
26	4wDH	TH	280V	1978	OOU
01569 EMMA	4wDH	TH	281V	1978	
28	4wDH	TH	282V	1979	OOU
"JAMES"	4wDH	TH	288V	1980	
9602 R.O.F. No.4	4wDH	TH	292V	1980	OOU

Tyne Dock
Gauge 4ft 8½in   NZ 348656

9	4wDH	TH	287V	1980

U.K. MINING VENTURES, ROGERLEY QUARRY

Gauge 2ft 0in   www.ukminingventures.com

–	4wBE	CE			

PRESERVATION SITES

A1 LOCOMOTIVE TRUST, DARLINGTON LOCOMOTIVE WORKS, STOCKTON & DARLINGTON RAILWAY CARRIAGE SHED, HOPETOWN LANE, DARLINGTON

Gauge 4ft 8½in   NZ 288156

60163 TORNADO	4-6-2	3C	Darlington	2195	2008

Based here between charter hirings

BOWES RAILWAY CO LTD, SPRINGWELL

Gauge 4ft 8½in   NZ 285589

W.S.T.	0-4-0ST	OC	AB	2361	1954
No.22 No.85	0-4-0ST	OC	AB	2274	1949
101	4wDM		FH	3922	1959
–	0-4-0DH		HE	6263	1964

Gauge 3ft 0in

No.1 9307/110	4wBE	CE	5921	1972
No.2 20/270/34	4wBE	CE	B3060	1983

Gauge 2ft 6in

B03	4w-4wDHF	_(HE	8515	1981
		(AB	651	1981
8	4wBE	CE	B1840	1978

Gauge 2ft 0in

20.123.945 SER No.2476					
PLANT No.2207/456	4wBEF	_(EE	2476	1958
		(RSHN	7980	1958
–	0-6-0DMF	HC	DM842	1954

TREVOR CATTERSON

Stored at private location
Gauge 4ft 8½in

(DB 965080)	2w-2PMR	Wkm	7595	1957
reb	2w-2DMR			1999

DARLINGTON RAILWAY MUSEUM, NORTH ROAD STATION
STATION ROAD, HOPETOWN, DARLINGTON
Gauge 4ft 8½in   NZ 288157

(63460)	901		0-8-0	3C	Dar		1919
No.1463			2-4-0	IC	Dar		1885
25	DERWENT		0-6-0	OC	Kitching		1845
	LOCOMOTION		0-4-0	VC	RS	1	1825

DARLINGTON RAILWAY PRESERVATION SOCIETY,
STATION ROAD, HOPETOWN, DARLINGTON
Gauge 4ft 8½in   NZ 290157 NZ 285160

78018		2-6-0	OC	Dar		1954
	LOCOMOTION	0-4-0	VC	LocoEnt	No.1	1975
	NORTHERN GAS BOARD No.1	0-4-0ST	OC	P	2142	1953
No.39		0-6-0T	OC	RSHD	6947	1938
	PATONS	0-4-0F	OC	WB	2898	1948
185	DAVID PAYNE	0-4-0DM		JF	4110006	1950
–		0-4-0DM		JF	4200018	1947
–		4wDM		RH	279591	1949
–		0-4-0DE		RH	312988	1952
–		0-4-0DM		_(RSHN	7925	1959
				(DC	2592	1959
1		4wWE		GEC		(1928?)
(DB 965096)		2w-2PMR		Wkm	7611	1957

Gauge 1ft 8in

–	4wDM	RH	375360	1955
–	4wDM	RH	476124	1962
–	4wDM	RH	354013	1953

D. FEATHERSTONE, IRESHOPEBURN
Gauge 2ft 0in   NY 871386

3	0-4-0BE	WR
9	0-4-0BE	WR

LOCOMOTION – THE NATIONAL RAILWAY MUSEUM AT SHILDON
Gauge 4ft 8½in   www.locomotion.uk.com

	"SANS PAREIL"	0-4-0	VC	Hackworth		1829
	(BRADYLL)	0-6-0	OC	Hackworth		1835
	SANS PAREIL	0-4-0	VC	BRE(S)		1980
–		0-4-0	VC	Hetton		c1852
No.2		0-6-2T	IC	Stoke		1923
No.563		4-4-0	OC	9E	380	1893
No.910		2-4-0	IC	Ghd		1875
1439		0-4-0ST	IC	Crewe	842	1862

(42700)	2700	2-6-0	OC	Hor		1926
(60800)	4771 GREEN ARROW	2-6-2	3C	Don	1837	1936
(65894)	2392	0-6-0	IC	Dar		1923
3020	CORNWALL	2-2-2	OC	Crewe		1858
68846		0-6-0ST	IC	SS	4492	1899
	IMPERIAL No.1	0-4-0F	OC	AB	2373	1956
	WOOLMER	0-6-0ST	OC	AE	1572	1910
–		0-6-0ST	IC	HE	3183	1944
	MERLIN/MYRDDIN	0-4-0ST	OC	P	1967	1939
(D2090)	03090	0-6-0DM		Don		1960
D6703	(37003)	Co-CoDE		_(EE	2866	1960
				(VF	D582	1960
D8000	(20050)	Bo-BoDE		_(EE	2347	1957
				(VF	D375	1957
E5001	(71001)	Bo-BoRE/WE		Don		1958
	DELTIC	Co-CoDE		EEDK	2007	1955
663	ANNETTE	0-6-0DE		_(EE	2160	1956
				(VF	D350	1956
DX50002		4wDHR		Matisa	PV5 570	1957
–		4wPM		MR	4217	1931
No.3		4wDM		RH	441934	1960
H 001		4wDH		S	10003	1959
(26500)	No.1	Bo-BoWE/RE		BE		1905
M49006		Bo-BoWE		Derby		1977
2090	(S10656)	4w-4wRER		_(Lancing		
				(Elh		1937
APT-E	PC1/TC1/TC2/PC2	4w-4w-4-4w4wArticGTE	Derby			1972
960209		2w-2PMR		Wkm	899	1933

Gauge 3ft 0in

No. 14	No.4 9306/108	0-6-0DMF	HC	DM1274	1961
No.9	20/125/101 M.T.R.	4w-4wDHF	HE	9227	1986

NORTH EASTERN LOCOMOTIVE PRESERVATION GROUP, HOPETOWN CARRIAGE WORKS, DARLINGTON

NZ 288157

Gauge 4ft 8½in — www.nelpg.org.uk

69023	JOEM	0-6-0T	IC	Dar	2151	1951

NORTH OF ENGLAND OPEN AIR MUSEUM, BEAMISH HALL

Gauge 4ft 8½in

NZ 217547

	"PUFFING BILLY"	4wG	VC	AK	71	2006
E No.1		2-4-0VBCT	OC	BH	897	1887
	STEAM ELEPHANT	6wG		_(Dorothea		2001
				(AK		2001
L.& H.C. 14		0-4-0ST	OC	HL	3056	1914
			reb	‡		1980
–		0-4-0VBT	VC	HW		1871
			reb	Wilton(ICI)		1984

17		0-4-0VBT	OC	HW	33	1873
–		0-4-0T	OC	Lewin	683	1877
No. 5		0-4-0ST	OC	SDSI(S)		1900
14		0-4-0DE		AW	D21	1933
–		0-4-0PM		Bg	680	1916
15097	IBIQUE	4wPM		MR	1930	1919
–		4wDM		RH	476140	1963
			reb	Wilton(ICI)		1982
2		4wWE		Siemens	455	1908

‡   rebuilt by Clark Hawthorn Ltd, Northumberland Engine Works, Wallsend-on-Tyne

SUNDERLAND CITY COUNCIL, TYNE & WEAR JOINT MUSEUMS SERVICE
WASHINGTON "F" PIT MUSEUM, WASHINGTON NEW TOWN
Gauge 2ft 0in   NZ 303574

–	0-4-0DMF		RH	392157	1956

PRIVATE OWNER
Loco stored at unknown location.
Gauge 2ft 0in

–	0-4-0BE		WR	8079	1980
rebuilt as	0-4-0DM		BrownGM		1993

STOCKTON-ON-TEES BOROUGH COUNCIL,
BRIDGE ROAD ROUNDABOUT, STOCKTON-ON-TEES
Gauge 4ft 8½in   NZ 446185

–	0-4-0VBT	VCG	HW	21	1870

TANFIELD RAILWAY PRESERVATION SOCIETY, MARLEY HILL
Gauge 4ft 8½in   NZ 207573

–		0-6-0ST	OC	AB	1015	1904
No.6		0-4-2ST	OC	AB	1193	1910
No.17		0-6-0T	OC	AB	1338	1913
32		0-4-0ST	OC	AB	1659	1920
	WELLINGTON	0-4-0ST	OC	BH	266	1873
	CITY OF ABERDEEN	0-4-0ST	OC	BH	912	1887
No.3		0-4-0WT	OC	EB	37	1898
RENISHAW IRONWORKS No.6		0-6-0ST	OC	HC	1366	1919
	IRWELL	0-4-0ST	OC	HC	1672	1937
38		0-6-0T	OC	HC	1823	1949
–		0-4-0ST	OC	HL	2711	1907
			reb	DL		1956
No.2		0-4-0ST	OC	HL	2859	1911
	STAGSHAW	0-6-0ST	OC	HL	3513	1927
	COAL PRODUCTS No.3	0-6-0ST	OC	HL	3575	1923
No.13		0-4-0ST	OC	HL	3732	1928

–		0-6-0F	OC	HL	3746	1929	
No.3	TWIZELL	0-6-0T	IC	RS	2730	1891	
–		0-4-0CT	OC	RSHN	7007	1940	
	LYSAGHT'S	0-6-0ST	OC	RSHD	7035	1940	
49		0-6-0ST	IC	RSHN	7098	1943	
	PROGRESS	0-6-0ST	IC	RSHN	7298	1946	
	SIR CECIL A.COCHRANE	0-4-0ST	OC	RSHN	7409	1948	
No.44	9103/44	0-6-0ST	OC	RSHN	7760	1953	
38		0-6-0ST	OC	RSHN	7763	1954	
21		0-4-0ST	OC	RSHN	7796	1954	
–		0-6-0ST	OC	RSHN	7800	1954	
No.16		0-6-0ST	OC	RSHN	7944	1957	
No.3		0-4-0ST	OC	RWH	2009	1884	
No.4		4wVBT	VCG	S	9559	1953	
No.20	TANFIELD	0-6-0ST	IC	WB	2779	1945	
	F.G.F.	0-4-0DH		AB	552	1968	
9		Bo-BoWE		AEG	1565	1913	
No.2		0-4-0DE		AW	D22	1933	
–		2w-2DHR		Bg	3565	1962	
–		4wDM		FH	3716	1955	
–		4wWE		GB	2508	1955	Dsm
–		4wWE		GB	2509	1955	Dsm
	2111-125	0-6-0DH		HE	6612	1965	
No.6		0-6-0DH		JF	4240010	1960	
T.I.C.No.35		0-4-0DE		RH	418600	1958	
–		0-6-0DM		RSHN	7697	1953	
–		0-4-0DM		RSHN	6980	1940	
–		0-6-0DM		RSHN	7746	1954	
–		0-4-0DM		RSHN	7901	1958	
	KEARSLEY No.3	Bo-BoWE		RSHN	7078	1944	
E10		4wWE		Siemens	862	1913	
DB 965079	68/016	2w-2PMR		Wkm	7594	1957	
DB 965097	68044	2w-2PMR		Wkm	7612	1957	

Gauge 3ft 6in

M2	4-6-2	OC	RSHD	7430	1951	

Gauge 2ft 6in

–	4wBEF		CE	B1886B	1980	

Gauge 600mm

No.11	ESCUCHA	0-4-0T	OC	BH	748	1883

Gauge 2ft 0in

No.2		4wBEF		CE	B3141B	1984
25		4wBEF		_(EE	2848	1960
				(RSHN	8201	1960
4	DM1067	0-6-0DMF		HC	DM1067	1959

2305/54	TYNESIDE GEORGE	0-6-0DMF	HC	DM1119	1958	
No.5	2201/266	0-6-0DMF	HC	DM1170	1960	
–		4wDM	HE	2577	1942	
2	AYLE	4wDM	HE	2607	1942	
No.1		4wDHF	HE	7332	1974	
–		4wDM	LB	53162	1962	
–		4wDM	LB	54781	1965	
–		4wDM	RH	244487	1946	
–		4wDM	RH	323587	1952	
–		0-4-0BE	WR		1972	
–		0-4-0BE	WR			

THE TERRIFIC TRAIN, THE NEW METROLAND, METRO CENTRE, DUNSTON, near GATESHEAD

Gauge 1ft 6in   NZ 211628

–	4-4-0RE	s/o	SwingStage		1988	Pvd
–	4-4-0RE	s/o	SL	321.11.90	1990	

TWEDDLE CHILDREN'S ANIMAL FARM, FILLPOKE LANE, BLACKHALL COLLIERY

Gauge 4ft 8½in   NZ 467378

1212	4w-4DMR	EK		1958	OOU

WEARDALE RAILWAY TRUST AND WEARDALE RAILWAYS LTD. c/o WEARDALE STEEL (WOLSINGHAM) LTD, WOLSINGHAM

Gauge 4ft 8½in   NZ 081370

No.77	NORWOOD	0-6-0ST	OC	RSHN	7412	1948
No.40		0-6-0T	OC	RSHN	7765	1954
(D5217)	25067	Bo-BoDE		Derby		1963
(D6987	37287) 37414	Co-CoDE		_(EE	3547	1965
				(EEV	D976	1965
56022		Co-CoDE		Electro		1976
25-1		0-6-0DH		EEV	3870	1969
–		0-6-0DH		RR	10187	1964
13		4wDH		RR	10197	1965
2		4wDH		RR	10232	1965
M14		4wDH		S	10077	1961
(E6041)	73134	Bo-BoDE/RE		_(EE	3713	1966
				(EEV	E373	1966
(E6046)	73139	Bo-BoDE/RE		_(EE	3718	1966
				(EEV	E378	1966
	141 103 55503	4wDMR		BRE(D)/Leyland		
					R4.030	1984
			reb	AB	741	1988

141 103	55523	4wDMR	BRE(D)/Leyland			
			R4.107		1984	
		reb	AB		740	1988
141 110	55510	4wDMR	BRE(D)/Leyland			
			R4.018		1984	
		reb	AB		739	1989
141 110	55530	4wDMR	BRE(D)/Leyland			
			R4.027		1984	
		reb	AB		738	1989
51356		2-2w-2w-2DMR	PSteel		1960	
51392		2-2w-2w-2DMR	PSteel		1960	
–		2w-2PMR	Wkm	6857	1954	
DX 68071		2w-2DMR	Wkm	10343	1969	
	DB 965950	2w-2PMR	Wkm	10646	1972	
DX 68080	DB 965993	2w-2DMR	Wkm	10706	1974	
DX 68090		2w-2DMR	Wkm	10843	1975	

WHORLTON LIDO, WHORLTON, near BARNARD CASTLE

Gauge 1ft 3in   CLOSED   NZ 106146

WENDY	4-4wDM	ColebySim	1972	OOU

ESSEX

INDUSTRIAL SITES

BP OIL CO LTD, CORYTON BULK TERMINAL, STANFORD-LE-HOPE

Gauge 4ft 8½in   TQ 746828

506/1		0-4-0DH	AB	506/1	1969	+
		reb	AB		1989	
506/2		0-4-0DH	AB	506/2	1969	+
		reb	AB		1989	
–		0-6-0DH	TH	291V	1980	
	HAMBLE-LE-RICE	0-6-0DH	TH	294V	1981	
–		0-6-0DH	TH	295V	1981	OOU

+   rebuild of AB 506/1965

CARLESS SOLVENTS LTD,
HARWICH REFINERY, REFINERY ROAD, PARKESTON, HARWICH

Gauge 4ft 8½in   TM 232323

Q240 JBV	4wDM	R/R	Unimog	092692	1982

ENGINEERING SERVICES, BROOKLYN FARM, NORTH HILL, HORNDON-ON-THE-HILL

Locomotives occasionally present for restoration or temporary storage whilst in transit.   TQ 668844

ROGER HARVEY, WALTON – ON – THE – NAZE
Gauge 4ft 8½in

–	4wWE	KS	1269	1912	Dsm

INDUSTRIAL CHEMICALS LTD, TITAN WORKS, TITAN INDUSTRIAL ESTATE, HOGG LANE, GRAYS
Gauge 4ft 8½in

–	4wDH	TH	144V	1964	OOU

MINISTRY OF DEFENCE, DEFENCE EVALUATION & RESEARCH AGENCY
Shoeburyness
See Section 6 for full details.

Shoeburyness (Project Avocet)
See Section 6 for full details.

TRANSFESA, TILBURY RIVERSIDE TERMINAL
Gauge 4ft 8½in

(D3932 08764) 003 FLORENCE	0-6-0DE	Hor		1961	a

a   on hire from Wabtec, South Yorkshire

PRESERVATION SITES

BRITISH POSTAL MUSEUM, STORE & ARCHIVE, DEBDEN
Gauge 2ft 0in

–		4w Atmospheric Car				1861	
807	211	2w-2-2-2wRE	EEDK	807	1931	Dsm	a
809		2w-2-2-2wRE	EEDK	809	1931	+	
21		2w-2-2-2wRE	_(GB	420461/21	1981		
			(HE	9120	1981		

a   consists of only one power bogie – no.211
+   built 1931 but originally carried plates dated 1930

COLNE VALLEY RAILWAY PRESERVATION SOCIETY LTD, CASTLE HEDINGHAM STATION, YELDHAM ROAD, CASTLE HEDINGHAM, HALSTEAD

35010	BLUE STAR		4-6-2	3C	Elh		1942
45163			4-6-0	OC	AW	1204	1935
45293			4-6-0	OC	AW	1348	1936
2199	VICTORY		0-4-0ST	OC	AB	2199	1945
1875	BARRINGTON		0-4-0ST	OC	AE	1875	1921
WD 190			0-6-0ST	IC	HE	3790	1952
No.1			0-4-0ST	OC	HL	3715	1928
No.60	JUPITER		0-6-0ST	IC	RSHN	7671	1950
(D1946)	47771		Co-CoDE		BT	708	1966
D2041			0-6-0DM		Sdn		1959
D2184			0-6-0DM		Sdn		1962
D3255			0-6-0DE		Derby		1956
D3476			0-6-0DE		Dar		1957
(D3526)	08411		0-6-0DE		Derby		1958
(D3556)	08441		0-6-0DE		Derby		1958
(D3575)	08460		0-6-0DE		Crewe		1958
(D4145)	08915		0-6-0DE		Hor		1962
(D5683)	31255		A1A-A1A DE		BT	284	1961
(55033)	977826	T003	2-2w-2w-2DMR		PSteel		1960
55508	141 108		(4wDMR		BRE(D)/Leyland		
			(			R4.016	1984
			(	reb	AB	759	1989
55528	141 108		(4wDMR		BRE(D)/Leyland		
			(			R4.033	1984
			(	reb	AB	758	1989	a
(68009)	9009		4w-4wRE/BER		Afd/Elh		1961
E79978			4wDMR		ACCars		1958
3211			0-4-0DM		AB	349	1941
–			4wDM		FH	3147	1947
	HENRY		4wDM		Lake&Elliot		c1924
				reb	FordTTC		1997
YD No.43			4wDM		RH	221639	1943
–			0-4-0DM		RH	281266	1950
–			4wDM	R/R	Unilok(G)	2109	1980
–			2w-2PMR		Wkm	1946	1935

a   141108 is a twin set

CRAVEN HERITAGE TRAINS LTD, EPPING
Gauge 4ft 8½in

L11		4w-4wRE		MetCam	1931/1932
			reb	Acton	1964

ROGER CRAVEN, PRIVATE LOCATION
Gauge 3ft 0in

–		4wDMF		RH	418803	1957

Gauge 750mm

5		4wDH		HE	8829	1979
16		4wDH		HE	9079	1984
15		4wDH		HE	9080	1984
11		4wDM		Moes		
13		4wDM		Moes		
27		4wDM		Moes		
–		4wDMF		RH	338438	1953
No.3		4wDMF		RH	375693	1954

Gauge 600mm

4	4wDM		Moes	
17	4wDM		Moes	

EAST ANGLIAN RAILWAY MUSEUM, CHAPPEL & WAKES COLNE STATION
Gauge 4ft 8½in TL 898289

No.11	STOREFIELD	0-4-0ST	OC	AB	1047	1905	
	ROBERT	0-6-0ST	OC	AE	2068	1933	
	KING GEORGE	0-6-0ST	IC	HE	2409	1942	
	JEFFREY	0-4-0ST	OC	P	2039	1943	
54	PEN GREEN	0-6-0ST	IC	RSHN	7031	1941	
	(JUBILEE)	0-4-0ST	OC	WB	2542	1936	
(D2279)	11249	0-6-0DM		_(RSHD	8097	1960	
				(DC	2656	1960	
(50599)	L990	2-2w-2w-2DMR		DerbyC&W		1958	
51213		2-2w-2w-2DMR		MetCam		1959	
A.M.W.No.144	JOHN PEEL	0-4-0DM		AB	333	1938	
7		0-4-0DH		JF	4220039	1965	+
–		4wPM		MR	2029	1920	
-		2w-2PMR		DC	1895	1950	DsmT
(TR 37)	(PWM 2797)	2w-2PMR		Wkm	6896	1954	

+   fitted with GER tram bodywork

EPPING & ONGAR RAILWAY, ONGAR GOODS YARD
Gauge 1524mm TL 551039

(1008)		4-6-2	OC	LO	157	1948
1060		2-8-2	OC	LO	172	1954

Gauge 4ft 8½in

D1995		0-4-0DM		_(VF	D293	1955
				(DC	2566	1955
–		4wDM		RH	398616	1956
–		4wDM		RH	512572	1965
PM002	BADGER	4wDHR		Perm	T002	1988
51342		2-2w-2w-2DMR		PSteel		1960
51384		2-2w-2w-2DMR		PSteel		1960

| – | 2w-2PMR | Bance | 2021 | 1995 |

GLENDALE FORGE, MONK STREET, near THAXTED
Gauge 2ft 0in   TL 612287

145	C.P.HUNTINGTON	4w-2-4wPH	s/o	Chance		
				76-50145-24	1976	
	ROCKET	0-2-2+4wPH	s/o	FRgroup4	1970	
	–	4wDM		RH		+ Dsm

+ either RH 217973 / 1942, or RH 213853 / 1942

LYNN TAIT GALLERY, THE OLD FOUNDRY, LEIGH-ON-SEA
Gauge 3ft 6in   TQ 889891

| 21 | 4wRER | ACCars | 1949 |

MANGAPPS FARM RAILWAY MUSEUM,
SOUTHMINSTER ROAD, BURNHAM-ON-CROUCH
Gauge 4ft 8½in   TQ 944980

	TOTO	0-4-0ST	OC	AB	1619	1919
ROF 8	No. 8	0-4-0ST	OC	AB	2157	1943
	MINNIE	0-6-0ST	OC	FW	358	1878
No.15	HASTINGS	0-6-0ST	IC	HE	469	1888
	BROOKFIELD	0-6-0PT	OC	WB	2613	1940
	EMPRESS	0-6-0ST	OC	WB	3061	1954
(D1778	47183 47579) 47793	Co-CoDE		BT	540	1964
(D2018	03018) 600 No.2	0-6-0DM		Sdn		1958
(D2081)	03081 LUCIE	0-6-0DM		Don		1960
(D2089)	03089	0-6-0DM		Don		1960
D2325		0-6-0DM		_(RSHD	8184	1961
				(DC	2706	1961
(D2399)	03399	0-6-0DM		Don		1961
ELLAND No.1	AUSTIN WALKER	0-4-0DM		HC	D1153	1959
DS 1169	IDRIS	4wDM		RH	207103	1941
	–	4wDM	R/R	S&H	7502	1966
11104		0-6-0DM		_(VF	D78	1948
				(DC	2252	1948
226		0-4-0DM		_(VF	5261	1945
				(DC	2180	1945
98401		4wBE		Perm	001	1987
1030		2-2w-2w-2RER		MetCam		1960
22624		2w-2-2-2wRER		GRC&W		1938
			reb	GRC&W		1950
W51381		2-2w-2w-2DMR		PSteel		1960
E79963		2w-2DMR		WMD	1268	1958

SANDFORD MILL MUSEUM, SANDFORD MILL ROAD, CHELMER, near CHELMSFORD

Gauge 2ft 8½in   TL 739061

8		4wRER		BE		1898
			reb	BE		c1911

SOUTHEND-ON-SEA BOROUGH COUNCIL,
SOUTHEND PIER RAILWAY, SOUTHEND-ON-SEA

Gauge 3ft 0in   TQ 884850

	A	SIR JOHN BETJEMAN	4w-4wDH	SL	SE4	1986
	B	SIR WILLIAM HEYGATE	4w-4wDH	SL	SE4	1986
No.1835			4wBER	?		1996

SOUTHEND PIER RAILWAY MUSEUM, SOUTHEND-ON-SEA

Gauge 3ft 6in   TQ 884850

11	4wRER	ACCars	1949
22	4wRER	ACCars	1949
6	2-2wRER	BE	1890

SUTTON HALL RAILWAY, ROCHFORD

Gauge 4ft 8½in   TQ 889891

NL 1305	2-2w-2w-2RER	MetCam	1961

WALTHAM ABBEY ROYAL GUNPOWDER MILLS CO LTD, WALTHAM ABBEY

Gauge 4ft 8½in   TL 376013

BARKING POWER	DUDLEY	4wDM	FH	(3294	1948?)

Gauge 3ft 0in

BB 307	2w-2DE	GB	6099	1964

Gauge 2ft 6in

1	4wBEF	CE	B3482A	1988	+
4	4wDH	HE	8828	1979	
—	4wDH	Ruhrthaler	3920	1969	

+   currently stored elsewhere.

Gauge 1ft 6in

No. 1		0-4-0T	OC	AE	1748	1916
	(CARNEGIE)	0-4-4-0DM		HE	4524	1954
	BUDLEIGH	4wDM		RH	235624	1945

Mr WILKES, near COLCHESTER
Gauge 4ft 8½in

–	4wVBT	VCG	S	7492	1928

GLOUCESTERSHIRE

INDUSTRIAL SITES

FIRE SERVICE COLLEGE, MORETON-IN-MARSH
Locos are used for static training purposes. SP 216329

Gauge 4ft 8½in

(E6033) 73126	Bo-BoRE/DE	_(EE	3595	1966	
		(EEV	E365	1966	
H 004	0-4-0DE	YE	2732	1959	

JOHN GERZ, c/o JOHN GOLDING HEAVY HAULAGE LTD,
ABBEY MILLS INDUSTRIAL ESTATE, KINGSWOOD, WOTTON-UNDER-EDGE
Dealer with locos for resale. ST 745922

Gauge 4ft 8½in

BE1	4wDM	RH	221561	1943	OOU
YARD No.766	0-4-0DM	RH	414300	1957	OOU

HANSON QUARRY PRODUCTS EUROPE LTD,
HANSON AGGREGATES, TYTHERINGTON QUARRY
Gauge 4ft 8½in ST 658888

HANSON	4wVBT	VCG	S	9387	1948	Pvd

MINISTRY OF DEFENCE, DEFENCE RAILWAY EXECUTIVE,
DEFENCE STORAGE & DISTRIBUTION CENTRE, ASHCHURCH
For full details see Section 6. SO 932338

THOMPSON RAIL ENGINEERING, VALLEY ROAD, CINDERFORD
Gauge 4ft 8½in

DR 98101	2w-2DMR	Schöma	4017	1974

PRESERVATION SITES

Mr. & Mrs. ASTBURY, OLD STATION HOUSE, BRIDGE ROAD, SHORTWOOD
Gauge 4ft 8½in   ST 672757

12	ALEXANDRA	0-4-0ST	OC	AB	929	1902	a	

a   carries plate AB 1054/1906.

AVON VALLEY RAILWAY CO LTD, BITTON STEAM CENTRE, BITTON STATION
BATH ROAD, BITTON
Gauge 4ft 8½in   www.avonvalleyrailway.org   ST 670705

34058	SIR FREDERICK PILE	4-6-2	3C	Bton		1947		
44123		0-6-0	IC	Crewe	5658	1925		
TKh 4015	KAREL	0-6-0T	OC	Chrz	4015	1954	c	
	EDWIN HULSE	0-6-0ST	OC	AE	1798	1918		
70		0-6-0T	IC	HC	1464	1921		
	LITTLETON No 5	0-6-0ST	IC	MW	2018	1922		
No.9		0-6-0T	OC	RSHN	7151	1944		
1		0-6-0T	IC	RSHN	7609	1950		
D2994	(07010)	0-6-0DE		RH	480695	1962		
51909	L231	2-2w-2w-2DMR		DerbyC&W		1960	a	
70043		0-4-0DM		AB	358	1941		
	KINGSWOOD	0-4-0DM		AB	446	1959		
D1171		0-6-0DM		HC	D1171	1959	a	
–		4wDM		RH	252823	1947	b	Dsm
429		0-6-0DH		RH	466618	1961		
D2	ARMY 610	0-8-0DH		S	10143	1963	a	
SC52006		2-2w-2w-2DMR		DerbyC&W		1961		
SC52025		2-2w-2w-2DMR		DerbyC&W		1961		
(B8W)	PWM 3769	2w-2PMR		Wkm	6648	1953		

a   currently in store elsewhere
b   converted to unpowered weed killing unit
c   carries plate Chrz 4939/1957

DEAN FOREST RAILWAY CO LTD, LYDNEY, Forest of Dean
Locos are kept at :–   Norchard Steam Centre   SO 629044
     Lydney Riverside Station   SO 634025

Gauge 4ft 8½in

1450		0-4-2T	IC	Sdn		1935	
5538		2-6-2T	OC	Sdn		1928	
5541		2-6-2T	OC	Sdn		1928	
9681		0-6-0PT	IC	Sdn		1949	
2		0-4-0ST	OC	AB	2221	1946	
WILBERT	REV.W.AWDRY	0-6-0ST	IC	HE	3806	1953	
63.000.432	FRED WARRIOR	0-6-0ST	IC	HE	3823	1954	
DFR 1	USKMOUTH 1	0-4-0ST	OC	P	2147	1952	

13308	08238 (D3308) CHARLIE	0-6-0DE	Dar		1956	
(D3588)	08473	0-6-0DE	Crewe		1958	Dsm
(D3902)	08734	0-6-0DE	Crewe		1960	
D5386	(27066 27103)	Bo-BoDE	BRCW	DEL229	1962	
(D5533)	31115	A1A-A1ADE	BT	132	1959	
D5634	(31210)	A1A-A1ADE	BT	234	1960	
E6001	(73001 73901)	Bo-BoDE/RE	Elh		1962	
(E6002)	73002	Bo-BoDE/RE	Elh		1962	
(E6007)	73101 THE ROYAL ALEX	Bo-BoDE/RE	_(EE	3569	1965	
			(EEV	E339	1965	
(D6963)	37263	Co-CoDE	_(EE	3523	1964	
			(EEV	D952	1964	
D7633	(25283 25904)	Bo-BoDE	BP	8043	1965	
D9555		0-6-0DH	Sdn		1965	
3947		4wDM	FH	3947	1960	
	BASIL	0-4-0DM	HE	2145	1940	
	DON CORBETT	0-4-0DH	HE	5622	1960	
–		0-4-0DM	JF	4210127	1957	
E50619	(53619) B 962	2-2w-2w-2DMR	DerbyC&W		1958	
M51566		2-2w-2w-2DMR	DerbyC&W		1959	
M51914		2-2w-2w-2DMR	DerbyC&W		1960	
1392	62378	4w-4wRER	York		1971	
1499	62364	4w-4wRER	York		1971	
(DS 3057)		4wPMR	Wkm	4254	1947	
(DB 965065)	68012	2w-2PMR	Wkm	7580	1956	
(DE 320501)	68019	2w-2PMR	Wkm	7598	1957	

BRIAN FAULKNER, POCKETS COTTAGE, CHURCHAM, GLOUCESTER
Gauge 2ft 0in   SO 763187

–		4wDM	L	8022	1936
–		4wDM	L	33650	1949
–		4wDM	LB	56371	1970
No.4	LITTLE OWL	2w-2DM	StokesMJ		1986

GLOUCESTERSHIRE WARWICKSHIRE STEAM RAILWAY plc
Locos are kept at :-

Toddington Goods Yard SP 049321
Winchcombe Carriage Works Yard SP 026297
Winchcombe Station Yard SP 025297

Gauge 4ft 8½in   **www.gwsr.com**

2807		2-8-0	OC	Sdn	2102	1905
4270		2-8-0T	OC	Sdn	2850	1919
5542		2-6-2T	OC	Sdn		1928
6984	OWSDEN HALL	4-6-0	OC	Sdn		1948
7903	FOREMARKE HALL	4-6-0	OC	Sdn		1949
9642		0-6-0PT	IC	Sdn		1946
35006	PENINSULAR & ORIENTAL S.N.CO					
		4-6-2	3C	Elh		1941
76077		2-6-0	OC	Hor		1956

92203	BLACK PRINCE		2-10-0	OC	Sdn		1959	
–			2-8-0	OC	NBH	24648	1941	
–			0-4-0ST	OC	P	1976	1939	

(D135)	45149 PHAETON		1Co-Co1DE		Crewe		1961	
(D1693)	47105 TIM LEVERTON		Co-CoDE		BT	455	1963	
(D1895)	47376 FREIGHTLINER 1995							
			Co-CoDE		BT	657	1965	
(D1932 | 47493)	47701	Co-CoDE		BT	694	1966	
(D2069)	03069		0-6-0DM		Don		1959	
D2182			0-6-0DM		Sdn		1962	
D4095	(08881)		0-6-0DE		Hor		1961	
(D5081)	24081		Bo-BoDE		Crewe		1960	
(D5343)	26043		Bo-BoDE		BRCW	DEL88	1959	
(D)5580	(31162)		A1A-A1ADE		BT	180	1960	
(D6799)	37099		Co-CoDE		_(EE	3228	1962	
					(VF	D753	1962	
(D6915)	37215		Co-CoDE		_(EE	3393	1963	
					(EEV	D859	1963	
D8137	(20137)		Bo-BoDE		_(EE	3608	1965	
					(EEV	D1007	1965	
D9553	54		0-6-0DH		Sdn		1965	
(E6036)	73129		Bo-BoDE/RE		_(EE	3598	1965	
					(EEV	E368	1965	
W51950			2-2w-2w-2DMR		DerbyC&W		1961	
W52062			2-2w-2w-2DMR		DerbyC&W		1961	
–			0-6-0DH		HE	5511	1960	
(7069)			0-6-0DE		HL	3841	1935	
No.21	(MAVIS)		0-4-0DM		JF	4210130	1957	
11230			0-6-0DM		_(RSHN	7860	1956	
					(DC	2574	1956	
372			0-6-0DE		YE	2760	1959	
	ARMY 9119		4wDMR		BD	3708	1975	
(9127)			4wDMR		BD	3743	1976	
(TR 13)	PWM 2189		2w-2PMR		Wkm	4166	1948	a
(TR 23 | B52)	PWM 4313	2w-2PMR		Wkm	7516	1956	

a   currently under restoration elsewhere

GREAT WESTERN RAILWAY MUSEUM
COLEFORD RAILWAY YARD, COLEFORD, Forest of Dean
Gauge 4ft 8½in   SO 576105

–	0-4-0ST	OC	P	1893	1936

HOPEWELL COLLIERY MUSEUM, near COLEFORD, Forest of Dean
Gauge 2ft 0in   SO 603114

	EILEEN	4wDM		RH	432648	1959	
1863	166 C.P.HUNTINGTON	4w-2-4wPH	s/o	Chance			
				79 50166 24	1979	a

a   currently under restoration elsewhere

LEA BAILEY MINE, NEWTOWN, near ROSS-ON-WYE

Not open to the public.   SO 645196

Gauge 2ft 6in

10		4wDHF	HE	9053	1981	Dsm

Gauge 2ft 0in

–		4wDHF	HE	8985	1981

NATIONAL WATERWAYS MUSEUM,
LLANTHONY WAREHOUSE, HISTORIC DOCKS, GLOUCESTER

Gauge 4ft 8½in   SO 827182

–		0-4-0F	OC	AB	2126	1942

B NICHOLLS, GOTHERINGTON STATION

Gauge 4ft 8½in   SP 974298

TR2	PWM 2779	2w-2PMR		Wkm	6878	1954

NORTH GLOUCESTERSHIRE RAILWAY CO LTD, TODDINGTON GOODS YARD

Gauge 2ft 0in   SP 048318

	CHAKA'S KRAAL No.6	0-4-2T	OC	HE	2075	1940
1091		0-8-0T	OC	Hen	15968	1918
7	JUSTINE	0-4-0WT	OC	Jung	939	1906
	"IVAN"	4wPM		FH	3317	1948
	YARD No. A497	4wDM		HE	6647	1967
2	DFK 538	4wDM		L	34523	1949
	"SPITFIRE"	4wPM		MR	7053	1937
6		4wDM		RH	166010	1932
5		4wDM		RH	354028	1953

BILL PARKER, FOREST LUBRICANTS,
THE FLOUR MILL, BREAM, Forest of Dean

Locos for repair and restoration are usually present.   SO 604067

Gauge 4ft 8½in

6960	RAVENINGHAM HALL	4-6-0	OC	Sdn		1944	
No.28		0-6-2T	IC	Cdf	306	1897	
D249		0-4-0WT	OC	KS	3063	1918	
No.229		0-4-0ST	OC	N	2119	1876	
1		4wDH		TH	133C	1963	+
	a rebuild of	4wVBT	VCG	S			

+   carries 133V on plate in error

Gauge 2ft 6in

No.1	CHEVALLIER	0-6-2T	OC	MW	1877	1915

Gauge 2ft 0in

JANET	4wDM		RH	504546	1963

J. RAINBOW, GLOUCESTER
Gauge 2ft 0in

FOXHANGER	4wDM		House	c1974

ROYAL FOREST OF DEAN'S MINING MUSEUM,
CLEARWELL CAVES, CLEARWELL, near COLEFORD, Forest of Dean
Gauge 2ft 6in   SO 576082

−	0-6-0DMF	_(HC	DM1435	1977	
		(HE	8583	1977	

Gauge 2ft 0in

K9	0-6-0DMF	HC	DM801	1954	
T42	0-6-0DMF	HC	DM841	1954	
R3	0-6-0DMF	_(HC	DM1442	1980	
		(HE	8842	1980	OOU
68	0-4-0DMF	HC	DM739	1950	Dsm
68	0-4-0DMF	HC	DM924	1955	Dsm
−	4wDHF	HE	7386	1976	a
7	4wDHF	HE	7446	1975	
−	4wDHF	HE	8986	1981	Dsm
−	4wDM	MR	21282	1957	
−	0-4-0BE	WR	L1009	1979	OOU

a   at Hawthorn Tunnel, near Drybrook

P. SADDINGTON
Gauge 2ft 0in

−	4wPM	Bg	2095	1936

TREASURE TRAIN LTD, PERRYGROVE RAILWAY,
MILKWALL, near COLEFORD, Forest of Dean
Gauge 1ft 3in   SO 579095

	LYDIA	0-6-2T	OC	AK	77	2008	
	SPIRIT OF ADVENTURE	0-6-0T	OC	ESR	295	1993	
No.3	URSULA	0-6-0T	OC	Waterfield		1999	
	JUBILEE	4wDH		HE	9337	1994	+
No.2	WORKHORSE	4wDM		MR	26014	1967	

+   altered from 2ft 0in gauge

WINCHCOMBE RAILWAY MUSEUM,
23 GLOUCESTER STREET, WINCHCOMBE, near CHELTENHAM
Gauge 2ft 0in   SP 022282

      AMOS   2w-2BE   FoxA   c1972 Dsm

HAMPSHIRE

INDUSTRIAL SITES

A.W. BIGGS & SON, WATERCRESS GROWERS,
DISTRICT HILL, HURSTBOURNE PRIORS, near WHITCHURCH   **(Closed)**
Gauge 600mm   SU 446462

      –   2w-2PM   Hutchings   Dsm

ESSO PETROLEUM CO LTD, ESSO REFINERY, FAWLEY, SOUTHAMPTON
Gauge 4ft 8½in   SU 452046, 453040, 462037

   552 BLUEBIRD   0-6-0DH   HE   8998 1981
   641 REDWING   0-6-0DH   HE   8999 1981

Mr. FARES, MALLARDS, BUCKLERS HARD, BEAULIEU
Loco used in connection with timber felling on this estate.   SZ 414997
Gauge 600mm

      –   4wBE   WR   D6905 1964

F.M.B. ENGINEERING CO LTD,
UNIT 10, SOUTHLANDS, LATCHFORD LANE, OAKHANGER, near BORDON
Locos under repair or restoration are usually present.   SU 769345

J. HIRST & SONS, ST MARY BOURNE, near ANDOVER
Locos for scrap or resale occasionally present
Gauge 600mm

      –   4wDH   BD   3698 1973 OOU

KNIGHTS RAIL SERVICES, EASTLEIGH WORKS, CAMPBELL ROAD, EASTLEIGH
Gauge 4ft 8½in   SU 457185

  (D2991) 07007   0-6-0DE   RH   480692 1962
  01507 425 VENOM   0-6-0DH   RH   459519 1961 a

(01508) 428		0-6-0DH	RH	466617	1961	
01509 433 VULCAN		0-6-0DH	RH	468043	1963	a
01583 422 VALIANT		0-6-0DH	RH	459517	1961	a
RRM 19 21 90 02		0-4-0DH	RH	504565	1965	Dsm

a   currently at East London Line Project, Greater London

MINISTRY OF DEFENCE, DEFENCE MUNITIONS, DEAN HILL
See Section 6 for full details.

MINISTRY OF DEFENCE, MARCHWOOD MILITARY PORT
See Section 6 for full details.   SU 395103
Also see entry under following sub-heading "Preservation Sites".

POLIMERI EUROPA UK LTD, CHARLESTON ROAD, HARDLEY, HYTHE
Gauge 4ft 8½in   R.T.C.   SU 442058

| – | | 4wDM | RH | 416568 | 1957 | OOU |

SIEMENS TRANSPORT – SOUTH WEST TRAINS, NORTHAM DEPOT
Gauge 4ft 8½in

LOUPY LOU		4wDH		RR	10241	1966	
			Reb	TH	247v	1973	
–		4wBE		Niteq	B193	2002	

WHITE HORSE FERRIES, HYTHE PIER RAILWAY
Gauge 2ft 0in   SU 423081

| – | | 4wRE | BE | 16302 | 1917 |
| – | | 4wRE | BE | 16307 | 1917 |

PRESERVATION SITES

DURLEY LIGHT RAILWAY, "FOUR WINDS", DURLEY, BISHOPS WALTHAM
Gauge 2ft 0in   SU 522173

–		0-8-0T	OC	Hano	8310	1918
D.L.R.No.2 NBA		0-4-2ST	OC	HE	1842	1936
	rebuilt as	0-4-2T	OC			
–		4wDM		FH	3787	1956
–		4wDM		OK	4013	1930
–		0-4-0DM		OK	20777	1936

EAST HAYLING LIGHT RAILWAY, BEACHLANDS, HAYLING ISLAND

Gauge 2ft 0in

SL 714988

No. 3	JACK	0-4-0DH	s/o	AK	23	1988
No. 1	ALAN B	4wDM		MR	7199	1937
4	ALISTAIR	4wDM		RH	201970	1940
5	EDWIN	4wDM		RH	7002-0967-5	1967

B. GENT

Stored at a private location.

Gauge 2ft 0in

	–	4wDM	MR	4023	1926

HAMPSHIRE BUILDINGS PRESERVATION TRUST LTD, CENTRE FOR THE CONSERVATION OF THE BUILT ENVIRONMENT, BURSLEDON BRICKWORKS, COAL PARK LANE, LOWER SWANWICK

Gauge 2ft 0in

SU 499098

	AGWI PET	4wPM	MR	4724	1939
LO 20		4wPM	MR	5226	1930
	BECCY	4wDM	MR	8694	1943

MARWELL'S WONDERFUL RAILWAY, MARWELL ZOOLOGICAL PARK, COLDEN COMMON, near WINCHESTER

Gauge 1ft 3in

SU 508216

	PRINCESS ANNE	2-6-0DH	s/o	SL	75.3.87	1987

MID-HANTS RAILWAY plc, "THE WATERCRESS LINE"

Locos are kept at :-

New Alresford Station SU 588325
Ropley Station SU 629324

Gauge 4ft 8½in

(30506)	S.R. 506	4-6-0	OC	Elh		1920	
(30828)	E828 HARRY E.FRITH	4-6-0	OC	Elh		1928	
(31625)	5 JAMES	2-6-0	OC	Afd		1929	
31806		2-6-0	OC	Bton		1926	
31874		2-6-0	OC	Woolwich		1925	
34007	WADEBRIDGE	4-6-2	3C	Bton		1945	
34016	BODMIN	4-6-2	3C	Bton		1945	
34105	SWANAGE	4-6-2	3C	Bton		1950	
35005	CANADIAN PACIFIC	4-6-2	3C	Elh		1941	
41312		2-6-2T	OC	Crewe		1952	
(45379)	5379	4-6-0	OC	AW	1434	1937	
60019	BITTERN	4-6-2	3C	Don	1866	1937	a
73096		4-6-0	OC	Derby		1955	
75079		4-6-0	OC	Sdn		1956	
76017		2-6-0	OC	Hor		1953	

No.			Type		Builder	Works No.	Date	Notes
92212			2-10-0	OC	Sdn		1959	
62.521	30076		0-6-0T	OC	DDak	521	1954	
10	DOUGLAS		0-6-0ST	IC	HE	2890	1943	
			reb		HE	3882	1962	
		rebuilt as	0-6-0	IC	Gartell		2001	
1			0-6-0ST	IC	HE	3781	1952	
		rebuilt as	0-6-0T	IC	MHR Ropley		1994	
(D22)	45132	D199	1Co-Co1DE		Derby		1961	
D3358	(08288)		0-6-0DE		Derby		1957	
D5353	(27007)		Bo-BoDE		BRCW	DEL196	1961	
(D6571)	33053		Bo-BoDE		BRCW	DEL175	1961	
D6593	(33208)		Bo-BoDE		BRCW	DEL164	1962	
12049			0-6-0DE		Derby		1948	
4			0-4-0DM		JF	22889	1939	
51363			2-2w-2w-2DMR		PSteel		1960	
W51400			2-2w-2w-2DMR		PSteel		1960	
51405			2-2w-2w-2DMR		PSteel		1960	
55003	103		2-2w-2w-2DMR		GRC&W		1958	
205.025	60124		4w-4DER		Afd/Elh		1959	
(TR22	PWM 4312)		2w-2PMR		Wkm	7515	1956	DsmT
(68084)	(DS3317)		2w-2PMR		Wkm	7824	1957	DsmT
(68075)	DB965991		2w-2DMR		Wkm	10707	1974	
(68082)	DB966031		2w-2DMR		Wkm	10839	1975	

a   carries plate Don 1818/1935

MINISTRY OF DEFENCE, 17 PORT & MARITIME REGIMENT, MARCHWOOD MILITARY PORT

Gauge 4ft 8½in   SU 395103

PERCY	0-4-0DM		JF	22503	1938	Pvd

PAULTONS RAILWAY, PAULTONS PARK, OWER, near ROMSEY

Gauge 1ft 3in   SU 316167

–	2-8-0DH	s/o	SL	RG.11.86	1987	

Mr SAMSON, BROOKLANDS FARM, MOCK BEGGAR, near IBSLEY, FORDINGBRIDGE

Gauge 2ft 0in   SU 162107

–	4wDM		LB	55070	1966
		reb	Gartell	1001	1987

TWYFORD WATERWORKS TRUST, TWYFORD WATERWORKS, HAZELEY ROAD, TWYFORD

Gauge 2ft 0in   Locomotives occasionally present at advertised public open days.   SU493248

(DOE 3983)	4wDM		FH	3983	1962
–	4wDM		L	3916	1931

–		4wDM	L	42494	1956	
–		4wPM	MR	5355	1932	
No.29	AYALA	4wDM	MR	7374	1939	

Unknown Owner, Private Location
Gauge 2ft 0in

18	0-8-0T	OC	Hano	8282	1917
8	0-8-0T	OC	OK	8356	1917
7	0-8-0T	OC	Schw	6728	1918

HEREFORDSHIRE

INDUSTRIAL SITES

ALAN KEEF LTD, LEA LINE, ROSS-ON-WYE
Locomotives under construction and repair are usually present.   SO 665214
The following is understood to be a complete FLEET LIST of locos currently owned by (or in the care of) Messrs
Keef. Some may be hired out from time to time, as shown by footnotes.
Gauge 3ft 0in

	NANCY	0-6-0T	OC	AE	1547	1908	
No.5	SLIEVE CALLAN	0-6-2T	OC	D	2890	1892	

Gauge 900mm

–		0-4-0WT	OC	OK	5102	1912	
–		4wDH	Rack	HE	9282	1988	OOU
RS106		4wDH		RFSD	L106	1989	OOU

Gauge 2ft 6in

ND 3308	YARD No.B50	2w-2BE	GB	3547	1948	

Gauge 2ft 0in

	TAFFY	0-4-0VBT	VC	AK	30	1994	+
	DIANA	0-4-0T	OC	KS	1158	1917	
	WOTO	0-4-0ST	OC	WB	2133	1924	
	SKIPPY	4wDM		AK	2	1976	
–		4wDM		MR	7066	1938	Dsm
–		4wDM		MR	8875	1944	Dsm
	DIGGER	4wDM		MR	8882	1944	
	PLANT No.34	4wDM		MR	40SD502	1975	
–		4wBE		WR	1393	1939	
			reb	AK		2006	

+   worksplate is dated 1990

Gauge monorail

M002	IVOR	2a-2DH	AK	M002	1989
–		2a-2DH	AK	M003	1989

PAINTER BROS LTD, ENGINEERS, MORTIMER ROAD, HEREFORD
(part of the BICC Group of Companies)

Gauge 2ft 0in   SO 508413

–	4wDM	L	40407	1954
–	4wDM	LB	54181	1964	OOU
–	4wBE	CE	B0142B	1973
–	4wBE	CE	5806	1970

UNKNOWN OWNER, HEREFORD AREA
Gauge 2ft 0in

ND 3052	YARD No. B3	0-4-0DM	HE	2263	1940	OOU
ND 3054	YARD No. B5	0-4-0DM	HE	2265	1940	OOU
ND 3064	YARD No. B23	0-4-0DM	HE	2402	1941	OOU

PRESERVATION SITES

D2578 LOCOMOTIVE GROUP, PRIVATE STORE, MORETON ON LUGG
The locos are under restoration inside a building on a secure industrial estate and visits are normally not possible. A contact for enquiries is at : d2578.aphra@virgin.net

Gauge 4ft 8½in   SO 508467

D2578		0-6-0DM	HE	5460	1958
		reb	HE	6999	1968
(D2145)	03145	0-6-0DM	Sdn		1961

M. DAVIES, STOKE EDITH STATION TARRINGTON
Gauge 4ft 8½in   SO 614414

–		4wDM	RH	463150	1961
A162	PWM 2194	2w-2PMR	Wkm	4171	1948

M. DEEM, LAMARO, ECCLES GREEN, NORTON CANON, HEREFORD
Gauge 1ft 3in   SO 374488

101	2-4wPM	TaylorJ		c1964

HEREFORDSHIRE WATERWORKS MUSEUM TRUST, HEREFORDSHIRE WATERWORKS MUSEUM, BROOMY HILL, HEREFORD

Gauge 2ft 0in   SO 497394

–	4wDM	LB	52886	1962	

R. HUNT, TITLEY JUNCTION STATION, near KINGTON

Private collection; cannot be viewed from any public place. No visitors without prior appointment.

Gauge 4ft 8½in   SO 328581

1	0-6-0DM	_(RSHN	7859	1956	
		(DC	2573	1956	
No.2	4wDH	TH	163V	1966	b
–	4wDM	FH	3906	1959	
DL 7	0-4-0DE	RH	458641	1963	
THE SHERIFF	4wDM	RH	458961	1962	
–	4wPM	Dowty			a
W51370	2-2w-2w-2DMR	PSteel		1960	
W51412	2-2w-2w-2DMR	PSteel		1960	

a   converted lorry
b   carries worksplate 173V 1966 in error

K. MATTHEWS, FENCOTE OLD STATION, HATFIELD, near LEOMINSTER

Gauge 4ft 8½in   SO 601589

TR40 PWM 4314	2w-2PMR	Wkm	7517	1956	

OWEN BROS MOTORS, c/o K. JONES, 13 NORBURY PLACE, TUPSLEY, HEREFORD

Gauge 1ft 3in   SO 542373

No.303	0-6-0PM	s/o	TaylorJ	1967	

BOB PALMER, BROMYARD & LINTON LIGHT RAILWAY, BROADBRIDGE HOUSE, BROMYARD

This railway does not operate public trains.   SO 657548, SO 669541

Gauge 2ft 6in

–	4wDM	Bg	3406	1953	Dsm

Gauge 2ft 0in

MESOZOIC	0-6-0ST	OC	P	1327	1913	Dsm
–	4wPM		MR	6031	1936	
–	4wDM		MR	9382	1948	
1	4wDM		MR	9676	1952	
2	4wDM		MR	9677	1952	
No.7	4wDM		MR	20082	1953	
–	4wDM		MR	102G038	1972	

–		4wDM	RH	187101	1937	
–		4wDM	RH	195849	1939	a
L 10		4wDM	RH	198241	1939	
–		4wDM	RH	213848	1942	
No.3	"NELL GWYNNE"	4wDM	RH	229648	1944	
No.6	"PRINCESS"	4wDM	RH	229655	1944	
–		4wDM	RH	229656	1944	
–		4wDM	RH	246793	1947	
–		4wDH	RH	437367	1959	
–		4wDM	RH	444200	1960	
–		2w-2PM	Wkm	3034	1941	Dsm

a   converted for use as a generating unit

A.J. WILKINSON, ROWDEN MILL STATION, near BROMYARD
Gauge 4ft 8½in   SO 627565

D2371	(03371)		0-6-0DM	Sdn		1958
A159	PWM 2191		2w-2PMR	Wkm	4168	1948
A13W	PWM 2801	(TR3)	2w-2PMR	Wkm	6884	1954
B30W	PWM 3956		2w-2PMR	Wkm	6941	1955

THE WOOLHOPE LIGHT RAILWAY,
P.J. FORTEY, THE HORNETS NEST, CHECKLEY, MORDIFORD, near HEREFORD
Gauge 1ft 3in   SO 608378

202	TREVOR	0-6-0PM	s/o	TaylorJ		c1974

HERTFORDSHIRE

INDUSTRIAL SITES

ENFIELD TIMBER, HEMEL HEMSTEAD
Gauge 1524mm

1151	1819	2-8-0	OC	Frichs	397	1949

McNICHOLAS CONSTRUCTION CO LTD,
PLANT DEPOT, LISMIRRANE INDUSTRIAL PARK, ELSTREE ROAD, ELSTREE
Locos are present in this yard between use on contracts.   TQ 166952

Gauge 1ft 6in

–	2w-2BE	Iso	T42	1973
–	2w-2BE	Iso	T51	1974

–	2w-2BE	Iso	T54	1974	
56	2w-2BE	Iso	T56	1974	
–	2w-2BE	Iso			
–	2w-2BE	Iso			
–	2w-2BE	Iso			
ML-2-17	4wBH	Tunn		c1982	

PRESERVATION SITES

B.LAWSON, BRY RAILWAY, TRING

Locos stored at various private locations.

Gauge 4ft 8½in

–	4wDM	RH	294269	1951	

Gauge 2ft 6in

No.2 6	4wBE	BV	694	1974	
No.3 9	4wBE	BV	696	1974	
3135B SP 03 426	4wBEF	CE	B3135B	1984	
	reb	CE	B4066RF	1994	
SP 03.425	4wBEF	CE	B3204A	1985	
No.03	4wDHF	HE	7384	1976	
–	4wDM	LB	55870	1968	Dsm
No.16	4wDM	RH	170200	1934	Dsm
–	4wDM	RH	247182	1947	
No.14	4wDM	RH	441945	1959	
No.12	0-4-0DH	RH	476133	1964	
No.17	4wDMF	RH	480680	1963	
No.13	4wDM	RH	506415	1964	
No.19	4wDM	RH	7002/0767/6	1967	
No.15	4wDM	RH	7002/0867/3	1967	
No.14 ND 3307 YARD No. B49	4wBE	GB	3546	1948	
No.15	4wBE	GB	3825	c1949	

Gauge 2ft 0in

–	4wDM	RH	280866	1949	
No.21 (LM 264)	4wDM	RH	371535	1954	
No.22 LM 265	4wDM	RH	375696	1954	
No.23 LM 112	4wDM	RH	375699	1954	
No.20	4wDMF	RH	381704	1955	
No.6 F	0-4-0BE	WR	M7544	1972	
No.1 MANDI MIS 47	0-4-0BE	WR	N7639	1973	

Gauge 1ft 6in

L 12	4wBE	CE	5965A	1973	
L 15	4wBE	CE	B0109A	1973	

–		2w-2BE	Iso	T6	1972	
–		2w-2BE	Iso	T9	1972	Dsm
–		2w-2BE	Iso	T15	1972	
–		2w-2BE	Iso	T40	1973	
No.9	SP 100 35	2w-2BE	WR	L800	1983	
No.10	SP 101 35T005	2w-2BE	WR	L801	1983	
No.11	SP 102	2w-2BE	WR	544901	1984	
No.12	JM 103	2w-2BE	WR	546001	1987	
No.13	SP 104	2w-2BE	WR	546601	1987	
–		2w-2BE	Iso	T53	1974	Dsm
–		2w-2BE	Iso	T71	1975	
–		2w-2BE	Iso	T79	1975	
–		2w-2BE	Iso	T81	1975	
–		2w-2BE	Iso			+
No.4		0-4-0BE	WR	F7117	1966	
		reb	WR	10142	1985	
No.5	1580	0-4-0BE	WR			

+ one of Iso T21 to T38

Gauge monorail

-		2wPH	RM	8111	1959

C.& D. LAWSON, DORCLIFF RAILWAY, TRING

Locos are currently stored elsewhere.

Gauge 2ft 6in

No.04			4wDM	Diema	3543	1974	
No.05			4wDM	Fisons		1976	
		rebuilt as	4wDH	Lawson		1999	
No.02			4wDM	HE	7366	1974	
No.01			4wDM	HE	7367	1974	
–			4wPM	L	34652	1949	
–			2w-2PH	Lawson	2	1998	
–			2w-2PH	Lawson	3	2000	
–			4wDH	Lawson	4	2001	
–			2w-2DMR	Lawson	5	2004	
–			2w-2DH	Lawson	6	2005	
–			4wDM	LB	53976	1964	
–			4wDM	LB	53977	1964	a
No.1			4wDM	RH	166045	1933	
No.7	ELLEN		4wDM	RH	200069	1939	
No.6			4wDM	RH	224315	1944	
No.9			4wDM	RH	229657	1945	
No.8			4wDM	RH	244559	1946	
No.2	CUCKOO BUSH		4wDM	RH	247178	1947	
No.3			4wDM	RH	297066	1950	
No.4			4wDM	RH	402439	1957	
No.5			4wDM	RH	432654	1959	
No.18	SIMBA		4wDH	RH	432661	1959	
		reb	Swanhaven		c1985	

No.10 TANIA			4wDM		RH	432665	1959	
No.11 SHEEBA			4wDM		RH	466594	1962	
–			2w-2PM		Wkm	3175	1942	
–			2w-2PM		Wkm	3431	1943	
		rebuilt as	2w-2DH		Lawson		1997	
–			2w-2PM		Wkm	3578	1944	
		rebuilt as	2w-2DH		Lawson		2002	

a currently on loan to County Borough of Doncaster Museum & Art Gallery, South Yorkshire

Gauge 2ft 0in

–		4wDM		RH	441944	1960	Dsm

PARADISE WILDLIFE PARK, WHITE STUBBS LANE, BROXBOURNE
Gauge 4ft 8½in   TL 338067

No.1		0-4-0DH	s/o	RH	512463	1965

ISLE OF WIGHT

PRESERVATION SITES

ISLE OF WIGHT RAILWAY CO LTD,
ISLE OF WIGHT STEAM RAILWAY, HAVENSTREET STATION
Gauge 4ft 8½in   SZ 556898

(32640)	11	NEWPORT	0-6-0T	IC	Bton		1878	
(32646)	W8	FRESHWATER	0-6-0T	IC	Bton		1876	
41313			2-6-2T	OC	Crewe		1952	
	W24	CALBOURNE	0-4-4T	IC	9E	341	1891	
	38	AJAX	0-6-0T	OC	AB	1605	1918	
ARMY 92		WAGGONER	0-6-0ST	IC	HE	3792	1953	
ARMY 198		ROYAL ENGINEER	0-6-0ST	IC	HE	3798	1953	
	37	INVINCIBLE	0-4-0ST	OC	HL	3135	1915	
D2059	(03059)	EDWARD	0-6-0DM		Don		1959	
D2554	(05001)		0-6-0DM		HE	4870	1956	
		ARMY 235	0-4-0DM		AB	371	1945	
–			4wDMR		Bg/DC	1647	1927	Dsm
DX 68809			4wDMR		Perm	010	1986	
DX 68810			4wDMR		Perm	011	1986	
DS 3320	PWM 3766		2w-2PMR		Wkm	6645	1953	

KENT

INDUSTRIAL SITES

THAMES STEEL LTD, SHEERNESS STEELWORKS, SHEERNESS, ISLE OF SHEPPEY
Gauge 4ft 8½in   TQ 912747

L127	BILL		0-6-0DH		EEV	D1199	1967	
				reb	YEC	L127	1996	OOU
L149	BEN		0-6-0DH		EEV	D1200	1967	
				reb	YEC	L149	1996	OOU
	–		4wDM	R/R	Unimog	107518		

AVONDALE ENVIRONMENTAL SERVICES LTD,
FORT HORSTED, PRIMROSE CLOSE, CHATHAM
Gauge 4ft 8½in   TQ 751651

	C959 YOR	4wDMR	R/R	Bruff	517	1986
	Y817 WER	4wDM	R/R	Unimog	197493	
	Y818 WER	4wDM	R/R	Unimog	197505	
	AF02UKS	4wDM	R/R	Unimog	200405	

BRETT AGGREGATES LTD, CLIFFE WHARF, NORTH SEA TERMINAL, SALT LANE, CLIFFE
Gauge 4ft 8½in   TQ 720755

331		4wDE		Werk	868	1950

CONTRACTED LANDS, GARDEN CLOSE, MAIDSTONE
Gauge 4ft 8½in

	K678 KHK	4wDMR	R/R	Landrover
	AXI 1400	4wDMR	R/R	RangeRover

DEPARTMENT OF TRANSPORT, LOCAL GOVERNMENT & REGIONS,
CINQUE PORTS TRAINING AREA, LYDD, ROMNEY MARSH
Also use Ministry of Defence locos; for details of these see Section 6.   TR 033198

Gauge 600mm

RTT/767184	2w-2PM	Wkm	2555	1939	Dsm
–	2w-2PM	Wkm	11680	1990	
–	2w-2PM	Wkm	11681	1990	
1	2w-2PM	Wkm	11684	1990	
3	2w-2PM	Wkm	11685	1990	
4	2w-2PM	Wkm	11679	1990	
6	2w-2PM	Wkm	11678	1990	
7	2w-2PM	Wkm	11677	1990	

EUROTUNNEL, CHERITON TERMINAL

These locos, used for shunting and maintenance, are also employed in the Channel Tunnel and at Coquelle Terminal, France, as required.

Gauge 4ft 8½in   TR 185375

0001		Bo-BoDE	MaK	1000.867	1993
0002		Bo-BoDE	MaK	1000.868	1993
0003		Bo-BoDE	MaK	1000.869	1993
0004		Bo-BoDE	MaK	1000.870	1993
0005		Bo-BoDE	MaK	1000.871	1993

0031	FRANCES	4wDH	Schöma	5366	1993
	Incorporates parts of	HE			
0032	ELISABETH	4wDH	Schöma	5367	1993
	Incorporates parts of	HE			
0033	SILKE	4wDH	Schöma	5263	1994
	Incorporates parts of	HE			
0034	AMANDA	4wDH	Schöma	5262	1994
	Incorporates parts of	HE			
0035	MARY	4wDH	Schöma	5269	1994
0036	LAURENCE	4wDH	Schöma	5268	1994
0037	LYDIE	4wDH	Schöma	5264	1994
0038	JENNY	4wDH	Schöma	5266	1994
0039	PACITA	4wDH	Schöma	5401	1994
0040	JILL	4wDH	Schöma	5402	1994
0041	KIM	4wDH	Schöma	5464	1995
0042	NICOLE	4wDH	Schöma	5465	1995

FOSTER YEOMAN QUARRIES LTD, ISLE OF GRAIN, near ALLHALLOWS

Gauge 4ft 8½in   TQ 875743

(D3817)	08650 ISLE OF GRAIN	0-6-0DE	Hor		1959

HITACHI, ASHFORD DEPOT

Gauge 4ft 8½in

–	0-4-0DH	S	10089	1962
–	4wBE	Scul		2007

IBSTOCK BUILDING PRODUCTS LTD,
FUNTON WORKS, SHEERNESS ROAD, LOWER HALSTOW, near SITTINGBOURNE

Gauge 2ft 0in   TQ 875677

69	2w-2BE	Red(F)		1979

ISTIL (UK) plc, QUEENBOROUGH STEEL MILL, ROLLING MILLS & WHARF,
ISLE OF SHEPPEY

Gauge 4ft 8½in   TQ 896716, 911716, 912719

870	BUSTER	0-6-0DH	AB	509	1966
871		0-6-0DH	AB	510	1966

| 872 | | 0-6-0DH | AB | 511 | 1966 | |
| 873 | | 0-6-0DH | AB | 512 | 1966 | |

OVERSEAS MINING & ENGINEERING EQUIPMENT LTD, RANGE ROAD INDUSTRIAL ESTATE, 24-27 RANGE ROAD, HYTHE

Second-hand locos occasionally present for resale.   TR 155342

POLICE TRAINING CENTRE, DENTON, GRAVESEND

London underground railcar used for instructional purposes.

Gauge 4ft 8½in

| 1306 | | 2-2w-2w-2RER | MetCam | | 1961 | |

RIDHAM SEA TERMINALS LTD, RIDHAM DOCK, SITTINGBOURNE

Gauge 4ft 8½in   RTC   TQ 918684

| – | | 0-6-0DH | EEV | D1227 | 1967 | OOU |

SEACON (TOWER WHARF), TOWER WHARF, NORTHFLEET

Gauge 4ft 8½in   TQ 612752

| – | | 2w-2BER | PWR BO.598W.01 | | 1993 | |

PRESERVATION SITES

A.J.R. BIRCH & SON LTD, HOPE FARM, SELLINDGE, near ASHFORD

Gauge 1524mm   TR 119388

| 799 | | 0-6-0T | OC | TK | 355 | 1925 |
| 1134 | | 2-8-0 | OC | TK | 531 | 1946 |

Gauge 4ft 8½in

34053	SIR KEITH PARK	4-6-2	3C	Bton		1947
68078		0-6-0ST	IC	AB	2212	1946
No.27		0-6-0ST	IC	RSHN	7086	1943
No.4		4wDH		S	10007	1959
4902	(4002) S13003S	4w-4wRER		Elh		1949

DAVID BREAKER, STALISFIELD

Gauge 4ft 8½in

| – | | 0-6-0ST | IC | MW | 1317 | 1895 |

currently stored elsewhere

BREDGAR & WORMSHILL LIGHT RAILWAY,
"THE WARREN", SWANTON STREET, BREDGAR, near SITTINGBOURNE
Gauge 750mm www.bwlr.co.uk TQ 873585

No.105	SIAM	0-6-0WT	OC	Hen	29582	1956

Gauge 2ft 0in

No. 7		0-4-2T	OC	Decauville	246	1897
No.1	LADY JOAN	0-4-0ST	OC	HE	1429	1922
SSE 1912		0-4-2T	OC	JF	13573	1912
9	LIMPOPO	0-6-0WT	OC	JF	18800	1930
2	KATIE	0-6-0WT	OC	Jung	3872	1931
No.6	EIGIAU	0-4-0WT	OC	OK	5668	1912
No.8		0-4-0WT	OC	OK	12722	1936
1	BRONHILDE	0-4-0WT	OC	Schw	9124	1927
No.4	ARMISTICE	0-4-0ST	OC	WB	2088	1919
5	BREDGAR	4wDH		BD	3775	1983
No.15	OLD HAIRY	0-6-0DMF		HC	DM1366	1965
			reb	STRPS		1997

Gauge 1ft 3in

	JACK	0-6-0	OC	LemonB	c1956

BRETT GRAVEL, MILTON MANOR FARM,
ASHFORD ROAD, CHARTHAM, near CANTERBURY
Gauge 2ft 0in TR 120558

–	4wDM	MR	8606	1941

THE CHATHAM STEAM RESTORATION COMPANY,
THE STEAM CENTRE, SLIP 6, HISTORIC DOCKYARD, CHATHAM
Works with steam locos occasionally present for restoration. TQ 758689

COLONEL STEPHENS RAILWAY MUSEUM,
TENTERDEN TOWN STATION, TENTERDEN
Gauge 4ft 8½in

GAZELLE	0-4-2WT	IC	Dodman	1893

DOVER TRANSPORT MUSEUM, WILLINGTON ROAD, OLD PARK, DOVER
Gauge 4ft 8½in

"ST THOMAS"	0-6-0ST	OC	AE	1971	1927

Gauge 900mm

RR10	4wDH	RACK	HE	9283	1988
TU 20 56404	4wDH		Moës		

Gauge 2ft 0in

–	4wPM	FH	3116	1946	
–	4wDM	MR	8730	1941	
STURRY	4wDM	RH	349061	1953	
–	4wDM	RH	444193	1960	

EAST KENT LIGHT RAILWAY SOCIETY, SHEPHERDSWELL

Gauge 4ft 8½in Shepherdswell TR 258483
Eythorne TR282496

	ST DUNSTAN	0-6-0ST	OC	AE	2004	1927
(D4113)	09025	0-6-0DE		Hor		1961
E.K.R.102	RICHBOROUGH CASTLE	0-6-0DH		EEV	D1197	1967
E.K.R.105	SNOWDOWN	0-4-0DM		JF	4160002	1952

THE BUFFS, ROYAL EAST KENT REGIMENT, 1572-1961
9th FIELD SQUADRON ROYAL ENGINEERS

	ARMY 427 C3 SA	0-6-0DH		RH	466616	1961
53256		2-2w-2w-2DMR		MetCam		1957
205001	60154	4-4wDER		Afd/Elh		1957
3142	S11161S	4w-4wRER		Elh		1937
3142	11201	4w-4wRER		Elh		1937
5759	S65373	4w-4wRER		Elh		1956
7105	(2325) 61229	4w-4RER		Afd/Elh		1958
7105	(2325) 61230	4w-4RER		Afd/Elh		1958
68001	931091	4w-4wBE/RER		Afd/Elh		1959
930 092	(9002) 68002	4w-4RE/BER		Afd/Elh		1959
931 098	(9008) 093	4w-4wRE/BER		Afd/Elh		1961

THE ELHAM VALLEY MUSEUM, PEENE YARD, PEENE, FOLKESTONE

Gauge 4ft 8½in TR 185378

32521	0-6-0T	OC	EVM			+

+ non-working replica loco

ELSA STEAM RAILWAY, near CANTERBURY

Gauge 2ft 0in

"ELSA"	0-6-0WT+T	OC	OK	7122	1914	+

+ currently on loan to Michael List-Brain, Preston

THE HOP FARM, BELTRING, near PADDOCK WOOD

Gauge 2ft 0in TQ 673472

OLIVER	4wDM	s/o	MR	9869	1953	OOU
BUSY BASIL	4wDH	s/o	SL		1986	OOU

KEN JACKSON, PROVAN GROUP, EYNSFORD

Gauge 2ft 0in   Locos stored at a private location.

3 DARENT		0-4-0T	OC	AB	984	1903
	reb	0-4-0ST		Provan Group		2003
–		4wDM		MR	9711	1952
AD 22		4wDM		RH	211609	1941

KENT COUNTY COUNCIL, CANTERBURY MUSEUM, STOUR STREET, CANTERBURY

Gauge 4ft 8½in   TR 146577

(INVICTA)	0-4-0	OC	RS	24	1830

MICHAEL LIST-BRAIN, PRESTON SERVICES, THE STEAM MUSEUM, COURT LANE, PRESTON, near CANTERBURY

Gauge 4ft 8½in   www.prestonservices.co.uk   TR 244604

E.K.R.101 CHISLET No.101	4wDM		RH	294268	1951

Gauge 1000mm

–	0-4-0WT	OC	Krauss	5742	1921

Gauge 2ft 0in

"ELSA"	0-6-0WT+T	OC	OK	7122	1914
–	0-10-0	OC	OK	11309	1927

Gauge 600mm

SMT T907	0-10-0T	OC	OK	10956	1925
SMT T912	0-10-0T	OC	OK	10957	1925
SMT T908	0-10-0T	OC	OK	12470	1934
SMT T911	0-10-0T	OC	OK	13101	1938

Gauge 1ft 6in

–	4-2-2	OC	WB	1425	1893

Gauge 1ft 3in

–	4-4-2	OC	Barnes	104	c1927
AO-TE-AROA	4-4-0	OC	Herschell		
3	0-4-0+0-4-0	4C	LJ		1990

J. MARTIN, "WAYSIDE", AMSBURY ROAD, HUNTON

Gauge 2ft 0in   TQ 732509

6	0-8-0T	OC	Hen	15551	1917	
49	4wDH		BD	3701	1973	a

a   currently stored elsewhere

Gauge 1ft 3in

–	4-4-0	OC	McGarigle		1904

ROMNEY HYTHE & DYMCHURCH RAILWAY, NEW ROMNEY
Gauge 1ft 3in   TR 074249

No.	Name	Type		Maker	No.	Year
1	GREEN GODDESS	4-6-2	OC	DP	21499	1925
2	NORTHERN CHIEF	4-6-2	OC	DP	21500	1925
3	SOUTHERN MAID	4-6-2	OC	DP	22070	1926
4	THE BUG	0-4-0TT	OC	Krauss	8378	1926
5	HERCULES	4-8-2	OC	DP	22071	1926
6	SAMSON	4-8-2	OC	DP	22072	1926
7	TYPHOON	4-6-2	OC	DP	22073	1926
8	HURRICANE	4-6-2	OC	DP	22074	1926
9	WINSTON CHURCHILL	4-6-2	OC	YE	2294	1931
10	DOCTOR SYN	4-6-2	OC	YE	2295	1931
11	BLACK PRINCE	4-6-2	OC	Krupp	1664	1937
No.12	JOHN SOUTHLAND	4w-4wDH		TMA	6143	1983
14	CAPTAIN HOWEY	4w-4wDH		TMA	2336	1989
15	PW3 3 REDGAUNLET "MULTUM IN PARBO"	4wPM		AK[1977]		1977
No.7	TREMBLY	4wDM		L	37658	1952
–		4wDM		MR	7059	1938
	rebuilt as	4wDH		TMA		1988
PW2	SCOOTER	2w-2PM		RHDR		1949

ROYAL ENGINEERS MUSEUM, PRINCE ARTHUR ROAD, GILLINGHAM
Gauge 4ft 8½in   TQ 767690

ARMY 9035	2w-2PMR	Wkm	8195	1958	a

a   currently stored at the Museum Store, Lodge Hill Camp, Chattenden (TQ 758735)

SITTINGBOURNE & KEMSLEY LIGHT RAILWAY LTD, SITTINGBOURNE and KEMSLEY
Gauge 4ft 8½in   Static exhibits   TQ 905643, 920662

–	0-4-0F	OC	AB	1876	1925
BEAR	0-4-0ST	OC	P	614	1896
		reb	AB	5997	1941

Gauge 2ft 6in

PREMIER	0-4-2ST	OC	KS	886	1905	OOU
LEADER	0-4-2ST	OC	KS	926	1905	
MELIOR	0-4-2ST	OC	KS	4219	1924	
UNIQUE	2-4-0F	OC	WB	2216	1923	OOU
ALPHA	0-6-2T	OC	WB	2472	1932	OOU
TRIUMPH	0-6-2T	OC	WB	2511	1934	
SUPERB	0-6-2T	OC	WB	2624	1940	
VICTOR	4wDM		HE	4182	1953	

P6495	BARTON HALL	4wDH		HE	6651	1965
	EDWARD LLOYD	0-4-0DM		RH	435403	1961

TENTERDEN RAILWAY CO LTD, (KENT & EAST SUSSEX RAILWAY)

Locos are kept at :-
Rolvenden Station   TQ 865328
Tenterden Station   TQ 882336
Wittersham Road Station   TQ 866288

Gauge 4ft 8½in

No. 30	1638	0-6-0PT	IC	Sdn		1951	
30065	DS 237 MAUNSELL	0-6-0T	OC	VIW	4441	1943	
(30070	DS 238) WD 1960 WAINWRIGHT						
		0-6-0T	OC	VIW	4433	1943	
(31556)	753	0-6-0T	IC	Afd		1909	
32670	No.3 BODIAM	0-6-0T	IC	Bton		1872	
32678	8	0-6-0T	IC	Bton		1880	
No.23	HOLMAN F.STEPHENS	0-6-0ST	IC	HE	3791	1952	
No.25	NORTHIAM	0-6-0ST	IC	HE	3797	1953	
No.24	ROLVENDEN	0-6-0ST	IC	HE	3800	1953	
14	CHARWELTON	0-6-0ST	IC	MW	1955	1917	
376	NORWEGIAN	2-6-0	OC	Nohab	1163	1919	
No.12	MARCIA	0-4-0T	OC	P	1631	1923	
(W20W)	20	4w-4wDMR		Sdn		1940	
D2023		0-6-0DM		Sdn		1958	
(D2024)	4	0-6-0DM		Sdn		1958	
(D)3174	(08108) DOVER CASTLE	0-6-0DE		Derby		1955	
D6570	(33052) ASHFORD	Bo-BoDE		BRCW	DEL174	1961	
D7594	(25244)	Bo-BoDE		Dar		1964	
(D9529)	14029	0-6-0DH		Sdn		1965	
M50971		2-2w-2w-2DMR		DerbyC&W		1959	
51571	L30	2-2w-2w-2DMR		DerbyC&W		1960	
1		Bo-BoDE		MV		1932	
No.1		0-4-0DE		RH	423661	1958	
	DR 98211A	4wDMR		Plasser	52766A	1985	
900312	YORK 21	2w-2PMR		Wkm		1931	
(900393)		2w-2PMR		Wkm	673	1932	DsmT
–		2w-2PMR		Wkm	6603	1953	
TR 1	6872	2w-2PMR		Wkm	6872	1954	
9043		2w-2PMR		Wkm	6965	1955	
			reb	Wkm		1961	
7438		2w-2PMR		Wkm	7438	1956	

TUNBRIDGE WELLS & ERIDGE RAILWAY PRESERVATION SOCIETY LTD
SPA VALLEY RAILWAY,
WEST STATION, NEVILL TERRACE, TUNBRIDGE WELLS

Gauge 4ft 8½in   TQ 579385

32650	SUTTON	0-6-0T	IC	Bton		1876
47493		0-6-0T	IC	VF	4195	1927
68077		0-6-0ST	IC	AB	2215	1947

2315	LADY INGRID	0-4-0ST	OC	AB		2315	1951
TKh 2871		0-6-0T	OC	Chrz		2871	1951
TKh 2944	HOTSPUR	0-6-0T	OC	Chrz		2944	1952
3135	SPARTAN	0-6-0T	OC	Chrz		3135	1953
1928	ALAN GLADDEN	2-6-4T	OC	Nohab		2229	1953
	FONMON	0-6-0ST	OC	P		1636	1924
No.57		0-6-0ST	IC	RSHN		7668	1950
62	UGLY	0-6-0ST	IC	RSHN		7673	1950
	NORTH DOWNS No.3	0-6-0T	OC	RSHN		7846	1955
No.10	TOPHAM	0-6-0ST	OC	WB		2193	1922
D3489		0-6-0DE		Dar			1958
(D3668)	09004	0-6-0DE		Dar			1959
(E6047)	73140	Bo-BoRE/DE		_(EE		3719	1966
				(EEV		E379	1966
(D)6583	(33063) R.J. MITCHELL	Bo-BoDE		BRCW		DEL187	1962
(D6585)	33065 SEALION	Bo-BoDE		BRCW		DEL189	1962
(D6954)	37254	Co-CoDE		_(EE		3511	1964
				(EEV		D942	1964
15224		0-6-0DE		Afd			1949
No.6	PRINCESS MARGARET	0-4-0DM		AB		376	1948
2591	SOUTHERHAM	0-4-0DM		_(RSHN		7924	1959
				(DC		2591	1959
51669		2-2w-2w-2DMR		DerbyC&W			1960
51849		2-2w-2w-2DMR		DerbyC&W			1960
207017	60142	4w-4wDER		Afd/Elh			1962
249	ESL 118A/ESL 118B	4w-4+4-4wRE		BRCW			1932
			reb	Acton			1961
	G997 PKO	4wDM	R/R				a

a   road/rail tipper lorry

WOODLANDS RAILWAY
Gauge 1ft 3in **(Closed)**

PAM	4wPM		Mace		1980	OOU
SIMON	6wPM	s/o	Mace		1985	OOU

WORLD NAVAL BASE, THE HISTORIC DOCKYARD, CHATHAM
Gauge 4ft 8½in TQ 758689

No.1140	ANNIE	0-4-0ST	OC	AB		945	1904
No.8	INVICTA	0-4-0ST	OC	AB		2220	1946
	SYDENHAM	4wWT	G	AP		3567	1895
	ACHILLES	0-4-0ST	OC	HL		2918	1912
	LITTLE LADY	0-4-0ST	OC	P		1903	1936
YARD No.361	AJAX	0-4-0ST	OC	RSHN		7042	1941
42	OVERLORD	0-4-0DM		AB		357	1941
YARD No.562		4wDM		FH		3738	1955
	PLUTO	4wDM		FH		3777	1956
R39		0-4-0DM		_(RSHN		7816	1954
				(DC		2503	1954

Gauge 600mm

LOD 758148	4wDM	RH	226276	1944

LANCASHIRE

INDUSTRIAL SITES

BLACKPOOL TRANSPORT SERVICES LTD,
BLUNDELL STREET DEPOT & WORKS, BLACKPOOL
Gauge 4ft 8½in   SD 307350

938	Q204 HFR	4wDM	R/R	Unimog	029065	1981
939	J271 TEC	4wDM	R/R	Unimog	172544	

BRITISH ENERGY, NUCLEAR ELECTRIC DIVISION, HEYSHAM POWER STATIONS
Gauge 4ft 8½in   SD 401599

2	DEREK SHEPHERD	Bo-BoWE	HL	3872	1936	
	rebuilt as	Bo-BoBE	Riley		1993	
No.1	DOUG TOTTMAN	Bo-BoBE	RSHN	7284	1945	
		reb	Kearsley		1982	
HO55		4wDH	S	10037	1960	a

a   on hire from RMS Locotec Ltd, Wakefield, West Yorkshire

BYZAK CONSTRUCTION LTD, PLANT SERVICES DIVISION,
PLANTATION ROAD, BURSCOUGH INDUSTRIAL ESTATE, BURSCOUGH
Locos are present in the yard between use on contracts.

Gauge 610mm   SD 426119

EL43A		4wBE	CE	B4246A	1998	
		reb	CE	B4381B	2002	
EL43B		4wBE	CE	B4246B	1998	
		reb	CE	B4381A	2002	
–		4wBEF	CE	5382	1966	
–		4wBEF	CE			

CASTLE CEMENT LTD, RIBBLESDALE WORKS,
WEST BRADFORD ROAD, CLITHEROE
Gauge 4ft 8½in   SD 749434

10	0-6-0DH	GECT	5396	1975
9	0-6-0DH	GECT	5401	1975

HELICAL SPRINGS LTD, PRECISION SPRING MANUFACTURERS, DOCK ROAD, LYTHAM ST ANNES. LYTHAM MOTIVE POWER MUSEUM.

Preserved locomotives in store, not on public display. SD 381276

Gauge 4ft 8½in

RIBBLESDALE No.3	0-4-0ST	OC	HC	1661	1936
HODBARROW No.6					
SNIPEY	0-4-0CT	IC	N	4004	1890
GARTSHERRIE No.20	0-4-0ST	OC	NBH	18386	1908

Gauge 2ft 0in

"No.37" JONATHAN	0-4-0ST	OC	HE	678	1898

Gauge 1ft 10¾in

MIRANDA	4wDM		HE	2198	1940

LANCASHIRE ENTERPRISES plc, LANCASHIRE ENTERPRISES BUSINESS PARK, CENTURION WAY, LEYLAND

Gauge 4ft 8½in   R.T.C. SD 544237

–	0-4-0DM	JF	4210108	1955	OOU

PRESERVATION SITES

BLACKPOOL MINIATURE RAILWAY CO LTD, RIO GRANDE EXPRESS, BLACKPOOL ZOO LTD, ZOOLOGICAL GARDENS, EAST PARK DRIVE, BLACKPOOL

Gauge 1ft 3in SD 335362

–	2-8-0DH	s/o	SL	7219	1972

FOLD HOUSE CARAVAN PARK, PILLING, near KNOTT-END-ON-SEA, PRESTON

Gauge 4ft 8½in SD 409477

THE PILLING PIG	0-6-0ST	OC	HC	1885	1955

FOULRIDGE CANAL CRUISES RECEPTION CENTRE, THE CANAL WHARF, FOULRIDGE, COLNE

Currently closed to the public. SD 888426

Gauge 2ft 0in

–	4wPM		L	9993	1938

PLEASURE BEACH RAILWAY, SOUTH SHORE, BLACKPOOL

Gauge 1ft 9in SD 305332

BARBIE	4wDM		AK	7	1982

4472	MARY LOUISE		4-6-2DH	s/o	HC	D578	1933	
4473	CAROL JEAN		4-6-2DH	s/o	HC	D579	1933	
		reb	4-6-4DH	s/o	Ravenglass		1988	
6200	GEOFFREY THOMPSON OBE DL							
			4-6-2DH	s/o	HC	D586	1935	
				reb	PBR		2004	

THE RIBBLE STEAM RAILWAY, off CHAIN CAUL ROAD, RIVERSWAY, PRESTON

Gauge 4ft 8½in   SD 504295

46441		2-6-0	OC	Crewe		1950	
	JOHN HOWE	0-4-0ST	OC	AB	1147	1908	
	EFFICIENT	0-4-0ST	OC	AB	1598	1918	
	ALEXANDER	0-4-0ST	OC	AB	1865	1926	
No.2	HEYSHAM	0-4-0F	OC	AB	1950	1928	
	J.N.DARBYSHIRE	0-4-0ST	OC	AB	1969	1929	
No.6		0-4-0ST	OC	AB	2261	1949	
_		0-6-0ST	OC	AE	1568	1909	
MDHB No 26		0-6-0ST	OC	AE	1810	1918	
	JOAN	0-6-0ST	OC	AE	1883	1922	
411,09		2-8-0	OC	BLW	69621	1943	Dsm
_		0-4-0ST	OC	GR	272	1894	
	"THE KING"	0-4-0WT	OC	EB	(48?)	1906	
	"KINSLEY"	0-6-0ST	IC	HE	1954	1939	
	"WALKDEN"	0-6-0ST	IC	HE	3155	1944	
1R		0-6-0ST	IC	HE	3696	1950	
_		0-6-0ST	IC	HE	3793	1953	
No.4	GLASSHOUGHTON No.4	0-6-0ST	IC	HE	3855	1954	
21	"LINDA"	0-6-0ST	OC	HL	3931	1938	
_		0-4-0ST	OC	Hor	1097	1910	
	LYTHAM ST.ANNES EXPRESS						
	DAPHNE	0-4-0ST	OC	P	737	1899	
	HORNET	0-4-0ST	OC	P	1935	1937	
_		0-4-0ST	OC	P	1999	1941	
	AGECROFT No.2	0-4-0ST	OC	RSHN	7485	1948	
	"GASBAG"	4wVBT	VCG	S	8024	1929	
	"ST MONANS"	4wVBT	VCG	S	9373	1947	
D2148		0-6-0DM		Sdn		1960	
(D2189)	03189	0-6-0DM		Sdn		1961	
D2595		0-6-0DM		HE	7179	1969	
		a rebuild of		HE	5644	1959	
D2870		0-4-0DH		YE	2677	1960	
D9539		0-6-0DH		Sdn		1965	
20/110/711		0-6-0DH		AB	615	1977	
		reb		AB	6719	1987	
	YELLOW BAT	4wBE		EEDK	788	1930	
(601	671)	0-6-0DE		EEDK	2098	1955	
_		4wBE		GB	2000	1945	
	HOTTO	4wPM		H	965	1930	
	MIGHTY ATOM	0-4-0DM		HC	D628	1943	

D629		0-4-0DM	HC	D629		1945
	MARGARET	0-4-0DM	HC	D1031		1956
	PERSIL	0-4-0DM	JF	4160001		1952
	BICC	0-4-0DH	NBQ	27653		1956
DH23	ENERGY	4wDH	RR	10226		1965
	ENTERPRISE	4wDH	RR	10282		1968
	PROGRESS	4wDH	RR	10283		1968
	STANLOW No.4	0-4-0DH	TH	160V		1966
98404		4wDHR	Perm	MTU 001		1991

THE WEST COAST RAILWAY COMPANY, WARTON ROAD, CARNFORTH

Other locos are occasionally present for repairs. Closed to the public.   SD 496708

Gauge 4ft 8½in

5972	OLTON HALL	4-6-0	OC	Sdn		1937	
45699	(GALATEA)	4-6-0	3C	Crewe	297	1936	
(46115)	6115 SCOTS GUARDSMAN	4-6-0	3C	NBQ	23610	1927	
48151		2-8-0	OC	Crewe		1942	
No.1	"LANCASTER"	0-6-0F	OC	AB	1572	1917	
	W.T.T.	0-4-0ST	OC	AB	2134	1942	
1		0-4-0ST	OC	AB	2230	1947	
	GLAXO	0-4-0F	OC	AB	2268	1949	
68009		0-6-0ST	IC	HE	3825	1954	
	CALIBAN	0-4-0ST	OC	P	1925	1937	
–		0-4-0ST	OC	P	2027	1942	
6		0-4-0ST	IC	SS	1585	1865	
	LINDSAY	0-6-0ST	IC	WCI		1887	
(D1656	47834) 47798	Co-CoDE		Crewe		1965	
(D2196)	03196						
40	JOYCE/GLYNIS	0-6-0DM		Sdn		1961	
D2381	03381	0-6-0DM		Sdn		1961	
(D3845)	08678 ARTILA	0-6-0DE		Hor		1959	
(D6808)	(37108)	Co-CoDE		_(EE	3237	1962	
				(VF	D762	1962	
(D6865)	37165	Co-CoDE		_(EE	3343	1963	
				(EES	8396	1963	+
(D6914)	37214 LOCH LAIDON	Co-CoDE		_(EE	3392	1963	
				(EEV	D858	1963	+
(D6922)	37222	Co-CoDE		_(EE	3408	1963	
				(EEV	D866	1963	+
(D6948)	37248 LOCH ARKAIG	Co-CoDE		_(EE	3505	1964	
				(EEV	D936	1964	
D7659	(25309 25909)	Bo-BoDE		BP	8069	1966	
	TRENCHARD	0-4-0DM		AB	401	1956	
	(ESKDALE)	0-6-0DE		YE	2718	1958	

+   property of Harry Needle Railroad Co Ltd, Merseyside

WEST LANCASHIRE LIGHT RAILWAY TRUST,
STATION ROAD, HESKETH BANK, near PRESTON
Gauge 2ft 0in   SD 448229

45		0-6-0T	OC	Chrz	3506	1957		
"No.3"	IRISH MAIL	0-4-0ST	OC	HE	823	1903		
47		0-8-0T	OC	Hen	14676	1917		
48		0-4-2T	OC	JF	15513	1920		
No.8	JOFFRE	0-6-0WTT	OC	KS	2405	1915		
"No.35" No.21	UTRILLAS	0-4-0WT	OC	OK	2378	1907		
"No.34" No.22	MONTALBAN	0-4-0WT	OC	OK	6641	1913		
"No.1"	"CLWYD"	4wDM		RH	264251	1951		
"No.2"	TAWD	4wDM		RH	222074	1943		
"No.4"	"BRADFIELD"	4wPM		FH	1777	1931		
No.5		4wDM		RH	200478	1940		
"No.7"		4wDM		MR	8992	1946		
10		4wDM		FH	2555	1942		
11		4wDM		MR	5906	1934		
12		4wDM		MR	11258	1964		
"No.12" No.2		4wDM		MR	7955	1945		
			reb	WLLR	No.2	1987	a	Dsm
"No.16"		4wDM		RH	202036	1941		Dsm
19		4wBE		BV	613	1972	b	
"No.19"		4wPM		L	10805	1939		
"No.20"		4wPM		Bg	3002	1937		
No.21		4wDM		HE	1963	1939		
25		4wBE		BV	692	1974	b	
"No.25"		4wDM		RH	297054	1950		
"No.26" 8		4wDM		MR	11223	1963		
No.31 "No.27"	MILL REEF	4wDM		MR	7371	1939		
36		4wDM		RH	339105	1953		
"No.38"		0-4-0DMF		HC	DM750	1949		
"No.39" P37829	"BLACK PIG"	4wDM		FH	3916	1959		
40		4wDM		RH	381705	1956		
49	SAMPSON	4wDM		FH	1887	1934		
51		4wDM		HE	4478	1953	+	
−		0-6-0DMF		HC	DM1393	1967		
640	WELSH PONY	4wWE		BEV	640	1926		
−		4wBE		GB	1840	1942		
−		4wDM		L	29890	1946	Dsm	

+   plate reads 4480/1953
a   converted into a brake van
b   currently stored elsewhere being/to be regauged from 2ft 6in

WINFIELD SHOE CO LTD,
HAZEL MILL, BLACKBURN ROAD, ACRE, HASLINGDEN, ROSSENDALE
Gauge 4ft 8½in   SD 787250

−	0-6-0DE		HC	D1075	1959

WINDMILL ANIMAL FARM MINIATURE RAILWAY, WINDMILL ANIMAL FARM, RED CAT LANE, BURSCOUGH

Gauge 1ft 3in

	ST.CHRISTOPHER	2-6-2T	OC	ESR	311	2001	
	SIÂN	2-4-2	OC	Guest	18	1963	
	KATIE	2-4-2	OC	Guest		1956	a
4	BLUE PACIFIC	4-6-2VB	OC	GuinnessNL		c1935	
11	BONNIE DUNDEE	0-4-0WT	OC	KS	720	1901	
	rebuilt as	0-4-2T	OC	Ravenglass		1981	
	rebuilt as	0-4-2	OC	Ravenglass		1996	
	RED DRAGON	4-4-2	OC	_(WalkerG		1991	
				(MossAJ		1991	
	incorporates parts of			BL	15	1909	
	PRINCESS ANNE	4-6w-2DE	s/o	Barlow		1948	b
	DUKE OF EDINBURGH	4-6-2DE	s/o	Barlow		1950	
2870	CITY OF LONDON	4-6-0DM	s/o	JMR		1978	
	WHIPPIT QUICK	4wPM		L	6502	1935	
	rebuilt as	4w-4PM		Fairbourne		1955	
	rebuilt as	4w-4PMR		Fairbourne		1962	
	rebuilt as	4w-4DMR		Moss AJ			
	GWRIL	4wPM		L	20886	1943	
–		2-2wPMR		MossAJ		1989	
	KONIGSWINTER	2-8-2DH	s/o	SL	7217	1972	
		reb	‡		1492	1992	
362	NEPTUNE	2-8-0gasH	s/o	SL	15.5.78	1978	
	converted to	2-8-0DH					
	BLACK SMOKE	2-4-2PM	s/o	SmithEL		c1956	
14		2w-2PM		WalkerG		1985	
5305		4-6-0BE		MossAJ		1999	
No.1	GORAM	2w-2-4BER	s/o	Hayne		1977	
–		4w-4BE		Hayne		1977	Dsm

a carries plate Guest 14/1954
b carries incorrect plate dated 1962 (an overhaul date ?)
‡ rebuilt by Cleethorpes Coast Light Rly Ltd

LEICESTERSHIRE

INDUSTRIAL SITES

AGGREGATE INDUSTRIES UK LTD
Bardon Hill Quarry, Bardon Hill, Coalville

Gauge 4ft 8½in

No.59	DUKE OF EDINBURGH	6wDH	RR	10273	1968
No.159	BARDON DUCHESS	6wDH	TH	297V	1981
D9504	(01566)	0-6-0DH	Sdn		1964

Croft Quarry, Croft

Gauge 4ft 8½in   SP 517960

01572	MS 5482 "KATHRYN"	0-6-0DH		RR	10256	1966
01562	MS 6475 CHUG	0-6-0DH		TH	257V	1975
			reb	RMS	LWO2918	2006

BRUSH TRACTION LTD, FALCON WORKS, NOTTINGHAM ROAD, LOUGHBOROUGH

Locos under construction or repair are usually present.

Gauge 4ft 8½in   SK 543207

(56009) 56201		Co-CoDE		Electro		1976	a
PLANT No.11079	SPRITE	0-4-0DH		HC	D1341	1966	
	GEORGE TOMS	0-4-0DH		_(WB	3209	1962	
				(RSHD	8364	1962	
	–	4wDM	R/R	Unimog			
				424121 10 072555		1981	

a   bodyshell used as engine carrier and test bed

LAFARGE AGGREGATES LTD, CENTRAL REGION, BARROW-UPON-SOAR RAIL-LOADING TERMINAL

Gauge 4ft 8½in   SK 587168

43266	AUTOLOC 503 NELLY	4wDH		ASEA	OC0488	1982
40905	"JO"	4wDH		DeDietrich	89134	1988
	CHLOE JADE	0-6-0DH		RR	10212	1964
	DANNY BOY	4wDM	R/R	Zephir	1928	2005
	–	4wDM	R/R	Zephir	2136	2008

METRONET RAIL, MIDLANDS TEST CENTRE, ASFORDBY and OLD DALBY

Gauge 4ft 8½in   SK 680239 SK 727207

| – | | 0-4-0DH | | S | 10128 | 1963 |
| | | | rep | YEC | L142 | 1995 |

PRESERVATION SITES

THE BATTLEFIELD LINE, (THE SHACKERSTONE RAILWAY SOCIETY LTD), SHACKERSTONE STATION, MARKET BOSWORTH

Gauge 4ft 8½in   SK 379066

	YVONNE	0-4-0VBT	OC	Cockerill	2945	1920
	WALESWOOD	0-4-0ST	OC	HC	750	1906
	SIR GOMER	0-6-0ST	OC	P	1859	1932
2		0-4-0ST	OC	P	2130	1951
	RICHARD III	0-6-0T	OC	RSHN	7537	1949
	LAMPORT No.3	0-6-0ST	OC	WB	2670	1942

(D14)	45015		1-Co-Co-1DE	Derby		1960	
(D1921)	47244	(47640 UNIVERSITY OF STRATHCLYDE)					
			Co-CoDE	BT	683	1965	
(D2170)	03170		0-6-0DM	Sdn		1960	+
(D2180)	03180		0-6-0DM	Sdn		1962	
(D2245)	11215		0-6-0DM	_(RSHN	7864	1956	
				(DC	2577	1956	
(D2310)			0-6-0DM	_(RSHN	8169	1960	+
				(DC	2691	1960	
(D2867)	DIANE		0-4-0DH	YE	2850	1961	+
(D3993)	08825		0-6-0DE	Derby		1960	
(D)5518	(31101)	BRUSH VETERAN					
			A1A-A1ADE	BT	89	1958	
(D5547	31129)	31461	A1A-A1ADE	BT	146	1956	
(D5548)	31130	CALDERHALL POWER STATION					
			A1A-A1ADE	BT	147	1959	
(E6011)	73105		Bo-BoDE/RE	_(EE	3573	1965	
				(EEV	E343	1965	a
(E6020)	73114		Bo-BoDE/RE	_(EE	3582	1965	
				(EEV	E352	1965	
(D6508)	33008		Bo-BoDE	BRCW	DEL100	1960	
(D6574)	33019	GRIFFON	Bo-BoDE	BRCW	DEL126	1960	
(D6836	37905)		Co-CoDE	_(EE	3281	1963	
				(VF	D810	1963	
(D6927)	37227		Co-CoDE	_(EE	3413	1963	
				(EEV	D871	1963	
(D8166)	20166	RIVER FOWEY	Bo-BoDE	_(EE	3637	1966	
				(EEV	D1036	1966	
12083	201276	M413	0-6-0DE	Derby		1950	
56098			Co-CoDE	Don		1981	
	HOTWHEELS		0-6-0DM	AB	422	1958	+
19			0-6-0DH	AB	594	1974	
7			4wDM	RH	235513	1945	
			reb	Shackerstone		2000	
–			4wDM	RH	263001	1949	
	HERCULES		0-4-0DM	RH	281271	1950	
M51131		T326	2-2w-2w-2DMR	DerbyC&W		1958	
W51321	(977753)	T316	2-2w-2w-2DMR	BRCW		1960	
W55005			2-2w-2w-2DMR	GRC&W		1958	
–			4wDMR	R/R	Bruff	519	1986	b

+ property of Harry Needle Railroad Co Ltd, Merseyside
a property of Rail Vehicle Engineering Ltd, Derby
b incorporates chassis from Bruff 519 and parts from 518 & 520

I.R. BENDALL, 46 ORSON DRIVE, WIGSTON
Gauge 2ft 0in SK 598993

EL 9		4wBE	CE	5961C	1972

"CONKERS", NATIONAL FOREST MILLENIUM DISCOVERY CENTRE, RAWDON ROAD MOIRA

Gauge 2ft 0in   www.visitconkers.com   SK 312161

CONKACHOO	4-4-0DH	s/o	SL	2121	2001

A.R. ETHERINGTON, STATION HOUSE, SHACKERSTONE

Gauge 4ft 8½in   SK 378064

5	4wDM	MR	9921	1959

Gauge 2ft 0in

S128 263 001	4wBE	CE	5882A	1971	a
CONTEX 1	4wBE	CE	5940A	1972	
–	4wBE	CE			
No. 1	4wBE	WR	7964	1978	

Gauge 1ft 6in

L 13	4wBE	CE	5965B	1973

a   frame used in replica and displayed on flat wagon

S. GEESON, PRIVATE LOCATION

Gauge 4ft 8½in

B.S.C.1	0-6-0DH	EEV	D1049	1965

GREAT CENTRAL RAILWAY plc, GREAT CENTRAL STATION, LOUGHBOROUGH

Locos are kept at :-   Loughborough Loco Shed SK 543194
Rothley Carriage & Wagon Works SK 569122
Quorn and Woodhouse SK 549161

Gauge 4ft 8½in

4141		2-6-2T	OC	Sdn		1946
6990	WITHERSLACK HALL	4-6-0	OC	Sdn		1948
30777	SIR LAMIEL	4-6-0	OC	NBH	23223	1925
34039	BOSCASTLE	4-6-2	3C	Bton		1946
42085		2-6-4T	OC	Bton		1951
45305	ALDERMAN A.E.DRAPER	4-6-0	OC	AW	1360	1937
46521		2-6-0	OC	Sdn		1953
47406		0-6-0T	IC	VF	3977	1926
48305		2-8-0	OC	Crewe		1943
63601	(102)	2-8-0	OC	Gorton		1912
69523		0-6-2T	IC	NBH	22600	1921
70013	OLIVER CROMWELL	4-6-2	OC	Crewe		1951
73156		4-6-0	OC	Don		1956
78019		2-6-0	OC	Dar		1954
	ROBERT	0-6-0ST	IC	HC	1752	1943

D123	(45125 89423)						
	LEICESTERSHIRE AND DERBYSHIRE YEOMANRY						
		1Co-Co1 DE		Crewe		1961	
D1705	(47117)	SPARROWHAWK	Co-CoDE		BT	467	1965
(D2989	07005)		0-6-0DE		RH	480690	1962
			reb	Resco	L106	1978	+
(D3101)	3101		0-6-0DE		Derby		1955
D4067	MARGARET ETHEL - THOMAS ALFRED NAYLOR						
		0-6-0DE		Dar		1961	
D5185	(25735 25035) CASTEL DINAS BRAN						
		Bo-BoDE		Dar		1963	
D5830	(31563)		A1A-A1A DE		BT	366	1962
6535	(33116)		Bo-BoDE		BRCW	DEL127	1960
(D6898)	37198		Co-CoDE		_(EE	3376	1964
				(EES	8419	1964	
(D6955)	37255		Co-CoDE		_(EE	3512	1964
				(EEV	D943	1964	
(D7615)	25265		Bo-BoDE		Derby		1966
D8098	(20098)		Bo-BoDE		_(EE	3003	1961
				(RSHD	8255	1961	
E6003	(73003)						
		SIR HERBERT WALKER	Bo-BoRE/DE		Elh		1962
		BARDON	0-4-0DM		AB	400	1956
		ARTHUR WRIGHT	0-4-0DM		JF	4210079	1952
W79976			4wDMR		ACCars		1958
(50193)	960 992 977898		2-2w-2w-2DMR		MetCam		1957
(50203)	960 992 977897		2-2w-2w-2DMR		MetCam		1957
E50321	(960 993 977900)		2-2w-2w-2DMR		MetCam		1958
E51427	(960 993 977899)		2-2w-2w-2DMR		MetCam		1959
(M51616)	ALF BENNEY		2-2w-2w-2DHR		DerbyC&W		1959
(M51622)			2-2w-2w-2DHR		DerbyC&W		1959
(50266)	53266		2-2w-2w-2DMR		MetCam		1957
1393	62384		4w-4wRER		York		1971
–			2-2wBER		Bance	020	1995

LEICESTER CITY COUNCIL, ARTS & LEISURE DEPARTMENT, ABBEY PUMPING STATION, CORPORATION ROAD, LEICESTER

Gauge 2ft 0in   SK 589067

LEONARD	0-4-0ST	OC	WB	2087	1919
"NEW STAR"	4wPM		L	4088	1931
–	4wPM		MR	5260	1931
–	4wDM		RH	223700	1943
–	4wDM		SMH	40SD515	1979

LEICESTERSHIRE COUNTY COUNCIL, MUSEUMS, ARTS & RECORDS SERVICE, SNIBSTON DISCOVERY PARK, former SNIBSTON MINE, ASHBY ROAD, COALVILLE

Gauge 4ft 8½in   SK 420144

No.2	0-4-0F	OC	AB	1815	1924

	–	0-4-0ST	OC	BE	314	1906	
CADLEY HILL No.1		0-6-0ST	IC	HE	3851	1962	
MARS II		0-4-0ST	OC	RSHN	7493	1948	
	–	0-6-0DH		HE	6289	1966	
	–	4wDM		RH	393304	1956	

Gauge 2ft 6in

	–	4wBEF		_(EE	2416	1957	
				(RSHN	7935	1957	
No.5		4wBEF		_(EE	2300	1956	
				(Bg	3436	1956	
	–	4wBEF		_(EE	2086	1955	
				(Bg	3434	1955	
	–	4wBEF		GECT	5424	1976	
	–	0-6-0DMF		HC	DM1238	1960	
	–	4wDH		HE	8973	1979	

Gauge monorail

A4	2wPH	RM	8253	1959	

P. MARTIN, KENNEL LANE, WITHERLEY
Gauge 2ft 0in   SP 328973

SYBIL MARY	0-4-0ST	OC	HE	921	1906

PETER THOMAS, BLABY "WAKES" SHOWGROUND, LEICESTER ROAD, BLABY
Gauge 4ft 8½in   SK 566983

–	0-6-0F	OC	WB	2370	1929	OOU

TWINLAKES PARK, MELTON SPINNEY ROAD, MELTON MOWBRAY
Gauge 1ft 3in

–	2-6-0DH	s/o	SL	RG11-86	1986	OOU
–	2-6-0DH	s/o	SL	76.3.88	1988	OOU

WELLAND VALLEY VINTAGE TRACTION CLUB, GLEBE ROAD, MARKET HARBOROUGH
Gauge 3ft 0in   SP 742868

KETTERING FURNACES No.8	0-6-0ST	OC	MW	1675	1906	a

a   currently under renovation at a private location

DAVID WHITE, GREENLEA LIGHT RAILWAY, WORKHOUSE LANE, BURBAGE
Gauge 2ft 0in   SP 447915

SIR GEORGE	4wDH	s/o	AK	12	1984

C.P.HUNTINGTON	4w-4wDH	s/o	Chance		
			78-50157-24	1978	
MERLIN	4wDH	s/o	HU	LX1001	1968
GOLIATH	4wDM		MR	5881	1935

LINCOLNSHIRE

INDUSTRIAL SITES

WILLIAM BLYTH, FAR INGS TILERIES, BARTON-UPON-HUMBER
Gauge 2ft 0in   RTC.   TA 023233

| IVOR | 4wDM | MR | 8678 | 1941 | OOU |

CONOCO LTD, HUMBER REFINERY, SOUTH KILLINGHOLME
Gauge 4ft 8½in   TA 163168

–		0-4-0DH	HE	6981	1968	
44	MITCHELL	0-6-0DH	HE	7396	1974	
			reb	Wilmott	2000	a
	EARL OF YARBOROUGH	6wDH	RFSK	V336	1991	
–		0-6-0DH	TH	312V	1984	

a   on hire from WB Power Services Ltd, Ilkeston, Derbyshire

CORUS, CONSTRUCTION AND INDUSTRIAL
Appleby Coke Ovens
Gauge 4ft 8½in   SE 917108

5	4wRE	Schalke	10-310-0054	1973	
6	4wRE	Schalke	10-310-0055	1973	
7	4wRE	Schalke	10-310-8070	1979	+

+   built under licence by Starco Engineering, Winterton Road, Scunthorpe

Appleby-Frodingham Works, Scunthorpe
Gauge 4ft 8½in   SE 910110, 915110, 916105

81 D8056 (20056)	Bo-BoDE	_(EE	2962	1961	
		(RSHD	8214	1961	+
82 (D8066) 20066	Bo-BoDE	_(EE	2972	1961	
		(RSHD	8224	1961	+
1	0-6-0DE	YE	2877	1963	OOU
5	0-6-0DE	YE	2909	1963	OOU
29	0-6-0DE	YE	2938	1964	
31	0-6-0DE	YE	2903	1963	OOU

44		0-6-0DE	YE	2768	1960	
46		0-6-0DE	YE	2945	1965	OOU
47		0-6-0DE	RR	10236	1966	OOU
No.51		0-6-0DE	YE	2709	1959	
53		0-6-0DE	YE	2793	1961	OOU
54		0-6-0DE	YE	2908	1963	OOU
58		0-6-0DH	HE	7409	1976	
61		6wDH	RR	10277	1968	+
63		6wDH	TH	317V	1987	+
70		Bo-BoDE	HE	7281	1972	
71		Bo-BoDE	HE	7282	1972	
72		Bo-BoDE	HE	7283	1972	
73		Bo-BoDE	HE	7284	1972	
74		Bo-BoDE	HE	7285	1972	
75		Bo-BoDE	HE	7286	1972	
76		Bo-BoDE	HE	7287	1973	
77		Bo-BoDE	HE	7288	1973	
78		Bo-BoDE	HE	7289	1973	
79	BIG KEITH	Bo-BoDE	HE	7290	1973	OOU
80		Bo-BoDE	HE	7474	1977	
90		0-6-0DE	YE	2943	1965	
92		0-6-0DE	YE	2788	1960	
93		0-6-0DE	YE	2902	1963	OOU
94		0-6-0DE	RR	10238	1967	
95		0-6-0DE	YE	2690	1959	
–		0-6-0DH	GECT	5365	1972	OOU

+   property of Harry Needle Railroad Co, Merseyside

Blast Furnace Highline, Appleby-Frodingham Works, Scunthorpe
Gauge 4ft 8½in   SE 917104

HL 1	0449-73-01	0-4-0DE	_(BD	3734	1977
			(GECT	5434	1977
HL 2	0448-73-02	0-4-0DE	_(BD	3735	1977
			(GECT	5435	1977
No.3	0448/73/03	0-4-0DE	_(BD	3736	1977
			(GECT	5436	1977
4	0448-73-04	0-4-0DE	_(BD	3737	1977
			(GECT	5437	1977
No.5	0448-73-05	0-4-0DE	_(BD	3738	1977
			(GECT	5438	1977
6	0448-73-06	0-4-0DE	_(BD	3739	1977
			(GECT	5439	1977
HL 7		0-4-0DE	_(BD	3740	1977
			(GECT	5440	1977

Dawes Lane Coke Ovens, Scunthorpe
Gauge 4ft 8½in   SE 921118

–	4wWE	GB	420383/1	1977
–	4wWE	GB	420383/2	1977

Rail Mill
Gauge 4ft 8½in

DAISY	4wCE	Vollert	2008

CORUS COGIFER, CIVIL ENGINEERS
APPLEBY-FRODINGHAM WORKS, SCUNTHORPE
Gauge 4ft 8½in   SE 925092

No.2	714/24 0714/78/06				
	GR 50932	4wDM	Robel	21.12 RN5	1973
No.3	714/22 0714/78/05	4wDM	Robel	54.12-56-RT1	1966
No.4	714/26 0714/78/07	4wDM	Robel	54.12-56-RW3	1974
5	0714/69/29	4wDM	Robel	54.12-56-AA169	1978

CORUS NORTHERN ENGINEERING SERVICES, STRUCTURE FABRICATION WORKS,
APPLEBY FRODINGHAM SITE, SCUNTHORPE
Gauge 3ft 6in

–	4wBER	James Lind & Son
–	4wBER	James Lind & Son

FLIXBOROUGH WHARF LTD, FLIXBOROUGH WHARF, FLIXBOROUGH STATHER
Gauge 4ft 8½in   SE 859147

(D3986)	08818 MOLLY	0-6-0DE	Derby		1960	b
29		0-6-0DH	HE	7017	1971	b
H 014		0-6-0DH	RR	10262	1967	a

a   hire loco, property of R.M.S.Locotec, Wakefield, West Yorkshire
b   property of Harry Needle Railroad Co, Merseyside

GRANT RAIL LTD, PLANT DEPOT, DAWES LANE, FRODINGHAM
The following is a FLEET LIST of the locomotives owned by this contractor. The locomotives are normally located at this Plant Depot between use on contracts.

Gauge 4ft 8½in   SE 904114

1	"GR 5099"	4wDM	R/R	S&H	7512	1972
	GR 5105	4wDH		Donelli	190/80	1980
6		4wDM		Robel 54-12-(65?)-RR1		
7	CE 9604	4wDM		Robel		
	FH 51 CHV	4wDM	R/R	Unimog	195421	

H.M. DETENTION CENTRE, NORTH SEA CAMP, FREISTON, near BOSTON
Gauge 2ft 0in   RTC   TF 385405

–	4wDM	LB	55413	1967	Pvd

PORT OF BOSTON LTD, BOSTON DOCKS
Gauge 4ft 8½in   TF 329431

| D2112 | (03112) | 0-6-0DM | Don | 1960 |
| D3871 | (08704) | 0-6-0DE | Hor | 1960 |

SIMON STORAGE, PORT OF IMMINGHAM, IMMINGHAM WEST TERMINAL, WEST SIDE, IMMINGHAM
Gauge 4ft 8½in   TA 195167

| 45 | TMC | 4wDH | R/R | NNM | 83506 | 1984 | a |

a   permanently coupled to a 4w wagon for brake assistance

TOTAL LINDSEY OIL REFINERY, KILLINGHOLME
Gauge 4ft 8½in   TA 160176

BEAVER	0-6-0DH		AB	630	1978	
		reb	YEC	L168	1999	
BADGER	0-6-0DH		AB	658	1980	
TIGGA	0-6-0DH		TH	285V	1979	
		Reb	HAB		1992	
DUNDERS	0-6-0DH		HE	6971	1968	+
LAURA	0-6-0DH		HE	8805	1978	

+   on hire from Staffordshire Locomotive Co Ltd, Staffordshire

PRESERVATION SITES

THE 5305 LOCO ASSOCIATION, BINBROOK TECHNICAL PARK, near LOUTH
Gauge 1524mm   TF 196970

| 1157 | 2-8-0 | OC | Frichs | 403 | 1949 |

Gauge 4ft 8½in

| 42859 | 2-6-0 | OC | Crewe | 5981 | 1930 |

JASON ALLEN, GRIMOLDBY
Gauge 2ft 0in   TF 388877

| – | 2w-2PM | Wkm | 4092 | 1946 |

Gauge 1ft 3in

| E1 | NUCLEAR ELECTRIC | 4wBE | HardyK | E1 | 1992 |

APPLEBY-FRODINGHAM RAILWAY PRESERVATION SOCIETY, c/o CORUS, APPLEBY-FRODINGHAM WORKS, SCUNTHORPE

Gauge 4ft 8½in   SE 913109

3138	HUTNIK	A11	0-6-0T	OC	Chrz	3138	1954	a
–			0-6-0ST	IC	HE	3846	1956	
(D2853)	02003		0-4-0DH		YE	2812	1960	+
D3000	(13000)		0-6-0DE		Derby		1952	
DL 15			0-4-0DH		HC	D1344	1965	
DL 2	01002	RICHARD CLARK	0-6-0DM		WB	3151	1962	
		ARNOLD MACHIN	0-6-0DE		YE	2661	1958	

a   carries plate Chrz 3140 in error
+   property of Harry Needle Railroad Co, Merseyside

TYSDALE FARM, TYDD ST. MARY

Gauge 2ft 0in

–	4wDM	OK	6931	1937
–	4wDM	OK	7734	1938

ANDREW BRIDDON, c/o CORUS, BLAST FURNACE SIDINGS, APPLEBY-FRODINGHAM WORKS, SCUNTHORPE

Gauge 4ft 8½in

D2128	0-6-0DM	Sdn		1960

P. CLARK, FULSTOW STEAM CENTRE, CARPENTERS ROW, MAIN STREET, FULSTOW, near LOUTH

Gauge 4ft 8½in   TF 331972

No.1	FULSTOW	0-4-0ST	OC	RSHN	7680	1950

CLEETHORPES COAST LIGHT RAILWAY LTD, THE MERIDIAN LINE, LAKESIDE STATION, KINGS ROAD, CLEETHORPES

Gauge 1ft 6in   TA 321073

–	4-4-2	OC	CurwenD	1951

Gauge 1ft 3in

No.1	SUTTON BELLE	4-4-2	OC	Cannon		1933	
			reb	HuntTG		1953	
No.2	SUTTON FLYER	4-4-2	OC	_(Cannon			
				(HuntTG		1950	
111	YVETTE	4-4-0	OC	CravenEA		1946	
24		2-6-2	OC	Fairbourne	No.4	1990	
	"KATIE"	0-4-0T	OC	FMB	001	1983	
	EFFIE	0-4-0T+T	OC	GNS	11	1999	
–		4wVBT	VCG	StanhopeT		c1987	+
	MOUNTAINEER	0-4-0TT	OC	W Van der Heiden Rotterdam			

No.5	BATTISON		2-6-4DH	s/o	Battison		1958	
DA1			4wDM		Bush Mill Rly		1986	
				reb	Bush Mill Rly		c1995	
No.4			4-4wPMR		G&S		1946	
–			4wDM	s/o	L	26366	1944	
–			4wPM		L	35811	1950	Dsm
	JOHN		4-4wDH		Minirail		1954	
	MOROG		2w-2PM		MossAJ		1992	
		rebuilt as	2w-2DH					

+ not yet completed

GREAT NORTHERN & EAST LINCOLNSHIRE RAILWAY plc,
THE LINCOLNSHIRE WOLDS RAILWAY,.LUDBOROUGH STATION
Gauge 4ft 8½in   TF 309960

2	LION	0-4-0ST	OC	P	1351	1914	
No.2		0-4-0ST	OC	P	1749	1928	
D3167	(08102)	0-6-0DE		Derby		1955	
97650	PWM 650	0-6-0DE		RH	312990	1952	
3793	COLONEL B	4wDM		HE	5308	1960	
			reb	Resco	L107	1981	
WD 1		0-4-0DM		JF	4210131	1957	
MS 8		0-4-0DM		JF	4210145	1958	
–		0-4-0DM		RH	375713	1954	
6		0-4-0DM		RH	414303	1957	
7		4wDM		RH	421418	1958	
–		0-6-0DH		S	10166	1963	
1303	62287	4w-4wRER		York		1970	

T. HALL, NORTH INGS FARM MUSEUM, DORRINGTON, near RUSKINGTON
Gauge 2ft 0in   TF 098527

No.9	SWIFT	4wVBT	HallT	1859401	1994	
–		4wDM	ClayCross		1961	+
	BULLFINCH	4wDM	HE	7120	1969	
–		4wDM	MR	7493	1940	
LOD/758022	PENELOPE	4wDM	MR	8826	1943	
–		4wDM	OK		c1932	
–		4wDM	RH	183773	1937	
	INDIAN RUNNER	4wDM	RH	200744	1940	
No.1		4wDM	RH	371937	1954	
–		4wDM	RH	375701	1954	Dsm
–		4wDM	RH	421433	1959	

+ constructed from parts supplied by Listers

JUNKTION ANTIQUES LTD, THE OLD RAILWAY STATION, NEW BOLINGBROKE, near BOSTON

Gauge 1ft 6in   TQ 308576

–		4wPM	?		?	OOU

LINCOLNSHIRE COUNTY COUNCIL, MUSEUM OF LINCOLNSHIRE LIFE, BURTON ROAD, LINCOLN

Gauge 4ft 8½in   SK 972723

–	4wDM	RH	463154	1961

Gauge 2ft 6in

–	4wPM	RP	52124	1918

Gauge 2ft 3in

–	4wDM	RH	192888	1939

Gauge 2ft 0in

–	4wDM	RH	421432	1959

PLEASURE ISLAND FAMILY THEME PARK, KINGS ROAD, CLEETHORPES

Gauge 600mm   TA 323065

1	ANNABEL	4-4-0DH	s/o	SL	495.10.92	1992

J. SCHOLES, THE OLD STATION, FEN ROAD, RIPPINGALE

Gauge 4ft 8½in   TF 115283

24	STAMFORD	0-6-0ST	OC	AE	1972	1927
D9537		0-6-0DH		Sdn		1965
7514	(PWM 4311)	2w-2PMR		Wkm	7514	1956

SKEGNESS WATER LEISURE PARK, LINCOLNSHIRE COAST LIGHT RAILWAY, WALLS LANE, WINTHORPE, SKEGNESS

Gauge 2ft 0in   Locos are stored.   TF 560627

2	JURASSIC	0-6-0ST	OC	P	1008	1903
7	NOCTON	4wDM		MR	1935	1920
1	PAUL	4wDM		MR	3995	1934
4		4wDM		MR	7481	1940
–		4wDM		MR	8622	1941
No.5		4wDM		MR	8874	1944
–		4wDM		MR	9264	1947

DAVID WELLS, SLEAFORD ROAD INDUSTRIAL ESTATE,
BRACEBRIDGE HEATH, LINCOLN
Gauge 4ft 8½in

| CHARLES | 4wDM | RH | 417889 | 1958 |

GREATER LONDON

INDUSTRIAL SITES

ALSTOM TRANSPORT LTD, MORDEN DEPOT
In use as a static meeting room.
Gauge 4ft 8½in   TQ 255680

| 1031 (1085) | 2-2w-2w-2RER | MetCam | 1959 |

AMEC CONSTRUCTION, DOCKLAND LIGHT RAILWAY EXTENSION CONTRACT, NORTH WOOLWICH to WOOLWICH ARSENAL
Gauge 900mm

| – | 4wDH | Schöma | 5610 | 1999 |
| – | 4wDH | Schöma | 5611 | 1999 |

BALFOUR BEATTY, ROMFORD OHLM DEPOT, ROMFORD
Gauge 4ft 8½in   TQ 499880

WALTER	4wBE	CE	B4427A	2006	a
ANNE	4wBE	CE	B4427B	2006	a
LOU	4wBE	CE	B4427C	2006	a
KITTY	4wBE	CE	B4427D	2006	a

a   currently on East London Line Project, New Cross

BOMBARDIER TRANSPORTATION INC. OF CANADA, ILFORD DEPOT, ILFORD
Gauge 4ft 8½in   TQ 445869

| (D3740) 08573 | 0-6-0DE | Crewe | 1959 | a |

a   property of RMS Locotec Ltd, Wakefield, West Yorkshire

DOCKLANDS LIGHT RAILWAY LTD, POPLAR & BECKTON DEPOTS
Gauge 4ft 8½in   TQ 376806

| 94 | 0-4-0DH | GECT | 5577 | 1979 |
| No.93 | 4wBE/RE | RFSK | V339 | 1991 |

No.95		4wDM	RH	466625	1962	
–		4wDM	Wkm	11622	1986	

EAST LONDON LINE PROJECT, SILWOOD ROAD DEPOT, NEW CROSS
Gauge 4ft 8½in   TQ 357783

		WALTER	4wBE	CE	B4427A	2006	a
		ANNE	4wBE	CE	B4427B	2006	a
		LOU	4wBE	CE	B4427C	2006	a
		KITTY	4wBE	CE	B4427D	2006	a
01507	425	VENOM	0-6-0DH	RH	459519	1961	b
01509	433	VULCAN	0-6-0DH	RH	468043	1963	b
01583	422	VALIANT	0-6-0DH	RH	459517	1961	b

a   property of Balfour Beatty
b   on hire from Knights Rail Services, Eastleigh, Hampshire

EUROSTAR LTD, TEMPLE MILLS DEPOT
Gauge 4ft 8½in

–		6wBE	Scul		2007	

FORD MOTOR CO LTD, DAGENHAM
Gauge 4ft 8½in   TQ 496825, 499827

	No.1		0-4-0DH		EEV	D1124	1966
		FLEET No.2	0-6-0DH		HC	D1396	1967
				reb	HAB	6385	1996
	3	MALCOLM	0-4-0DH		S	10127	1963
GT/PL/1		P 260 C	4wDM		Robel		
						21 11 RK1	1966

J. MURPHY & SONS LTD, LOWER LEA VALLEY REGENERATION, "OLYMPICS 2012", CONTRACT
Gauge 2ft 0in

–	4wDH	Schöma	5712	2001
–	4wDH	Schöma	5713	2001
–	4wDH	Schöma	5714	2001

J. MURPHY & SONS LTD,
PLANT DEPOT, HIGHVIEW HOUSE, HIGHGATE ROAD, KENTISH TOWN
Locos are present at this depot between use on contracts.   TQ 287855

Gauge 2ft 0in

JMLM2	0-4-0BE	WR	M7550	1972
LM03	4wBE	WR	N7607	1973
DN04	4wBE	WR	N7605	1973
(JMLM5)	4wBE	WR	N7606	1973

LM08		4wBE	WR	N7621	1973
LM09		4wBE	WR	N7620	1973
LM10		4wBE	CE	B3329B	1986
			reb CE	B3804	1991
LM11		4wBE	CE	B3329A	1986
			reb CE	B3791	1991
LM12		4wBE	CE	B3070C	1983
			reb CE	B3804	1991
LM13		4wBE	CE	B3070D	1983
			reb CE	B3782	1991
LM14		4wBE	CE	B3070B	1983
			reb CE	B3804	1991
LM15		4wBE	CE	B3070A	1983
			reb CE	B3782	1991
JMLM16	JM95	4wBE	CE	B1534B	1977
			reb CE	B3672	1990
JMLM17	JM93	4wBE	CE	B1547B	1977
			reb CE	B3672	1990
JMLM18	JM94	4wBE	CE	B1534A	1977
			reb CE	B3672	1990
JMLM19		4wBE	WR	6502	1962
			reb WR	10102	1983
JMLM20		4wBE	WR	6505	1962
			reb WR	10105	1983
JMLM21		4wBE	WR	6503	1962
			reb WR	10104	1983
JMLM22	4951	4wBE	WR	6504	1962
			reb WR	10106	1983
LM24		4wBE	CE	B0167	1974
			reb CE	B3786A	1991
JMLM25		4wBE	CE	B0145A	1973
			reb CE	B3786B	1991
LM26JM		4wBE	CE	B0145C	1973
			reb CE	B3799	1991
LM 27		4wDH	Schöma	5694	2001
LM 28	11	4wDH	Schöma	5695	2001
(LM 29)		4wDH	Schöma	5696	2001
(LM 30)		4wDH	Schöma	5697	2001
LM 31	14	4wDH	Schöma	5698	2001
(LM 32)		4wDH	Schöma	5699	2001
LM 33	6	4wDH	Schöma	5700	2001
LM 34		4wDH	Schöma	5701	2001
LM 35	10	4wDH	Schöma	5702	200

Gauge 1ft 6in

(JMLM6)		0-4-0BE	WR	7617	1973

EDMUND NUTTALL LTD, CIVIL ENGINEERS,
PLANT DEPOT, RAYLAMB WAY, off MANOR ROAD, SLADE GREEN, ERITH
Locos are present at this depot between use on contracts. TQ 537777

Gauge 2ft 0in

RR51-075		4wBE		CE	5590	1969
			reb	CE	B4174B	1996
RR51-052		4wBE		CE	5590/1	1969
RR51-053	IVOR	4wBE		CE	5590/2	1969
RR51-074		4wBE		CE	5590/6	1969
			reb	CE	B4174A	1996
RR51-059		4wBE		CE	5590/8	1969
RR51-069		4wBE		CE	5943	1972
RR51-070		4wBE		CE	5949A	1972
RR51-065		4wBE		CE	5949B	1972
RR51-071		4wBE		CE	5949D	1972
RR51-068	HERBIE	4wBE		CE	5949G	1972
RR51-073		4wBE		CE	B0129	1973
TO.11		4wBE		CE	B4071.4	1995

PLASSER MACHINERY PARTS AND SERVICES LTD,
DRAYTON GREEN ROAD, WEST EALING
Gauge 4ft 8½in TQ 161809

–	0-4-0DM	Bg/DC	2724	1963

ROYAL MAIL LETTERS LTD, THE POST OFFICE UNDERGROUND RAILWAY
(part of London Region of Post Office Letters Ltd) **(Closed-On care and maintenance)**

Locos are kept at :- King Edward Building, St Pauls TQ 319813
Mount Pleasant Parcels Office, Clerkenwell TQ 311823
New Western District Office, Rathbone Place TQ 296814

Gauge 2ft 0in

–			4wRE	EEDK	601	1926	Pvd	
–			4wRE	EEDK	652	1926	OOU	a
1			4wBE	EEDK	702	1926		
2			4wBE	EEDK	703	1926		
3			4wBE	EEDK	704	1926		
66	[104	104]	2w-2-2-2wRE	_(EE	3335	1962		e
				(EES	8314	1962	OOU	
01	[169	170]	2w-2-2-2wRE	HE	9134	1982	OOU	d
02	[103	104]	2w-2-2-2wRE	GB	420461/2	1980	OOU	
03	[105	106	2w-2-2-2wRE	GB	420461/3	1980	OOU	
04	[107	108]	2w-2-2-2wRE	_(GB	420461/4	1980		
				(HE	9103	1980	OOU	
05	[109	110]	2w-2-2-2wRE	_(GB	420461/5	1980		
				(HE	9104	1980	OOU	
06	[111	112]	2w-2-2-2wRE	_(GB	420461/6	1980		
				(HE	9105	1980	OOU	
07	[113	114]	2w-2-2-2wRE	_(GB	420461/7	1980		
				(HE	9106	1980	OOU	

08	GREAT WEST EXPRESS						
	[115 116]	2w-2-2-2wRE	_(GB	420461/8	1980		
			(HE	9107	1980	OOU	
09	[117 118]	2w-2-2-2wRE	_(GB	420461/9	1981		
			(HE	9108	1981	OOU	
10	[119 120]	2w-2-2-2wRE	_(GB	420461/10	1981		
			(HE	9109	1981	OOU	
11	[121 122]	2w-2-2-2wRE	_(GB	420461/11	1981		
			(HE	9110	1981	OOU	
12	[123 124]	2w-2-2-2wRE	_(GB	420461/12	1981		
			(HE	9111	1981	OOU	
13	[125 126]	2w-2-2-2wRE	_(GB	420461/13	1981		
			(HE	9112	1981	OOU	
14	CAPITAL EXPRESS						
	[127 128]	2w-2-2-2wRE	_(GB	420461/14	1981		
			(HE	9113	1981	OOU	
15	[129 130]	2w-2-2-2wRE	_(GB	420461/15	1981		
			(HE	9114	1981	OOU	
16	[131 132]	2w-2-2-2wRE	_(GB	420461/16	1981		
			(HE	9115	1981	OOU	
17	[133 134]	2w-2-2-2wRE	_(GB	420461/17	1981		
			(HE	9116	1981	OOU	
18	[135 136]	2w-2-2-2wRE	_(GB	420461/18	1981		
			(HE	9117	1981	OOU	
19	[137 138]	2w-2-2-2wRE	_(GB	420461/19	1981		
			(HE	9118	1981	OOU	
20	[139 140]	2w-2-2-2wRE	_(GB	420461/20	1981		
			(HE	9119	1981	OOU	
23	[145 146]	2w-2-2-2wRE	_(GB	420461/23	1981		
			(HE	9122	1981	OOU	
24	[147 148]	2w-2-2-2wRE	_(GB	420461/24	1981		
			(HE	9123	1981	OOU	
25	[149 150]	2w-2-2-2wRE	_(GB	420461/25	1981		
			(HE	9124	1981	OOU	
26	[151 152]	2w-2-2-2wRE	_(GB	420461/26	1981		
			(HE	9125	1981	OOU	
27	[153 154]	2w-2-2-2wRE	_(GB	420461/27	1982		
			(HE	9126	1982	OOU	
28	[155 156]	2w-2-2-2wRE	_(GB	420461/28	1982		
			(HE	9127	1982	OOU	
29	[157 158]	2w-2-2-2wRE	_(GB	420461/29	1982		
			(HE	9128	1982	OOU	
30	[159 160]	2w-2-2-2wRE	_(GB	420461/30	1982		
			(HE	9129	1982	OOU	
31	[161 162]	2w-2-2-2wRE	_(GB	420461/31	1982		
			(HE	9130	1982	OOU	
32	S.S.J.ROBERTSON H.M.CHIEF INSPECTOR OF RAILWAYS						
	[163 164]	2w-2-2-2wRE	_(GB	420461/32	1982		
			(HE	9131	1982	OOU	
33	GREAT EAST EXPRESS	2w-2-2-2wRE	_(GB	420461/33	1982		
	[165 166]		(HE	9132	1982	OOU	
34	[167 168]	2w-2-2-2wRE	_(GB	420461/34	1982		
			(HE	9133	1982	OOU	
752	[101 102]	2w-2-2-2wRE	EEDK	752	1930	OOU	c
–		2w-2-2-2wRE	EEDK	753	1930		b
35	[107 108]	2w-2-2-2wRE	EEDK	755	1930	OOU	
36	[105 106]	2w-2-2-2wRE	EEDK	756	1930	OOU	

759	[110	115]	2w-2-2-2wRE	EEDK	759	1930	OOU	c
39	[121	122]	2w-2-2-2wRE	EEDK	762	1930	OOU	
763	[123	124]	2w-2-2-2wRE	EEDK	763	1930	OOU	c
793	[183	184]	2w-2-2-2wRE	EEDK	793	1930	OOU	c
795	[187	188]	2w-2-2-2wRE	EEDK	795	1930	OOU	c
797	[191	192]	2w-2-2-2wRE	EEDK	797	1930	OOU	
799	[195	196]	2w-2-2-2wRE	EEDK	799	1930	OOU	c
802	[201	202]	2w-2-2-2wRE	EEDK	802	1930	OOU	c
804	[205	206]	2w-2-2-2wRE	EEDK	804	1930	OOU	c
41	[207	208]	2w-2-2-2wRE	EEDK	805	1930	OOU	
810	[217	218]	2w-2-2-2wRE	EEDK	810	1930	OOU	
43	[219	220]	2w-2-2-2wRE	EEDK	811	1930	OOU	
813	[223	224]	2w-2-2-2wRE	EEDK	813	1930	OOU	c
45	[225	226]	2w-2-2-2wRE	EEDK	814	1930	OOU	
46	[227	228]	2w-2-2-2wRE	EEDK	815	1930	OOU	
816	[229	230]	2w-2-2-2wRE	EEDK	816	1930	OOU	c
817	[231	232]	2w-2-2-2wRE	EEDK	817	1930	OOU	c
818	[233	233]	2w-2-2-2wRE	EEDK	818	1930	OOU	c
820	[237	238]	2w-2-2-2wRE	EEDK	820	1931	OOU	c
–	[239	240]	2w-2-2-2wRE	EEDK	821	1931	OOU	b
822	[241	242]	2w-2-2-2wRE	EEDK	822	1931	OOU	c
48	[245	246]	2w-2-2-2wRE	EEDK	824	1931	OOU	
826	[249	250]	2w-2-2-2wRE	EEDK	826	1931	OOU	c
49	[251	252]	2w-2-2-2wRE	EEDK	827	1931	OOU	
830	[257	258]	2w-2-2-2wRE	EEDK	830	1931	OOU	c
925	[445	446]	2w-2-2-2wRE	EEDK	925	1936	OOU	c
51	[457	458]	2w-2-2-2wRE	EEDK	931	1936	OOU	
932	[459	460]	2w-2-2-2wRE	EEDK	932	1936	OOU	c
50	[235	451]	2w-2-2-2wRE	EE			OOU	f
55	[236	452]	2w-2-2-2wRE	EE			OOU	f

a converted to a battery carrier
b converted to a passenger car
c stored in a disused tunnel at Rathbone Place
d supplied as spare power units for 01 to 34 (orig 501 to 534) but now forming 01
e also contains parts of EE 3334-EES 8313 / 1962
f contains a power unit from EEDK 819/1930 and EEDK 928/1936

TARMAC SOUTHERN LTD, HAYES ASPHALT WORKS, PUMP LANE, HAYES
Gauge 4ft 8½in   TQ 105795

220		0-4-0DM	AB	359	1941

TRANSPORT FOR LONDON, CROYDON TRAMLINK LTD, THERAPIA LANE DEPOT, CROYDON
Gauge 4ft 8½in   TQ 298669

058	2w-2DMR	(German)
059	2w-2DMR	(German)

TRANSPLANT LTD and METRONET RAIL & TUBE LINES

(Transplant – A Division of Tubelines)

London underground railways maintenance. Some lines are maintained by Metronet Rail.

Locos are kept at :-

Acton Works, Bollo Lane	TQ 196791
Cockfosters Depot	TQ 288962
Ealing Common Depot, Uxbridge Road	TQ 189802
Golders Green Depot, Finchley Road	TQ 253875
Hainault Depot	TQ 450918
Hammersmith Depot	TQ 234787
Highgate Depot	TQ 279886
Lillie Bridge Depot	TQ 250782
Morden Depot	TQ 255680
Neasden Depot	TQ 206858
New Cross Depot	TQ 360778
Northfields Depot, Northfields Avenue	TQ 167789
Northumberland Park Depot	TQ 34x88x
Stonebridge Park Depot	TQ 192845
Stratford Market Depot	
Upminster Depot	TQ 570871
Waterloo (Waterloo & City Line)	TQ 309799
Waterloo T&RSED, Waterloo & City Line	TQ 309799
West Ruislip Depot	TQ 094862

Locos may also be found temporarily in depots/sidings at -
Aldgate, Amersham Station, Arnos Grove, Barking, Brixton (Underground), Chalfont & Latimer Station, Edgware, Edgware Road, Elephant & Castle (Underground), Farringdon, High Barnet, High Street Kensington, London Road, Loughton, Moorgate, Parsons Green, Queens Park, Rickmansworth Station, South Harrow, Stanmore, Triangle Sidings, Uxbridge, Walthamstow (Underground), Wembley Park Depot, White City and Woodford

Gauge 4ft 8½in

1	BRITTA LOTTA	4wDH	Schöma	5403	1996
2	NIKKI	4wDH	Schöma	5404	1996
3	CLAIRE	4wDH	Schöma	5405	1996
4	PAM	4wDH	Schöma	5406	1996
5	SOPHIE	4wDH	Schöma	5407	1996
6	DENISE	4wDH	Schöma	5408	1996
7	ANNEMARIE	4wDH	Schöma	5409	1996
8	EMMA	4wDH	Schöma	5410	1996
9	DEBORA	4wDH	Schöma	5411	1996
10	CLEMENTINE	4wDH	Schöma	5412	1996
11	JOAN	4wDH	Schöma	5413	1996
12	MELANIE	4wDH	Schöma	5414	1996
13	MICHELE	4wDH	Schöma	5415	1996
14	CAROL	4wDH	Schöma	5416	1996
L 15	69015 97715	4w-4wBE/RE	MetCam		1970
L 16	69016	4w-4wBE/RE	MetCam		1970
L 17	17	4w-4wBE/RE	MetCam		1970
L 18	69018	4w-4wBE/RE	MetCam		1970
L 19	69019	4w-4wBE/RE	MetCam		1970
L 20	64020 97720	4w-4wBE/RE	MetCam		1964
L 21	64021	4w-4wBE/RE	MetCam		1964
L 22		4w-4wBE/RE	MetCam		1965
L 23		4w-4wBE/RE	MetCam		1965

L 24	64024		4w-4wBE/RE	MetCam		1965	
L 25	64025		4w-4wBE/RE	MetCam		1965	
L 26	64026		4w-4wBE/RE	MetCam		1965	
L 27	64027		4w-4wBE/RE	MetCam		1965	
L 28			4w-4wBE/RE	MetCam		1965	
L 29	64029		4w-4wBE/RE	MetCam		1965	
L 30	64030		4w-4wBE/RE	MetCam		1965	
L 31			4w-4wBE/RE	MetCam		1965	
L 32	64032	97732	4w-4wBE/RE	MetCam		1965	
L 44	73044		4w-4wBE/RE	Don	L44	1973	
L 45	73045		4w-4wBE/RE	Don	L45	1974	
L 46	73046		4w-4wBE/RE	Don	L46	1974	
L 47	73047	97747	4w-4wBE/RE	Don	L47	1974	
L 48	73048		4w-4wBE/RE	Don	L48	1974	
L 49	73049		4w-4wBE/RE	Don	L49	1974	
L 50	73050	97750	4w-4wBE/RE	Don	L50	1974	
L 51	51		4w-4wBE/RE	Don	L51	1974	
L 52	73052	97752	4w-4wBE/RE	Don	L52	1974	
L 53	73053	97753	4w-4wBE/RE	Don	L53	1974	
L 54			4w-4wBE/RE	Don	L54	1974	OOU
L 62	85062		4w-4wBE/RE	MetCam		1985	OOU
L 63	85063		4w-4wBE/RE	MetCam		1985	OOU
L 64	85064		4w-4wBE/RE	MetCam		1985	OOU
L 65			4w-4wBE/RE	MetCam		1985	OOU
L 66	85066		4w-4wBE/RE	MetCam		1985	OOU
L 67	85067		4w-4wBE/RE	MetCam		1986	OOU
L 130			4w-4RE	MetCam		1934	e
			reb	Acton		1967	
L 132			4w-4wRE	Cravens		1960	d
			reb	Derby		1987	
L 133			4w-4wRE	Cravens		1960	d
			reb	Derby		1987	
L 135			4w-4RE	MetCam		1934	e
			reb	Acton		1967	
L 150			2-2w-2w-2RE	MetCam		1938	a
			reb	Acton		1978	OOU
L 151			2-2w-2w-2RE	MetCam		1938	a
			reb	Acton		1978	OOU
TCC 1			4w-4wRE	MetCam		1939	
			reb	Acton		1978	
TCC 5			4w-4wRE	MetCam		1938	
			reb	Acton		1978	
2	(3706)		4w-4RER	MetCam		1935	e Pvd
7	(3209)		4w-4RER	MetCam		1932	e Pvd
1406			2-2w-2w-2RER	MetCam		c1962	j
1407			2-2w-2w-2RER	MetCam		c1962	b
1441			2-2w-2w-2RER	MetCam		c1962	f
1481			2-2w-2w-2RER	MetCam		c1962	g
1515			2-2w-2w-2RER	MetCam		c1960	OOU
1532			2-2w-2w-2RER	MetCam		c1962	h
1560			2-2w-2w-2RER	MetCam		c1962	c
1561			2-2w-2w-2RER	MetCam		c1962	c

1570		2-2w-2w-2RER	MetCam		c1960	c
1576		2-2w-2w-2RER	MetCam		c1960	j
1577		2-2w-2w-2RER	MetCam		c1960	j
1672		2-2w-2w-2RER	MetCam		c1962	h
1673		2-2w-2w-2RER	MetCam		c1962	h
1680		2-2w-2w-2RER	MetCam		c1962	i OOU
1681		2-2w-2w-2RER	MetCam		c1962	j
1682		2-2w-2w-2RER	MetCam		c1960	b
1690		2-2w-2w-2RER	MetCam		c1962	j
1691		2-2w-2w-2RER	MetCam		c1962	i
3215		2-2w-2w-2RER	MetCam		c1972	j
3229		2-2w-2w-2RER	MetCam		c1972	k
3315		2-2w-2w-2RER	MetCam		c1972	j
3329		2-2w-2w-2RER	MetCam		c1972	k
9125		2-2w-2w-2RER	MetCam		c1960	j
9441		2-2w-2w-2RER	MetCam		c1960	c
9459		2-2w-2w-2RER	MetCam		c1960	b
9533		2-2w-2w-2RER	MetCam		c1960	h
9561		2-2w-2w-2RER	MetCam		c1960	c
9577		2-2w-2w-2RER	MetCam		c1960	j
9691		2-2w-2w-2RER	MetCam		c1960	
12 SARAH SIDDONS		4w-4wRE	VL		1922	
–		2w-2BER	Bance LUL2BSBACO	07098	1998	
–		4wBER	Bance LUL4SBACO	07699	1998	
–		4wBER	Bance LUL4SBACO	06898	1998	
–		2w-2BER	Bance LUL2SBACO	07198	1998	
–		2w-2BER	Bance LUL2SBACO	07298	1998	
–		2w-2BER	Bance LUL2SBACO	07398	1998	
–		2w-2BER	Bance LUL2SBACO	07498	1998	
–		2w-2BER	Bance LUL2SBACO	07598	1998	
–		4wBE	SET		2003	
–		4wBE	Niteq	B168	2001	
–		4wBE	Niteq	B184	2001	
–		4wBE	Niteq	B217	2005	
–		4wBE	Niteq	B222	2005	
A456 NWX	L84	4wDM R/R	Unimog 424121.10.101335	1035/83	1983	
C622 EWT	L85	4wDM R/R	Unimog 424121.10.126262	1130/86	1986	
–		4wDMR R/R	Landrover		c2004	m

a converted to weedkilling train
b Sandite Car pilot
c pilot motor cars
d track recording pilot motor cars
e heritage train

f   supplies inspection unit
g   new works unit
h   emergency training unit
i   inspection unit
j   engineering unit
k   training and filming unit (Aldwych Branch)
m   property of Metronet Rail

PRESERVATION SITES

BLUMSUM WOODYARD, RIVER ROAD, BARKING
Gauge 1524mm

794		0-6-0T	OC	TK	350	1925

CRAVENS HERITAGE TRAINS LTD,
c/o LONDON UNDERGROUND LTD, WEST RUISLIP DEPOT
Gauge 4ft 8½in   TQ 094862

3906	4w-4wRER	Cravens	1960
3907	4w-4wRER	Cravens	1960

c/o LONDON UNDERGROUND LTD, HAINAULT DEPOT
Gauge 4ft 8½in   TQ 450918

1506	2-2w-2w-2RER	MetCam	c1960
1507	2-2w-2w-2RER	Metcam	c1960
9507	2-2w-2w-2RER	MetCam	c1960

ENFIELD TIMBER COMPANY,
1-23 HERTFORD ROAD, ENFIELD HIGHWAY, ENFIELD
Gauge 1524mm   TQ 352966

792 HEN		0-6-0T	OC	TK	373	1927

EUROSTORAGE LTD, WEST DRAYTON
Gauge 4ft 8½in   TQ 054802

21147	4w-4wRER	MetCam	1949	OOU

FLYING SCOTSMAN SERVICES, SOUTHALL M.P.D., SOUTHALL
Gauge 4ft 8½in   TQ 133798

34067	TANGMERE	4-6-2	3C	Bton	1947	
35022	HOLLAND-AMERICA LINE	4-6-2	3C	Elh	1948	
35027	PORT LINE	4-6-2	3C	Elh	1948	
(46100) 6100	ROYAL SCOT	4-6-0	3C	Derby	1930	
			reb	Crewe	1950	

D2447	LORD LEVERHULME	0-4-0DM		AB	388	1953	
(D3948)	08780	0-6-0DE		Derby		1960	

THE FRIENDS OF THE PUMP HOUSE, LOW HALL LANE, WALTHAMSTOW, E17
Gauge 4ft 8½in TQ 363882

60138	(977907)	4-4wDER		Afd/Elh		1962	
54256		2w-2-2-2wRER		BRCW		1939	
3016		2w-2-2-2wRER		MetCam		1968	

GREAT ORMOND STREET CHILDRENS HOSPITAL
Gauge 4ft 8½in

3634	4w-4wRER		MetCam		1988	Dsm

Reduced in length to 32ft and converted to hospital radio studio.

G.W.R. PRESERVATION GROUP LTD,
SOUTHALL RAILWAY CENTRE, GLADE LANE, SOUTHALL   (Closed)
Gauge 4ft 8½in   www.gwrpg.co.uk   TQ 133798

2	WILLIAM MURDOCH	0-4-0ST	OC	P	2100	1949	
	BIRKENHEAD	0-4-0ST	OC	RSHN	7386	1948	
A.E.C. No.1		4wDM		AEC		1938	
ARMY 251	FRANCIS BAILY OF THATCHAM						
		0-4-0DM		RH	390772	1956	
–		4wDMR		BD	3706	1975	

KEW BRIDGE STEAM MUSEUM,
KEW BRIDGE MUSEUM STEAM RAILWAY, GREEN DRAGON LANE, BRENTFORD
Gauge 2ft 0in   TQ 188780

	CLOISTER	0-4-0ST	OC	HE	542	1891	
–		0-4-0ST	OC	Kew		1995	+
2	"ALISTER"	4wDM		L	44052	1958	

+   not yet completed

KINGS COLLEGE, STRAND
Gauge 1ft 3in   TQ 308808

	PEARL	2-2-2	IC	B(C)		1860	

LONDON REGIONAL TRANSPORT, LONDON TRANSPORT MUSEUM
Museum Depot, Gunnersbury Lane, Acton Town
Gauge 4ft 8½in

4416		2w-2-2-2wRE	BRCW		1939
ESL107		4w-4-4-4wRE	_(BRCW		1903
			(MetAmal		1903
		reb	Acton		1939
61		4w-4wRER	EEDK	1151	1940
L35		4w-4wBE/RE	GRC&W	0/7903	1938
4184		4w-4RER	GRC&W	0/5026	1924
4417		2w-2-2-2wRE	GRC&W		1939
(320)	L134	4w-4RE	MetC&W		1927
		reb	Acton		1967
3327		4w-4RER	MetCam		1929
(3693)	L131	4w-4RE	MetCam		1934
		reb	Acton		1967
12048		4w-4wRER	MetCam		1938
10012		4w-4wRER	MetCam		1938
11012		4w-4wRER	MetCam		1938
(S11187	3135)	2-2w-2w-2RER	EE/Elh		1937
22679		2w-2-2-2wRER	MetCam		1952
16		4w-4wRER	MetCam		1986
3530		4w-4wRER	MetCam		1972
3734		4w-4wRER	MetCam		1988

LONDON'S TRANSPORT MUSEUM, COVENT GARDEN PIAZZA
Gauge 4ft 8½in   TQ 303809

23		4-4-0T	OC	BP	710	1866
5	JOHN HAMPDEN	Bo-BoRE		VL		1922
4248		4w-4RER		GRC&W	0/5026	1924
11182		2-2w-2w-2RER		MetCam		1939
No.13		4wRE		M&P/BP		1890 +

+   carried plate from No.1 until probable identity established c1990

METROPOLITAN WATERBOARD RAILWAY SOCIETY, HAMPTON WATERWORKS,
Gauge 2ft 0in

HOUNSLOW	4wPH	SPL	No.1	2008

MUSEUM OF LONDON, RESERVE STORE, MORTIMER WHEELER HOUSE, WHARF ROAD, HACKNEY
Gauge 2ft 0in

–	4w Atmospheric Car	1861

currently not on public display. Cut into two halves, Inventory no.s 31.85/1 and 31.85/2.

NETWORK RAIL, STEWARTS LANE DEPOT

Privateley preserved locomotives and multiple units based here.

Gauge 4ft 8½in TQ 288766

35028	CLAN LINE		4-6-2	3C	Elh		1948
(E6043)	73136 PERSEVERENCE		Bo-BoDE/RE		_(EE	3715	1966
					(EEV	E375	1966
3051	CAR No.88	S288S	4w-4wRER		MetCam		1932
3053	CAR No.92		4w-4wRER		MetCam		1932
3053	CAR No.93		4w-4wRER		MetCam		1932

RIVIERA TRAINS, OLD OAK COMMON DEPOT

Preserved locomotives based here whilst working mainline charters.

Gauge 4ft 8½in

D1015	WESTERN CHAMPION			
	C-CDH	Sdn		1962

S.C. ROBINSON, 47 WAVERLEY GARDENS

Gauge 2ft 0in TQ 187831

–	4wDMF	RH	209429	1943

ROYAL AIR FORCE MUSEUM, GRAHAME PARK WAY, HENDON

Gauge 2ft 0in

NG 23	4wBE	BD	3702	1973	
	reb	AB		1987	a
A.M.W. No.165	4wDM	RH	194784	1939	a

a   currently stored in museum reserve store at an Operational RAF base in the midlands

SCIENCE MUSEUM, SOUTH KENSINGTON

Gauge 5ft 0in TQ 268793

"PUFFING BILLY"	4w	VCG	Hedley	1827-1832	a

a   incorporates parts of loco of same name built c1814

Gauge 4ft 8½in

1868	2-2-2	OC	Crewe	20	1845
No.1 ROCKET	0-2-2	OC	RS	19	1829

VILLAGE UNDERGROUND, 54 HOLYWELL LANE, GREAT EASTERN STREET, SHOREDITCH

Gauge 4ft 8½in TQ 334823

3662	4w-4wRER	MetCam	1988
3733	4w-4wRER	MetCam	1988

GREATER MANCHESTER

INDUSTRIAL SITES

ASHTON PACKET BOAT CO LTD, ASHTON BOATYARD, HANOVER STREET NORTH, GUIDE BRIDGE

Gauge 2ft 0in   SJ 920978

–	4wDM	FH	2325	1941	a
–	4wDM	HE	2820	1943	
–	4wDM	HE	6012	1960	
–	4wDM	MR	22031	1959	
–	4wDM	RH	200761	1941	

a   stored on behalf of owners.

CORUS TRACK PRODUCTS, CASTLETON WORKS, HEYWOOD ROAD, CASTLETON

Gauge 4ft 8½in   SJ 880102

(D3759 08592) 08994	0-6-0DE	Crewe	1959

CREATIVE LOGISTICS LTD, FREIGHT TERMINAL, DUNCAN STREET, off REGENT ROAD, SALFORD

Gauge 4ft 8½in   SJ 823981

"SHARON"	0-4-0DH	EEV	3987	1970	+	OOU
(D2985 07001)	0-6-0DE	RH	480686	1962	+	
–	0-6-0DH	RR	10240	1965	+	OOU
–	0-6-0DH	S	10072	1961	+	OOU
109189	0-6-0DH	S	10157	1963	+	OOU
01552 BH	0-6-0DH	TH	167V	1966	+	

+   property of Harry Needle Railroad Co Ltd, Merseyside

MIKE DARNALL, c/o CHAIRFILLINGS, C.F.HOUSE, RELIANCE INDUSTRIAL ESTATE, EAGAR STREET, NEWTON HEATH, MANCHESTER

This is understood to be a complete FLEET LIST of the locos owned by (or in the care of) this company, which operates from the above address. Some locos are for hire or resale, and are in use or stored at a number of locations.

Gauge 4ft 8½in

(D3503)	08388	0-6-0DE	Derby		1958	
(D3560)	08445	0-6-0DE	Derby		1958	
(D3761)	08594	0-6-0DE	Crewe		1959	
(D4174)	08944	0-6-0DE	Dar		1962	a
(D5562)	31144	A1A-A1A DE	BT	161	1959	
(D5823)	31556	A1A-A1A DE	BT	324	1961	a

a   currently at East Lancashire Railway, Greater Manchester

D.C.T. CIVIL ENGINEERING,
PLANT DEPOT, PROSPECT HOUSE, GEORGE STREET, SHAW, OLDHAM
Locos are present in this yard between use on contracts.

Gauge 2ft 0in

03	4wBE	CE	B1524/2	1977
–	4wBE	CE		

V.J. DONEGHAN (PLANT) LTD,
TUNNELLING & CIVIL ENGINEERING CONTRACTORS,
BIRD HALL INDUSTRIAL PARK, BIRD HALL LANE, STOCKPORT
Locos are present in this yard between use on contracts.

Gauge 1ft 6in   SJ 879886

–	4wBE	CE	5640	1969
2	4wBE	CE		
–	4wBE	CE		
4	4wBE	CE		

Three of the four battery boxes used by the above locos carry CE plates:- 5841/68, 5628/69 and 5866/71 respectively.

J. DOYLE LTD,
SCRAP MERCHANTS, CHEQUERBENT, WESTHOUGHTON
Gauge 4ft 8½in   SD 674062

–	0-6-0ST	OC	AE	1600	1912	Pvd

MANCHESTER SHIP CANAL CO LTD,
BARTON DOCK LOCO SHED, TRAFFORD PARK
Gauge 4ft 8½in   SJ 791955

(D3953)	08785	0-6-0DE	Derby	1960
D3991	(08823)	0-6-0DE	Derby	1960
(D4143)	08913	0-6-0DE	Hor	1962

MARSH TRACKWORK, BARTON DOCK, TRAFFORD PARK
Gauge 4ft 8½in

	N338 CNE	4wDM	R/R	_(Perm/Landrover (Hy-rail	29932	1996	
	A341 SCW	4wDM	R/R	Unimog	099195		
	(DB 965051)	2w-2PMR		Wkm	(7574)	1956	DsmT
9036		2w-2PMR		Wkm	8196	1958	a
–		2w-2PMR		GeismarST/99/37		1999	

a   currently on display at The Museum of Science & Industry in Manchester, Liverpool road, Castlefield, Manchester

RILEY & SON (E) LTD, BUCKLEY WELLS LOCOMOTIVE WORKS, BURY

Locos usually present for maintenance, repair and /or restoration.

Gauge 4ft 8½in   SD 799101

34073	249 SQUADRON	4-6-2	3C	Bton	1948	
35009	SHAW SAVILL	4-6-2	3C	Elh	1942	

SERCO METROLINK LTD,
QUEENS ROAD DEPOT, CHEETHAM HILL, MANCHESTER

Gauge 4ft 8½in   SD 848005

–	4wDH		_(GECT	5862	1991
			(RFSK	V337	1991
L253 HKK	4wDM	R/R	Volkswagen/Perm		
–	4wPMR		Bance		

SIEMENS TRANSPORT, ARDWICK DEPOT

Gauge 4ft 8½in

–	0-4-0DH		EEV	D1122	1966
–	4wBE		CPM	1731.02UK	

A.E. YATES LTD,
CRANFIELD ROAD, LOSTOCK INDUSTRIAL ESTATE, LOSTOCK, BOLTON

Locos are present in this yard between contracts.   SD 650098

Gauge 2ft 0in

–	4wBE		CE	5640	1969
PLANT No.432/43	4wBE		CE	5866A	1971
–	4wBE		CE		

PRESERVATION SITES

EAST LANCASHIRE LIGHT RAILWAY CO LTD,
BURY TRANSPORT MUSEUM

Locos are kept at :-

Bolton Street Station, Bury	SD 802107
Buckley Wells Carriage Shops, Bury	SD 800103
Bury Depot	SD 799101
Castlecroft Road Goods Shed, Bury	SD 803109

Gauge 5ft 3in

99	4w-4wDER		Derby C&W	1978	OOU

Gauge 4ft 8½in

3855	2-8-0	OC	Sdn	1942	
7229	2-8-2T	OC	Sdn	1935	

30499		4-6-0	OC	Elh		1920
42765		2-6-0	OC	Crewe	5757	1927
44871 SOVEREIGN		4-6-0	OC	Crewe		1945
45231 THE SHERWOOD FORESTER						
		4-6-0	OC	AW	1286	1936
45337		4-6-0	OC	AW	1392	1937
(45690) 5690 LEANDER		4-6-0	3C	Crewe	288	1936
			reb	Derby		1973
(46201) 6201 PRINCESS ELIZABETH						
		4-6-2	4C	Crewe	107	1933
46428		2-6-0	OC	Crewe		1948
47324		0-6-0T	IC	NBH	23403	1926
(52322) 1300		0-6-0	IC	Hor	420	1896
71000 DUKE OF GLOUCESTER		4-6-2	3C	Crewe		1954
76079		2-6-0	OC	Hor		1957
80097		2-6-4T	OC	Bton		1954
92214		2-10-0	OC	Sdn		1959
No.1		0-4-0ST	OC	AB	1927	1927
1 "GOTHENBURG"		0-6-0T	IC	HC	680	1903
–		0-4-0ST	OC	P	1370	1915
1151		0-4-0ST	OC	P	1438	1916
(D99) 45135 3rd CARABINIER		1Co-Co1DE		Crewe		1961
D335 (40135)		1Co-Co1DE		_(EE	3081	1961
				(VF	D631	1961
(D345) 40145 EAST LANCASHIRE RAILWAY						
		1Co-Co1DE		_(EE	3091	1961
				(VF	D641	1961
(D415) 50015 VALIANT		Co-CoDE		_(EE	3785	1967
				(EEV	D1156	1967
D1041 WESTERN PRINCE		C-CDH		Crewe		1962
(D1501) 47402 GATESHEAD		Co-CoDE		BT	343	1962
2062 (D2062 03062)		0-6-0DM		Don		1959
D2956 (01003)		0-4-0DM		AB	398	1956
D3232 (08164)		0-6-0DE		Dar		1956
(D3594) 08479		0-6-0DE		Hor		1958
(D4174) 08944		0-6-0DE		Dar		1962	a
D5054 (24054) PHIL SOUTHERN		Bo-BoDE		Crewe		1959
D5705 (TDB 968006)		Co-BoDE		MV		1958
(D5823) 31556		A1A-A1ADE		BT	324	1961	a
D6525 (33109) CAPTAIN BILL SMITH RNR						
		Bo-BoDE		BRCW	DEL117	1960
(D6536) 33117		Bo-BoDE		BRCW	DEL128	1960
(D6809) 37109		Co-CoDE		_(EE	3238	1963
				(VF	D763	1963
(D6971) 37418		Co-CoDE		_(EE	3531	1965
				(EEV	D960	1965	c
D7076		B-BDH		BPH	7980	1963
(D8087) 20087		Bo-BoDE		_(EE	2993	1961
				(RSHD	8245	1961
D8233		Bo-BoDE		BTH	1131	1959	b
D9531		0-6-0DH		Sdn		1965

BENZOLE	4wDM		FH	3438	1950
4002	0-6-0DE		HC	D1076	1959
–	4wDM		MR	9009	1948
2	2w-2DH	R/R	TH	V327	1988
M51192	2-2w-2w-2DMR		MetCam		1958
51485	2-2w-2w-2DMR		Cravens		1959
(55001) 01 TDB 975023 THUNDERBIRD 1	2-2w-2w-2DMR		GRC&W		1958
1305 S60130	4w-4wDER		Afd/Elh		1962
M 65451	4w-4wRER		Wolverton		1959

a   property of Mike Darnall, Greater Manchester
b   carries plate 1118/1959
c   currently at Barrow Hill Roundhouse Railway Centre, Derbyshire for restoration

Gauge 1ft 3in

42869	2-6-0	OC	GibbonsCL	1993	a

a   not yet completed

JOHN MARROW, BRYN ENGINEERING, HORWICH, near WIGAN
Other locos here, occasionally, for repairs, etc.

Gauge 4ft 8½in

20/109/89	0-6-0DH		AB	647	1979	+

+   property of Harry Needle Railroad Co Ltd

THE MUSEUM OF SCIENCE & INDUSTRY IN MANCHESTER, LIVERPOOL ROAD, CASTLEFIELD, MANCHESTER

Gauge 5ft 6in   SJ 831978

No.3157	4-4-0	IC	VF	2759	1911

Gauge 4ft 8½in

PLANET	2-2-0	OC	MSI		1992	
"NOVELTY"	2-2-0VBWT	VC	ScienceMus		1929	a
(27001) ARIADNE 1505	Co-CoWE		Gorton	1066	1954	
–	4wBE		_(EE	1378	1944	
			(Bg	3217	1944	
9036	2w-2PMR		Wkm	8196	1958	

Gauge 3ft 6in

2352	4-8-2+2-8-4T	4C	BP	6639	1930

Gauge 3ft 0in

No.3 PENDER	2-4-0T	OC	BP	1255	1873	+

+   loco is sectioned to show moving parts
a   a replica of original loco built 1829 by Braithwaite & Ericsson

PRIVATE SITE, BLACKROD, near BOLTON

Gauge 4ft 8½in   Loco stored for unknown owner

(D3795) 08628	0-6-0DE	Derby		1959

PRIVATE SITE, MANCHESTER

Gauge 2ft 0in

–	4wDM	JF	18892	1931

RED ROSE STEAM SOCIETY, HIGHER GREEN LANE, ASTLEY GREEN COLLIERY MUSEUM, ASTLEY GREEN, TYLDESLEY

Gauge 4ft 8½in   SJ 705998

–	4wDM	RH	244580	1946

Gauge 3ft 0in

No.17		0-6-0DMF	HC	DM781	1953
No.11		0-6-0DMF	HC	DM1058	1957
BEM 401	No.20	0-6-0DMF	HC	DM1120	1958
No.8 9306/103		0-6-0DMF	HC	DM1270	1961
No.5 20/105/624		0-6-0DMF	_(HC	DM1439	1978
			(HE	8821	1978
–		0-6-0DMF	HE	4816	1955

Gauge 2ft 6in

–		4wDHF	_(AB	621	1981
			(HE	8567	1981
–		4wDHF	_(AB	622	1981
			(HE	8568	1981
3		4wBEF	_(EE	2417	1957
			(RSHN	7936	1957
6	PLT No.1/44/19	0-6-0DMF	HC	DM1413	1970
7	1/44/20	0-6-0DMF	HC	DM1414	1970
4	1/44/17	0-6-0DMF	HC	DM1173	1959
5	1/44/18	0-6-0DMF	HC	DM1352	1967
–		0-4-0DMF	HE	3411	1947
1-44-170		0-6-0DMF	HE	8575	1978
1-44-174		0-6-0DMF	HE	8577	1978
NEWTON		4wDH	HE	8975	1979

Gauge 2ft 4in

–	0-6-0DMF	HC	DM970	1957

Gauge 2ft 1in

2 KESTREL	0-6-0DMF	HC	DM647	1954

Gauge 2ft 0in

STACY	0-6-0DMF	HC	DM804	1951

T1		0-6-0DMF	HC	DM840	1954
14	GEORGE	0-6-0DMF	HC	DM929	1955
No.16	WARRIOR	0-6-0DMF	HC	DM933	1956
–		0-4-0DMF	HC	DM1164	1959
R4		0-6-0DMF	_(HC	DM1443	1980
			(HE	8843	1980
3		0-4-0DMF	HE	6048	1961
75	ROGER BOWEN	0-4-0DMF	HE	7375	1973
09	CALVERTON	4wDHF	HE	7519	1977
	MOLE	4wDMF	HE	8834	1978
03	LIONHEART	4wDHF	HE	8909	1979
	SANDY	4wDM	MR	11218	1962
	POINT OF AYR	4wDMF	RH	497547	1963
A19		4wBEF	MV/BP	989	1955

SALFORD CITY COUNCIL,
CADISHEAD BY - PASS, MARTENS ROAD, IRLAM
Gauge 4ft 8½in   SJ 716922

1		0-4-0F	OC	P	2155	1955

JOHN STEIN, THE WILLOW TRAMWAY, 26 WILLOW AVENUE, CHEADLE HULME
Gauge 2ft 0in   SJ 867867

2	TAMAR	4wBE	Red(T)		1980

WIGAN METROPOLITAN BOROUGH COUNCIL, DEPARTMENT OF LEISURE,
HAIGH RAILWAY, HAIGH COUNTRY PARK, COPPERAS LANE, HAIGH, WIGAN
Gauge 1ft 3in   SD 601082

–		0-6-2DH	s/o	AK	41	1992	
15	W.BROGAN B.E.M.	0-6-0DM		G&S		1961	a

a   carries plates G&S 15/1959

MERSEYSIDE

INDUSTRIAL SITES

ALSTOM TRANSPORT LTD, EDGE HILL CARRIAGE SIDINGS, LIVERPOOL
Gauge 4ft 8½in

–		0-4-0DH	HE	9225	1984
		rep	YEC	L173	2001

HARRY NEEDLE RAILROAD CO LTD, P.O.BOX 60, ST.HELENS, WA11 8GD

Registered Office Address. Locomotives are usually maintained at Barrow Hill, Barrow Hill Roundhouse Railway Centre, Derbyshire.The locos are for hire or resale, and are in use or stored at a number of locations.

THE POTTER GROUP, RAIL FREIGHT TERMINAL, WOODWARD ROAD, KNOWSLEY INDUSTRIAL ESTATE, KNOWSLEY

Gauge 4ft 8½in

(D3272)	08202	0-6-0DE	Derby	1956
(D3765)	08598 H 016	0-6-0DE	Derby	1959

PRESERVATION SITES

G. FAIRHURST, PRIVATE LOCATION

Gauge 2ft 0in

–	4wPM	LancTan	1958

KNOWSLEY SAFARI PARK, KNOWSLEY HALL, near PRESCOT

Gauge 1ft 3in   SJ 460936

–	2-6-0DH	s/o	SL	343.2.91	1991

LAKESIDE MINIATURE RAILWAY, MARINE LAKE, SOUTHPORT

Gauge 1ft 3in   SD 331174

No.4468	DUKE OF EDINBURGH	4-6-2DE	s/o	Barlow	1948
No.2510	PRINCE CHARLES	4-6-2DE	s/o	Barlow	1954
GOLDEN JUBILEE 1911-1961		4-6wDE	s/o	Barlow	1963
–		2-6-2DM	s/o	MossAJ	2006
	PRINCESS ANNE	6-6wDH		SL	1971

MERSEYSIDE DEVELOPMENT CORPORATION, junction of DERBY ROAD and BANKFIELDS STREET, BOOTLE, LIVERPOOL

Gauge 4ft 8½in   SJ 339937

–	4wDM	RH	224347	1945

NATIONAL MUSEUM & GALLERIES OF MERSEYSIDE, LARGE OBJECT STORE JUNIPER STREET, BOOTLE   (Closed)

Gauge 4ft 8½in   SJ 349908

M.D.& H.B. No.1	0-6-0ST	OC	AE	1465	1904
(CECIL RAIKES)	0-6-4T	IC	BP	2605	1885
LION	0-4-2	IC	Todd Kitson & Laird		1838

| No.3 | 4w-4wRER | BM | 1892 |

Locos not on public display

NEWTON-LE-WILLOWS COMMUNITY HIGH SCHOOL, NEWTON-LE-WILLOWS
Gauge 2ft 6in   SJ 586964

PARKSIDE	4wDH	HE	8825	1978

SOUTHPORT PIER RAILWAY, SOUTHPORT
Gauge 600mm   SD 335176

2-2w-2w-2+2-2w-2w-2BER	SL/UK LOCO	2005	

NORFOLK

PRESERVATION SITES

BRESSINGHAM STEAM PRESERVATION COMPANY,
BRESSINGHAM LIVE STEAM MUSEUM, BRESSINGHAM HALL, near DISS
Gauge 5ft 0in   TM 080806

1144	2-8-0	OC	TK	571	1948	OOU

Gauge 4ft 8½in

(30102)	GRANVILLE	0-4-0T	OC	9E	406	1893
(32662)	662	0-6-0T	IC	Bton		1875
(41966)	80 THUNDERSLEY	4-4-2T	OC	RS	3367	1909
(62785)	No.490	2-4-0	IC	Str	836	1894
No.251		4-4-2	OC	Don	991	1902
	ROBERT KETT	0-4-0F	OC	AB	1472	1916
6841	WILLIAM FRANCIS	0-4-0+0-4-0T 4C		BP	6841	1937
990	HENRY OAKLEY	4-4-2	OC	Don	769	1898
No.1		0-4-0T	OC	N	4444	1892
No.25		0-4-0ST	OC	N	5087	1896
377	KING HAAKON 7	2-6-0	OC	Nohab	1164	1919
	MILLFIELD	0-4-0CT	OC	RSHN	7070	1942
5865	PEER GYNT	2-10-0	OC	Schichau	4216	1944
1	COUNTY SCHOOL	0-4-0DH		RH	497753	1963

Gauge 2ft 0in

–	4wBEF	HE	9155	1991	

Gauge 1ft 11in — Nursery Line

GWYNEDD	0-4-0STT	OC	HE	316	1883

| No.994 | BILL HARVEY | 0-4-0ST | OC | HE | 994 | 1909 | |
| 7 | "TOBY" | 4wDM | s/o | MR | 22210 | 1964 | |

Gauge 1ft 3in — Waveney Valley Railway

No.1662	ROSENKAVALIER	4-6-2	OC	Krupp	1662	1937	
1663	MÄNNERTREU	4-6-2	OC	Krupp	1663	1937	
4472	FLYING SCOTSMAN	4-6-2	3C	StewartWP		1976	
D6353	JOE BROWN ENGINEER	4w-4wDM		BrownJ		1998	
	IVOR	4wDH		Frenze		1979	
			reb	‡	No.1	1986	

‡ rebuilt by Gray's Engineering, Diss

BURE VALLEY RAILWAY (1991) LTD, THE BROADLAND LINE, AYLSHAM
Gauge 1ft 3in   TG 197265

1	WROXHAM BROAD	2-6-2DM	s/o	Guest		1964	a
	rebuilt as	2-6-4T	OC	Winson		1992	
–		2-8-0	OC	TurnerT/BVR			b
6	BLICKLING HALL	2-6-2	OC	Winson	12	1994	
7	SPITFIRE	2-6-2	OC	Winson	14	1994	
8		2-6-2T	OC	Winson/BVR	16	1998	
9	MARK TIMOTHY	2-6-4T	OC	Winson	20	1999	
			rebuilt	AK	69R	2003	
3	2nd AIR DIVISION USAAF	4w-4wDH		BVR		1989	
4	RUSTY	4wDM		HE	4556	1954	
	rebuilt as	4wDH		EAGIT		1994	
7		4wDM		LB	51989	1960	

a   carries plates G&S 20/1964
b   currently under construction elsewhere

THE LATE G.T. CUSHING, STEAM MUSEUM,
THURSFORD GREEN, THURSFORD, near FAKENHAM
Gauge 1ft 10¾in   R.T.C.   TF 980345

| | CACKLER | 0-4-0ST | OC | HE | 671 | 1898 | OOU |

J. EDWARDS, BELTON, GREAT YARMOUTH
Gauge 1ft 3in

| – | | 2-2w-4BEF | | GB | 6132 | 1966 | |

FENGATE AGRICULTURAL LIGHT RAILWAY, WEETING, near BRANDON
Gauge 4ft 8½in   TL 770885

Visiting locomotives occasionally present.

GREAT EASTERN TRACTION,
HARDINGHAM STATION, HARDINGHAM, near WYMONDHAM
Gauge 4ft 8½in   TG 050055

60		0-6-0DE	BT	804	1978
8	DL 82	0-6-0DH	RR	10272	1967
2		0-4-0DH	_(RSHD	8368	1962
			(WB	3213	1962
No.9	BATMAN	0-4-0DE	RH	512842	1965

HILL FAMILY, CAISTER CASTLE, near YARMOUTH
Gauge 4ft 8½in   TG 504123

42	RHONDDA	0-6-0ST	IC	MW	2010	1921

R.& A. JENKINS, FRANSHAM STATION, GREAT FRANSHAM, near SWAFFHAM
Gauge 4ft 8½in   TF 888135

–	4wDM	RH	398611	1956

Gauge 2ft 0in

–	4wDM	RH	422573	1958

M. MAYES
Gauge 4ft 8½in

–		0-4-0VBT	OC	Cockerill	2525	1907
	WISSINGTON	0-6-0ST	IC	HC	1700	1938
–		0-4-0ST	OC	RSHN	7818	1954

Gauge 2ft 0in

3010	0-6-0T	OC	KS	3010	1916

MID-NORFOLK RAILWAY SOCIETY, DEREHAM STATION
Gauge 4ft 8½in   TF 995128

(D419)	50019	RAMILLIES		Co-CoDE	_(EE	3789	1967
					(EEV	D1160	1967
(D1933	47255)	47596		Co-CoDE	BT	695	1966
(D3798)	08631	EAGLE		0-6-0DE	Derby		1959
(D5557)	31538			A1A-A1A DE	BT	156	1959
(D5662)	31235			A1A-A1A DE	BT	262	1960
(D5695)	31530			A1A-A1A DE	BT	296	1961
(E6022	73116)	73210	SELHURST	Bo-BoDE/RE	_(EE	3584	1966
					(EEV	E354	1966
(D8069)	20069			Bo-BoDE	_(EE	2975	1961
					(RSHD	8227	1961
	56040			Co-CoDE	Don		1977
51226				2-2w-2w-2DMR	MetCam		1958

51434 MATTHEW SMITH 1974-2002

		2-2w-2w-2DMR	MetCam		1959
51499		2-2w-2w-2DMR	MetCam		1959
51503		2-2w-2w-2DMR	MetCam		1959
55009	109	2-2w-2w-2DMR	GRC&W		1958
68004	931 094 (9004)	4w-4wRE/BER	Afd/Elh		1960
960225	GEORGE T.RASEY	2w-2PMR	Wkm	1308	1933

NORTH NORFOLK RAILWAY plc, THE STATION, SHERINGHAM

Locos are kept at :-
Sheringham TG 156430
Weybourne TG 118419

Gauge 4ft 8½in

34081	92 SQUADRON	4-6-2	3C	Bton		1948	
61572		4-6-0	IC	BP	6488	1928	
		reb		MaLoWa		1994	
65033		0-6-0	IC	Ghd		1889	
65462	(564)	0-6-0	IC	Str		1912	
68088	(No.985)	0-4-0T	IC	Dar	(1205)	1923	
69621	(7999) A.J. HILL	0-6-2T	IC	Str		1924	
90775		2-10-0	OC	NBH	25438	1943	
1982	RING HAW	0-6-0ST	IC	HE	1982	1940	
(D1886)	47367	Co-CoDE		BT	648	1965	
(D2051)		0-6-0DM		Don		1959	
D2063	(03063)	0-6-0DM		Don		1959	
(D2280)	FORD No.02	0-6-0DM		_(RSHD	8098	1960	
				(DC	2657	1960	
D3935	(08767)	0-6-0DE		Hor		1961	
D3940	(08772)	0-6-0DE		Derby		1960	
D5207	(25057)	Bo-BoDE		Derby		1963	
(D5631)	31207	A1A-A1A DE		BT	231	1960	
D6732	(37032) MIRAGE	Co-CoDE		_(EE	2895	1961	
				(VF	D611	1961	
12131		0-6-0DE		Dar		1952	
51228		2-2w-2w-2DMR		MetCam		1958	
E79960		2w-2DMR		WMD	1265	1958	
98801		4wDHR		Kershaw45.121A		1992	
RDB 975874	LEV 1	4wDMR		Leyland		1978	
Q454 JTT		4wDM	R/R	Unimog			
				416141 10 027869			
M.& G.N. No.1		2w-2PMR		Wkm	1521	1934	Dsm
No.2		2w-2PMR		Wkm	1522	1934	Dsm

ALAN POWELL, NORWICH
Gauge 1ft 3in

–		2-4wPM	s/o	Powell	1997

FRED ROUT, BROOMHILL FARM, LEYS LANE, BUCKENHAM, near ATTLEBOROUGH
Gauge 4ft 8½in

No.21		0-6-0DM		HC	D707	1950

STRUMPSHAW HALL STEAM MUSEUM, STRUMPSHAW HALL, near ACLE
Gauge 1ft 11½in   TG 345065

No.6	GINETTE MARIE	0-4-0WT	OC	Jung	7509	1937
No.1		4wDM	s/o	MR	7192	1937

Gauge 1ft 3in

2	CAGNEY	4-4-0	OC	McGarigle		1902

DAVID TURNER, WYMONDHAM STATION
Gauge 4ft 8½in   TG 114009

11103	0-4-0DM	_(VF	D297	1956
		(DC	2583	1956

WHITWELL & REEPHAM STATION
Gauge 4ft 8½in   www.whitwellstation.com   TG 092216

–	4wDH	BD	3733	1977

YAXHAM LIGHT RAILWAYS, YAXHAM STATION YARD, YAXHAM, near DEREHAM
Gauge 1ft 11½in   TG 003102

No.1		0-4-0VBT	VCG	Potter		1970
"No.16"	ELIN	0-4-0ST	OC	HE	705	1899
	KIDBROOKE	0-4-0ST	OC	WB	2043	1917
No.2	RUSTY	4wDM		L	32801	1948
No.3	PEST	4wDM		L	40011	1954
No.4	GOOFY	4wDM		OK	(6501?)	c1936
No.6	LOD/758097 COLONEL	4wDM		RH	202967	1940
No.7		4wDM		RH	170369	1934
No.10	OUSEL	4wDM		MR	7153	1937
No.13		4wDM		MR	7474	1940
No.14	LOD 758375 ARMY 25	4wDM		RH	222100	1943
No.18	DOE 3982	4wDM		FH	3982	1962
No.19	PENLEE	4wDM		HE	2666	1942

NORTHAMPTONSHIRE

INDUSTRIAL SITES

GEISMAR (UK) LTD,
SALTHOUSE ROAD, BRACKMILLS INDUSTRIAL ESTATE, NORTHAMPTON
Railcars under construction or repair are usually present.　　　　　　　SP 781858

GEO-TEK, FARADAY CLOSE, DAVENTRY
Locomotives under construction are usually present.　　　　　　　SP 564368

Parts of frames of 2ft gauge 4wDHF HE 8518-AB 632 / 1977 may still be here; they were utilised in a wheel press.

J. REDDEN (SCRAP MERCHANTS), FINEDON ROAD, WELLINGBOROUGH
Gauge　4ft 8½in　　　　　　　　　　　　　　　　　　SP 906695

L8	4wDM	RH	393303	1956	Dsm

SALCEY ABORCARE & FORESTRY, FOREST ROAD, HANSLOPE
Road/Rail vehicles are present in this yard between contracts.

Gauge　4ft 8½in

B636 TEC	4wDM	R/R	Unimog	114455
J646 EAT	4wDM	R/R	Unimog	166990
N744 DVV	4wDM	R/R	Unimog	184641

SIEMENS TRANSPORT, KINGS HEATH TRAINCARE FACILITY, NORTHAMPTON
Gauge　4ft 8½in　　　　　　　　　　　　　　　　　　SP 745612

–	4wBE	CPM	1731.01	2005

PRESERVATION SITES

BILLING AQUADROME LTD, CROW LANE, BILLING, near NORTHAMPTON
Gauge　2ft 0in　　　　　　　　　　　　　　　　　　SP 808615

–	4wDH	s/o	AK	14	1984

CORBY DISTRICT COUNCIL,
EAST CARLTON COUNTRYSIDE PARK AND STEEL HERITAGE CENTRE, CORBY
Gauge　4ft 8½in　　　　　　　　　　　　　　　　　　SP 834893

–	0-6-0ST	OC	HL	3827	1934

HIGHAM FERRERS LOCOMOTIVES
Site near Rushden
Gauge 1000mm

| ND 3647 | | 4wDM | | MR | 22144 | 1962 | + |

+   loco at private site

Gauge 600mm

| 5662 | | 0-4-0WTT | OC | OK | 5662 | 1912 |

Site near Wellingborough
Gauge 3ft 0in

| 18 | | 4wBE | | GB | 1570 | 1938 |
| – | | 4wDMF | | RH | 433388 | 1959 |

IRCHESTER NARROW GAUGE RAILWAY TRUST, IRCHESTER COUNTRY PARK, IRCHESTER
Gauge 1000mm   SP 906660

(4)	CAMBRAI	0-6-0T	OC	Corpet	493	1888
No.85	1		0-6-0ST	OC	P	1870	1934
(No.86 | 2)		0-6-0ST	OC	P	1871	1934
(No.87	3	89-12) 8315/87	0-6-0ST	OC	P	2029	1942

	9	THE ROCK	0-4-0DM		HE	2419	1941
ND 3645	10	MILFORD	4wDM		RH	211679	1941
(ED 10)	11						
		EDWARD CHARLES HAMPTON	4wDM		RH	411322	1958

Gauge 3ft 0in

LR 3084	14		4wDM		MR	3797	1926
				a rebuild of	MR	1363	1918
	12		0-6-0DM		RH	281290	1949	a
	5		4wDMF		RH	338439	1953

a   currently on loan to R.M.S. Locotec Ltd, Wakefield, West Yorkshire

NORTHAMPTON STEAM RAILWAY, PITSFORD & BRAMPTON STATION, CHAPEL BRAMPTON, NORTHAMPTON
Gauge 4ft 8½in   SP 735667, 736664

3862		2-8-0	OC	Sdn		1942
5374	VANGUARD	0-6-0T	OC	Chrz	5374	1959
5967	BICKMARSH HALL	4-6-0	OC	Sdn		1937
45	COLWYN	0-6-0ST	IC	K	5470	1933
	WESTMINSTER	0-6-0ST	OC	P	1378	1914
–		0-4-0ST	OC	P	2104	1950	+

| (D67) | 45118 | | | | | |
| | THE ROYAL ARTILLERYMAN | 1Co-Co1DE | | Crewe | | 1962 |

(D1855) 47205	Co-CoDE	Crewe		1965
D5401 (27056)	Bo-BoDE	BRCW	DEL244	1962
(D5821) 31289 PHOENIX	A1A-A1ADE	BT	322	1961
(D6823 37123) 37679	Co-CoDE	_(EE	3268	1963
		(RSHD	8383	1963
No.21	0-4-0DM	JF	4210094	1954
rebuilt as	0-4-0DH	JF		1966
(No.1 MERRY TOM)	4wDM	RH	275886	1949
(764 SIR GILES ISHAM)	0-4-0DM	RH	319286	1953
No.53 SIR ALFRED WOOD	0-6-0DM	RH	319294	1953
–	0-4-0DH	TH	146C	1964
a rebuild of	0-4-0DM	JF	4210018	1950 a
51359 L703	2-2w-2w-2DMR	PSteel		1960

+   actually built 1948 but plates are dated as shown
a   TH 146C incorporates frame and wheels (only) of the JF loco

NORTHAMPTONSHIRE IRONSTONE RAILWAY TRUST LTD, HUNSBURY HILL INDUSTRIAL MUSEUM

Gauge 4ft 8½in   SP 735584

89-94	TRYM	0-4-0ST	OC	HE	287	1883
9365 89-17	BELVEDERE	4wVBT	VCG	S	9365	1946
	MUSKETEER	4wVBT	VCG	S	9369	1946
–		0-4-0ST	OC	WB	2565	1936
–		4wDH		FH	3967	1961
–		0-4-0DM		HC	D697	1950
No.16		0-4-0DM		HE	2087	1940
	CHARLIE WAKE	0-4-0DM		JF	4220001	1959
No.46	MUFFIN	4wDM		RH	242868	1946
–		4wDM		RH	321734	1952 a Dsm
4002 S 13004 S		4w-4wRER		Elh		1949
5176 S14351		4w-4wRER		Lancing/Elh		1951
5176 S14352		4w-4wRER		Lancing/Elh		1951

a   frame in use as a wagon

PRIVATE OWNER, near NORTHAMPTON

Gauge 3ft 0in

–	4wDM	RH	418764	1957

RUSHDEN HISTORICAL TRANSPORT SOCIETY, THE OLD STATION, STATION APPROACH, RECTORY ROAD, RUSHDEN

Gauge 4ft 8½in   SP 957672

	EDMUNDSONS	0-4-0ST	OC	AB	2168	1943 a
–		0-4-0ST	OC	AB	2323	1952
001	"CHERWELL"	0-6-0ST	OC	WB	2654	1942
(D5630) 31206		A1A-A1A DE		BT	230	1960

WD 70048	0-4-0DM	AB	363	1942
LES FORSTER	4wDH	S	10159	1963

a   currently at Tyseley Locomotive Works, West Midlands for overhaul.

WICKSTEED PARK LAKESIDE RAILWAY,
WICKSTEED LEISURE PARK, KETTERING
Gauge 2ft 0in   SP 883770

2042	LADY OF THE LAKE	0-4-0DM	s/o	Bg	2042	1931
2043	KING ARTHUR	0-4-0DH	s/o	Bg	2043	1931
	CHEYENNE	4wDM	s/o	MR	22224	1966

J. WOOLMER, 15 BAKERS LANE, WOODFORD, KETTERING
Gauge 2ft 0in   SP 969769

89-18	4wPM	L	14006	1940
–	4wDM	L	36743	1951

NORTHUMBERLAND

OUR DEFINITION OF "NORTHUMBERLAND" INCLUDES THOSE LOCATIONS WHICH WERE SITUATED WITHIN THAT PART, OF THE FORMER COUNTY OF TYNE & WEAR, WHICH IS NORTH OF THE RIVER TYNE AND NOW CONSISTS OF A NUMBER OF UNITARY AUTHORITIES.

INDUSTRIAL SITES

ALCAN SMELTER & POWER, LYNEMOUTH
Gauge 4ft 8½in   NZ 302903

		2-2wPMR	BanceSTD2NPAC/057/098 1999
–			

DEPARTMENT OF THE ENVIRONMENT, TRANSPORT AND THE REGIONS, REDESDALE RANGES MILITARY TARGET RAILWAY
Gauge 2ft 6in   NT 827016

–	2w-2PM	Wkm	3245	1943
–	2w-2PM	Wkm	11686	1990
–	2w-2PM	Wkm	11687	1990
–	2w-2PM	Wkm	11688	1990
–	2w-2PM	Wkm	11689	1990

IAN STOREY ENGINEERING LTD, HEPSCOTT, near MORPETH
Gauge 4ft 8½in

44767	GEORGE STEPHENSON	4-6-0	OC	Crewe		1947	
76084		2-6-0	OC	Hor		1957	
(DB 965053)		2w-2PMR		Wkm	7576	1956	a
DB 965071		2w-2PMR		Wkm	7586	1957	a

a   property of the Eden Valley Railway Trust, Warcop, Cumbria

NEXUS, TYNE WEAR METRO, SOUTH GOSFORTH CAR SHEDS, NEWCASTLE-UPON-TYNE
Gauge 4ft 8½in   NZ 250686

BL1		4wBE/WE		HE	9174	1989
BL2		4wBE/WE		HE	9175	1989
BL3		4wBE/WE		HE	9176	1989
	T597 OKK	4wDM	R/R	SRS		1999
	D640 JWW	4wDM	R/R	Unimog	126899	1987
	F171 DUA	4wDM	R/R	Unimog WDB4241261-W140729		1988
	NA 52 JNN	4wDM	R/R	Unimog	200083	
	NK 54 SDY	4wDM	R/R	Unimog		
	NK 54 SDZ	4wDM	R/R	Unimog		
	NR 05 VRE	4wDM	R/R	Mercedes/		c2005

UK COAL MINING LTD
Headquarters: Harworth Park, Blyth Road, Harworth, Nottinghamshire DN11 8DB
Widdrington Disposal Point, Widdrington
(operated by Johnson's (Chopwell) Ltd)

Gauge 4ft 8½in — Surface NZ 237957

(01564) 12088		0-6-0DE	Derby	1951	+

+   on hire from Harry Needle Railroad Co Ltd, Merseyside

PRESERVATION SITES

ALLENHEADS HERITAGE CENTRE, ALLENHEADS
Gauge 2ft 0in   NY 859453

–	0-4-0BE	WR	

ALN VALLEY RAILWAY, LONGHOUGHTON GOODS YARD, ALNWICK
Gauge 4ft 8½in   NU 240150

–	4wDM	RH	265617	1948	
L2 312989	0-4-0DE	RH	312989	1952	
68030 70/008 (DB965369)	2w-2DMR	Matisa	D8.005	1971	
		reb Kilmarnock		1979	
(DX 68805)	4wDMR	Perm	006	1986	
(DX 68806)	4wDMR	Perm	007	1986	
(DX 68702)	4wDMR	Perm	007	1986	
(68706) 98706	4wDHR	Perm	010	1986	
(98707)	4wDHR	Perm	012	1986	

M. FAIRNINGTON, AGRICULTURAL ENGINEERS, UNIT A, BERWICK ROAD, WOOLER
Gauge 4ft 8½in   NT 995287

–	0-6-0T	OC	HC	1243	1917
PENICUIK	0-4-0ST	OC	HL	3799	1935
DB 965952	2w-2PMR		Wkm	10648	1972
PWM 2807 (B170W)	2w-2PMR		Wkm	4985	1949

HEATHERSLAW LIGHT RAILWAY CO LTD, HEATHERSLAW MILL, CORNHILL-ON-TWEED
Gauge 1ft 3in   NT 933385

THE LADY AUGUSTA	0-4-2	OC	TaylorB	1989
CLIVE	4w-4wDH		SmithN	2000

NORTH TYNESIDE COUNCIL, TYNE & WEAR JOINT MUSEUMS SERVICE
STEPHENSON RAILWAY MUSEUM, MIDDLE ENGINE LANE, near CHIRTON
Museum locos work services for the North Tyneside Steam Railway

Gauge 4ft 8½in   NZ 323693

A.No.5	0-6-0PT	IC	K	2509	1883
1313	4-6-0	OC	Motala	586	1917
ASHINGTON No.5					
JACKIE MILBURN 1924-1988	0-6-0ST	OC	P	1970	1939
"BILLY"	0-4-0	VC	RS	A4	1826
No.1 TED GARRETT JP,DL,MP	0-6-0T	OC	RSHN	7683	1951
401 THOMAS BURT M.P. 1837-1922					
	0-6-0ST	OC	WB	2994	1950
(D2078 03078)	0-6-0DM		Don		1959
3267	4w-4wRER		York		1904
10	0-6-0DM		Consett		1958
E4	Bo-BoWE/BE		Siemens	457	1909

NORTHUMBRIAN RAIL LTD, c/o M. FAIRNINGTON, AGRICULTURAL ENGINEERS, UNIT A,
BERWICK ROAD,WOOLER

Gauge 4ft 8½in   www.northumbria-rail.co.uk   NT 995287

50 (323.674-2) SIMONSIDE	4wDH	Gmd	4991	1957
51 (323.539-7) CHEVIOT	4wDH	Gmd	4861	1955
801	Bo-BoDE	Alco	77120	1950
424839 NORTHUMBRIA	0-4-0DE	RH	424839	1959

WOODHORN COLLIERY MUSEUM, ASHINGTON

Gauge 2ft 0in   NZ 287884

EXMOOR RANGER	4wDM	HE	6348	1975
–	4wDH	Schöma	5240	1991

NOTTINGHAMSHIRE

INDUSTRIAL SITES

HARSCO TRACK TECHNOLOGIES,
UNIT 1 CHEWTON STREET, EASTWOOD, NOTTINGHAM
Road/Rail vehicles under construction, repair, or for hire, are usually present.

Gauge 4ft 8½in   SK 475462

F511 LRR	4wDM	R/R	Perm	1989
G276 NAU	4wDM	R/R	Perm	1989
L975 MNU	4wDM	R/R	Perm	1990

M491 PTV	4wDM	R/R	Perm	1994
N517 YAU	4wDM	R/R	Perm	1996
N798 XRA	4wDM	R/R	Perm	1996
P161 FAU	4wDM	R/R	Perm	1997
P758 GNN	4wDM	R/R	Perm	1998
P580 JVC	4wDM	R/R	Perm/Landrover	1998
R913 MAU	4wDM	R/R	Perm	1998
R447 XRA	4wDM	R/R	Perm	1998
S292 NAU	4wDM	R/R	Perm	1999

NOTTINGHAM EXPRESS TRANSIT, WILKINSON STREET DEPOT, NOTTINGHAM
Gauge 4ft 8½in   SK 553423

–		4wBE		Niteq	B183	2003
FG52WCC		4wDM	R/R	Unimog	199635	

SIMS METAL UK, HARRIMANS LANE, DUNKIRK, NOTTINGHAM
Locomotives for scrap are occasionally present   SK 549337
Gauge 4ft 8½in

–		0-6-0DH		S	10140	1962

RICHARD C. TUXFORD EXPORT LTD, HOLLINWOOD LANE, CALVERTON
Locomotives in transit or for resale occasionally present.   SK 604500

UK COAL MINING LTD
Headquarters: Harworth Park, Blyth Road, Harworth, Nottinghamshire DN11 8DB

Harworth Colliery, Bircotes
Production ceased. Mothballed from 9/2006
Gauge 2ft 6in — Underground   SK 623903

–		4wDHF		CE	B1530	1977
No.1		4wBEF		CE	B1831A	1979
			reb	CE	B3290	1986
No.2		4wBEF		CE	B1831B	1979
–		4wBEF		CE	B3155A	1984
–		4wBEF		CE	B3157A	1984
			reb	CE	B3570	1989
–		4wBEF		CE	B3157B	1984
			reb	CE	B3532	1988
–		4wBEF		CE	B3249B	1986
11B	297/154	4w-4wBEF		CE	B3322A	1987
10B	297/029	4w-4wBEF		CE	B3322B	1987
12B		4w-4wBEF		CE	B3322C	1987
–		4wBEF		CE	B3410	1988
–		4wBEF		CE	B3411	1988
14B	297/305	4w-4wBEF		CE	B3502A	1989
15B	297/315	4w-4wBEF		CE	B3502B	1989
–		4wBEF		CE	B3634A	1990
–		4wBEF		CE	B3634B	1990

–		4w-4wBEF	CE		B3689B	1991	
–		4w-4wBEF	CE		B3689C	1991	
–		4w-4wBEF	CE		B3800A	1991	
–		4w-4wBEF	CE		B3800B	1991	
–		4w-4wBEF	CE		B3800C	1991	
PL 1		4wBEF	CE				
PL 2		4wBEF	CE				
–		4wBEF	_(EE		2083	1955	
			(Bg		3435	1955	
–		4wBEF	_(EE		2301	1956	
			(Bg		3437	1956	
–		4wBEF	_(EE		2521	1957	
			(RSHN		7963	1957	
–		4wBEF	_(EE				a
			(				
–		4wBEF	_(EE				a
			(				
15/20		4wBEF	EEV		3768	1966	
No.1	820/32099	0-6-0DMF	HC		DM724	1949	
No.2	820/32100	0-6-0DMF	HC		DM725	1949	
No.3	820/32101	0-6-0DMF	HC		DM726	1949	
No.4	820/32102 PHILLIP	0-6-0DMF	HC		DM727	1949	
No.5	820/32103	0-6-0DMF	HC		DM729	1949	
No.6	820/34204	0-6-0DMF	HC		DM1309	1963	
–		0-6-0DMF	_(HE		8848	1981	
			(HC		DM1448	1981	
–		0-6-0DMF	_(HE		8849	1982	
			(HC		DM1449	1982	
–		0-6-0DMF	_(HE		8850	1982	
			(HC		DM1450	1982	

a   one may be EE 2522-RSHN 7964 / 1958

Harworth Equipment Holding Centre, Harworth Park, Blyth Road, Harworth

Locos stored on the surface pending further use elsewhere or disposal.

Gauge 2ft 6in   SK 623903

1	4wBEF		CE	B2935A	1982	
		reb	CE	B3118C	1983	
2	4wBEF		CE	B2935B	1982	
		reb	CE	B3118B	1983	
3	4wBEF		CE	B3433	1988	
4	4wEF		CE	B3439	1988	
5	4wBEF		CE	B3193A	1985	
		reb	CE	B3555	1989	
7	4wBEF		CE	B3635	1990	
(4)?	4w-4wBEF		CE			
5	4w-4wBEF		CE	B3332A	1987	Dsm
P7	4wBEF		CE			
–	4wBEF		CE	B3340	1987	
31	4w-4wBEF		CE	B3467	1988	
32	4w-4wBEF		CE	B3850	1992	

(33)?		4w-4wBEF	CE	(B3198C	1985)?	
(34)?		4w-4wBEF	CE	(B3707	1991)?	
Gauge 2ft 4in						
–		4wBEF	CE	B3501	1990	

Thoresby Colliery, Edwinstowe

Gauge 3ft 0in — Underground   SK 636676

E2	74832	4wBEF		CE	B1504A	1977
			reb	CE	B3156	1984
E3	74835	4wBEF		CE	B1504B	1977
			reb	CE	B3239	1985
E1	74813	4wBEF		CE	B1504C	1977
			reb	CE	B3102	1984
E5	74485	4wBEF		CE	B1843A	1979
E6	73431	4wBEF		CE	B1850A	1979
E7	73433	4wBEF		CE	B1850B	1979
E10	76123	4wBEF		CE	B2273A	1981
E11	76138	4wBEF		CE	B2273B	1981
E9	76158	4wBEF		CE	B2274A	1981
E8	76159	4wBEF		CE	B2274B	1981
E12	71365	4wBEF		CE	B2986A	1982
E14	71364	4wBEF		CE	B2986B	1982
E16	72434	4wBEF		CE	B3045A	1983
E15	72430	4wBEF		CE	B3045B	1983
No.2	70331	4w-4wBEF		CE	B3224B	1985
No.3	70332	4w-4wBEF		CE	B3224C	1985
–		4w-4wBEF		CE	B3352A	1987
			reb	CE	B3478	1988
No.4	70724	4w-4wBEF		CE	B3352B	1987
			reb	CE	B3565	1989
–		4w-4wBEF		CE	B3477A	1989
BB7		4w-4wBEF		CE	B3477B	1989
			reb	CE	B4355	2001
–		4w-4wBEF		CE	B3591	1990
			reb	CE	B4423	2006
A1	72920	4wBERF		TH	SE107	1979
A2	72427	4w-4wBERF		TH	SE117	1983

Welbeck Colliery, Welbeck Colliery Village

Gauge 2ft 4in — Underground   SK 582704

No.2B	87830		4wBEF	CE	B2205A	1980
No.3B	87829		4wBEF	CE	B2205B	1980
No.4B	84800	4	4wBEF	CE	B3034A	1983
No.5B	84801	5	4wBEF	CE	B3034B	1983
–			4wBEF	CE	B3161	1985
–			4wBEF	CE	B3234	1985
No.6			4w-4wBEF	CE	B3246	1986
–			4wDHF	CE	B3270A	1986
–			4wDHF	CE	B3270B	1986
–			4wDHF	CE	B3270C	1986

–		4wDHF	CE	B3270D	1986	
–		4wDHF	CE	B3270E	1986	
No.10		4w-4wBEF	CE	B3363A	1987	
No.11		4w-4wBEF	CE	B3363B	1987	
–		4w-4wBEF	CE	B3445	1988	
No.2	820/45106	0-4-0DMF	HC	DM771	1950	
No.4	820/45105	0-4-0DMF	HC	DM772	1950	
No.1	820/45104	0-4-0DMF	HC	DM773	1950	
No.5	820/24691	0-6-0DMF	HC	DM971	1957	
No.3	820/24692	0-6-0DMF	HC	DM1011	1957	
No.4	820/55033 No.8	0-6-0DMF	HC	DM1287	1962	
No.7	820/55489 No.9	0-6-0DMF	HC	DM1332	1964	

PRESERVATION SITES

GREAT CENTRAL RAILWAY (NOTTINGHAM) LTD
NOTTINGHAM TRANSPORT HERITAGE CENTRE, MERE WAY, RUDDINGTON, NOTTINGHAM
Gauge 4ft 8½in   SK 575322

411.388		2-8-0	OC	Alco	70284	1942	
–		2-8-0	OC	Alco	(70610	1943?)	Dsm
	"JULIA"	0-6-0ST	IC	HC	1682	1937	
	(ABERNANT)	0-6-0ST	IC	MW	1762	1910	
No.15	8310/41	0-6-0ST	IC	MW	2009	1921	
5	ABERNANT	0-6-0ST	IC	MW	2015	1921	
56		0-6-0ST	IC	RSHN	7667	1950	
(D1643	47059 47631) 47765	Co-CoDE		Crewe		1964	
(D1994)	47292	Co-CoDE		Crewe		1966	
D2959		0-4-0DE		RH	449754	1961	
(D3180	08114) 13180	0-6-0DE		Derby		1955	
(E6016)	73110	Bo-BoDE/RE		_(EE	3578	1965	
				(EEV	E348	1965	
(D6709)	37340	Co-CoDE		_(EE	2872	1960	
				(VF	D588	1960	
D7629	(25279)	Bo-BoDE		BP	8039	1965	
(D8007)	20007	Bo-BoDE		_(EE	2354	1957	
				(VF	D382	1957	
D8048	(20048)	Bo-BoDE		_(EE	2770	1959	
				(VF	D495	1959	
D8154	(20154)	Bo-BoDE		_(EE	3625	1966	
				(EEV	D1024	1966	
56097		Co-CoDE		Don		1981	
	MORRIS	4wDM		MR	2026	1920	a
No. 2	MARBLAEGIS	4wDM		RH	236364	1946	
	QWAG	4wDM		RH	371971	1954	
(423)	CROMWELL	0-6-0DH		RH	459518	1961	
W51138	T003	2-2w-2w-2DMR		DerbyC&W		1958	
W51151	T004	2-2w-2w-2DMR		DerbyC&W		1958	

52060	977813	2-2w-2w-2DMR	DerbyC&W		1960
M53645		2-2w-2w-2DMR	DerbyC&W		1958
(53926	977814)	2-2w-2w-2DMR	DerbyC&W		1959
68800		4wDHR	Perm	001	1985
DX68807		4wDMR	Perm	008	1986

a   plate reads MR 2028

SHERWOOD FOREST RAILWAY,
SHERWOOD FOREST FARM PARK, EDWINSTOWE, MANSFIELD
Gauge 1ft 3in   SK 586655

No.1 SMOKEY JOE	0-4-0STT	OC	HardyK	01	1991	
No.2 PET	0-4-0ST	OC	HardyK	02	1998	
E3 ANNE	4wBE		HardyK	E3	1993	
1	2-2wPM	s/o	Rosewall		1947	
		reb	Vanstone		1980	OOU
–	4wPM		SherwoodForest		2005	

SUNDOWN ADVENTURELAND, RAMPTON, near RETFORD
Gauge 1ft 6in   SK 793792

–	2-4-0RE	s/o	SL	546.4.93	1993

NEIL WHITE, PRIVATE LOCATION
Gauge 4ft 8½in

1677	2-2w-2w-2RER	MetCam	c1960

OXFORDSHIRE

INDUSTRIAL SITES

FOUNTAIN FORESTRY LTD, P.O.BOX 307, MALTHOUSE WALK, BANBURY
Gauge 4ft 8½in

P213 PMA	4wDM	R/R	Unimog
			WDB-4271122-W187252
P399 ERP	4wDM	R/R	Unimog
			WDB-4271172-W185674

MINISTRY OF DEFENCE, DEFENCE DISTRIBUTION AND AGENCY,
BICESTER MILITARY RAILWAY
See Section 6 for full details.

PRESERVATION SITES

PETER ALEXANDER, OXFORD AREA
Gauge 4ft 8½in

| B55W | PWM 4316 | | 2w-2PMR | | Wkm | 7519 | 1956 | |

THE BEECHES LIGHT RAILWAY
A private railway, not open to the public.

Gauge 2ft 0in

19		0-4-0ST+WT	OC	SS	3518	1888	
	COL. FREDERICK WYLIE	4wDH		HE	9349	1994	
			reb	AK		2004	
	MAJOR GERALD SCOTT	4wDM		MR	21619	1957	
	WING CDR BERTIE BILLINGS						
		4wDM		RH	200512	1940	
37		2w-2-2-2wRE		EEDK	760	1930	
44		2w-2-2-2wRE		EEDK	812	1930	
–		2-2wPMR		Statfold		2008	
–		2w-2PMR		Wkm	1548	1934	DsmT

BLENHEIM PALACE RAILWAY, WOODSTOCK
Gauge 1ft 3in   SP 444163

| | SIR WINSTON CHURCHILL | 0-6-2DH | s/o | AK | 39 | 1992 | |
| | – | 4-6wDM | | Guest | | 1960 | |

CHINNOR & PRINCES RISBOROUGH RAILWAY ASSOCIATION, CHINNOR CEMENT WORKS, CHINNOR
Gauge 4ft 8½in   SP 756002

9682		0-6-0PT	IC	Sdn		1949	
	THE BLUE CIRCLE	2-2-0WT	G	AP	9449	1926	
13018	(D3018 08011)	0-6-0DE		Derby		1953	
D5581	(31163)	A1A-A1ADE		BT	181	1960	
(D6816)	37116	Co-CoDE		_(EE	3245	1963	
				(VF	D770	1963	
(D6919)	37219 SHIRLEY ANN SMITH						
		Co-CoDE		_(EE	3405	1963	
				(EEV	D863	1963	
D8568		Bo-BoDE		CE	4365U/69	1963	
459515	IRIS	0-6-0DH		RH	459515	1961	
W55023	L123	2-2w-2w-2DMR		PSteel		1960	
105701		2w-2PMR		Bance	AL2025	1995	
1		2w-2PMR		Wkm	7090	1955	

CHOLSEY & WALLINGFORD RAILWAY, ST.JOHNS ROAD, WALLINGFORD
Gauge 4ft 8½in   SU 600891

701	SPITFIRE		0-4-0ST	OC	AB	1964	1929	
–			0-4-0ST	OC	P	1555	1920	
–			0-4-0F	OC	WB	2473	1932	
(08022	D3030)	LION	0-6-0DE		Derby		1953	
(08060	D3074)	UNICORN	0-6-0DE		Dar		1953	
(D3190)	(08123)							
	"GEORGE MASON"		0-6-0DE		Derby		1955	
803			Bo-BoDE		Alco	77777	1950	
	"CARPENTER"		0-4-0DM		FH	3270	1948	
T003	CEPS 68097		4wDHR		Perm	T003	1988	
No.1	WILLY SKUNK		2w-2PMR		Wkm	8774	1960	

COTSWOLD WILD LIFE PARK, BURFORD
Gauge 2ft 0in   SP 237084

No.3		0-4-0DH	s/o	AK	17	1985	
No.4	BELLA	0-4-0DH	s/o	AK	68	2003	

GREAT WESTERN SOCIETY, DIDCOT RAILWAY CENTRE
Gauge 7ft 0¼in   SU 524906

	FIRE FLY	2-2-2	IC	FFP		1989	

Gauge 4ft 8½in

1338		0-4-0ST	OC	K	3799	1898	
1340	TROJAN	0-4-0ST	OC	AE	1386	1897	
1363		0-6-0ST	OC	Sdn	2377	1910	
(1466)	4866	0-4-2T	IC	Sdn		1936	
3650		0-6-0PT	IC	Sdn		1939	
3738		0-6-0PT	IC	Sdn		1937	
3822		2-8-0	OC	Sdn		1940	
4079	PENDENNIS CASTLE	4-6-0	4C	Sdn		1924	
4144		2-6-2T	OC	Sdn		1946	
2999	LADY OF LEGEND	(4942	MAINDY HALL)				
		4-6-0	OC	Sdn		1929	
		reb		Riley/GWS		2006	
5051	EARL BATHURST	4-6-0	4C	Sdn		1936	
5322		2-6-0	OC	Sdn		1917	
5572		2-6-2T	OC	Sdn		1929	
5900	HINDERTON HALL	4-6-0	OC	Sdn		1931	
6023	KING EDWARD II	4-6-0	4C	Sdn		1930	
6106		2-6-2T	OC	Sdn		1931	
6697		0-6-2T	IC	AW	985	1928	
6998	BURTON AGNES HALL	4-6-0	OC	Sdn		1949	
7202		2-8-2T	OC	Sdn		1934	
7808	COOKHAM MANOR	4-6-0	OC	Sdn		1938	
7927	WILLINGTON HALL	4-6-0	OC	Sdn		1950	
No.5		0-4-0WT	OC	GE		1857	

No.1	BONNIE PRINCE CHARLIE	0-4-0ST	OC	RSHN	7544	1949	
(D3771	08604) 604 PHANTOM	0-6-0DE		Derby		1959	
(W22W)	No.22	Bo-BoDMR		Sdn		1940	
(5)		0-4-0PM		DerbyC&W		1960	
DL26		0-6-0DM		HE	5238	1962	
(A 21 W)		2w-2PMR		Wkm	6892	1954	DsmT
(B 37 W	PWM 3963)	2w-2PMR		Wkm	6948	1955	DsmT
68007	PWM 4303	2w-2PMR		Wkm	7506	1956	
68009	(PWM 4305)	2w-2PMR		Wkm	7508	1956	

NIGEL HEATH, WITNEY
Loco is stored at a private location.

Gauge 2ft 0in

| 15 | 0-8-0T | OC | Hen | 14968 | 1917 |

P. ROGERS, PRIVATE LOCATION
Gauge 4ft 8½in

| (A144 | PWM 2176) | 2w-2PMR | | Wkm | 4153 | 1946 | OOU |
| | PWM 4310 | 2w-2PMR | | Wkm | 7513 | 1956 | Dsm |

JIM SHACKELL, WITNEY
Gauge 1ft 3in

| – | 2-6-2 | OC | LemonB | | 1967 | + |

+   not yet completed

PAUL SPACKLEN,
Gauge 4ft 8½in   currently stored at Old Oak Common Depot, London

(D426	50026) 89426					
	INDOMITABLE	Co-CoDE	_(EE	3796	1968
			(EEV	D1167	1968

RUTLAND

INDUSTRIAL SITES

CASTLE CEMENT (KETTON) LTD, KETTON WORKS
Heidelberg Cement Group

A class 08 diesel shunter is also hired from EWS when required.   SK 987057

Gauge 4ft 8½in

| H024 | 08870 (D4038) | 0-6-0DE | Dar | | 1960 | a |

a   on hire from RMS Locotec Ltd, Wakefield.

PRESERVATION SITES

RUTLAND RAILWAY MUSEUM, COTTESMORE IRON ORE MINES SIDINGS, ASHWELL ROAD, COTTESMORE, near OAKHAM
Gauge 4ft 8½in   SK 887137

	(FIREFLY)	0-4-0ST	OC	AB	776	1899
RRM 2		0-4-0ST	OC	AB	1931	1927
RRM 6	SIR THOMAS ROYDEN	0-4-0ST	OC	AB	2088	1940
2350	BELVOIR	0-6-0ST	OC	AB	2350	1954
RRM 3	DORA	0-4-0ST	OC	AE	1973	1927
–	"No.24"	0-6-0ST	IC	HE	2411	1941
RRM 28	"No.65"	0-6-0ST	IC	HE	3889	1964
–		0-6-0ST	OC	HL	3138	1915
	SINGAPORE	0-4-0ST	OC	HL	3865	1936
RRM 1	(UPPINGHAM)	0-4-0ST	OC	P	1257	1912
RRM 4	ELIZABETH	0-4-0ST	OC	P	1759	1928
RRM 10	8	0-4-0ST	OC	P	2110	1950
	No.7	4wVBT	VCG	S	9376	1947
			reb	TH		1960
	CRANFORD No.2	0-6-0ST	OC	WB	2668	1942

RRM 11	"CARLTON IRONWORKS No.2"					
		0-4-0DM		AB	352	1941
RRM 18		0-4-0DH		AB	499	1965
No.1		0-4-0DH		JF	4220007	1960
	KETTON No.4	0-6-0DH		JF	4240012	1961
–		0-6-0DH		JF	4240015	1962
RRM 106	3	0-4-0DH		NBQ	27656	1957
RRM 12		4wDM		RH	306092	1950
ARMY 110	A2 EQ	4wDM		RH	411319	1958
No.3	"ELIZABETH"	0-4-0DE		RH	421436	1958
–		0-4-0DE		RH	544997	1969
RRM 21	(BETTY)	0-4-0DH		RR	10201	1964
61	689/171 GRAHAM	0-4-0DH		RR	10207	1965
	KEN 67	0-6-0DH		S	10180	1964
–		0-4-0DH		TH	132C	1963
	a rebuild of	0-4-0DM		JF	22982	1942
No.4		4wDH		TH	186V	1967
RRM 16	"D.E.5"	0-6-0DE		YE	2791	1962
RRM 15	1382	0-6-0DE		YE	2872	1962

SHROPSHIRE

PRESERVATION SITES

CAMBRIAN RAILWAYS SOCIETY LTD, OSWESTRY CYCLE & RAILWAY MUSEUM
Station Yard, Oswald Road, Oswestry
Gauge 4ft 8½in   SJ 294297

–		0-6-0ST	OC	AB	885	1900	
	NORMA	0-6-0ST	IC	HE	3770	1952	
	ADAM	0-4-0ST	OC	P	1430	1916	
	OLIVER VELTOM	0-4-0ST	OC	P	2131	1951	
–		4wDM		FH	3057	1946	Dsm
	CYRIL	4wDM		FH	3541	1952	
–		4wDM		FH	3953	1960	
–		0-4-0DM		HC	D843	1954	
–		0-6-0DM		HE	3526	1947	
No.1	SCOTTIE	4wDM		RH	412427	1957	
	TELEMON	0-4-0DM		_(VF	D295	1955	
				(DC	2568	1955	
W38	PWM 3764	2w-2PMR		Wkm	6643	1953	a
	DR 98205A	4wDMR		Plasser	52760A	1985	

Gauge 2ft 0in   SJ 298277

–		4wDM		RH	496038	1963	+
–		4wDM		RH	496039	1963	+

a   kept at Llanddu Yard, Nantmawr branch (SJ 256233)
+   currently at M. Hignetts Farm, The Lees Farm, Rednall (SJ 375288)

CAMBRIAN RAILWAY TRUST, LLYNCLYS GOODS YARD, LLYNLYS,
OSWESTRY   www.cambrianrailwaytrust.com
Gauge 4ft 8½in   SJ 285239

5952	COGAN HALL	4-6-0	OC	Sdn		1935	
	ISABEL	0-6-0ST	OC	HL	3437	1919	
–		0-4-0ST	OC	P	1738	1928	
D2094	(03094)	0-6-0DM		Don		1960	
D3019		0-6-0DE		Derby		1953	
875	ADOLF	0-4-0DH		HE	9222	1984	Dsm
2	JAMES	0-4-0DH		YE	2675	1961	
51187		2-2w-2w-2DMR		MetCam		1958	
51205		2-2w-2w-2DMR		MetCam		1958	
51512		2-2w-2w-2DMR		MetCam		1959	

G.FAIRHURST, c/o ENGLISH NATURE, MANOR HOUSE WORKS, near WHIXALL
Gauge 2ft 0in   SJ 505366

–	4wPM	MR	1934	1919	a
–	4wDM	RH	191679	1938	a

a   locos stored at a private location

IRONBRIDGE GORGE MUSEUM TRUST LTD
Blists Hill Victorian Town, Madeley, Telford
Locomotive frequently demonstrated in steam within museum premises.   SJ 693033
Operates on plateway-type flanged rails.

Gauge 3ft 0in

–	4wG	OC	CastleGKN	1990	+

+   working replica of Trevithick loco.

Coalbrookdale Museum of Iron
Locomotives on static display.   SJ 667048, 668047

Gauge 4ft 8½in

–		0-6-0ST	OC	AB	782	1896
5		0-4-0ST	OC	Coalbrookdale		c1865
–		0-4-0VBT	VCG	S	6155	1925
	a rebuild of	0-4-0ST	OC	MW	437	1873
–		0-4-0VBT	VCG	S	6185	1925
	a rebuild of (6)	0-4-0ST	OC	Coalbrookdale		c1865

DAVID LEWIS, WHITCHURCH
Gauge 4ft 8½in

–	0-4-0DM	JF	4210074	1952

POOL HOUSE, BRIDGE ROAD, HORSEHAY, TELFORD
Gauge 2ft 0in

339209	4wDM	RH	339209	1952

J. REES, SHREWSBURY AREA
Gauge 2ft 0in

3	0-8-0T	OC	Hen	14928	1917

SEVERN VALLEY RAILWAY CO LTD
Locos are kept at :-

Arley, Worcestershire   SO 800764
Bewdley, Worcestershire   SO 793753
Bridgnorth   SO 715926
Hampton Loade   SO 744863
Highley   SO 749831

Gauge 4ft 8½in

813		0-6-0ST	IC	HC	555	1900
1501		0-6-0PT	OC	Sdn		1949
2857		2-8-0	OC	Sdn		1918
4150		2-6-2T	OC	Sdn		1947
4566		2-6-2T	OC	Sdn		1924
4930	HAGLEY HALL	4-6-0	OC	Sdn		1929
5164		2-6-2T	OC	Sdn		1930
5764		0-6-0PT	IC	Sdn		1929
7325		2-6-0	OC	Sdn		1932
7714		0-6-0PT	IC	KS	4449	1930
7802	BRADLEY MANOR	4-6-0	OC	Sdn		1938
7812	ERLESTOKE MANOR	4-6-0	OC	Sdn		1939
34027	TAW VALLEY	4-6-2	3C	Bton		1946
42968		2-6-0	OC	Crewe	136	1934
43106		2-6-0	OC	Dar	2148	1951
45110		4-6-0	OC	VF	4653	1935
46443		2-6-0	OC	Crewe		1950
47383		0-6-0T	IC	VF	3954	1926
48773		2-8-0	OC	NBH	24607	1940
75069		4-6-0	OC	Sdn		1955
80079		2-6-4T	OC	Bton		1954
(THE LADY ARMAGHDALE)						
		0-6-0T	IC	HE	686	1898
	WARWICKSHIRE	0-6-0ST	IC	MW	2047	1926
WD 600	GORDON	2-10-0	OC	NBH	25437	1943
(D435) 50035	ARK ROYAL	Co-CoDE		_(EE	3805	1968
				(EEV	D1176	1968
D444 (50044)	EXETER	Co-CoDE		_(EE	3814	1968
				(EEV	D1185	1968
D821	GREYHOUND	B-BDH		Sdn		1960
D1013	WESTERN RANGER	C-CDH		Sdn		1962
D1062	WESTERN COURIER	C-CDH		Crewe		1963
D3022 (08015)		0-6-0DE		Derby		1953
(D3201) 08133		0-6-0DE		Derby		1955
D3586 (08471)		0-6-0DE		Crewe		1958
(D3802) 08635		0-6-0DE		Derby		1959
D3937 08769	GLADYS	0-6-0DE		Derby		1960
D5410 (27059)		Bo-BoDE		BRCW	DEL253	1962
E6005 (73005)		Bo-Bo DE/RE		Elh		1962
E6006 (73006)		Bo-Bo DE/RE		Elh		1962
(D6906) 37906		Co-CoDE		_(EE	3384	1963
				(EEV	D850	1963
D7029		B-BDH		BPH	7923	1962
12099		0-6-0DE		Derby		1952
D2957		0-4-0DM		RH	319290	1953
D2960	SILVER SPOON	0-4-0DM		RH	281269	1950
D2961		0-4-0DE		RH	418596	1957
M50933		2-2w-2w-2DMR		DerbyC&W		1960

M51935		2-2w-2w-2DMR	DerbyC&W		1960	
M51941		2-2w-2w-2DMR	DerbyC&W		1960	
M52064		2-2w-2w-2DMR	DerbyC&W		1961	
(PT 2P)		2w-2PMR	Wkm	1580	1934	
PWM 3189		2w-2PMR	Wkm	5019	1948	DsmT
DB 965054		2w-2PMR	Wkm	7577	1957	DsmT
(PT 1P TP 49P)		2w-2PMR	Wkm	7690	1957	
(9021) 6		2w-2PMR	Wkm	8085	1958	

SHROPSHIRE LOCOMOTIVE COLLECTION, CROSS HOUSES, near ATCHAM

Locomotives are stored on secure private premises with no public access without appointment.

Gauge 4ft 8½in

–	0-6-0F	OC	WB	3019	1952

SHROPSHIRE MINES TRUST, SNAILBEACH LEAD MINES

Locos are kept at another, private, site.

Gauge 1ft 11½in   SJ 375022

–		0-4-0BE	WR	S7950	1978
RED DWARF		0-4-0BE	WR	5655	1956
	rebuilt as	4wBE	ShepherdFG		1980

TELFORD CENTRAL RAILWAY STATION, TELFORD

Non-working replica loco on static display in station building.

Gauge 4ft 0in   SJ 704092

–	4wG		TU	1987

TELFORD HORSEHAY STEAM TRUST, TELFORD STEAM RAILWAY, THE OLD LOCO SHED, BRIDGE ROAD, HORSEHAY, TELFORD

Gauge 4ft 8½in   www.telfordsteamrailway.co.uk   SJ 675073

5619		0-6-2T	IC	Sdn		1925	
–		0-4-0F	OC	AB	1944	1927	OOU
"139 BEATTY"		0-4-0ST	OC	HL	3240	1917	
ROCKET		0-4-0ST	OC	P	1722	1926	a
3		0-4-0ST	OC	P	1990	1940	
50556 (53556) N682		2-2w-2w-2DMR	BRCW			1958	
M50479 (53479)		2-2w-2w-2DMR	BRCW			1958	
50531 (53531)		2-2w-2w-2DMR	BRCW			1958	
D3429 (08359)		0-6-0DE	Crewe			1958	
–		0-4-0DH	NBQ	27414		1954	
183062 FOLLY		4wDM	RH	183062		1937	
D2959		4wDM	RH	382824		1955	
2991		0-4-0DH	RH	525947		1968	
JOANNA		4wDH	TH	177C		1967	b
	a rebuild of	4wVBT	VCG	S	9401	1950	

–		0-4-0DE	YE	2687	1958	
(390)	AMESBURY	0-6-0DE	YE	2756	1959	b
RB004		4wDMR	Leyland/Derby C&W			
			RB004	1984		
(TR36	PWM 2786) A14W	2w-2PMR	Wkm	6885	1954	OOU

a   property of Somerset & Dorset Locomotive Co Ltd
b   property of WB Power Services Ltd, Ilkeston, Derbyshire

Gauge 2ft 0in

–	4wVBTram VCG	_(Kierstead			
		(AK		1979	
–	4wDM	RH	222101	1943	OOU

SOMERSET

INDUSTRIAL SITES

FOSTER YEOMAN QUARRIES LTD,
MEREHEAD STONE TERMINAL, TORR WORKS, SHEPTON MALLET
(operated by Mendip Rail Ltd)
Gauge 4ft 8½in   ST 693426

(D3044)	08032	0-6-0DE	Derby		1954	
(D3739	08572) 08731	0-6-0DE	Crewe		1959	a
(D3810)	08643	0-6-0DE	Hor		1959	
(D3994)	08826	0-6-0DE	Derby		1960	
44	WESTERN YEOMAN II	Bo-BoDE	GM	798033-1	1980	

a   08731 rebuilt Swindon Works 1983 using frame from 08572

HANSON QUARRY PRODUCTS EUROPE LTD, HANSON AGGREGATES,
WHATLEY QUARRY, near FROME
(operated by Mendip Rail Ltd)
Gauge 4ft 8½in   ST 733479

(D3763)	08596	0-6-0DE	Derby		1959	a
(D4177)	08947	0-6-0DE	Dar		1962	
120	WHATLEY ENDEAVOR	4w-4wDE	GM	37903	1972	
No.4		4wDH	TH	200V	1968	

a   currently on hire from Wabtec Rail Ltd, South Yorkshire

PRESERVATION SITES

BLATCHFORD LIGHT RAILWAY,
EMBOROUGH QUARRY, EMBOROUGH, near WELLS

This a private railway, not open to the public.

Gauge 4ft 8½in

–		0-6-0DE	YE	2641	1957

Gauge 2ft 6in

9	YARD No.24	0-4-0DM		HE	2017	1939
2	YARD No. B6	0-4-0DM		HE	2266	1940
ND 3060		0-4-0DM		HE	2398	1941
	YARD No.1075	4wDH		HE	7447	1976
	YARD No. 1073	4wDH		HE	7450	1976
	YARD No.1074	4wDH		HE	7451	1976
10		4wDHF	RACK	HE	9057	1981
–		4wDM		RH	398101	1956
L4134		2w-2PM		Wkm	3174	1942

Gauge 2ft 4in

	CORRIS	4wDM	RH	398102	1956

Gauge 2ft 0in

–	4wDM	MR	60S318	1964	a

a   brake column is stamped 11164 in error

Mr. BOND, YEOVIL AREA

Gauge 3ft 0in

–	4wDM	JF	3930048	1951
Stored at unknown location				

B. CLARKE, 11 PENN GARDENS, BATH

These locos are not on public display.

Gauge 2ft 0in

CLARA	4wPM	Bonnymount		c1986
–	4wDM	L	38296	1952
ADAM	4wDM	MR	9978	1954
–	4wDM	OK	7595	1937
–	4wDM	RH	213834	1942

EAST SOMERSET RAILWAY CO LTD,
WEST CRANMORE RAILWAY STATION, SHEPTON MALLET

Gauge 4ft 8½in   ST 664429

5637		0-6-2T	IC	Sdn		1925	
No.110	(32110) B110	0-6-0T	IC	Bton		1877	
1398	LORD FISHER	0-4-0ST	OC	AB	1398	1915	
1719	LADY NAN	0-4-0ST	OC	AB	1719	1920	
705		0-4-0ST	OC	AB	2047	1937	
30075		0-6-0T	OC	DDak	669	1960	
–		0-6-0DH		HC	D1373	1965	
	CATTEWATER	4wDH		RR	10199	1964	
39	CABOT	0-6-0DH		RR	10218	1965	
	ERIC	0-6-0DH		RR	10221	1965	
2	JOAN	0-4-0DH		S	10165	1964	
2	WILLIAM ELLIS	4wDH		TH	136C	1964	
	a rebuild of	4wVBT	VCG	S			

GARTELL LIGHT RAILWAY, COMMON LANE, YENSTON, near TEMPLECOMBE

Gauge 2ft 0in   ST 718218

	AXE	0-6-0T	OC	Gartell		2006	a
No.6	Mr.G	0-4-2T	OC	NDLW	698	1998	
No.5	ALISON	4wDH		AK	No.10	1983	
No.2	ANDREW	4wDH		BD	3699	1973	
No.1	AMANDA	Bo-BoDH		Gartell		2003	
–		4wDM		RH	193984	1939	Dsm
–		Bo-BoDH		SL		1973	Dsm

a   loco built with new frames, incorporating parts from KS 2451

P. HAY, PRIVATE LOCATION

Gauge 2ft 0in

–	BLONDIE	4wPM		H	984	1931
–		2w-2PM		Rhiwbach		

ANDREW JOHNSTON, WEDMORE

Gauge 2ft 0in

	TOBY	4wPM		Carter		1986	+
–		4wDM	s/o	MR	8727	1941

+   stored at another, private, location

P.D. NICHOLSON,
CROSSING KEEPERS LODGE, 87 WHITSTONE ROAD, SHEPTON MALLET

Gauge 4ft 8½in   ST 626429

TR12	(PWM 2188) A156W	2w-2PMR		Wkm	4165	1948	+

+   currently in store at a private location

Gauge 2ft 0in

–	4wPM	FH	1830	1933
–	4wPM	RT&Co(C)		1941

SOMERSET & DORSET RAILWAY HERITAGE TRUST, MIDSOMER NORTON SOUTH STATION

Gauge 4ft 8½in   ST 664536

37		4wVBT	VCG	S	7109	1927
	DAVID JAMES COOK	0-6-0DH		EEV	D1120	1966

SOMERSET & DORSET RAILWAY MUSEUM TRUST, WASHFORD STATION

Gauge 4ft 8½in   ST 044412

6	KILMERSDON	0-4-0ST	OC	P	1788	1929
–		4wDM		RH	210479	1942

Gauge 2ft 0in

–	4wDM	L	42319	1956

UNKNOWN OWNER, HENSTRIDGE

Gauge 4ft 8½in

–	0-6-0T	OC	HC	1857	1952

UNKNOWN OWNER, PRIVATE SITE, near CLUTTON

Gauge 4ft 8½in

(TP57P)	2w-2PMR	Wkm	8267	1959

UNKNOWN OWNER, PRIVATE LOCATION, near TAUNTON

Gauge 2ft 6in

–	4wDM	MR	5879	1935

WARNERS HOLIDAYS, CRICKET ST.THOMAS WILDLIFE PARK, near CHARD

Gauge 1ft 3in   ST 376086

–		0-6-2DH	s/o	AK	51	1995
	SAINT THOMAS	4w-4wDH		Guest		1957

WEST SOMERSET RAILWAY plc

Locos are kept at :-

	Bishops Lydeard	ST 164290
	Dunster	SS 996447
	Minehead	SS 975463
	Williton Goods Yard	ST 085416

Gauge 4ft 8½in

2874		2-8-0	OC	Sdn	2780	1918
3850		2-8-0	OC	Sdn		1942
4160		2-6-2T	OC	Sdn		1948
4561		2-6-2T	OC	Sdn		1924
5224		2-8-0T	OC	Sdn		1924
6412		0-6-0PT	IC	Sdn		1934
6695		0-6-2T	IC	AW	983	1928
9351		2-6-0	OC	WSR		2004
	rebuilt from 5193	2-6-2T	OC	Sdn		1934
7820	DINMORE MANOR	4-6-0	OC	Sdn		1950
7828	ODNEY MANOR	4-6-0	OC	Sdn		1950
34046	BRAUNTON	4-6-2	3C	Bton		1946
35011	GENERAL STEAM NAVIGATION					
		4-6-2	3C	Elh		1944
44422		0-6-0	IC	Derby		1927
(53808)	88	2-8-0	OC	RS	3894	1925
–		4wVBT	VCG	S	9374	1947
D832	ONSLAUGHT	B-BDH		Sdn		1960
D1010	WESTERN CAMPAIGNER	C-CDH		Sdn		1962
D1661	(47076 47613 47840)	NORTH STAR				
		Co-CoDE		Crewe		1965
(D2119)	03119	0-6-0DM		Sdn		1959
D2133		0-6-0DM		Sdn		1960
D2205		0-6-0DM		_(VF	D212	1953
				(DC	2486	1953
D2271		0-6-0DM		_(RSHD	7913	1958
				(DC	2615	1958
D3462	(08377)	0-6-0DE		Dar		1957
(D)6566	(33048)	Bo-BoDE		BRCW	DEL170	1961
(D6575)	33057	Bo-BoDE		BRCW	DEL179	1961
D7017		B-BDH		BPH	7911	1961
D7018		B-BDH		BPH	7912	1961
D7523	(25173) JOHN F. KENNEDY					
		Bo-BoDE		Derby		1965
D9526		0-6-0DH		Sdn		1964
–		0-4-0DH		AB	578	1972
–		0-4-0DH		AB	579	1972
DH16		4wDH		S	10175	1964
51663		2-2w-2w-2DMR		DerbyC&W		1960	a Dsm
51852		2-2w-2w-2DMR		DerbyC&W		1960
51859	859	2-2w-2w-2DMR		DerbyC&W		1960
51880	880	2-2w-2w-2DMR		DerbyC&W		1960
(51887)		2-2w-2w-2DMR		DerbyC&W		1960
901 002	RDB977693	(53222)	2-2w+2w-2DMR	MetCam		1957
901 002	RDB977694	(53338)	2-2w+2w-2DMR	MetCam		1958

a   used as advertising hoarding at Norton Junction

WESTONZOYLAND ENGINE TRUST,
WESTONZOYLAND PUMPING STATION, near BRIDGWATER
Gauge 2ft 0in ST 340328

–		4wDM	L	34758	1949	
87030	30	4wDM	MR	40S310	1968	

YEOVIL RAILWAY CENTRE,
THE YEOVIL COUNTRY RAILWAY, YEOVIL JUNCTION
Gauge 4ft 8½in ST 570140

	PECTIN		0-4-0ST	OC	P	1579	1921
(D400)	50050	FEARLESS	Co-CoDE		_(EE	3770	1967
					(EEV	D1141	1967
23			0-4-0DM		JF	22898	1940
			0-4-0DM		JF	22900	1941
–							
44	COCKNEY REBEL		0-4-0DM		JF	4000007	1947
DS1174	YEO		4wDM		RH	458959	1961

STAFFORDSHIRE

INDUSTRIAL SITES

AMEC CONSTRUCTION, PLANT DEPOT, COLD MEECE, SWYNNERTON, STONE
Locos are present in this yard between use on contracts. SJ 850325

Gauge 2ft 0in

	263 022	4wBE		CE	5955A	1972
	263 051	4wBE		CE	B0119B	1973
S191	263 023	4wBE		CE	B0131A	1973
S213	263 024	4wBE		CE	B0183A	1974
S232	263 025	4wBE		CE	B0459A	1975
	263 021	4wBE		CE	B0465	1974
S237	263 008	4wBE		CE	B0471A	1975
S238	263 009	4wBE		CE	B0471B	1975
S241	263 026	4wBE		CE	B0471E	1975
S242	263 027	4wBE		CE	B0471F	1975
			reb	CE	B3480/1A	1988
S261	263 028	4wBE		CE	B0941A	1976
S263	263 029	4wBE		CE	B0941C	1976
S264	263 030	4wBE		CE	B0948.1	1976
S265	263 031	4wBE		CE	B0948.2	1976
S271	263 032	4wBE		CE	B0952.2	1976
			reb	CE	B3787	1991

S275	263 033	4wBE		CE	B0957B	1976
			reb	CE	B3480/1B	1988
	263 077	4wBE		CE	B1559	1977
			reb	CE	B3214B	1985
	263 075	4wBE		CE	B3642A	1990
			reb	CE	B3766A	1991
	263 073	4wBE		CE	B3642B	1990
			reb	CE	B3766B	1991
	263 076	4wBE		CE	B3766C	1991
	263 074	4wBE		CE	B3766D	1991
1	263 053	4wBE		CE	5512/1	1968
5	263 054	4wBE		CE		
6	263 058	4wBE		CE		
8	263 059	4wBE		CE	5839B	1971
9	263 057	4wBE		CE	5839C	1971
L28		4wDH		Schöma	5571	1998
L29		4wDH		Schöma	5572	1998
L24		4wDH		Schöma	5573	1998
L25		4wDH		Schöma	5574	1998
L26		4wDH		Schöma	5575	1998
L27		4wDH		Schöma	5576	1998

ɓauge 1ft 6in

S179	263.040	4wBE	CE	B0111C	1973
S206	263 006	4wBE	CE	B0152	1973
S147	263 016	4wBE	CE	5926/2	1972

ɓOMBADIER TRANSPORTATION, CENTRAL RIVERS DEPOT, BARTON UNDER NEED-ʍOOD

ɓauge 4ft 8½in   SJ 203177

(D3662)	08507	0-6-0DE	Don	1958	+

+   on hire from Harry Needle Railroad Co Ltd

ɔLAYTON EQUIPMENT LTD, SECOND AVENUE, CENTRUM 100, BURTON-ON-TRENT

ɴew CE locos under construction, and locos for repair, usually present.

ɭH GROUP SERVICES LTD, HUNSLET ENGINE COMPANY & ANDREW BARCLAY LOCO-ʍOTIVES, UNITS 150-152, GREYCAR INDUSTRIAL ESTATE, BARTON-UNDER-NEED-ʍOOD

ɭocos for repair / overhaul / resale and hire usually present.

ɓauge 4ft 8½in   SJ ȝ06185

(D3819)	08652	0-6-0DE	Hor	1959	
(D4041)	08873	0-6-0DE	Dar	1960	
(D4143)	08913	0-6-0DE	Hor	1962	d

	SAM	0-6-0DH		ABG	659	2004	+ g
			reb of	HAB	6768	1990	
			reb of	AB	659	1982	
1	EMILY	0-6-0DH		ABG	660	2004	* g
			reb of	HAB	6769	1990	
			reb of	AB	660	1982	
	GILLIAN	0-6-0DH		EEV	D1137	1966	f
9		0-6-0DH		HE	7304	1972	
–		0-6-0DH		HE	8979	1979	
	WILLIAM	4wDH		S	10048	1960	bc
	(RONA)	0-6-0DH		S	10151	1964	
			reb	TH		1987	
			reb	HAB	6432	1997	a
DH11	EDWARD	4wDH		TH	267V	1976	e
–		6wDH		TH	V325	1987	h
	GR 5143	4wDM	R/R	Unimog 416141 10 025642			
	AE 55 MZJ	4wDM	R/R	Unimog	207425	2005	

a frame of S 10151 rebuilt by TH with parts from RR 10213
b currently on hire to Corus, Skinningrove, North Yorkshire
c Property of Staffordshire Locomotive Co Ltd
d currently at Manchester Ship Canal Co Ltd, Greater Manchester
e currently at Total Oil, Herbrandston, Milford Haven, South West Wales
f currently at Coopers (Metals) Ltd, South Yorkshire
g currently at Cleveland Potash Ltd, Tees Dock, Grangetown, North Yorkshire
h currently at Tarmac Buxton Lime & Cement, Derbyshire
+ carried ABG 660 plates from 2004 to 2007
* carried ABG 659 plates from 2004 to 2007

Gauge 3ft 6in

–	4wDHR	WkmR	11730	1991

MARCROFT ENGINEERING, STOKE WORKS, WHIELDON ROAD, FENTON, STOKE-ON-TRENT
Gauge 4ft 8½in SJ 881439

	CHRISTOPHER	4wDH	RR	10269	1967	
	ANDREW	4wDH	TH	164V	1966	a
1	545/001	4wDH	TH	183V	1967	
2		4wDH	TH	184V	1967	

a on hire from WB Power Services Ltd, Derbyshire

STAFFORDSHIRE LOCOMOTIVE CO LTD, P.O.BOX 125, LICHFIELD
This is understood to be a complete FLEET LIST of the locos owned by (or in the care of) this company, which operates from the above address. Some locos are for hire or resale, and all are in use or stored at a number of locations.

Gauge 4ft 8½in

No.2	800	0-6-0DH	HE	6971	1968	a
No.6		4wDH	S	10048	1960	b

a   currently at Total Lindsey Oil Refinery, Lincolnshire
b   currently at Corus, Skinnigrove, North Yorkshire

Gauge 2ft 0in

–	4wPM	L	1626	1928	+
–	4wDM	RH	7002/1067/2	1968	

+   built as a road truck with bolt-on steel railway wheels

PRESERVATION SITES

COORS BREWERY LTD, THE MUSEUM OF BREWING, HORNINGLOW STREET, BURTON-ON-TRENT (Closed)

Gauge 4ft 8½in   SK 248234

No.9	0-4-0ST	OC	NR	5907	1901
20	4wDM		KC		1926

CHASEWATER RAILWAY, THE COLLIERY LINE, CHASEWATER PLEASURE PARK, BROWNHILLS

Gauge 4ft 8½in   SK 034070

No.3	"COLIN McANDREW"	0-4-0ST	OC	AB	1223	1911
No.4	BRITISH GYPSUM	0-4-0ST	OC	AB	2343	1953
431		0-6-0ST	OC	HC	431	1895
10		0-6-0T	OC	HC	1822	1949
	ASBESTOS	0-4-0ST	OC	HL	2780	1909
	ALFRED PAGET	0-4-0ST	OC	N	2937	1882
917		0-4-0ST	OC	P	917	1902
5		4wVBT	VCG	S	9632	1957
	LINDA	0-4-0ST	OC	WB	2648	1941
(50160)	53160	2-2w-2w-2DMR		MetCam		1956
W51372		2-2w-2w-2DMR		PSteel		1960
34		0-4-0DE		BBT	3097	1956
No.5		0-4-0DM		Bg	3027	1939
MARSTON THOMPSON EVERSHED		0-4-0DM		Bg	3410	1955
53		0-4-0DH		HE	6678	1969
		reb		HE		1982
ROD462	WD462	4wDM		FH	1891	1934
–		0-4-0DM		JF	4100013	1948
–		0-4-0DH		JF	4220015	1962
–		4wDM		KC	1612	1929
D2911		0-4-0DH		NBQ	27876	1959
–		4wDM		RH	279597	1949	Dsm
–		4wDM		RH	305306	1952
7		0-4-0DE		RH	499435	1963
–		0-4-0DE		RH	544998	1969	Dsm
	HEM HEATH 3D	0-6-0DM		WB	3119	1956

Gauge 2ft 6in

8	4wDHF	HE	7385	1976	OOU

Gauge 2ft 0in

YARD No.1076	4wDM	HE	7448	1976
14	4wDH	HE	9081	1984
BOLTON FELL	4wDM	LB	52726	1961
SO 30	4wDM	MR	5609	1931
–	4wDM	RH	174535	1936
YD No.988	4wDM	RH	235729	1944
–	4wDMF	RH	441424	1960
NEATH ABBEY	4wDH	RH	476106	1964

CHATTERLEY WHITFIELD MINING MUSEUM, TUNSTALL (Closed)
Gauge 2ft 6in SJ 883531

3	TOM	4wBEF	Bg	3555	1961
2	CW 1986 111 JERRY	4wBEF	Bg	3578	1961
	–	4wBEF	_(EE	3223	1962
			(RSHD	8344	1962

CHURNET VALLEY RAILWAY (1992) plc, CHEDDLETON STATION, near LEEK
Gauge 4ft 8½in SJ 983519

7821	DITCHEAT MANOR	4-6-0	OC	Sdn		1950
48173		2-8-0	OC	Crewe		1943
80098		2-6-4T	OC	Bton		1954
411.144		2-8-0	OC	BLW	72080	1945	Dsm
5197		2-8-0	OC	Lima	8856	1945
(D1107)	47524	Co-CoDE		Crewe		1966
D1842	(47192)	Co-CoDE		Crewe		1965
D2334		0-6-0DM		_(RSHD	8193	1961
				(DC	2715	1961
(D)6513	33102	Bo-BoDE		BRCW	DEL105	1960
(D6606	37305) 37407	Co-CoDE		_(EE	3565	1965
				(EEV	D994	1965
(D6775)	37075	Co-CoDE		_(EE	3067	1962
				(RSHD	8321	1962
(D6979	37279) 37424	Co-CoDE		_(EE	3539	1965
				(EEV	D968	1965
D7672	(25322 25912)					
	TAMWORTH CASTLE	Bo-BoDE		Derby		1967
	–	4wDH		TH	103C	1960
	a rebuild of	4wVBT	VCG	S	9390	1949
	"BRIGHTSIDE"	0-4-0DH		YE	2672	1959
	ROGER H BENNETT	0-6-0DE		YE	2748	1959
3822	62351	4w-4wRER		York		1973
M50517	(53517)	2-2w-2w-2DMR		BRCW		1957
(M50437)	53437	2-2w-2w-2DMR		BRCW		1957
M50455	(53455)	2-2w-2w-2DMR		BRCW		1957

(M50494)	53494		2-2w-2w-2DMR	BRCW	1957	
901 001	DB977391	(51433)	2-2w-2w-2DMR	MetCam	1959	
901 001	DB977392	(53167)	2-2w-2w-2DMR	MetCam	1959	

DRAYTON MANOR PARK, FAZELEY, TAMWORTH
Gauge 2ft 0in SK 194016

1	THOMAS	4-4wDH	s/o	Emmeln	081309	2008	
6	PERCY	4-4wDH	s/o	Emmeln		2008	
	POLPERRO EXPRESS	4-4-0+4w-4wDH	s/o	SL	2151	2003	

FOXFIELD LIGHT RAILWAY SOCIETY, FOXFIELD STEAM RAILWAY, BLYTHE BRIDGE, near STOKE-ON-TRENT
Locos are kept at :- Blythe Bridge (Caverswall Road) Station SJ 957421
Site of former Foxfield Colliery, near Dilhorne SJ 976446

Gauge 4ft 8½in

		0-4-0F	OC	AB	1984	1930	
–		0-4-0F	OC	AB	1984	1930	
–		0-4-0ST	OC	AE	1563	1908	
–		0-6-0ST	OC	AE	1919	1924	
–		0-4-0ST	OC	BP	1827	1879	
4101		0-4-0CT	OC	D	4101	1901	
	WHISTON	0-6-0ST	IC	HE	3694	1950	
	WIMBLEBURY	0-6-0ST	IC	HE	3839	1956	
6		0-4-0ST	OC	Heath		1885	
			reb	CW		1934	
	BELLEROPHON	0-6-0WT	OC	Haydock	C	1874	a
–		0-4-0ST	OC	HL	3581	1924	
	MOSS BAY	0-4-0ST	OC	KS	4167	1920	
–		0-4-0ST	OC	KS	4388	1926	
	HENRY CORT	0-4-0ST	OC	P	933	1903	
	"IRONBRIDGE"	0-4-0ST	OC	P	1803	1933	
No.11		0-4-0ST	OC	P	2081	1947	
No.15	ROKER	0-4-0CT	OC	RSHN	7006	1940	
	MEAFORD No.2	0-6-0T	OC	RSHN	7684	1951	
–		4wVBT	VCG	S	9535	1952	
	LEWISHAM	0-6-0ST	OC	WB	2221	1927	
	HAWARDEN	0-4-0ST	OC	WB	2623	1940	
–		0-4-0ST	OC	WB	2842	1946	
	FLORENCE No.2	0-6-0ST	OC	WB	3059	1953	

MEAFORD POWER STATION LOCOMOTIVE No.4

		0-6-0DH		AB	486	1964	
	WD 820	0-4-0DM		_(EE	1188	1941	
				(DC	2157	1941	
–		6wDM		KS	4421	1929	
	HELEN	4wDM		MR	2262	1923	
	"HERCULES"	4wDM		RH	242915	1946	+
		4wDM		RH	408496	1957	
–		0-4-0DE		RH	423657	1958	
–		0-4-0DE		RH	424841	1960	

5300003	MYFANWY		0-4-0DH		_(RSHD	8366	1962
					(WB	3211	1962
–			4wDH		TH	111C	1961
		a rebuild of	4wVBT	VCG	S		
	WOLSTANTON No.3		0-6-0DM		WB	3150	1959
	BAGNALL		4wDH		WB	3207	1961
	LUDSTONE		0-6-0DE		YE	2868	1962
–			4wBE/WE		EEDK	1130	1939
–			2w-2BER		Bance	054	1998
–			2w-2PMR		Wkm	7139	1955

+ rebuilt from 2ft 0in gauge
a carries works plate D

LAWRENCE HODGKINSON, 17 BILLINGTON AVENUE, LITTLE HAYWOOD
These locos are kept at a private location.
Gauge 2ft 6in

–	4wDM	RH	441948	1959
–	4wDM	RH	476112	1962

Gauge 2ft 0in

–	4wPM	L	962	1928

A. HODGSON
These locos are kept at a private location.
Gauge 2ft 6in

5	4wBE	BV	690	1974
–	4wBE	WR	892	1935

Gauge 2ft 0in

No.1 BESSIE	4wDM	RH	170374	1934

G. LEE, STATFOLD BARN RAILWAY
Gauge 4ft 8½in   www.statfoldbarnrailway.co.uk

No.1	GLENFIELD		0-4-0CT	OC	AB	880	1902
	COAL PRODUCTS No.6		0-6-0ST	IC	HE	2868	1943
				reb	HE	3883	1963
No.3			0-4-0ST	OC	HL	3597	1926
	POLDARK MINING CO LTD 6		0-4-0ST	OC	P	1530	1919
–			0-4-0VBT	OC	Cockerill	3083	1924
–			4wDM		RH	305302	1951
	No.24		4wDH		TH	188C	1967
		a rebuild of	4wVBT	VCG	S	9597	1955
	LIBBIE		2w-2PMR		BgDC	1097	1920

Gauge 3ft 6in

–	4wPMR		Wkm	5864	1951

Gauge 2ft 6in

6	0-4-0T	OC	LaMeuse	3243	1926	b
YARD No.26 ND 6506 SAM	0-4-0DM		HE	2019	1939	
19	4wDHF	RACK	HE	9294	1990	

Gauge 750mm

5 TJEPPER	0-4-4-0T	4C	Jung	2279	1914
1 PAKIS BARU	0-4-0WT	OC	OK	614	1900
5	0-4-4-0T	4C	OK	1473	1905

Gauge 2ft 0in

TRANGKIL No.4	0-4-2ST	OC	HE	3902	1971	a
STATFOLD	0-4-0ST	OC	HE	3903	2005	
JACK LANE	0-4-0ST	OC	HE	3904	2006	
9 SF. DJATIBARANG	0-4-4-0T	OC	Jung	4878	1930	
1	0-4-2T	OC	KraussS	4045	1899	
740 MATHERAN	0-6-0T	OC	OK	2343	1907	
SRAGI 14 MAX	0-6-0WT	OC	OK	10750	1923	
No.1 HARROGATE	0-6-0ST	OC	P	2050	1944	
ISIBUTU	4-4-0T	OC	WB	2820	1945	
–	4wPM		FH	(1776	1931 ?)	
No.1 D4	4wDM		Funkey			
No.4 D5	4wDM		Funkey			
reb	4wDH					
No.6 BADGER	0-6-0DH		HB	D1418	1971	
NITH	0-4-0DMF		HC	DM1002	1956	
–	4wDM		HE	3621	1947	
–	4wDM		HE	6285	1968	
VICKACHTAR	4wDH		HE	8819	1979	
7	4wDHF		HE	8911	1980	
–	4wDH		HE	9351	1994	
No.2	4wDH		HT	6720	1965	
D7 3 N13	4wDH		HT	7588	1968	
5 BRAKE SERVICE WAGON No.17						
	4wDM		MR	8640	1941	
–	4wDM		MR	8995	1946	Dsm
CHARLEY	4wDM		MR	9976	1954	
ND6455	4wDM		RH	221625	1943	
(A155W TR11 PWM 2187)	4wDMR		CravenJ		1987	c
JMLM23 280537	4wBE		GB	420253	1970	
		reb	WR		1983	
–	4wBE		WR	6092	1958	

a   convertible to 2ft 6in gauge.
b   carries La Meuse worksplate 3355 1929
c   built by J. Craven, Walesby, Nottinghamshire. Incorporates parts from Wkm 4164. Convertible to all gauges from 2ft 0in to 4ft 8½in.

THE LES OAKES COLLECTION, OAKAMOOR ROAD, CHEADLE

Gauge 4ft 8½in

	0-4-0DH	AB	478	1963
–	0-6-0DE	BBT	3021	1951
–	0-4-0DE	BBT	3096	1956

LIME KILN WHARFE INDUSTRIAL RAILWAY,
LIME KILN BASIN, WHITEBRIDGE INDUSTRIAL ESTATE,
WHITEBRIDGE LANE, STONE

Gauge 2ft 0in   SJ 894345

LOD 758227	4wDM	MR	8813	1943	
LOD 758019	4wDM	MR	8820	1943	
–	4wDM	RH	171901	1934	+

+   carries plate RH 191679

MILL MEECE PUMPING STATION PRESERVATION TRUST LTD,
MILL MEECE PUMPING STATION, COTES HEATH, near ECCLESHALL

Gauge 2ft 0in   SJ 831339

–	4wDM	L	39419	1953

DUNCAN MILNER, BUTE STREET, LONGTON, STOKE ON TRENT

Locomotives stored for third parties occasionally present   SJ 904438

Gauge 2ft 0in

RTT 767165	2w-2PM	Wkm	3238	1943

NORTH STAFFS & CHESHIRE TRACTION ENGINE CLUB, KLONDYKE MILL, DRAYCOTT –
IN – THE – CLAY

Gauge 2ft 0in   currently away for restoration   SK 156289

DOROTHY	0-4-0ST	OC	WB	1568	1899

R. PHILLIPS

These locomotives are kept at a private location.

Gauge2ft 0in

(4)	4wDM	RH	260716	1949
–	4wDM	MR	9778	1953
–	4wPM	SkinnerD		c1975

REFRESH RESTORATIONS, 17 STAFFORD ROAD, UTTOXETER

This is an Administration address, Locomotives are restored elsewhere.

Gauge 2ft 6in   SJ 823484

12	ELECTRA	4wBE		BV	565	1970
"20"	YARD No.54 TO 235	4wDMR		FH	2196	1940
–		4wDH		Ruhrthaler	3909	1969
"70"	"CRYSTAL"	4wBE		WR	K7070	1970

Gauge 2ft 0in

9		0-6-0WT	OC	HC	1238	1916
–		4-6-0T	OC	HE	1215	1916
	STANHOPE	0-4-2ST	OC	KS	2395	1917
"1"	BILLET	4wBE		WR	C6717	1963
"2"	CABLE MILL	4wBE		WR	C6716	1963
3		4wDM		MR	8878	1944
5		4wDM		RH	223667	1943
6		4wPM		MR	9104	1941
7		4wDM		MR	8663	1941
13	"THE PILK"	4wDM		MR	11142	1960
14	KNOTHOLE WORKER	4wDM		MR	22045	1959
"16"	MARGARET	4wDHF		HE	9056	1982
"No.18"	8103 L.C.W.W. 18	4wDM		HE	6299	1964
20		4wDM		MR	8748	1942
21		4wDM		MR	8669	1941
A.T.4535	LISTER	4wPM		L	3834	1931
24		4wDM		HE	1974	1939
25	(ND 10448)	4wDM		HE	6007	1963
"26"		4wDM		HE	6018	1961
	ANNIE	4wDM		RH	198297	1939
28	24	4wDM		RH	198228	1940
29	VANGUARD	4wDM		RH	195846	1939
"30"	"FRIDEN"	4wDM		RH	237914	1946
–		4wDM		RH	189972	1938
"33"		4wPM		MR	7033	1936
"34"		4wDM		RH	164350	1933
No.35 (DX 68061)	TR26 PWM 2214	2w-2DMR		Wkm	4131	1947
No.36	"COMMERCIAL"	4wDM		RH	280865	1949
7		4wDM		RH	260719	1948
"No.38"	KENNETH	4wDM		RH	223749	1944
"No.39"	LR 2832	4wPM		MR	1111	1918
"40"	739	4wDM		SMH	40SD516	1979
41		4wDM		MR	5821	1934
42		4wDM		MR	7710	1939
–		4wDM		SMH	104G063	1976
"44"	CHAUMONT	4wDH		HU	LX1002	1968
	LR 3090	4wPM		MR	1369	1918
	87008	4wDM		RH	179870	1936
"48"	R12	4wDM		RH	235725	1944
"49"	4470	4wPM		OK	4470	1931

	DELTA	0-4-0DM		Dtz	10050	1931	
	–	0-4-0PM	s/o	Bg	1695	1928	
	–	4wDM		FH	2306	1940	
	–	4wDM		HC	D558	1930	
	4588	4wPM		OK	4588	1932	
	"60"	4wPM		MR	6035	1937	
	–	4wDM		MR	1320	1918	
62	P396 81A03	4wDM		RH	497542	1963	
	–	4wDMF		RH	256314	1949	
24.8		4wBE		PWR	B0366	1993	
6	"AMENE"	4wBE		WR	D6912	1964	
71		4wBE		CE	5843	1971	
	–	4wDM		OK	(3444 1930?)		
	–	4wPM		MR	5038	1930	
	–	4wDM		LB	52610	1961	
	87004	4wDM		MR	2197	1923	
	–	4wDM		FH	2586	1941	Dsm

Gauge 1ft 6in

"72	LADY ANN"	4wBE		CE	B0922A	1975

THE STAFFORDSHIRE NARROW GAUGE SOCIETY LTD, AMERTON RAILWAY, AMERTON WORKING FARM, STOWE-BY-CHARTLEY, near WESTON, STAFFORD

Gauge 3ft 0in

No.1	(ED 10)	0-4-0ST	OC	WB	1889	1911

Gauge 2ft 0in SJ 993278

	–	0-8-0T	OC	Hen	14019	1916	
	HOWARD	0-4-0ST	OC	HE	3905	2007	a
No.56	(LORNA DOONE)	0-4-0ST	OC	KS	4250	1922	
	EMMETT	0-4-0T		Moors Valley 20		1995	
	a rebuild of	0-4-0DM		OK	21160	1938	
	ISABEL	0-4-0ST	OC	WB	1491	1897	
	PADDY	0-4-0VB	VC	Wbton	2	2007	
774	OAKLEY	0-4-0PM		Bg	774	1919	
	THE TRENTHAM EXPRESS						
		0-4-0DM	s/o	Bg	2085	1934	
	DREADNOUGHT	0-4-0DM	s/o	Bg	3024	1939	
	GORDON	4wDHF		HE	8561	1978	
	reb	4wDH				/2004	
	–	4wDM		Jung	5869	1934	
	–	4wDM		MR	7471	1940	
87033		4wDM		MR	40SD501	1975	
ND 6507		4wDM		RH	221623	1943	
	–	4wDM		RH	506491	1964	

a   carries plate dated 2005.

. TWEEDY, IVY DENE, CHAPEL LANE, GRATTON ENDON
Gauge 1ft 6in

JMLM7	0-4-0BE	WR	M7548	1972

CHRIS WITHINGTON, BANK CLOSE COTTAGE, UTTOXETER
Gauge 4ft 8½in

(900332)	2w-2PMR	Wkm	497	1932

SUFFOLK

INDUSTRIAL SITES

JOHN APPLETON ENGINEERING,
3A MASTERLORD INDUSTRIAL PARK, STATION ROAD, LEISTON
Works with locos occasionally present for restoration.   TM 440628

FELIXSTOWE DOCK & RAILWAY CO LTD, PORT OF FELIXSTOWE
Gauge 4ft 8½in   TM 285331

(D3599)	08484	CAPTAIN NATHANIEL DARELL				
			0-6-0DE	Hor		1958
01531	H4323	COLONEL TOMLINE	0-6-0DH	HE	7018	1971
			reb	HAB	6578	1999

PRESERVATION SITES

EAST ANGLIA TRANSPORT MUSEUM SOCIETY,
EAST SUFFOLK LIGHT RAILWAY,
CHAPEL ROAD, CARLTON COLVILLE, LOWESTOFT
Gauge 2ft 0in   TM 505903

–		4wDM	MR	5902	1932	+	Dsm
2	ALDBURGH	4wDM	MR	5912	1934		
No.6	THORPNESS	4wDM	MR	22209	1964		
No.5	ORFORDNESS	4wDM	MR	22211	1964		
4	LEISTON	4wDM	RH	177604	1936		

+   converted to a brake van

ANTHONY GOFF
Gauge **4ft 8½in**   Locomotive stored at private location.

No. 1		0-4-0DM		JF	20337	1934

IPSWICH TRANSPORT MUSEUM, COBHAM ROAD, IPSWICH
Gauge **monorail**   TM 193428

–		1w1PH		RM	11345	1963

LONG SHOP MUSEUM, LEISTON
Gauge **4ft 8½in**   TM 443626

SIRAPITE		4wT	G	AP	6158	1906

THE MID-SUFFOLK LIGHT RAILWAY COMPANY, BROCKFORD STATION, WETHERINGSETT, near STOWMARKET
Gauge **4ft 8½in**   TM 128659

	LITTLE BARFORD	0-4-0ST	OC	AB	2069	1939
	No.4	0-6-0ST	OC	HC	1604	1928
	–	0-4-0DM		RH	304470	1951
DE 960220		2w-2PMR		Wkm	1949	1935
(B154W PWM 2222)		2w-2PMR		Wkm	4139	1947
RLC/009023 MAINTENANCE 003		2w-2PMR		Wkm	8087	1958

NETWORK SOUTHEAST RAILWAY SOCIETY, ELLOUGH AIRFIELD, BECCLES
Gauge **4ft 8½in**

1753 62043		4w-4wRER		York		1965

PLEASUREWOOD HILLS AMERICAN THEME PARK, CORTON ROAD, LOWESTOFT
Gauge **4ft 8½in**   TM 545965

–		4wDM		RH	305315	1952

Gauge **2ft 0in**

167 ANNIE OAKLEY		4w-2-4wPH	s/o	Chance	79.50167.24	1979

S.A. PYE, 109 PAPER MILL LANE, BRAMFORD, IPSWICH
Gauge **4ft 8½in**   TM 127472

No.35		0-4-0F	OC	RSHN	7803	1954
No.4 "BIRCHENWOOD"		0-6-0ST	OC	WB	2680	1942
D2700		0-4-0DH		NBQ	27426	1955

S. SMITH, HERRINGFLEET HILLS, HERRINGFLEET
This is a private location.

Gauge 2ft 0in

–	4wDM	s/o	MR	9774	1953

**STEAM TRACTION LTD, c/o WEBB TRUCK EQUIPMENT,
ACTON PLACE INDUSTRIAL ESTATE, ACTON, near SUDBURY**

Gauge 1524mm   TL 883455

1077	2-8-2	OC	Jung	11787	1953

SURREY

INDUSTRIAL SITES

R. MARNER, HORSEHILL FARM, NORWOOD HILL, HORLEY
Locos under renovation here occasionally.

**THREE VALLEYS WATER COMPANY, WALTON TREATMENT WORKS
DESBOROUGH ISLAND, WALTON-ON-THAMES**
(subsidiary of Colne Valley Water)

Gauge 3ft 6in

–	4wDH	AK	55	1998

PRESERVATION SITES

I.L. BUTLER, 5 HEATH RISE, GROVE HEATH, RIPLEY

Gauge 600mm   TQ 046557

3		0-4-0DM	Dtz	19531	1937
12	ARCHER	4wDM	MR	4709	1936
11	BARGEE	4wDM	MR	8540	1940

CARL da COSTA, 11 BRIDGEFIELDS, FARNHAM

Gauge 2ft 0in

–	2-4wBE	WR	887	1935	Dsm

JOHN EWING
Gauge 2ft 0in

–	0-6-0WT	OC	OK	9239	1921

Locomotive currently at the Festiniog Railway Company, North Wales for restoration

TONY GUY, HASLEMERE
Gauge 2ft 0in

ALTONIA	0-4-0DM	s/o	Bg	1769	1929
rebuilt as	0-4-0DH	s/o	BES		1992

M. HAYTER, No.1 HEATHER VIEW COTTAGES, SHORTFIELD COMMON, FRENSHAM, FARNHAM
Gauge 2ft 0in   SU 843423

–	2w-2PM	Wkm	2981	1941
–	2w-2PM	Wkm	3032	1941

DAVID JEFFCOT, HASLEMERE
Gauge 2ft 0in

–	4wDM	MR	22235	1965

ANDREW JOHNSTON, MIDHURST
Gauge 2ft 0in

–	4wDM	FH	2544	1942

BRYCE LATHAM, CAMBERLEY
Locomotive stored at a private location
Gauge 3ft 2¼in

No.5 WILLIAM FINLAY	0-4-0T	OC	FJ	173L	1880

MOLE VALLEY DISTRICT COUNCIL, LEISURE CENTRE, WATER PARK, LEATHERHEAD
Gauge 4ft 8½in   TQ 164558

BIWATER EXPRESS	0-6-0ST	OC	HL	3837	1934

OLD KILN LIGHT RAILWAY, THE RURAL LIFE CENTRE, OLD KILN MUSEUM, THE REEDS, REEDS ROAD, TILFORD, near FARNHAM
Gauge 2ft 0in   SU 858434

PAMELA	0-4-0ST	OC	HE	920	1906
M.N.No.1 ELOUISE	0-6-0WT	OC	OK	9998	1922
–	4wDM		FH	2528	1941

1 STINKER		4wDM		HE	1944	1939
–		4wPM		MR	5297	1931
–		4wDM		MR	5713	1936
.OD/758039 PHOEBE		4wDM		MR	8887	1944
–		4wDM		MR	8981	1946
SANDROCK		4wDM		RH	177639	1936
RED DWARF		4wDM		RH	181820	1936
NORDEN		4wDM		RH	392117	1956
–		4wDM		Schöma	1676	1955
No.4 L12 RTT 767093 LIZ		2w-2PM		Wkm	3031	1941
	rebuilt as	4wDM		Haytor		1973
SUE		2w-2PM		Wkm	3287	1943
	rebuilt as	2w-2PMR		‡		1977

‡   rebuilt by E.J.Stephens, Wey Valley Light Railway, Farnham, Surrey

Gauge 600mm

NG 35		4wDH		HE	7010	1971
			reb	HAB	6941	1988
36 GALLOWAYS		4wDH		HE	7011	1971
NG 37		4wDH		HE	7012	1971
			reb	HAB	6014	1988
NG 38		4wDH		HE	7013	1971

P. RAMPTON, HAMBLEDON

The following locomotives are stored at private locations.   TQ 001381
The locos are not available for viewing or photography.

Gauge 2ft 6in

695		0-6-4T	OC	KS	4408	1928
666		4-6-2	OC	NB	17111	1906
AK16		2-6-2T	OC	WB	2029	1916
No.3 CONQUEROR		0-6-2T	OC	WB	2192	1922

Gauge 2ft 0in

121		2-8-2	OC	AFB	2668	1951
SSE 1912		4-4-0	OC	FE	265	1897
LISBOA		4-4-0	OC	FE	266	1897
82		2-6-2+2-6-2T	4C	Hano	10634	1928
38		4-6-2	OC	WB	2457	1932
41		4-6-2	OC	WB	2460	1932

Gauge 600mm

RENISHAW 4		0-4-4-0T	VCG	AE	2057	1931
–		0-4-0WT	OC	Borsig	5913	1908
7 SOTILLOS		0-6-2T	OC	Borsig	6022	1906
1 SABERO		0-6-0T	OC	Couillet	1140	1895
2 SAMELICES		0-6-0T	OC	Couillet	1209	1898
3 OLLEROS		0-6-0T	OC	Couillet	1318	1900
101		0-4-2T	OC	Hen	16073	1918

102		0-4-0T	OC	Hen	16043	1918
103		0-4-0T	OC	Hen	16045	1918
6	LA HERRERA	0-6-0T	OC	Sabero		c1937
	RENISHAW 5	0-4-4-0T	OC	WB	2545	1936
	–	0-4-2T	OC	WB	2895	1948
No.18		4wDE		DK		c1918

Gauge 550mm

| 4 | SAN JUSTO | 0-4-2ST | OC | HC | 639 | 1902 |
| 5 | SANTA ANA | 0-4-2ST | OC | HC | 640 | 1902 |

FRANK SAXBY, GUILDFORD
Gauge 2ft 0in

| | SUE | 4wG | IC | Saxby | 1943 | 1999 |

THORPE PLEASURE PARK, STAINES ROAD, CHERTSEY
(a member of the R.M.C.Group)

Gauge 2ft 0in — Treasure Island Railway   TQ 027685

| | IVOR | 4wDH | s/o | AK | 11 | 1984 |

Gauge 2ft 0in — Canada Creek Railway   TQ 035681

C.C.R.89 No.1	4-4-0DH	s/o	SL	139/1.2.89	1989
C.C.R.89 No.2	4-4-0DH	s/o	SL	139/2.1.89	1989
C.C.R.94 No.3	4-4-0DH	s/o	SL	606.3.94	1994

EAST SUSSEX

PRESERVATION SITES

BLUEBELL RAILWAY CO LTD
Locos are kept at :-

Horsted Keynes, West Sussex TQ 372293
Kingscote TQ 367355
Sheffield Park TQ 403238

Gauge 4ft 8½in

3217	(9017)					
	EARL OF BERKELEY	4-4-0	IC	Sdn		1938
(30064)	WD 1959	0-6-0T	OC	VIW	4432	1943
(30096)	96 NORMANDY	0-4-0T	OC	9E	396	1893
(30541)	541	0-6-0	IC	Elh		1939
(30583)	No.488	4-4-2T	OC	N	3209	1885
(30847)	847	4-6-0	OC	Elh		1936
(30928)	No.928 STOWE	4-4-0	3C	Elh		1934

(31027)	No.27 PRIMROSE	0-6-0T	IC	Afd		1910
(31065)	No.65	0-6-0	IC	Afd		1896
31178		0-6-0T	IC	Afd		1910
(31263)	No.263	0-4-4T	IC	Afd		1905
(31323)	323 BLUEBELL	0-6-0T	IC	Afd		1910
(31592)	No.592	0-6-0	IC	Longhedge		1901
(31618)	No.1618	2-6-0	OC	Bton		1928
(31638)	1638	2-6-0	OC	Afd		1931
32473	(473) BIRCH GROVE	0-6-2T	IC	Bton		1898
(32636)	No.672 FENCHURCH	0-6-0T	IC	Bton		1872
(32655)	55 STEPNEY	0-6-0T	IC	Bton		1875
(34023)	21 C 123 BLACKMOOR VALE	4-6-2	3C	Bton		1946
34059	SIR ARCHIBALD SINCLAIR	4-6-2	3C	Bton		1947
(58850)	27505	0-6-0T	OC	Bow	181	1880
73082	CAMELOT	4-6-0	OC	Derby		1955
75027		4-6-0	OC	Sdn		1954
78059		2-6-0	OC	Dar		1956
80064		2-6-4T	OC	Bton		1953
80100		2-6-4T	OC	Bton		1955
80151		2-6-4T	OC	Bton		1957
92240		2-10-0	OC	Crewe		1958
	No.3 BAXTER	0-4-0T	OC	FJ	158	1877
	No.4 SHARPTHORN	0-6-0ST	IC	MW	641	1877
(D3236)	08168	0-6-0DE		Dar		1956
	BRITANNIA	4wPM		H	957	1926	a
6944	PWM 3959	2w-2PMR		Wkm	6944	1955
(TR 39	B45W DB 965564) PWM 4306	2w-2PMR		Wkm	7509	1956
	–	2w-2PMR		Wkm	7581	1956	DsmT
ƆXN 68001 00		2w-2DMR		Wkm	10705	1974
			reb	Ashford		1993
ƆXN 68001 01		2w-2DMR		Wkm	10708	1974
			reb	Ashford		1993
	–	2w-2PMR		Wkm			DsmT

a   runs on propane gas

BRIGHTON RAILWAY MUSEUM, PRESTON PARK, BRIGHTON (Closed)
Gauge 4ft 8½in   TQ 302061

	–	0-4-0DM		RH	260754	1950
	BESSIE	0-4-0DM		RH	260755	1950

DRUSILLA'S ZOO PARK, BERWICK, near EASTBOURNE
Gauge 2ft 0in   TQ 524050

	–	0-4-2+4-4wDH	s/o	MetalbauE		2007
2	BILL	4wDM		MR	9409	1948

THE CLAUDE JESSETT TRUST COMPANY, THE GREAT BUSH RAILWAY, TINKERS PARK, HADLOW DOWN, near UCKFIELD

Gauge 2ft 0in   TQ 538241

No.3	SAO DOMINGOS	0-6-0WT	OC	OK	11784	1928	
1	AMINAL	4wDM		MR		c1931	
				reb	‡		
4	MILD	4wDM		MR	8687	1941	
4		4wDM		RH	177638	1936	+
5	ALPHA	4wDM		RH	183744	1937	
14	ALBANY	4wDM		RH	213840	1941	
22		4wDM		RH	226302	1944	
24		4wDM		RH	382820	1955	
21		4wBE		WR	5035	1954	Dsm
No.22	LAMA	4wBE		WR	5033	1953	
23		0-4-0BE		WR	M7534	1972	Dsm
No.24	TITCH	0-4-0BE		WR	M7535	1972	
No.25	WOLF	4wDM		MR	7469	1940	

‡   rebuilt by Ludlay Brick Co, Berwick, near Eastbourne, Sussex
+   carries plate RH 177642/1936

LAVENDER LINE PRESERVATION SOCIETY, ISFIELD STATION, STATION ROAD, ISFIELD, near UCKFIELD

Gauge 4ft 8½in   TQ 452171

68012	BLACKIE		0-6-0ST	IC	HE	3193	1944	
				reb	HE	3887	1964	
	LADY ANGELA		0-4-0ST	OC	P	1690	1926	
V47			0-4-0ST	OC	P	2012	1941	
(D2020)	03020	F134L	0-6-0DM		Sdn		1958	+
(D2197)	03197		0-6-0DM		Sdn		1961	+
WD 825	15	QUEENBOROUGH	0-4-0DM		AB	354	1941	
				reb	BIS		1957	
–			4wDM		FH	3658	1953	
				rep	Resco	L112		
No.16	WEM		0-4-0DM		_(VF	5257	1945	
					(DC	2176	1945	
(205023)	60122		4-4wDER		Afd/Elh		1957	
205033	60151		4-4wDER		Afd/Elh		1957	
PW2	PWM 3951		2w-2PMR		Wkm	6936	1955	

+   property of Harry Needle Railroad Co Ltd, Merseyside

A. PRAGNELL, PRIVATE LOCATION, near HORSTED KEYNES

Gauge 4ft 8½in

–		2w-2PMR	Syl	14384		
(900855)		2w-2PMR	Wkm	6967	1954	a
–		2w-2PMR	Wkm	7445	1956	DsmT
–		2w-2PMR	Wkm		1932	b

a   carries plate Wkm 7445/1956
b   carries plate Wkm 7581/1956

ROTHER VALLEY RAILWAY LTD,
STATION HOUSE, STATION ROAD, ROBERTSBRIDGE
Gauge 4ft 8½in   TQ 734235

D99	11790		0-4-0DM	_(VF	D77	1947	
				(DC	2251	1947	
	TITAN		0-4-0DM	_(VF	D140	1951	
				(DC	2274	1951	
97701			4wDE	Matisa	2655	1975	
		reb		Kilmarnock		1986	
PX 205			2w-2DH	RVR		c2005	a

a   rebuilt from a Track-lifting machine

ST.LEONARDS RAILWAY ENGINEERING LTD,
ST.LEONARDS WEST MARINA RAILWAY DEPOT, BRIDGE WAY, ST.LEONARDS
Gauge 4ft 8½in   TQ 775084

(D2995)	07011		0-6-0DE	RH	480696	1962
		reb		Resco	L105	1978
1001	S 60000	HASTINGS	4-4wDER	Afd/Elh		1957
1001	S 60001		4-4wDER	Afd/Elh		1957
1012	S 60016	(S60016 S60226)				
		MOUNTFIELD	4-4wDER	Afd/Elh		1957
1013	S60118					
		TUNBRIDGE WELLS	4-4wDER	Afd/Elh		1957
	S 60019		4-4wDER	Afd/Elh		1957
	(S60145)	977939	4-4wDER	Afd/Elh		1960
	(S60149)	977940	4-4wDER	Afd/Elh		1961

VOLKS ELECTRIC RAILWAY, BRIGHTON
Gauge 2ft 8½in   TQ 326035

3		4wRE	VER		1892	
4		4wRE	VER		1892	
6		4wRE	VER		1901	
7		4wRE	VER		1901	
8		4wRE	VER		1901	
9		4wRER	BE		1898	
	reb		BE		c1911	
	reb		‡		1950	OOU a
9		4wRE	VER		1910	
10		4wRE	VER		1926	
–		4wDM	AK	40SD530	1987	

‡   rebuilt by Brighton Corporation Tramway Department
a   currently at South Downs Heritage Centre, Hassocks

WEST SUSSEX

INDUSTRIAL SITES

TUNNEQUIP LTD, WEALDEN WORKS (REDLAND), LANGHURSTWOOD ROAD, HORSHAM
Gauge 1ft 6in

–		4wBH		Tunn	TQ121	1980
			reb	Tunn		1996
–		4wBH		Tunn	TQ122	1980
			reb	Tunn		1996
–		4wBH		Tunn	TQ123	1980
			reb	Tunn		1996
–		4wBH		Tunn	TQ124	1980
			reb	Tunn		1996
–		4wBH		Tunn	TQ125	1980
			reb	Tunn		1996
–		4wBH		Tunn	TQ126	1980
			reb	Tunn		1996

PRESERVATION SITES

A. CROUCHER, LANCING AREA
Gauge 4ft 8½in   Kept at a private location

1		2w-2PMR	Wkm	6952	1955

HOLLYCOMBE STEAM & WOODLAND GARDEN SOCIETY, HOLLYCOMBE STEAM COLLECTION, IRON HILL, LIPHOOK
Gauge 4ft 8½in   SU 852295

50	COMMANDER B	0-4-0ST	OC	HL	2450	1899
3	JACK	0-4-0DH		YE	2679	1962

Gauge 3ft 0in

	"EXCELSIOR"	2-2-0WT	G	AP	1607	1880

Gauge 2ft 0in

70	CALEDONIA	0-4-0WT	OC	AB	1995	1931
38	JERRY M	0-4-0ST	OC	HE	638	1895
	PIXIE	0-4-0ST	OC	WB	2090	1919
	JOFFRE	4wDM		MR	8994	1943
16	JACK	4wDM		RH	203016	1940

THE KINGSTON LIGHT RAILWAY, c/o N. KELLY, 4 KINGSTON CLOSE, SHOREHAM-BY-SEA
Gauge 600mm

CLAY CROSS	4wDM	L	41803	1955

SOUTHERN INDUSTRIAL HISTORY CENTRE TRUST, AMBERLEY MUSEUM, HOUGHTON BRIDGE, AMBERLEY, ARUNDEL

Gauge 4ft 8½in   www.amberleymuseum.co.uk   TQ 031122

No.2 BURT	4wDM	MR	9019	1950

Gauge 3ft 2¼in

1 TOWNSEND HOOK	0-4-0T	OC	FJ	172L	1880
MONTY	4wDM		OK	7269	1936

Gauge 3ft 0in

SCALDWELL	0-6-0ST	OC	P	1316	1913

Gauge 2ft 11in

–	4wDM		MR	10161	1950

Gauge 2ft 6in

T0001 ND10261 00 NZ 26	4wDH		BD	3751	1980
–	4wPM		HU	45913	1932

Gauge 2ft 0in

BARBOUILLEUR	0-4-0WT	OC	Decauville	1126	1947
POLAR BEAR	2-4-0T	OC	WB	1781	1905
PETER	0-4-0ST	OC	WB	2067	1918
WENDY	0-4-0ST	OC	WB	2091	1919
808	2w-2-2-2wRE		EEDK	808	1931
–	4wDM		FH	1980	1936
–	4wPM		(FH	3627	1953 ?)
–	0-4-0DMF		HC	DM686	1948
THAKEHAM TILES No.3	4wDM		HE	2208	1941
–	4wDM		HE	3097	1944
THAKEHAM TILES No.4	4wDM		HE	3653	1948
12	4wDH		HE	8969	1980
–	4wDM		HE		
PELDON	4wDM		JF	21295	1936
–	4wPM		L	33937	1949
–	4wPM		L	34521	1949
–	4wPM		MR	872	1918
		reb	MR	3720	1925
3101	4wPM		MR	1381	1918
27	4wDM		MR	5863	1934

–		4wDM	MR	11001	1956	
6193	REDLAND	4wDM	OK	6193	1935	
7741	THE MAJOR	4wDM	OK	7741	1937	
No.2		4wDM	RH	166024	1933	
18		4wDM	RH	187081	1937	
–		4wDM	R&R	80	1937	
–		4wDH	Schöma	5239	1991	
–		4wPM	Thakeham		c1946	
–		4wPM	Thakeham		c1950	
–		4wBE	BE	16303	c1917	
–		4wBE	BE	16306	c1917	Dsm
–		4wBE	WR	4998	1953	
2 50		4wBE	WR	5031	1953	
–		4wBE	WR	(5034	1953?)	
–		0-4-0BE	WR	T8033	1979	
	RTT/767159	2w-2PM	Wkm	3161	c1943	
WD 904		2w-2PMR	Wkm	3403	1943	

Gauge 1ft 10in

23	0-4-0T	IC	Spence	29L	1920

Gauge monorail

–	2wPH	RM	9514	1960

WARWICKSHIRE

INDUSTRIAL SITES

ALLELYS HEAVY HAULAGE LTD, THE SLOUGH, STUDLEY
Locomotives in transit are also stored in the yard for short periods of time.
Gauge 4ft 8½in

TEUCER	0-4-0DM	_(VF	D294	1955	
		(DC	2567	1955	OOU

EUROPEAN METAL RECYCLING LTD, METAL MERCHANTS AND PROCESSORS, TRINITY ROAD, KINGSBURY
Locomotives for scrap are occasionally present at this location.   SP 219969

MINISTRY OF DEFENCE, DEFENCE MUNITIONS, KINETON
See Section 6 for full details of MOD locos.
The following are stored on site for third parties:
Gauge 4ft 8½in

65217	306 017	4w-4wWER	MetCam	1949	Pvd

MORGAN EST, PLANT DEPOT, WATLING STREET, RUGBY
Locos are occasionally present for repair   SP 533788

MOTORAIL LOGISTICS, LONG MARSTON
Also mainline and former mainline locomotives and rolling stock stored for reuse/resale.
Gauge 4ft 8½in

(D1754	47160)	47746	Co-CoDE	BT	482	1964
(D3415)	08345	RUSSELL	0-6-0DE	Derby		1958
(D3679)	08517		0-6-0DE	Dar		1958 +
(D3835)	08668		0-6-0DE	Crewe		1960 +
(D3896)	08728		0-6-0DE	Crewe		1960
(D3904)	08736	LOCO 4	0-6-0DE	Crewe		1960
(D3981)	08813		0-6-0DE	Derby		1960 +
(D3995)	08827		0-6-0DE	Derby		1960 +
(D4037)	08869		0-6-0DE	Dar		1960 +
(D4158)	08928		0-6-0DE	Dar		1962 +
(D8016)	20016		Bo-BoDE	_(EE	2363	1957
				(VF	D391	1957 +
(D8032)	20032		Bo-BoDE	_(EE	2754	1957
				(RSHD	8064	1957 +
(D8057)	20057		Bo-BoDE	_(EE	2963	1961
				(RSHD	8215	1961 +
(D8060	20060)	20902	Bo-BoDE	_(EE	2966	1961
				(RSHD	8218	1961 +
(D8072)	20072		Bo-BoDE	_(EE	2978	1961
				(RSHD	8230	1961 +

(D8081)	20081		Bo-BoDE	_(EE	2987	1961		
				(RSHD	8239	1961	+	
(D8083)	20903		Bo-BoDE	_(EE	2989	1961		
				(RSHD	8241	1961	+	
(D8088)	20088 2017 37		Bo-BoDE	_(EE	2994	1961		
				(RSHD	8246	1961	+	
(D8315)	20215		Bo-BoDE	_(EE	3696	1967		
				(EEV	D1091	1967	+	
(E3199	86001) 86401		Bo-BoWE	_(EEV	3491	1965		
				(VF	E337	1965		
(E6045)	73138		Bo-BoDE/RE	_(EE	3717	1966		
				(EEV	E377	1966		
51352			2-2w-2w-2DMR	PSteel		1960		
51376			2-2w-2w-2DMR	PSteel		1960		
RRM 22			0-6-0DH	EEV	D1231	1967	+	
X7202	KEMIRA 2		0-6-0DH	EEV	D1233	1968	+	
–			0-6-0DH	EEV	5352	1971	+	
No.503			0-6-0DH	HE	6614	1965		
	RACHAEL		0-6-0DH	HE	7003	1971	+	
No.5			0-4-0DH	HE	7161	1970	+	
28	3D 63/000/316		0-6-0DH	HE	7181	1970	+	
–			0-6-0DH	HE	7276	1972	+	
28			0-6-0DH	HE	7279	1972	+	
	EMMA		0-6-0DH	HE	8902	1978	+	
–			0-4-0DH	RR	10204	1965	+	
	H021		4wDH	RR	10251	1966	OOU	+
014	SUZIE		0-4-0DH	S	10119	1962	OOU	+
LB2	H013 No.10137		0-4-0DH	S	10137	1962	OOU	+
			8wDH	R/R	Minilok	160	1991	
			4wDH	R/R	Minilok			
TH 104			2w-2DMR	Robel				
				56.27-10-AG35		1983	+	

+   property of Harry Needle Railroad Co Ltd, Merseyside

A.C. Electrics Ltd

13	(692)	0-6-0DE	_(EE	2146	1956	
			(VF	D336	1956	a

a   Property of RMS Locotec Ltd, Wakefield, West Yorkshire

MOVERIGHT INTERNATIONAL c/o
JOHN WATTS FARMS, RYE FARM, RYEFIELD LANE, WISHAW
Gauge 4ft 8½in   SP 180945

3845		2-8-0	OC	Sdn		1942	
(D1662)	47484	Co-CoDE		Crewe		1965	
(D4157)	08927	0-6-0DE		Hor		1962	
2001	AT3 DJ 053 (D8035 20035)	Bo-BoDE		(EE	2757	1959	
				(VF	D482	1959	
2002	AT3 DJ 054 (D8063 20063)	Bo-BoDE		(EE	2969	1961	
				(RSHD	8221	1961	

```
2003  AT3 DJ 051 (D8139 20139)  Bo-BoDE        (EE    3610   1966
                                               (EEV   D1009  1966
(685)                           0-6-0DE        (EE    2124   1956
                                               (VF    D314   1956
–                               4wDH           WB     3208   1961   OOU
```

Gauge 3ft 6in

```
390                             4-8-0    OC    SS     4150   1896
```

Locomotives in transit are also stored in the yard for short periods of time.

PRISON SERVICE COLLEGE,
NEWBOLD REVEL, STRETTON-UNDER-FOSSE, near RUGBY
Gauge 2ft 0in   SP 455808

```
–                               4wDM           L      33651  1949   Pvd
```


SEVERN LAMB UK LTD, ARDEN INDUSTRIAL ESTATE, TYTHING ROAD, ALCESTER
New miniature locos under construction, and locos in for repair, usually present.   SP 097587

TNT LOGISTICS UK LTD, VW CARS DISTRIBUTION CENTRE, BIRCH COPPICE
BUSINESS PARK, DORDON
Gauge 4ft 8½in   SK 252005

```
9210                            4wDM     R/R   Unimog
                                               WDB4951021W199146    2002
```


UK COAL MINING LTD, DAW MILL COLLIERY, OVER WHITACRE
Headquarters: Harworth Park, Blyth Road, Harworth, Nottinghamshire DN11 8DB
                                                                    SP 257902
Gauge 3ft 0in — Underground

```
No.1                            4wBEF          CE     B0990A  1976
No.2                            4wBEF          CE     B0990B  1976
No.3                            4wBEF          CE     B1839   1979
No.4                            4wBEF          CE     B3040A  1983
No.5                            4wBEF          CE     B3040B  1983
No.6                            4wBEF          CE     B3201A  1985
                                         reb   CE     B4338   2000
No.7                            4wBEF          CE     B3201B  1985
                                         reb   CE     B4308   1999
–                               4wBEF          CE     B3517   1988
No.10  LAURA                    4w-4wBEF       HE     9310    1992
No.11  LINZI                    4w-4wBEF       HE     9311    1992
```

PRESERVATION SITES

ANDREW BRIDDON, LONG MARSTON
This is the complete FLEET LIST of all locos owned, but some may be stored at other sites.

Gauge 4ft 8½in

–	2w-2DMR	Wkm	(6607	1953?)	a

a   currently stored eleswhere

COVENTRY ELECTRIC RAILWAY CENTRE, ROWLEY ROAD, BAGINTON, COVENTRY
Gauge 4ft 8½in   SP 354751

4311	61287		4w-4wRER	Afd/Elh		1959
4732	12795		4w-4wRER	Lancing/Elh		1951
4732	12796		4w-4wRER	Lancing/Elh		1951
(6307)	(14573)		4w-4wRER	Lancing/Elh		1959
28690			4w-4wRER	DerbyC&W		c1939
(S65321)	ADB 977505	(930053)	4w-4RER	Elh		1954
(936.003)	No.3 ADB977349	(M61183)	4w-4wRER	Afd/Elh		1957
–			4wBE/WE	EEDK	905	1935
–			4wPM	FH	2895	1944
42			Bo-BoWE	HL	3682	1927
–			0-4-0DE	RH	268881	1949
–			4wDM	RH	338416	1953

THE ENGINEERING EMPORIUM, BRAMCOTE WORKS, BRAMCOTE FIELDS FARM
Gauge 2ft 0in

81.04	19	4wDM	HE	6298	1964	OOU
81.02		4wDM	RH	260712	1948	OOU
–		4wDM	RH	452294	1960	Dsm

J.W.LEWIS, BEACON VIEW, BENTLEYS LANE, MAXSTOKE
Gauge 4ft 8½in   SP 244875

AD 9124	4wDMR	BD	3713	1975
RS/140	4wDM	FH	3892	1958

OHN PAYNE, PRIVATE LOCATION

his is understood to be a complete FLEET LIST of the locos owned by (or in the care of) this firm. Some
cos are for hire or resale, and may be in use or stored at a number of locations.

auge 4ft 8½in

97653	0-6-0DE		RH	431760	1959	Dsm
D No.26653 TANGO	4wDH		BD	3730	1977	
00 NZ 66	4wDH		BD	3732	1977	
RMY 413 C2SA ND10490	0-4-0DH		NBQ	27648	1959	
–	4wDM		RH	210481	1941	Dsm
–	4wDM		RH	235519	1945	
–	4wDH		RR	10242	1966	
YARD No.10433	0-4-0DM		_(VF	5258	1945	
			(DC	2177	1945	
		reb	YEC	L121	1993	
–	0-4-0DE		YE	2856	1961	

HE STRATFORD & BROADWAY RAILWAY SOCIETY,
ONG MARSTON, near STRATFORD-UPON-AVON

auge 4ft 8½in   SP 153473

MET	0-4-0ST	OC	HL	2800	1909
No.4	0-4-0ST	OC	HL	3719	1928
No.3 AGECROFT No.1	0-4-0ST	OC	RSHN	7416	1948
D70047 MULBERRY	0-4-0DM		AB	362	1942
OF CHORLEY 4 18242	0-4-0DH		JF	4220022	1962

WESTMACOTT, 13 ALCESTER ROAD, STUDLEY

auge 1ft 11½in   SP 074639

–	4wDM	RH	193974	1938

. WINCOTE, NUNEATON

auge 4ft 8½in

(TR18) PWM 4301	2w-2PMR	Wkm	7504	1956
WM 4302 THE HAVEN	2w-2PMR	Wkm	7505	1956

WEST MIDLANDS

INDUSTRIAL SITES

DHL, PROLOGIS PARK INDUSTRIAL ESTATE, COVENTRY
Gauge 4ft 8½in   SP 32X84X

(D3460)	08375	0-6-0DE	Dar	1957	a

a   on hire from RMS Locotec Ltd, Wakefield, West Yorkshire

TRAVEL MIDLAND METRO,
WEDNESBURY DEPOT, POTTERS LANE, WEDNESBURY
Gauge 4ft 8½in   SO 984945

R199 EOX	4wDM	R/R	Iveco	1998	
Q179 VOH	4wDM	R/R	Unimog		
			4271151 W166200	1991	a

a   property of Centro

J.P.M. PARRY & ASSOCIATES LTD,
CORNGREAVES TRADING ESTATE, OVEREND ROAD, CRADLEY HEATH
Gauge 610mm / 760mm   SO 948853

–	2w-2FER	Parry	8	1994	+	Dsm

+   test-bed vehicle

PARRY PEOPLE MOVERS LTD,
CORNGREAVES TRADING ESTATE, OVEREND ROAD, CRADLEY HEATH
PPM vehicles occasionally present under construction or repair.   SO 948853

INNOVATE RAIL LTD, ROUND OAK RAIL TERMINAL, PEDMORE ROAD, BRIERLEY HILL
Gauge 4ft 8½in   SO 925879

–	0-6-0DH	AB	491	1964
LANCE	0-6-0DH	S	10150	1963
293V	0-6-0DH	TH	293V	1980

SALFORD METALS LTD, LONG ACRE, LITCHFIELD ROAD
Gauge 4ft 8½in

SIR HENRY TARONI EXPRESS	0-4-0DH	HE	7259	1971
	reb	HE	9286	1987

STONE BROTHERS, 41 ROUND ROAD, COSELEY, BILSTON, WOLVERHAMPTON
Gauge 2ft 6in

YARD No.B48	ND 3306	2w-2BE	GB	3545	1948

T.M.A. ENGINEERING LTD, TYBURN ROAD, ERDINGTON, BIRMINGHAM
New locos under construction, and locos for repair, are occasionally present.

PRESERVATION SITES

BIRMINGHAM ALLIANCE, MOOR STREET STATION, BIRMINGHAM
Gauge 4ft 8½in   SP 074867

2885	2-8-0	OC	Sdn	1938

CADBURY WORLD, BOURNVILLE
Gauge 4ft 8½in

No.14	CADBURY	0-4-0DM	HC	D1012	1956

W.T. HUNT, PRIVATE LOCATION
Gauge 1ft 3in

	PRINCE OF WALES	4-4-2	OC	BL	11	1908	OOU

L.C.P. PROPERTIES LTD, PENSNETT TRADING ESTATE, SHUT END
Gauge 4ft 8½in   SO 900894, 901897

2025	WINSTON CHURCHILL	0-6-0ST	IC	MW	2025	1923
–		4wDM		RH	215755	1942

STANDARD GAUGE STEAM TRUST, TYSELEY LOCOMOTIVE WORKS, THE STEAM DEPOT, WARWICK ROAD, TYSELEY, BIRMINGHAM
Gauge 4ft 8½in   SP 105841

4110		2-6-2T	OC	Sdn	1936
4121		2-6-2T	OC	Sdn	1937
4936	KINLET HALL	4-6-0	OC	Sdn	1929
4953	PITCHFORD HALL	4-6-0	OC	Sdn	1929
4965	ROOD ASHTON HALL	4-6-0	OC	Sdn	1929
5029	NUNNEY CASTLE	4-6-0	OC	Sdn	1934
5043	EARL OF MOUNT EDGCUMBE	4-6-0	4C	Sdn	1936
6024	KING EDWARD I	4-6-0	4C	Sdn	1930
7029	CLUN CASTLE	4-6-0	4C	Sdn	1950

7752		0-6-0PT	IC	NBQ	24040	1930	
7760		0-6-0PT	IC	NBQ	24048	1930	
–		0-6-0ST	IC	RSHN	7289	1945	
9600		0-6-0PT	IC	Sdn		1945	
	EDMUNDSONS	0-4-0ST	OC	AB	2168	1943	
No.1	CADBURY	0-4-0T	OC	AE	1977	1925	
6	1	0-4-0ST	OC	P	2004	1941	
No.670		2-2-2	IC	TyseleyLW		1989	+

(D318	97408)	40118	1Co-Co1DE	_(EE	2853	1961	
				(RSHD	8148	1961	
(D417)	50017	(50117)					
		ROYAL OAK	Co-CoDE	_(EE	3787	1967	
				(EEV	D1158	1967	
(D421)	50021	RODNEY	Co-CoDE	_(EE	3791	1968	
				(EEV	D1162	1968	
(D433)	50033	GLORIOUS	Co-CoDE	_(EE	3803	1968	
				(EEV	D1174	1968	
(D449	50149)	50049 DEFIANCE	Co-CoDE	_(EE	3819	1968	
				(EEV	D1190	1968	
(D1755	47161 47541)	47773	Co-CoDE	BT	483	1964	
(D1762	47167 47580)	47732	Co-CoDE	BT	524	1964	
(D1943	47500)	47770	Co-CoDE	BT	705	1966	
(D3029	08021)	13029	0-6-0DE	Derby		1953	
(D6964)	37264		Co-CoDE	_(EE	3524	1965	
				(EEV	D953	1965	
(D8059)	20059		Bo-BoDE	_(EE	2965	1961	
				(RSHD	8217	1961	
(D8177)	20177		Bo-BoDE	_(EE	3648	1966	
				(EEV	D1047	1966	
(E3137	86045)	86259	Bo-BoWE	Don		1965	
	87031		Bo-BoWE	Crewe		1974	
No.800			0-4-0PM	Bg	800	1920	
13	–		4wDM	RH	299099	1950	
	–		0-6-0DM	RH	347747	1957	
	–		0-6-0DH	RR	10255	1966	a
(55034)	(977828)		2-2w-2w-2DMR	PSteel		1961	

+   not yet completed
a   property of Somerset & Dorset Loco Company

SMITH'S of LYE, LYE CROSS
Gauge 4ft 8½in   SO 921847

–	0-4-0DM	Bg	3590	1962

THINKTANK, MILLENNIUM POINT, CURZON STREET, BIRMINGHAM
Gauge 4ft 8½in   SP 084875

46235	CITY OF BIRMINGHAM	4-6-2	4C	Crewe	1939

JK COUNTY DONEGAL GROUP, BIRMINGHAM
Gauge 3ft 0in

–	2w-2PMR	Wkm	4091	1946	Dsm	

WILTSHIRE

INDUSTRIAL SITES

BATH & PORTLAND STONE LTD, MONKS PARK MINE, CORSHAM
Mine currently closed - Locomotive stored underground.   ST 878682
Gauge 2ft 6in

8	4wBE	GB	2920	1958	OOU

**LAFARGE CEMENT, WESTBURY BUSINESS UNIT (CEMENT WORKS),
CROWBRIDGE ROAD, WESTBURY**
(division of Blue Circle Industries plc)
Gauge 4ft 8½in   ST 885527

–	0-6-0DH	S	10108	1963	
	reb	TH		1987	
–	0-6-0DH	TH	278V	1978	

**COOPERS (METALS) LTD,
BRIDGE HOUSE, GIPSY LANE WORKS, GIPSY LANE, SWINDON**
(part of European Metal Recycling)
Gauge 4ft 8½in   SU 165860

–	0-6-0DH	HC	D1377	1966	
	reb	HE	9036	1979	
	reb	YEC	L186	2000	

MERYS MINERALS LTD, BROADLANDS QUARRY, QUIDHAMPTON, SALISBURY
Gauge 4ft 8½in   SU 114314

01571	CORAL	0-6-0DH	TH	261V	1976
		reb	YEC	L124	1996

**MINISTRY OF DEFENCE, DEFENCE COMMUNICATIONS SERVICES AGENCY,
BASIL HILL SITE, PARK LANE, CORSHAM**
Gauge 600mm Underground   ST 851694

WD No.1	MW 11025	4wDM	RH	179009	1936	OOU
28	M.W. 11026	4wDM	RH	(?))	1938	OOU

MINISTRY OF DEFENCE, LUDGERSHALL RAILHEAD

See Section 6 for full details.

CHILMARK STONE – HURDCOTT STONE, CHILMARK MINE, MoD AFD CHILMARK DEPOT

Gauge 2ft 0in   ST 976312

–	4wDM		MR	9932	1972
		reb	AK		1988

Mrs. WHITES GARDEN LTD, NURSERY

Gauge monorail

–	2a-2DH	AK	M001	1988

PRESERVATION SITES

Mr. S. CLARKE

Locomotive stored at a private location
Gauge 2ft 0in

–	4wDM	MR	8720	1941

GREAT WESTERN DESIGNER OUTLET VILLAGE, SWINDON

Gauge 4ft 8½in   SU 138847

7819	HINTON MANOR	4-6-0	OC	Sdn	1939

LONGLEAT LIGHT RAILWAY, LONGLEAT, WARMINSTER

Gauge 1ft 3in   ST 808432

6	JOHN HAYTON		0-6-2T	OC	ESR	323	2004
7	FLYNN		0-6-0DH		AK	79	2007
4	LENKA		4-4wDHR		Longleat		1984
5	CEAWLIN		2-8-2DH	s/o	Longleat		1989
	a rebuild of		2-8-0DH	s/o	SL	75 356	1975
	rebuilt		0-6-2DH	s/o	Longleat		

PRIVATE OWNER, UNKNOWN LOCATION

Gauge 1ft 6in

GNR No.1	2-2-2	IC	?		c1863

SCIENCE MUSEUM, ANNEXE, WROUGHTON, near SWINDON
Not on public display.   SU 131790

Gauge 2ft 0in

| 807 | | 2w-2-2-2wRE | EEDK | 807 | 1931 | Dsm | a |

a   one power bogie at British Postal Museum, Essex

STEAM MUSEUM OF THE GREAT WESTERN RAILWAY,
SWINDON HERITAGE CENTRE, SWINDON WORKS.
Gauge 7ft 0¼in

| | NORTH STAR | 2-2-2 | IC | Sdn | | 1925 | + |

+   replica, incorporating parts of the original, RS 150/1837

Gauge 4ft 8½in

2516		0-6-0	IC	Sdn	1557	1897	
4073	CAERPHILLY CASTLE	4-6-0	4C	Sdn		1923	
4248		2-8-0T	3C	Sdn		1916	
6000	KING GEORGE V	4-6-0	4C	Sdn		1927	
9400		0-6-0PT	IC	Sdn		1947	
92220	EVENING STAR	2-10-0	OC	Sdn		1960	
	AGECROFT No.3	0-4-0ST	OC	RSHN	7681	1951	
(W4W)	No.4	4w-2w+2DMR		_(AEC (852004?)		1934	
				(PRoyal B3550		1934	
A38W		2w-2PMR		Wkm	8505	1960	

SWINDON & CRICKLADE RAILWAY SOCIETY, near SWINDON
Locomotives are kept at::–   Blunsdon Road Station SU 110897
                                                   Hayes Knoll SU 106907

Gauge 4ft 8½in

	SWORDFISH	0-6-0ST	OC	AB	2138	1941	
	SALMON	0-6-0ST	OC	AB	2139	1942	
45		0-4-0ST	OC	AB	2352	1954	
	RICHARD TREVITHICK	0-4-0ST	OC	AB	2354	1954	
	SLOUGH ESTATES No.3	0-6-0ST	OC	HC	1544	1924	
	GUNBY	0-6-0ST	IC	HE	2413	1941	
2022	(03022)	0-6-0DM		Sdn		1958	
D2152	(03152)	0-6-0DM		Sdn		1960	
(D3261)	13261	0-6-0DE		Derby		1956	
	WOODBINE	0-4-0DM		JF	21442	1936	
–		0-4-0DM		JF	4210137	1958	+
–		0-4-0DH		JF	4220031	1964	
51074	595	2-2w-2w-2DMR		GRC&W		1959	
51104	119 021	2-2w-2w-2DMR		GRC&W		1959	
207203	60127	4w-4wDER		Afd/Elh		1962	
	DR 98504	4wDHR		Plasser	52792	1985	
–		2w-2PMR		Wkm	8089	1958	

+   incorporates parts of JF 4210082 / 1953

THE COLLEGE, SWINDON, DEPARTMENT OF ENGINEERING,
NORTH STAR SITE, NORTH STAR AVENUE, SWINDON
Gauge 1ft 2in   SU 148855

	NORTH STAR	2-2-2	IC	SdnCol		1978

THE UNDERGROUND QUARRY CENTRE,
PICKWICK QUARRY, PARK LANE, CORSHAM
Gauge 2ft 6in   ST 855702

	–	4wDM	RH	359169	1953

(Quarry has been re-opened by Hanson Quarry Products Europe Ltd. Locomotive stored on surface)

P.S. WEAVER, NEW FARM, LACOCK, near CORSHAM
Gauge 1ft 9in   ST 899691

	–	0-4-0VBT	VCG	WeaverP	1978

WORCESTERSHIRE

INDUSTRIAL SITES

SIMS BIRDS LTD, LONG MARSTON DEPOT
Locos for scrap occasionally present   SP 154458

PRESERVATION SITES

EVESHAM VALE LIGHT RAILWAY, EVESHAM COUNTRY PARK
Gauge 1ft 3in   SP 044465

No.103	JOHN	4-4-2	OC	Barnes	103	1921	
	COUNT LOUIS	4-4-2	OC	BL	32	1923	
	–	4-4-0	OC	Cagney		c1924	a
3	DOUGAL	0-6-2T	OC	SL		1970	
5751	PRINCE WILLIAM	4-6-2	OC	G&S		1949	+
712		0-4-0	OC	Morse		1951	
	SIR EGWYN	0-4-0TT	OC	ESR	312	2003	
	–	4wDM		L	41545	1955	
	–	4wDM		Eddy Knowell		2002	
	–	4wPMR		Eddy Knowell		2004	
	–	4-4-0PM		Morse		1939	

CROMWELL	4wDM	RH	452280	1960
rebuilt as	4wDH	AK	13R	1984

+   carries plate G&S 9/1946
a   currently away for restoration

SEVERN VALLEY RAILWAY CO LTD, BEWDLEY & ARLEY STATIONS
Gauge 4ft 8½in   SO 793753, 800764

For details of locos see under Shropshire entry.

D. TURNER, "FAIRHAVEN", WYCHBOLD
Gauge 2ft 0in   SO 922660

–	4wDM	MR	8600	1940

WEST MIDLANDS SAFARI PARK, BEWDLEY
SIMBA KIDDIES TRAIN
Gauge 400mm   SO 801756, 805755

–	4-6wRE	s/o	_(Dotto		1991
			(SL	365.3.91	1991

Gauge 1ft 3in

SAFARI EXPRESS	2-8-0DH	s/o	SL	15/2/79	1979

EAST YORKSHIRE

INDUSTRIAL SITES

CAVE HILL TRACTORS, SOUTH CAVE, near KINGSTON UPON HULL
Unimog vehicles for resale/conversion occasionally present.

OMYA UK MELTON DEPOT, MELTON, near KINGSTON UPON HULL
Gauge 4ft 8½in   SE 965258

–	0-6-0DH	JF	4240017	1966	OOU

WANSFORD TROUT FARM, near DRIFFIELD
Gauge 2ft 0in   TA 051568

–	4wPH	(? Denmark)

| – | 4wPH | (? Denmark) |
| – | 4wDH | (? Driffield) |

PRESERVATION SITES

**HULL CITY MUSEUM & ART GALLERIES,
'STREETLIFE', HULL MUSEUM OF TRANSPORT,
40 HIGH STREET, KINGSTON UPON HULL** **(Closed)**
Gauge **3ft 0in**   TA 103287

| 1 | 0-4-0Tram | OC | K | 2551 T56 | 1882 |

COLIN SHUTT, HOWDEN
Gauge **4ft 8½in**

| – | 2-2wPMR | ShuttC | c2005 |

NORTH YORKSHIRE

INDUSTRIAL SITES

FRANK ATKINSON LTD, WENNING AVENUE, HIGH BENTHAM
Unimog vehicles for resale/conversion occasionally present.

B.O.C.M. PAULS LTD, OLYMPIA MILLS, BARLBY ROAD, SELBY
Gauge **4ft 8½in**   R.T.C   SE 624326, 625327

| – | 4wDM | R/R | S&H | 7501 | 1966 | OOU |

CLEVELAND POTASH LTD
Boulby Mine, Loftus
Gauge **4ft 8½in**   NZ 763183

| MADDIE | 0-6-0DH | HE | 6662 | 1966 |
| KAREN | 0-6-0DH | S | 10147 | 1963 |

Gauge **1ft 6in** — Underground   NZ 765189

| – | 0-4-0BE | WR | 7654 | 1974 |

Tees Dock, Grangetown
Gauge 4ft 8½in   NZ 549235

SAM	0-6-0DH	ABG	659	2004	a
		reb of HAB	6768	1990	
		reb of AB	659	1982	
1 EMILY	0-6-0DH	ABG	660	2004	a
		reb of HAB	6769	1990	
		reb of AB	660	1982	
H 029 DUNCAN	0-6-0DH	RR	10286	1969	+
H 012	0-6-0DH	RR	10289	1970	+

+   on hire from R.M.S.Locotec Ltd, West Yorkshire
a   on hire from LH Group Services Ltd, Staffordshire

COBRA RAILFREIGHT LTD, NORTH ROAD, MIDDLESBROUGH
Gauge 4ft 8½in   NZ 488209

–	0-6-0DH	EEV	3994	1970	
	rep	YEC	L180	2000	+

+   on hire from R.M.S.Locotec Ltd, West Yorkshire

CORUS, SECTIONS, PLATES & COMMERCIAL STEELS, TEESSIDE WORKS
Redcar Coke Ovens, Redcar

Gauge 4ft 8½in   NZ 562257

1	4wWE	GB	420355/1	1976
2	4wWE	GB	420355/2	1976
3	4wWE	GB	420408	1977

South Bank Coke Ovens
Gauge 4ft 8½in   NZ 536214

1	4wWE	HartlepoolBSC	1986
2	4wWE	HartlepoolBSC	1986

CORUS CONSTRUCTIONAL AND INDUSTRIAL, TEESIDE CAST PRODUCTS, LACKENBY WORKS, MIDDLESBOROUGH
Gauge 4ft 8½in   NZ 563223

251	WALTER URWIN	6wDE	GECT	5414	1976	
252	BOULBY	6wDE	GECT	5415	1976	
253	ESTON	6wDE	GECT	5416	1976	
255	LIVERTON	6wDE	GECT	5418	1976	
–		6wDE	GECT	5421	1977	Dsm
257	NORTH SKELTON	6wDE	GECT	5426	1977	
258	GRINKLE	6wDE	GECT	5427	1977	
259	CARLIN HOW	6wDE	GECT	5428	1977	Dsm
260	ROSEDALE	6wDE	GECT	5429	1977	
261	STAITHES	6wDE	GECT	5430	1977	
262	LOFTUS	6wDE	GECT	5431	1977	

263	LUMPSEY	6wDE		GECT	5432	1977	OOU
265	ROSEBERRY	6wDE		GECT	5462	1977	
266	SHERRIFFS	6wDE		GECT	5463	1977	
267	SLAPEWATH	6wDE		GECT	5464	1977	
268	KIRKLEATHAM	6wDE		GECT	5465	1977	
269	LONGACRES	6wDE		GECT	5466	1977	
270	CHALONER	6wDE		GECT	5467	1977	OOU
271	GLAISDALE	6wDE		GECT	5469	1978	
273	KILTON	6wDE		GECT	5471	1978	OOU
274	ESKDALESIDE	6wDE		GECT	5472	1978	OOU
275	RAITHWAITE	6wDE		GECT	5473	1978	OOU
276	SPAWOOD	6wDE		GECT	5474	1978	
277	WATERFALL	6wDE		GECT	5475	1978	
279		6wDE		GECT	5478	1979	OOU
	"WESTERN QUEEN"	6wDE		GECT	5480	1979	Dsm
LM 20	LACKENBY 1	4wDM	Robel	54.12-107	AD184	1980	
LM 21	REDCAR No.2	4wDM	Robel	54.12-107	AD183	1980	

CORUS, SPECIAL SECTIONS, SKINNINGROVE WORKS, CARLIN HOW, SALTBURN-BY-THE-SEA

Gauge 4ft 8½in   NZ 708194

	WILLIAM	4wDH	S	10048	1960	a
309		0-6-0DH	YE	2825	1961	
No.314		0-6-0DH	YE	2832	1962	

a   on hire from Staffordshire Locomotives Ltd

A.V. DAWSON LTD

Locos kept at :-   Depot Road, Middlesbrough Wharf, Middlesbrough NZ 488213

                          Ayrton Store and Railhead, Forty Foot Road, Middlesbrough NZ 493215

Gauge 4ft 8½in

(D3767)	08600		0-6-0DE	Derby		1959	
(D3942)	08774	ARTHUR VERNON DAWSON					
			0-6-0DE	Derby		1960	
(D3975)	08807		0-6-0DE	Derby		1960	
(D4142)	08912		0-6-0DE	Hor		1962	Dsm
	ELEANOR DAWSON		0-4-0DM	Bg/DC	2725	1963	
–			0-4-0DM	RSHN	7900	1958	Pvd

FASTLINE, RAIL PLANT WORKSHOPS, LEEMAN ROAD, YORK

Gauge 4ft 8½in   SE 587520

01565	0-6-0DH	S	10144	1963

NATIONAL POWER plc, DRAX NATURE TRAIL, BARLOW, NEAR SELBY
Gauge 4ft 8½in — SE 653285

ALICE		0-6-0DM	EES	8199	1963	Pvd

PD PORTS TEESPORT, TEES DOCK, GRANGETOWN
Gauge 4ft 8½in — NZ 546232

4 (D3538)	08423	H 011	0-6-0DE	Derby		1958	a
(D3755)	08588		0-6-0DE	Crewe		1959	a
(625	690)	H 043	0-6-0DE	_(EE	2122	1956	
				(VF	D312	1956	a
(687)		H 046	0-6-0DE	_(EE	2129	1956	
				(VF	D319	1956	a
5	20/110/710		0-6-0DH	AB	614	1977	OOU
6			0-6-0DH	RR	10215	1965	OOU
2			0-6-0DH	RR	10239	1965	OOU
1			0-6-0DH	S	10161	1964	OOU

a   on hire from R.M.S. Locotec Ltd, West Yorkshire

PLASMOR LTD, CONCRETE BLOCK MANUFACTURERS,
BLOCK WORKS RAIL TERMINAL, HECK WORKS, GREEN LANE, GREAT HECK
Gauge 4ft 8½in — SE 597213

–		0-4-0DH	JF	4220038	1966

SELBY STORAGE & FREIGHT COMPANY LTD,
RAIL DISTRIBUTION CENTRE, SELBY
(Member of the Potter Group)
Gauge 4ft 8½in — SE 629322

–		0-6-0DH	RR	10220	1965	
–		0-6-0DH	RR	10214	1964	+

+   on hire from Harry Needle Railroad Co Ltd, Merseyside

SEMBCORP UTILITIES TEESSIDE LTD,
WILTON INTERNATIONAL MANUFACTURING SITE, MIDDLESBROUGH
serves   Enron Power Ltd
          Freightliner Ltd, Wilton Freightliner Terminal

Gauge 4ft 8½in — NZ 564218

(D3911)	08743	BRYAN TURNER	0-6-0DE		Crewe		1960
(D4133)	08903						
		JOHN W. ANTILL	0-6-0DE		Hor		1962
1			4wDH	R/R	NNM	82503	1983
T2			4wDH	R/R	NNM	83501	1983
T4	02/573		4wDH	R/R	NNM	83503	1984

T5		4wDH	R/R	NNM	83504	1984	
RO.OO5 "WILTONIA"		2w-2DMR		Wkm	7591	1957	
	rebuilt as	2w-2DHR		YEC	L112	1992	
–		2w-2PMR		Wkm	7603	1957	DsmT

TARMAC (NORTHERN) LTD, SWINDEN QUARRY, LINTON, near SKIPTON
Gauge 4ft 8½in   SD 983614

CRACOE	6w-6wDH	RFSD	
		067/GA/57000/001	1994

TRINITY RAIL, HOLGATE ROAD, YORK
Gauge 4ft 8½in   SE 585518

TM 4150 MAGNUM	4wDM	R/R	Trackmobile	
			LGN971310798	1998

UK COAL MINING LTD
Headquarters: Harworth Park, Blyth Road, Harworth, Nottinghamshire DN11 8DB
Kellingley Colliery, Kellingley

Gauge 2ft 6in — Surface   SE 527233

No.6 1-43-86	4wBEF	GB	6121	1965	Dsm

Gauge 2ft 4in — Surface

	4w-4wBEF	CE	B3224A	1985	OOU
	4w-4wBEF	CE			OOU

Gauge 2ft 6in — Underground

P3	4wBEF		CE	B1574G	1978
		reb	CE	B3864A	1992
No.2 1.43.102	4wBEF		CE	B3168	1985
No.3 1.43.101	4w-4wBEF		CE	B3198A	1985
–	4w-4wBEF		CE	B3198B	1985
No.1 ML54	4wBEF		CE	B3262	1986
No.3 1.43.104	4wBEF		CE	B3266	1986
No.2 1-43-96	4wBEF		CE	B3530A	1989
No.1 1-43-97	4wBEF		CE	B3530B	1989
–	4w-4wBEF		CE	B3602A	1990
–	4w-4wBEF		CE	B3602B	1990
		reb	CE	B4388	2005
–	4wBEF		CE	B3649A	1990
–	4wBEF		CE	B3649B	1990
No.3 1.43.98	4wBEF		CE	B3644	1990
–	4w-4wBEF		CE	B3656	1990
No.4 1.43.103	4w-4wBEF		CE	B3773A	1991
No.1 1.43.296	4w-4wBEF		CE	B3832A	1992
–	4w-4wBEF		CE	B3875	1992
No.2 1.43.100	4w-4wBEF		CE	B3963	1993

–			4wBEF		CE		
				reb	CE	B4023	1994
–			6w-6wBEF		CE	B4162	1996
				reb	CE	B4349	2001
No.4	1-43-81	No.1	4wBEF		GB	6081	1964
				reb	GB	420435	1977
No.2	1-43-82		4wBEF		GB	6082	1964
No.4	1-43-92		4wBEF		GB	6083	1964
				reb	GB	420099	1968
No.11	1-43-91		4wBEF		GB	6135	1965
No.10	1-43-90		4wBEF		GB	6136	1965
	1-44-166		0-6-0DMF		_(HC	DM1426	1977
					(HE	7486	1977
	1-44-46		0-6-0DMF		_(HC	DM1434	1979
					(HE	8582	1979
	1-44-47		0-6-0DMF		_(HC	DM1441	1979
					(HE	8841	1979
	1-44-163		4wDHF		HE	7381	1976
	1-44-164		4wDHF		HE	7383	1976
No.4	1-44-177		4wDHF	RACK	HE	7490	1980
	1-44-168		4wDHF		HE	7521	1977
	1-44-180		4wDHF		HE	8833	1978
No.3	1-44-176		4wDHF	RACK	HE	8953	1978
No.10	1-44-183		4wDHF	RACK	HE	8990	1982

Becorit Heavy Duty Suspended Monorail System — Underground

	1-46-41	?	BGB	916/6/001	1979
	1-46-42	?	BGB	916/6/002	1983
	1-46-43	?	BGB	916/6/003	1983
	1-46-44	?	BGB	916/6/004	1983

Kellingley Training Centre, Kellingley

Gauge 2ft 6in — Surface · SE 529231

No.1	1-44-251	8566	4wDHF	_(HE	8566	1981
				(AB	618	1981
	1-44-161A		4wDHF	_(HE	8802	1987
				(AB	637	1987

PRESERVATION SITES

EMBSAY & BOLTON ABBEY STEAM RAILWAY, EMBSAY STATION, EMBSAY, near SKIPTON

Locomotives are kept at :– · Embsay Station SE 007533 · Bolton Abbey SE 060533

Gauge 4ft 8½in

No.22	FISHBURN COKE WORKS	0-4-0ST	OC	AB	2320	1952
	ILLINGWORTH	0-6-0ST	OC	HC	1208	1916

223 - North Yorkshire

–	0-6-0ST	OC	HC	1450	1922	
rebuilt as	0-6-0T	OC	Byworth		2000	
SLOUGH ESTATES LTD No.5	0-6-0ST	OC	HC	1709	1939	
71499	0-6-0ST	IC	HC	1776	1944	
No.140	0-6-0T	OC	HC	1821	1948	
(AIREDALE No.3)	0-6-0ST	IC	HE	1440	1923	
S112 SPITFIRE	0-6-0ST	IC	HE	2414	1941	
No.7 BEATRICE	0-6-0ST	IC	HE	2705	1945	
S.134 WHELDALE	0-6-0ST	IC	HE	3168	1944	
S.121 PRIMROSE No.2	0-6-0ST	IC	HE	3715	1952	
8 SIR ROBERT PEEL	0-6-0ST	IC	HE	3776	1952	
DARFIELD No.1	0-6-0ST	IC	HE	3783	1953	
69	0-6-0ST	IC	HE	3785	1953	
N.C.B.MONCKTON No.1	0-6-0ST	IC	HE	3788	1953	
9 6 ANNIE	0-4-0ST	OC	P	1159	1908	
68005	0-6-0ST	IC	RSHN	7169	1944	
No.4	0-4-0ST	OC	RSHN	7661	1950	
7164 ANN	4wVBT	VCG	S	7232	1927	
No.3	0-4-0ST	OC	YE	2474	1949	
D1524 (47004)	Co-CoDE		BT	419	1963	
D2203	0-6-0DM		_(VF	D145	1952	
			(DC	2400	1952	
(D3067) 08054	0-6-0DE		Dar		1953	
D3867 (08700)	0-6-0DE		Hor		1960	
(D3941) 08773	0-6-0DE		Derby		1960	
(D5537) 31119	A1A-A1ADE		BT	136	1959	
D5600 (31435) NEWTON HEATH TMD						
	A1A-A1ADE		BT	200	1960	
(D9513 N.C.B. 38)	0-6-0DH		Sdn		1964	
MEAFORD POWER STATION LOCO No.1						
	0-4-0DH		AB	440	1958	
–	4wDM		Bg/DC	2136	1938	Dsm
No.36	0-6-0DM		HC	D1037	1958	
H.W.ROBINSON	0-4-0DM		JF	4100003	1946	
	0-4-0DM		JF	4200003	1946	
–	4wDM		RH	394009	1955	
–	4wDM		Robel			
(51993) 977834 S003 960933	2-2w-2w-2DMR		DerbyC&W		1961	
SC52005 (977832)	2-2w-2w-2DMR		DerbyC&W		1961	
(52012) 977835 S003 960933	2-2w-2w-2DMR		DerbyC&W		1960	
SC52031	2-2w-2w-2DMR		DerbyC&W		1961	
DB 965095	2w-2PMR		Wkm	7610	1957	

Gauge 2ft 6in

–	4wDM	SMH	60SD755	1980	

Gauge 2ft 0in

–	4wPM	L	10225	1938	
P 1215	4wDM	MR	5213	1930	
–	4wDM	MR	8979	1946	Dsm

–		4wDM	RH	175418	1936	Dsm
.W.A. L2		4wDM	RH		
754		4wDM	SMH	60SD754	1980
RTT/767172		2w-2PM	Wkm	3164	c1943

FLAMINGOLAND, FLAMINGO PARK ZOO, KIRBY MISPERTON, near PICKERING

Gauge 2ft 0in   SE 778800

97	C.P.HUNTINGTON	4w-2-4wPH	s/o	Chance		
				73 5097-24	1973
1863	C.P.HUNTINGTON	4w-2-4wPH	s/o	Chance	
				76 50141 24	1976

GREAT YORKSHIRE RAILWAY PRESERVATION SOCIETY, DERWENT VALLEY LIGHT RAILWAY, MURTON, near YORK

Gauge 4ft 8½in   SE 650524

No.8			0-4-0ST	OC	AB	2369	1955
No.65			0-6-0ST	OC	HC	1631	1929
		rebuilt as	0-6-0T	OC			1994
(D2079)	03079		0-6-0DM		Don		1960
	CHURCHILL		0-4-0DM		JF	4100005	1947
			0-4-0DM		JF	4200022	1948
–	BRITISH SUGAR YORK		0-4-0DM		RH	327964	1953
No.1	JIM		4wDM		RH	417892	1959
No.4	OCTAVIUS ATKINSON						
088	97088		4wDM		RH	466630	1962

LIGHTWATER VALLEY LEISURE LTD, LIGHTWATER VALLEY FARM, RIPON

Gauge 1ft 3in   SE 285756

278	7	2-8-0DH	s/o	SL	17/6/79	1979
278	7	2-8-0DH	s/o	SL	1/84	1984

J.LLOYD, CASTLETON LIGHT RAILWAY, CASTLETON

Gauge 2ft 0in

–		4wDM	MR	7333	1938
7494	ALNE	4wDM	MR	7494	1940
		reb	York(BRE)		1991
–		4wDM	Eclipse		c1956

MK2 COACH PRESERVATION SOCIETY, c/o SEWARD AGRICULTURAL SUPPLIES, SINDERBY STATION near RIPON

Gauge 4ft 8½in   SE 334813

(D1723	47132)	47540	THE INSTITUTION OF CIVIL ENGINEERS			
			Co-CoDE	BT	494	1966

NATIONAL RAILWAY MUSEUM, LEEMAN ROAD, YORK

Some of the collection is exhibited at, Locomotion – at Shildon and is rotated quite frequently. Certain locomotives will be used on 'Special Runs' and also exhibited at other sites.

Gauge 7ft 0¼in   SE 594519

	IRON DUKE	4-2-2	IC	Resco		1985	+

+   incorporates parts of RSHN 7135 / 1944

Gauge 4ft 8½in

	ROCKET	0-2-2	OC	RS	4089	1934	+
	THE AGENORIA	0-4-0	VC	FosterRastrick		1829	
	ROCKET	0-2-2	OC	LocoEnt	No.2	1979	
No.1		4-2-2	OC	Don	50	1870	
No.3		0-4-0	IC	BuryC&K		1846	
No.66	AEROLITE	2-2-4T	IC	Ghd		1869	
82	BOXHILL	0-6-0T	IC	Bton		1880	
214	GLADSTONE	0-4-2	IC	Bton		1882	
673		4-2-2	IC	Derby		1897	
790	HARDWICKE	2-4-0	IC	Crewe	3286	1892	
No.1275		0-6-0	IC	D	708	1874	
No.1621		4-4-0	IC	Ghd		1893	
2818		2-8-0	OC	Sdn	2122	1905	
3440	(3717) CITY OF TRURO	4-4-0	IC	Sdn	2000	1903	
4003	LODE STAR	4-6-0	4C	Sdn	2231	1907	
(30245)	245	0-4-4T	IC	9E	501	1897	
(30850)	850 LORD NELSON	4-6-0	4C	Elh		1926	
(30925)	925 CHELTENHAM	4-4-0	3C	Elh		1934	
(31737)	No. 737	4-4-0	IC	Afd		1901	
(33001)	C1	0-6-0	IC	Bton		1942	
34051	WINSTON CHURCHILL	4-6-2	3C	Bton		1946	
35029	ELLERMAN LINES	4-6-2	3C	Elh		1949	a
(41000)	1000	4-4-0	3C	Derby		1902	
(42500)	2500	2-6-4T	3C	Derby		1934	
(45000)	5000	4-6-0	OC	Crewe	216	1934	
46229	DUCHESS OF HAMILTON	4-6-2	4C	Crewe		1938	
(50621)	No.1008	2-4-2T	IC	Hor	1	1889	
(60022)	4468 MALLARD	4-6-2	3C	Don	1870	1938	
60103	FLYING SCOTSMAN	4-6-2	3C	Don	1564	1923	
(65567)	No.8217	0-6-0	IC	Str		1905	
(68633)	No.87	0-6-0T	IC	Str	1249	1904	
	BAUXITE No.2	0-4-0ST	OC	BH	305	1874	
–		0-4-0ST	OC	RSHN	7063	1942	
	FRANK GALBRAITH	4wVBT	VCG	S	9629	1957	
KF7		4-8-4	OC	VF	4674	1935	

D1023	WESTERN FUSILIER	C-CDH		Sdn		1963	
D2860		0-4-0DH		YE	2843	1961	
(D3079 08064)	13079	0-6-0DE		Dar		1954	
(D4141)	08911 MATEY	0-6-0DE		Hor		1962	
(D5500)	31018	A1A-A1ADE		BT	71	1957	

(D9002)	55002	THE KINGS OWN YORKSHIRE LIGHT INFANTRY				
		Co-CoDE	_(EE	2907	1960	
			(VF	D559	1960	
26020	(76020)	Bo-BoWE	Gorton	1027	1951	
87001	STEPHENSON	Bo-BoWE	Crewe		1973	
252001	41001	Bo-BoDE	Crewe		1972	
M)28361(M)		4w-4wRER	DerbyC&W		c1939	b
22-141		4w-4wWER			1976	
8143	1293	4w-4RER	MV		1925	
			MetC&W		1925	
11179	3131	4w-4RER	EE/Elh		1938	
61275	4308	4w-4wRER	Afd/Elh		1959	
28249		4w-4wRER	Oerlikon		1915	
M51562		2-2w-2w-2DMR	DerbyC&W		1959	
M51922		2-2w-2w-2DMR	DerbyC&W		1960	
"7050"		0-4-0DM	_(EEDK	874	1934	
			(DC	2047	1934	
(BEL 2)	No.1	4wBE	Stoke		1917	

+   replica of loco in original condition as built in 1829
a   loco is sectioned
b   in store at MOD Kineton,

Gauge 3ft 0in

"HANDYMAN"	0-4-0ST	OC	HC	573	1900

Gauge 900mm

RA 36	4wBE/WE	HE	9423	1990

Gauge 1ft 6in

WREN	0-4-0STT	OC	BP	2825	1887
PET	0-4-0ST	IC	Crewe		1865

Gauge 1ft 4½in

–	2-4-0	OC	Young&Co	1856

Gauge 1ft 3in

LITTLE GIANT	4-4-2	OC	BL	10	1905

NORTH BAY RAILWAY CO, NORTH BAY RAILWAY, NORTHSTEAD MANOR GARDENS, NORTH BAY, SCARBOROUGH

Gauge 1ft 8in
TA 035898

1931	NEPTUNE	4-6-2DH	s/o	HC	D565	1931
No.570	ROBIN HOOD	4-6-4DH	s/o	HC	D570	1932
			reb	AK		1982
1932	TRITON	4-6-2DH	s/o	HC	D573	1932
1933	POSEIDON	4-6-2DM	s/o	HC	D582	1933
	rebuilt as	4-6-2DH	s/o	#		1991

L11	4wBE	CE	5920	1972

rebuilt by Lenwade Hydraulic Services, loco was probably DH from new and not as shown.

NORTH YORKSHIRE MOORS HISTORICAL RAILWAY TRUST LTD
NORTH YORKSHIRE MOORS RAILWAY

Locos are kept at :-

Grosmont   NZ 828049, 828053
Levisham   SE 818909
New Bridge   SE 803854
Pickering   SE 797842

Gauge 4ft 8½in

No.3672	DAME VERA LYNN	2-10-0	OC	NBH	25458	1944
3814		2-8-0	OC	Sdn		1940
6619		0-6-2T	IC	Sdn		1928
(30825)	825	4-6-0	OC	Elh		1927
30830		4-6-0	OC	Elh		1930
30841		4-6-0	OC	Elh		1936	Dsm
30926	REPTON	4-4-0	3C	Elh		1934
34101	HARTLAND	4-6-2	3C	Elh		1950
45212		4-6-0	OC	AW	1253	1935
45407		4-6-0	OC	AW	1462	1937
45428	(5428) ERIC TREACY	4-6-0	OC	AW	1483	1937
(49395)	9395	0-8-0	IC	Crewe	5662	1921
60007	SIR NIGEL GRESLEY	4-6-2	3C	Don	1863	1937
62005		2-6-0	OC	NBQ	26609	1949
(63395)	No.2238	0-8-0	OC	Dar		1918
75029		4-6-0	OC	Sdn		1954
80135		2-6-4T	OC	Bton		1956
2253		2-8-0	OC	BLW	69496	1944
No.3180	ANTWERP	0-6-0ST	IC	HE	3180	1944
No.29		0-6-2T	IC	K	4263	1904
No.5		0-6-2T	IC	RS	3377	1909

D200	(40122)	1Co-Co1DE	_(EE	2367	1957
			(VF	D395	1957
(D427)	50027 LION	Co-CoDE	_(EE	3797	1968
			(EEV	D1168	1968
D2207		0-6-0DM	_(VF	D208	1953
			(DC	2482	1953
(D3723)	08556	0-6-0DE	Dar		1959
(D)4018	(08850)	0-6-0DE	Hor		1961
D5032	(24032) HELEN TURNER	Bo-BoDE	Crewe		1959
D5061	(24061) (97201)	Bo-BoDE	Crewe		1960
D6700	(37350)	Co-CoDE	_(EE	2863	1960
			(VF	D579	1960
D7541	(25191) THE DIANA	Bo-BoDE	Derby		1965
D7628	(25278) SYBILLA	Bo-BoDE	BP	8038	1965
	DEPARTMENTAL LOCOMOTIVE No.16				
		0-4-0DM	_(EEDK	1195	1941
			(DC	2164	1941
12139	NEIL D.BARKER	0-6-0DE	EEDK	1553	1948

1		4wDM	RH	421419	1958	
No.1	RON ROTHWELL	4wDH	TH	129V	1963	
No.2		4wDH	TH	131V	1963	
205205	60110	4w-4wDER	Afd/Elh		1957	
E50204	(53204) 101680	2-2w-2w-2DMR	MetCam		1957	
E51511	101680	2-2w-2w-2DMR	MetCam		1959	
–		2w-2PMR	Wkm	417	1931	DsmT
–		2w-2PMR	Wkm	1305	1933	DsmT
4	(DB 965108)	2w-2PMR	Wkm	7623	1957	
–		2w-2PMR	Wkm			DsmT

RIPON & DISTRICT LIGHT RAILWAY, CANALSIDE, DALLAMIRES LANE, RIPON
Gauge 1ft 11½in   SE 319708

–	4wDM	L	7954	1936
No.8	4wDM	L	50191	1957

Gauge 1ft 3in

–	4wDM	StanhopeT	c1977

SALTBURN MINIATURE RAILWAY, VALLEY GARDENS, SALTBURN
Gauge 1ft 3in   NZ 667216

4472	FLYING SCOTSMAN	4-6-2gas	s/o	Artisair	1972
	PRINCE CHARLES	4-6-2DE	s/o	Barlow	1953
	GEORGE OUTHWAITE	0-4-0DH	s/o	_(SMR	1994
				(WiltonICI	1994

GRAEME WALTON-BINNS, CARGO FLEET
Gauge 2ft 0in

SINEMBE	4-4-0T	OC	WB	2287	1926
A. BOULLE	4-4-0T	OC	WB	2627	1940
CHARLES WYTOCK	4-4-0T	OC	WB	2819	1946

WENSLEYDALE RAILWAY ASSOCIATION, LEEMING BAR STATION
Gauge 4ft 8½in   SE 013889

(D1945 47502) 47715	Co-CoDE	BT	707	1966	
D5584 (31166)	A1A-A1ADE	BT	184	1960	
WESTERN WAGGONER (D2144 03144)					
	0-6-0DM	Sdn		1961	
WENSLEY	4wDM	RH	476141	1963	
(S68010) 931 090 (9010)	4w-4wRE/BER	Afd/Elh		1961	
51210	2-2w-2w-2DMR	MetCam		1958	
51247	2-2w-2w-2DMR	MetCam		1959	

(50746)	53746	2-2w-2w-2DMR	MetCam		1957	
	51572	2-2w-2w-2DMR	DerbyC&W		1960	
E 51813		2-2w-2w-2DMR	BRCW		1961	
E 51842		2-2w-2w-2DMR	BRCW		1961	
C958 YOR		4wDMR	R/R	Bruff	516	1986
(DB965045	68/011) WR 3002	2w-2PMR	Wkm		7073	1955
MPP	0010	2w-2PMR	Wkm		10731	1974

J.D. WIGGINS, MANLESS GREEN FARM, BOROUGHGATE LANE, SKELTON GREEN, SALTBURN
Gauge 2ft 0in

No.9	4wDM	RH	202969	1940	Dsm

YORKSHIRE DALES NATIONAL PARK AUTHORITY, DALES COUNTRYSIDE MUSEUM, HAWES STATION, HAWES
Gauge 4ft 8½in   SD 872900

67345	0-6-0T	OC	RSHN	7845	1955

SOUTH YORKSHIRE

INDUSTRIAL SITES

AMALGAMATED CONSTRUCTION CO LTD, MINING & CIVIL ENGINEERS, WHALEY BRIDGE, BARUGH, BARNSLEY
Locomotives are present in yard between use on contracts.
Gauge 2ft 0in   SE 320085

	713 004 091760	4wBE		CE	5238	1966
	713 005	4wBE		CE	5481	1968
	713 010	4wBE		CE	5868/3	1971
10	713 007	4wBE		CE	B0182B	1974
	713 009 T/E 332	4wBE		CE	B0182A	1974
25	713 001	4wBEF		CE	B3100A	1984
26	713 002	4wBEF		CE	B3100B	1984
No.515	091774	4wBE		CE	B3259A	1986
No.517	091775	4wBE		CE	B3259B	1986
No.516	091776	4wBE		CE	B3259C	1986

Gauge 1ft 6in

T/E 300 091756	4wBE	CE		
T/E 301 719 001	4wBE	WR	N7608	1973

rebuilt Donelon

	719 004	4wBE	CE	B0151	1973
12	T/E 333 091763	4wBE	CE	B0171B	1974
7	719 009	4wBEF	CE	B0171	1974
3	719 007	4wBEF	CE	B0171C	1974
2	719 005 LOCO 313	4wBE	CE	B1570	1978
16	719 003 LOCO 405	4wBEF	CE	B0171D	1974
	719 006	4wBE	CE	5911C	1972
	719 008	4wBE	CE	B2200A	1979

BOMBARDIER TRANSPORTATION INC. OF CANADA.,
DONCASTER WORKS, DONCASTER (Closed)
Gauge 4ft 8½in

(D3849) 08682	0-6-0DE	Hor		1959

C.F. BOOTH LTD, SCRAP MERCHANTS,
CLARENCE METAL WORKS, ARMER STREET, ROTHERHAM
Locos for scrap are also usually present at this location.

Gauge 4ft 8½in SK 421924

(LAURA)	0-6-0DH		ABG	646	2004	
		reb of	HAB	6767	1990	
		reb of	AB	646	1979	
R2 D4	0-6-0DH		EEV	D1194	1967	
LRH 08302	0-4-0DE		RH	421435	1958	OOU
426	4wDH		TH	170V	1966	

COOPERS (METALS) LTD, (incorporating Marple & Gillot),
EAST COAST ROAD, ATTERCLIFFE, SHEFFIELD
(part of European Metal Recycling)
Locomotives for scrap or resale are present at this yard from time to time. SK 373888

Gauge 4ft 8½in

33	0-6-0DH	EEV	3998	1970
GILLIAN	0-6-0DH	EEV	D1137	1966
–	0-6-0DE	YE	2714	1958

CORUS, ENGINEERING STEELS
Aldwarke Works, Rotherham
Gauge 4ft 8½in SK 447951, 449953, 449962, 451954, 452963, 456957, 459958

No. 2	0-6-0DH	GECT	5395	1974
H 025 R.A.LAWDAY	0-6-0DE	YE	2878	1963
31	0-6-0DE	YE	2904	1964
32	0-6-0DE	YE	2935	1964
35	0-6-0DE	YE	2635	1957
91	0-6-0DE	YE	2944	1965
93	0-6-0DE	YE	2889	1962

94		0-6-0DE	YE	2890	1962	
96		0-6-0DE	YE	2905	1963	
97		0-6-0DE	YE	2906	1963	

Stocksbridge Works, Stocksbridge, Sheffield
Gauge 4ft 8½in   SK 260990, 267992

No.1	714/37	4wDM	Robel	21.12RK3	1969
30		0-6-0DE	YE	2750	1959
33		0-6-0DE	YE	2740	1959
34		0-6-0DE	YE	2594	1956
37		0-6-0DE	YE	2736	1959
STOCKSBRIDGE RAILWAY CO	38	0-6-0DE	YE	2798	1961

FASTLINE, ROBERTS ROAD DEPOT, DONCASTER
Gauge 4ft 8½in

(D3689)	08527	0-6-0DE	Dar	1959	+

+   on hire from Harry Needle Railroad Co Ltd

H.M.P. LINDHOLME, BAWTRY ROAD, HATFIELD WOODHOUSE, DONCASTER
Gauge 4ft 8½in

–		0-4-0DH	GECT	5576	1979	OOU

MALTBY COLLIERY LTD, MALTBY COLLIERY, MALTBY
Gauge 2ft 6in — Surface   SK 550925

No.1	SL1	4wBEF		CE	B3434A	1987	

Gauge 2ft 6in — Underground

No.1	524/61	4wBEF		CE	B1574B	1978
No.29	524/124	4wBEF		CE	B1575E	1978
			reb	CE	B3245	1986
No.23	524/111	4wBEF		CE	B1575C	1978
No.24	524/115	4wBEF		CE	B2238A	1980
No.25	524/116	4wBEF		CE	B2238B	1980
No.26	524/121	4wBEF		CE	B2964A	1982
No.27	524/122	4wBEF		CE	B2964B	1982
No.28	524/123	4wBEF		CE	B3142B	1984
–		4w-4wBEF		CE	B3289B	1986
–		4w-4wBEF		CE	B3362B	1987
			reb	CE	B3723	1991
No.2	SL2	4wBEF		CE	B3434B	1987
No.40		4w-4wBEF		CE	B3797	1992
–		4w-4wBEF		CE	B3830B	1992
No.33	524/118	4wDHF		HE	7455	1979
No.32	524/117	4wDHF		HE	7456	1979
No.36	390/75	4wDHF		HE	8507	1984

DAVY MARKHAM, PRINCE OF WALES ROAD, DARNALL, SHEFFIELD

Gauge 4ft 8½in   SK 395875

RUNAR		4wDH		TH	189C	1967	
	a rebuild of	4wVBT	VCG	S	9536	1952	

NATIONAL GRID plc, NORTH WEST AREA,
WOODHEAD CABLE TUNNEL, DUNFORD BRIDGE & WOODHEAD

Gauge 2ft 0in   SK 114998, SE 156022

–	4wDH	AK	46	1993	
–	4wBE	CE	B4299	1998	

POWERFUEL, HATFIELD COLLIERY, STAINFORTH

Gauge 2ft 0in — Underground   SE 654113

P3			4wBEF		CE	B1574A	1978	
P1			4wBEF		CE	B1574D	1978	
P2			4wBEF		CE	B2259	1980	
				reb	CE	B3417	1988	OOU
P6			4wBEF		CE	B3101A	1984	
P5			4wBEF		CE	B3518	1988	
–			4w-4wBEF		CE	B3603	1990	
				reb	CE	B4444	2007	
P4			4wBEF		CE	B3615	1990	
–			4w-4wBEF		CE	B4447	2008	
No.111	390/HA/M/0717	No.14	0-6-0DMF		HC	DM717	1951	OOU
No.114	390/HA/M/0786	No.17	0-6-0DMF		HC	DM786	1953	Dsm
	390/MM/M/2581		0-6-0DMF		HC	DM797	1953	Dsm
	390/MM/M/2593		0-6-0DMF		HC	DM798	1953	OOU
	390/MM/M/2606		0-6-0DMF		HC	DM799	1953	Dsm
No.19	390/HA/M/0932		0-6-0DMF		HC	DM932	1956	
No.101	390/HA/M/0980	No.21	0-6-0DMF		HC	DM980	1955	Dsm
No.20	390/HA/M/0981		0-6-0DMF		HC	DM981	1956	
No.22	390/HA/M/0986		0-6-0DMF		HC	DM986	1956	Dsm
	390/T/M/3057		0-6-0DMF		HC	DM1108	1959	
–			0-6-0DMF		_(HC	DM1444	1980	
					(HE	8844	1980	Dsm

THE SCOTTS COMPANY (UK) LTD,
HATFIELD PEAT WORKS, STAINFORTH MOOR ROAD, THORNE, DONCASTER

Gauge 3ft 0in   SE 713084

–		4wDH		Schöma	5129	1990	
			reb	AK		1998	
–		4wDH		Schöma	5130	1990	
–		4wDH		Schöma	5131	1990	+
			reb	AK		1998	
–		4wDH		Schöma	5132	1990	+ OOU
	THE THOMAS BUCK	4wDH		Schöma	5220	1991	OOU

		4wDH		Schöma	5221	1991	+

+   slave unit for use with a master unit, 5129, 5130 and 5220

STAGECOACH SUPERTRAM, (Sub of Stagecoach Holdings)
NUNNERY SUPERTRAM DEPOT, WOODBOURN ROAD, SHEFFIELD
Gauge 4ft 8½in   SK 374878

M992 NNB	4wDM	R/R	Volkswagen/Perm 1995
YM 02 DJY	4wDM	R/R	Volkswagen/Harsco

UK COAL MINING LTD
Headquarters: Harworth Park, Blyth Road, Harworth, Nottinghamshire DN11 8DB

Rossington Colliery, Rossington   (Closed 31/03/2006)
Gauge 2ft 0in — Underground   SK 601985

–		4wBEF		CE	B0498.2	1977	+
			reb	CE	B4000	1994	
–		4wBEF		CE	B0498.3	1977	+
			reb	CE	B3942	1993	
–		4wBEF		CE	B1574C	1978	
			reb	CE	B3864B	1992	
–		4wBEF		CE	B2972B	1982	
			reb	CE	B3906/2	1992	
–		4wBEF		CE	B3043A	1983	
–		4wBEF		CE	B3645A	1990	
–		4wBEF		CE	B3645B	1990	
–		4w-4wBEF		CE	B3794	1991	
–		4w-4wBEF		CE			a
	KATIE	4w-4wBEF		GMT		1987	
	TRACEY	4w-4wBEF		GMT		1987	
No.19	390/R/M/2216	0-6-0DMF		HC	DM936	1956	OOU

+   locos named SHIRLEY and SUE
a   either B3335/1987 or B3732/1991

WABTEC RAIL LTD, DONCASTER WORKS, HEXTHORPE ROAD, DONCASTER
Locos under construction and repair usually present.   SE 569031

This is understood to be a complete FLEET LIST of the locos owned by (or in the care of) this company, which operates from the above address. Some locos are for hire or resale, and may be in use or stored at a number of locations.

Gauge 4ft 8½in

(D3401)	08331	H001	0-6-0DE	Derby	1957	d
(D3587)	08472		0-6-0DE	Crewe	1958	
(D3738)	08571		0-6-0DE	Crewe	1959	
(D3763	08596)		0-6-0DE	Derby	1959	a
(D3782)	08615		0-6-0DE	Derby	1959	
(D3836)	08669		0-6-0DE	Crewe	1960	
(D3858)	08691		0-6-0DE	Hor	1959	

(D3892) 08724		0-6-0DE	Crewe		1960	c
(D3932 08764) 003 FLORENCE		0-6-0DE	Hor		1961	b
(D3953 08785) 004		0-6-0DE	Derby		1960	e
(D4002) 08834 (H024) RS75		0-6-0DE	Derby		1960	
(D4021) 08853		0-6-0DE	Hor		1961	
(D8189) 20189		Bo-BoDE	_(EE	3670	1966	
			(EEV	D1065	1966	
–		4wDH	TH	166V	1966	

a   currently at Hanson Quarry Products, Somerset
b   currently at Transfesa, Tilbury Riverside Terminal, Essex
c   currently at Leeds Neville Hill Depot, West Yorkshire
d   currently at Midland Railway, Butterley, Derbyshire
e   currently at Manchester Ship Canal Co Ltd, Barton Dock, Greater Manchester

PRESERVATION SITES

COUNTY BOROUGH OF DONCASTER, MUSEUM & ART GALLERY, CHEQUER ROAD, DONCASTER
Gauge 2ft 6in

–	4wDM	LB	53977	1964	+

+   on loan from C.& D.Lawson, Hertfordshire

ELSECAR STEAM RAILWAY, ELSECAR HERITAGE WORKSHOPS, ELSECAR, BARNSLEY
Gauge 4ft 8½in   SE 386998

	EARL FITZWILLIAM	0-6-0ST	OC	AE	1917	1923	
	–	0-6-0ST	OC	AE	1945	1926	
2150		0-6-0ST	OC	P	2150	1954	
No.10	GERVASE	0-4-0VBT	VCG	S	6807	1928	
	a rebuild of	0-4-0ST		MW	1472	1900	a
–		4wVBT	VCG	S	9596	1955	
	WILLIAM	4wVBT	VCG	S	9599	1956	
(D9524)	14901	0-6-0DH		Sdn		1964	
	LOUISE	0-6-0DH		HE	6950	1967	
–		0-4-0DH		NBQ	27097	1953	
	COUNTESS FITZWILLIAM	4wDH		RH	544996	1968	

	72229	0-4-0DM		_(VF	5265	1945	
				(DC	2184	1945	
			reb	YEC	L120	1993	
	EARL OF STRAFFORD	0-6-0DE		YE	2895	1964	
DB965949	DX 68005	2w-2PMR		Wkm	10645	1972	
	–	2w-2DM					

a carries plate S 6710

Gauge 2ft 2in

	–	4wDM		RH	382808	1955

KELHAM ISLAND INDUSTRIAL MUSEUM, off ALMA STREET, SHEFFIELD

This loco is not on public display. SK 352882

Gauge 4ft 8½in

	0-4-0DE		YE	2481	1950

SOUTH YORKSHIRE TRANSPORT MUSEUM, WADDINGTON WAY, ALDWARKE, ROTHER-HAM

Gauge 4ft 8½in

	BROWN BAYLEY No.7	0-4-0ST	OC	HC	1689	1937

WEST YORKSHIRE

INDUSTRIAL SITES

CROSSLEY EVANS LTD, METAL PROCESSORS, STATION ROAD, SHIPLEY

Gauge 4ft 8½in SE 148372

42 M	PRINCE OF WALES	0-4-0DH	HE	7159	1969	
0040		4wDM	RH	284838	1950	OOU
9	BETH	4wDM	RH	425483	1958	OOU
	KATIE	4wDH	S	10023	1960	
109 L		0-4-0DH	S	10118	1962	

DUFFY CIVIL ENGINEERING, LEEDS

Gauge 2ft 0in

	–	4wBE	CE	5956	1972

ENGLISH WELSH & SCOTTISH RAILWAY, FERRYBRIDGE POWER STATION

Gauge 4ft 8½in   SE 482252

PADIHAM			0-4-0DH	AB		473	1961	OOU

R.M.S. LOCOTEC LTD, UNIT 1, GREENS INDUSTRIAL PARK, CALDER VALE ROAD, WAKEFIELD

Locos for repair/overhaul/resale and hire are usually present.   SE 249200

The following is believed to include a complete FLEET LIST of the current loco stock owned by, or in the care of, this company. Several of the locos will be out on hire at any given time (as shown in other entries in this Handbook) whilst others will be located here at Wakefield.

Gauge 4ft 8½in

68006			0-6-0ST	IC	HE	3192	1944	
				reb	HE	3888	1964	I
3809			0-6-0ST	IC	HE	3809	1954	
No.47			0-6-0ST	OC	RSHN	7849	1955	
D2199			0-6-0DM		Sdn		1961	I
(D3378)	08308		0-6-0DE		Derby		1957	
(D3460)	08375		0-6-0DE		Dar		1957	e
(D3538)	08423	H 011	0-6-0DE		Derby		1958	n
(D3685)	08523		0-6-0DE		Don		1958	s
(D3699)	08535		0-6-0DE		Dar		1959	r
(D3740)	08573		0-6-0DE		Crewe		1959	k
(D3755)	08588		0-6-0DE		Crewe		1959	n
(D3780)	08613		0-6-0DE		Derby		1959	q
(D3789)	08622	H 028	0-6-0DE		Derby		1959	m
(D3815)	08648		0-6-0DE		Hor		1959	
(D3918)	08750		0-6-0DE		Crewe		1960	
(D3922)	08754	H 041	0-6-0DE		Hor		1961	
(D3924)	08756		0-6-0DE		Hor		1961	c
(D3930)	08762		0-6-0DE		Hor		1961	
(D3956)	08788		0-6-0DE		Derby		1960	
(D3977)	08809		0-6-0DE		Derby		1960	
(D4015)	08847		0-6-0DE		Hor		1961	
(D4038)	08870	H 024	0-6-0DE		Dar		1960	h
(D4039)	08871		0-6-0DE		Dar		1960	
(D4042)	08874		0-6-0DE		Dar		1960	
(D4115)	08885	H 042	0-6-0DE		Hor		1962	c
(D4166)	08936		0-6-0DE		Dar		1962	q
(687)		H 043	0-6-0DE		_(EE	2129	1956	
					(VF	D319	1956	n
653			0-6-0DE		_(EE	2150	1956	
					(VF	D340	1956	n
(625	690)		0-6-0DE		_(EE	2122	1957	
					(VF	D312	1957	n
13	(649)	692 H.049	0-6-0DE		_(EE	2146	1956	
					(VF	D336	1956	r
MP 201			0-6-0DH		EEV	D1202	1967	*

–		0-6-0DH	EEV	3994	1970	
	rep		YEC	L180	2000	g
01573	H 006	0-6-0DH	HE	6294	1965	
HL005		0-6-0DH	HE	6295	1965	
H 015	SYLGWYN	0-6-0DH	HE	7410	1976	m
H 032	PETE GANNON	0-6-0DH	HE	7541	1976	
AD 02		2-2wDMR	Robel	56.27-10-AG36	1982	
AD 03		2-2wDMR	Robel	56.27-10-AG37	1982	
PE9803		2-2wDMR	Robel	56.27-10-AG38	1983	a
–		0-6-0DH	RR	10188	1964	
H 014		0-6-0DH	RR	10262	1967	d +
H 058		4wDH	RR	10280	1968	b
H 029	DUNCAN	0-6-0DH	RR	10286	1969	f
H 012		0-6-0DH	RR	10289	1970	f
H 055		4wDH	S	10037	1960	p
H 003	ROSEDALE	4wDH	S	10070	1961	j
H 002		4wDH	S	10164	1963	
H 057	DL2	4wDH	S	10177	1964	j
–		2w-2PMR	Wkm	7031	1954	DsmT
DX 68086	SM 02	2w-2DMR	Wkm	10841	1975	a
(DX 68088)	SM 01	2w-2DMR	Wkm	10842	1975	a

+ carries plate RR 10287
* stored elsewhere
a currently at Meldon Quarry, Devon
b currently at British Energy, Co.Durham
c currently at Network Rail, Whitemoor Yard, Cambridgeshire
d currently at Flixborough Wharf Ltd, Lincolnshire
e currently at DHL, Coventry, West Midlands
f currently at Cleveland Potash, Tees Dock, North Yorkshire
g currently at Cobra Railfreight, North Yorkshire
h currently at Castle Cement (Ketton) Ltd, Ketton Works, Rutland
j currently at Mostyn Docks Ltd, North Wales
k currently at Bombadier Transportation, Ilford Depot, Greater London
l currently at Peak Rail Ltd, Derbyshire
m currently at Corus, Trostre Works, South-West Wales
n currently at PD Ports Teesport, Tees Dock
p currently at British Energy, Nuclear Electric Division, Heysham Power Stations, Lancs
q currently at Corus, Shotton Works, North Wales
r currently at A.C. Electrics Ltd, Motorail Logistics, Long Marston, Warwickshire
s currently at Celtic Energy Ltd, Onllwyn, South West Wales

Gauge 3ft 0in

H 048		0-6-0DM	RH	281290	1949	o

o currently at Isle of Man Transport, Isle of Man

THYSSEN (GB) GROUP OF COMPANIES, THYSSEN TUNNELLING LTD, PLANT DEPOT, LANGTHWAITE GRANGE INDUSTRIAL ESTATE, SOUTH KIRKBY, PONTEFRACT

Gauge 2ft 0in   SE 457108

–	4wBEF	CE	B3086	1984	

TILITY TREE SERVICES, OAKWORTH, KEIGHLEY
auge 4ft 8½in

337 CNE	4wDM	R/R	_(Perm/Landrover		
			(Hy-rail 29930	1996	
?71 HAO	4wDM	R/R	_(Perm/Landrover		
			(Hy-rail 31101	1996	

PRESERVATION SITES

ITY OF BRADFORD METROPOLITAN COUNCIL ART GALLERIES & MUSEUMS,
RADFORD INDUSTRIAL & HORSES AT WORK MUSEUM,
OORSIDE MILLS, MOORSIDE ROAD, BRADFORD
auge 4ft 8½in   SE 184353

NELLIE	0-4-0ST	OC	HC	1435	1922

UREKA !, THE CHILDRENS MUSEUM LTD, DISCOVERY ROAD, HALIFAX
auge 4ft 8½in   SE 097247

No.96	0-4-0DM	HE	2641	1941

EIGHLEY & WORTH VALLEY LIGHT RAILWAY LTD
ocos are kept at :-   Haworth   SE 034371
                                                                               Ingrow   SE 058399
                                                                               Oxenhope SE 032355
auge 4ft 8½in

5775		0-6-0PT	IC	Sdn		1929	
(30072)	72	0-6-0T	OC	VIW	4446	1943	
34092	CITY OF WELLS	4-6-2	3C	Bton		1949	
41241		2-6-2T	OC	Crewe		1949	
43924		0-6-0	IC	Derby		1920	
45596	BAHAMAS	4-6-0	3C	NBQ	24154	1935	
			reb	HE	5596	1968	
47279		0-6-0T	IC	VF	3736	1924	
48431		2-8-0	OC	Sdn		1944	
(51218)	68	0-4-0ST	OC	Hor	811	1901	
957	(52044)	0-6-0	IC	BP	2840	1887	
(58926)	1054	0-6-2T	IC	Crewe	2979	1888	
75078		4-6-0	OC	Sdn		1956	
78022		2-6-0	OC	Dar		1954	
80002		2-6-4T	OC	Derby		1952	
No.2258	TINY	0-4-0ST	OC	AB	2258	1949	

752		0-6-0ST	IC	BP	1989	1881	
	LORD MAYOR	0-4-0ST	OC	HC	402	1893	
31	HAMBURG	0-6-0T	IC	HC	679	1903	
No.1704	NUNLOW	0-6-0T	OC	HC	1704	1938	
118	BRUSSELS	0-6-0ST	IC	HC	1782	1945	
5820		2-8-0	OC	Lima	8758	1945	
85		0-6-2T	IC	NR	5408	1899	
–		0-4-0CT	OC	RSHN	7069	1942	
90733		2-8-0	OC	VF	5200	1945	
D2511		0-6-0DM		HC	D1202	1961	
(D3336 13336)	08266	0-6-0DE		Dar		1957	
(D5209)	25059	Bo-BoDE		Derby		1963	
(D8031)	20031	Bo-BoDE		_(EE	2753	1959	
				(RSHD	8063	1959	
D 226	VULCAN	0-6-0DE		_(EE	2345	1956	
				(VF	D226	1956	
23	MERLIN	0-6-0DM		HC	D761	1951	
32	HUSKISSON	0-6-0DM		HE	2699	1944	
	"JAMES"	0-4-0DE		RH	431763	1959	
M50928		2-2w-2w-2DMR		DerbyC&W		1959	
51189		2-2w-2w-2DMR		MetCam		1958	
M51565		2-2w-2w-2DMR		DerbyC&W		1959	
51803		2-2w-2w-2DMR		MetCam		1959	
(50268)	53268	2-2w-2w-2DMR		MetCam		1958	
E79962		4wDMR		WMD	1267	1958	
M79964		4wDMR		WMD	1269	1958	
950021		2w-2PMR		Wkm	590	1932	
–		2w-2PMR		Wkm			DsmT

KIRKLEES LIGHT RAILWAY CO LTD, CLAYTON WEST, near HUDDERSFIELD
Gauge 1ft 3in   SE 258112

	FOX	2-6-2T	OC	TaylorB	No.9	1987
	BADGER	0-6-4ST	OC	TaylorB	No.10	1991
	HAWK	0-4-4-0T	4C	TaylorB	No.11	1998
			reb	TaylorB		2007
	OWL	4w-4wT	VC	TaylorB	No.12	2000
7		2-2wPH	s/o	TaylorB		1991
	JAY	4wDH		TaylorB		1992

LEEDS CITY COUNCIL, DEPARTMENT OF LEISURE SERVICES,
LEEDS INDUSTRIAL MUSEUM, ARMLEY MILLS, CANAL ROAD, LEEDS
Gauge 4ft 8½in   SE 275342

(GWR 252)		0-6-0	IC	EBW		1855	Dsm
	"ELIZABETH"	0-4-0ST	OC	HC	1888	1958	
	"HODBARROW"	0-4-0ST	OC	HE	299	1882	
R.A.F.No.111	ALDWYTH	0-6-0ST	IC	MW	865	1882	

–		4wBE		GB	1210	1930	
			reb	HE	9146	1987	
–		0-4-0WE		GB	2543	1955	
	SOUTHAM 2	0-4-0DM		HC	D625	1942	
B16	ND 3066	0-4-0DM		HE	2390	1941	
–		0-4-0DM		JF	22060	1937	
No.10	MP 351	0-4-0DM		JF	22893	1940	

Gauge 3ft 6in

	PIONEER	0-6-0DMF	HC	DM634	1946	
–		0-6-0DMF	HC	DM733	1950	

Gauge 3ft 0in

	"LORD GRANBY"	0-4-0ST	OC	HC	633	1902
4057		0-6-0DMF		HE	4057	1953
–		2-4-0DM		JF	20685	1935

Gauge 2ft 11in

–	4wDM		HC	D571	1932

Gauge 2ft 8in

H 881	0-4-0DMF		HE	3200	1945

Gauge 2ft 6in

	"JUNIN"	2-6-2DM	HC	D557	1930
–		4wBE	HT	9728	1985

Gauge 2ft 1½in

No.5	0-4-0DMF		HE	4019	1949

Gauge 2ft 0in

3	(CHEETAL)	0-6-0WT	OC	JF	15991	1923
	FAITH	0-4-0DMF		HC	DM664	1952
–		0-4-0DMF		HC	DM749	1949
–		0-6-0DMF		HC	DM803	1954
1368		4wDMF		HC	DM1368	1965
1		0-4-0DMF		HE	2008	1939
–		4wDM		HE	2959	1944
8		4wDMF		HE	4756	1954
–		0-4-0DMF		HE	5340	1957
–		4wDM		HU	36863	1929
21294	LAYER	4wDM		JF	21294	1936

Gauge 1ft 6in

	JACK	0-4-0WT	OC	HE	684	1898	
–		4wBE		GB	1325	1933	Dsm
4	5A	4wBE		GB	1326	1933	

P.N. LOWE, ABBEY LIGHT RAILWAY, BRIDGE ROAD, KIRKSTALL, LEEDS

Gauge 2ft 0in
SE 262357

"No.10"		0-4-0PM	BgC	736	1917	Dsm
11		0-4-0PM	BgC	760	1918	
12	GEORGE	4wBE	GB	2848	1957	
2	ATLAS	4wDM	HE	2463	1944	
		reb	ALR	No.2	1983	
"No.8"		4wPM	HU	39924	1924	
No.1	LOWECO	4wDM	L	20449	1942	
		reb	ALR	No.1	1978	
"No.9"		4wPM	MH	A110	1925	Dsm
3	ODIN 41	4wDM	MR	5859	1934	
		reb	ALR	No.3	1989	
6	DRUID	4wDM	MR	8644	1941	
		reb	ALR	6	1999	
"No.7"		4wDM	OK	5926	1935	
4	VULCAN A.M.W.No.197	4wDM	RH	198287	1940	
5		4wDM	RH	235654	1946	
		reb	ALR	5	2002	

MIDDLETON RAILWAY TRUST, TUNSTALL ROAD, HUNSLET, LEEDS

Gauge 4ft 8½in
SE 305310

68153	59	4wVBT	VCG	S	8837	1933
	"LUCIE"	0-4-0VBT	OC	Cockerill	1625	1890
		reb		Dorothea		1988
No.53	WINDLE	0-4-0WT	OC	EB	53	1909
No.1310		0-4-0T	IC	Ghd	(38?)	1891
Nr.385		0-4-0WT	OC	Hart	2110	1895
	"HENRY DE LACY II"	0-4-0ST	OC	HC	1309	1917
67		0-6-0T	IC	HC	1369	1919
	MIRVALE	0-4-0ST	OC	HC	1882	1955
–		0-4-0ST	OC	HE	1493	1925
	"PICTON"	2-6-2T	OC	HE	1540	1927
–		0-4-0T	OC	HE	1684	1931
	"BROOKES No.1"	0-6-0ST	IC	HE	2387	1941
	rebuilt as	0-6-0T	IC	Middleton		1999
	reb	0-6-0ST	IC	Middleton		2007
6	PERCY	0-4-0ST	OC	HL	3860	1935
44	CONWAY	0-6-0ST	IC	K	5469	1933
	SIR BERKELEY	0-6-0ST	IC	MW	1210	1891
	MATTHEW MURRAY	0-6-0ST	IC	MW	1601	1903
–		0-4-0ST	OC	MW	1795	1912
	JOHN BLENKINSOP	0-4-0ST	OC	P	2003	1941
–		0-4-0ST	OC	P	2103	1950
–		0-4-0ST	OC	WB	2702	1943
(R)DB 998901	"OLIVE"	2w-2DMR		Bg/DC	2268	1950
D2999		0-4-0DE		_(BT	91	1958
				(BP	7856	1958
	MARY	0-4-0DM		HC	D577	1932

CARROLL		0-4-0DM		HC	D631	1946
GRACE		0-4-0DH		HC	D1345	1970
.M.S.7051 "JOHN ALCOCK"		0-6-0DM		HE	1697	1932
			reb	HE		1949
"COURAGE"		4wDM		HE	1786	1935
–		0-4-0DM		JF	3900002	1945
LOIS		0-4-0DH		JF	4220033	1965
AUSTIN'S No.1		0-4-0DM		P	5003	1961
(DS 75) 75S		4wRE		_(Siemens	6	1898
				(HC		1898
–		4wDH		TH	138C	1964
	a rebuild of	4wVBT	VCG	S	9584	1955
(03-03-PO300)		4wWE		GB	420452	1979
DE 320467 DB 965049)		2w-2PMR		Wkm	7564	1956
999507		4wDMR		Wkm	8025	1958

Gauge 3ft 0in

BEM 404	4wDHF	HE	8505	1981

Gauge 2ft 2in

–	4wDM	HE	6273	1965

ANDREW NEALE, LEEDS
Gauge 1ft 10¾in

EDWARD SHOLTO	0-4-0ST	OC	HE	996	1909

Currently under restoration at a private location.

Executors of T. STANHOPE, CLIFFORD, BOSTON SPA
Locos occasionally here for renovation, etc.

Gauge 2ft 0in

–	4wBE	CE	B0107A	1973

A.J. WILSON, 35 HOLT PARK ROAD, LEEDS
Gauge 3ft 0in

06/22/6/2	4wDM	RH	224337	1944

Gauge 2ft 0in

THE WASP	2-2wPM	WilsonAJ		1969

YORKSHIRE MINING MUSEUM TRUST,
NATIONAL COAL MINING MUSEUM FOR ENGLAND,
CAPHOUSE COLLIERY, NEW ROAD, OVERTON, WAKEFIELD

Gauge 4ft 8½in   SE 253164

–		0-6-0ST	IC	P	1567	1920
NCB 44		0-6-0DH		HE	6684	1968
–		0-6-0DH		HE	7307	1973
(No.47)		0-6-0DH		TH	249V	1974

Gauge 3ft 0in

BEM 403	0-4-0DMF	HE	3614	1948

Gauge 2ft 6in

No.17		4w-4wBEF		CE	B3162A	1985	Dsm +
No. 1		4w-4wBEF		CE	B3538	1989	
	KIRSTIN	4w-4wDHF		GMT	0592	1981	
	STEPHANIE	4w-4wDHF		GMT	0593	1981	
	ANNA	4w-4wDHF		GMT		1984	
18		4wDHF	RACK	HE	9212	1987	
20		4wDHF	RACK	HE	9271	1987	
746	ENO 596						
	YKS MM 1992.196	0-4-0DMF		HC	DM746	1951	
No.2	"DEBORAH"	0-4-0DMF		HC	DM1356	1965	
–		0-6-0DMF		_(HC	DM1433	1978	
				(HE	8581	1978	
–		4wDMF		RH	480679	1961	

Gauge 2ft 4in

–	4wBEF	Atlas	2463	1944
–	4wDM	RH	375347	1954

Gauge 2ft 3in

CAPHOUSE FLIER	4wDHF	HE	8832	1978

Gauge 2ft 2in

–	4wDH	HE	7530	1977

Gauge 2ft 1½in

–	4wDM	RH	379659	1955

Gauge 2ft 0in

0-4-0DMF	HC	DM655	1949

+   only one cab - i.e. 4wBEF, prev at Wistow Colliery, North Yorkshire.

Consequent upon the fragmentation of the County Geography of Scotland, due to the creation of a number of autonomous Unitary Authorities and similar bodies, and in view of the relatively few remaining locations hosting locomotives, this Section of this Handbook is now presented in two parts. Industrial sites and Preservation sites.

Defining Areas in accordance with the 1974-1996 "large counties" era, now provides a direct relationship between this volume and the "Historic Handbook" series which is also published by the Industrial Railway Society. The historic books contain the recorded details of all past and recent locomotives, at all known past and present locations, in the areas they cover, together with extensive texts describing the locations and the businesses they served.

INDUSTRIAL SITES

ALSTOM, GLASGOW WORKS, SPRINGBURN ROAD, GLASGOW

Gauge 4ft 8½in   City of Glasgow NS 605665

(D3735)	08568	ST ROLLOX	0-6-0DE		Crewe	1959
(D3898)	08730	THE CALEY	0-6-0DE		Crewe	1960
2777			4wDM	R/R	Unilok	2091	1982

ALSTOM TRANSPORT – VIRGIN TRAINS, POLMADIE DEPOT

Gauge 4ft 8½in   City of Glasgow NS 598625

–	0-6-0DH	HE	7041	1971

BABCOCK MARINE, ROSYTH BUSINESS PARK, ROSYTH

Gauge 4ft 8½in   Fife NT 108821

236		0-4-0DM	AB	372	1945
		reb	YEC	L123	1994
BRIL 001	"JINTY"	0-6-0DM	AB	385	1952
1	YARD No.DP35	0-4-0DM	RH	313390	1952

1ST BATTALION, THE ROYAL HIGHLAND FUSILIERS, FORT GEORGE RANGE, INVERNESS

Gauge 600mm   Highland NH 783571

BEN	2w-2PM	Wkm	11682	1990
BRUCE	2w-2PM	Wkm	11683	1990

BRITISH NUCLEAR FUELS plc, CHAPELCROSS WORKS, ANNAN

Gauge 5ft 4in   (Closed)   Dumfries & Galloway NY 216695

No.1	4wDM	RH	411320	1958
No.2	4wDM	RH	411321	1958

BRUSH-BARCLAY LTD, CALEDONIA WORKS, WEST LANGLANDS STREET, KIL-MARNOCK

Locos under construction or repair are usually present.

Gauge 4ft 8½in   East Ayrshire NS 425382

		0-4-0DH	AB	482	1963	
–						

CALEDONIAN PAPER plc, LONG DRIVE, SHEWALTON, IRVINE

Gauge 4ft 8½in   North Ayrshire NS 335354

174D001		0-6-0DH		HE	9092	1988
	CHRISTIAN	0-6-0DH		RR	10217	1965
			reb	HE	9371	2006

CHEMRING ENERGENTICS, ARDEER WORKS

Gauge 2ft 6in   North Ayrshire NS 290401, 290405

05/582	4wDH	AK	21	1987
05/583	4wDH	AK	22	1987

C.P.L. SCOTLAND LTD, MOSSEND COAL DEPOT, MAIN ROAD BELLSHILL

Gauge 4ft 8½in   North Lanarkshire NS 749605

–	0-4-0DH	_(RSHD	8365	1962	
		(WB	3210	1962	OOU

DALMUNZIE RAILWAY, DALMUNZIE HOTEL, DALMUNZIE

Gauge 2ft 6in   Perth & Kinross NO 091713

DALMUNZIE	4wPM	MR	2014	1920	OOU

DEANSIDE TRANSIT LTD, DEANSIDE ROAD, HILLINGTON, GLASGOW

Gauge 4ft 8½in   City of Glasgow NS 522659

(D3562)	08447	0-6-0DE	Derby	1958	
12082	01553	0-6-0DE	Derby	1950	+

+   on hire from Harry Needle Railroad Co Ltd, Merseyside

E.G. STEELE & CO LTD, WINTON WAGON WORKS, 25 DALZELL STREET, HAMILTON

Gauge 4ft 8½in   North Lanarkshire NS 708561

–	4wDH	R/R	NNM	75511	1979
–	4wDH	R/R	NNM	81504	1983

INEOS, GRANGEMOUTH REFINERY, BO'NESS ROAD, GRANGEMOUTH

Gauge 4ft 8½in   Falkirk NS 942817, 944814, 952822

10	0-6-0DH	AB	600	1976	+

11	0-6-0DH		AB	649	1980	+
	reb	HE	Greycar	750215	2006	
2	0-6-0DH		EEV	D917	1965	
	reb	AB			1981	
	reb	HAB		6694	1990	OOU
3	0-6-0DH		EEV	D1232	1968	
	reb	AB			1980	+
12	0-6-0DH		TH	290V	1980	+

\+ property of LH Group Services Ltd, Staffordshire, England

LAFARGE CEMENT, OXWELLMAINS CEMENT WORKS, DUNBAR
Gauge 4ft 8½in   East Lothian   NT 708768

No.1	ADAM	4wDH	S	10022	1959	
No.2		4wDH	RR	10266	1967	
No.3		4wDH	S	10006	1959	OOU
1		4wDH	RR	10247	1966	Dsm
2		4wDH	RR	10248	1966	Dsm
3		4wDH	RR	10249	1966	OOU
3		4wDH	S	10021	1959	
–		4wDH	S	10033	1960	Dsm

LITHGOWS LTD, NETHERTON, LANGBANK
Gauge 2ft 0in   RTC   Renfrewshire   NS 393722

–	4wPM	MR	2097	1922	OOU
–	4wPM	MR	2171	1922	OOU
No.2	4wDM	MR	8700	1941	OOU

MINISTRY OF DEFENCE, DEFENCE MUNITIONS, GLEN DOUGLAS, near ARROCHAR
Argyle & Bute

See Section 6 for full details.

MINISTRY OF DEFENCE, DEFENCE MUNITIONS, EASTRIGGS
See Section 6 for full details.   Dumfries & Galloway   NY 246656

THOS MUIR HAULAGE & METALS LTD, DEN ROAD, KIRKCALDY
Gauge 4ft 8½in   Fife   NT 282926

No.3		0-4-0ST	OC	AB	946	1902	OOU
No.22		0-4-0ST	OC	AB	1069	1906	OOU
–		0-4-0ST	OC	AB	1807	1923	OOU
No.7		0-4-0ST	OC	AB	2262	1949	OOU
No.2	HP 515	0-4-0DH		AB	515	1966	OOU
No.1	HP 299	0-4-0DH		AB	516	1966	OOU
No.12	H 662	0-4-0DH		NBQ	27732	1957	OOU

OMYA UK, WATERLOO BRANCH, ABERDEEN
Gauge 4ft 8½in   Aberdeen

–	0-4-0DH	RH	513139	1967	

R.& M. SUPPLIES (INVERKEITHING) LTD, THE BAY, INVERKEITHING
(leased from Forth Ports Authority)
Gauge 4ft 8½in   RTC   Fife NT 127823

–	0-4-0DM	JF	4210138	1958	OOU

ROCHE PRODUCTS LTD, DALRY
Gauge 4ft 8½in   North Ayrshire NS 295503

50 GC 8	0-6-0DH	RR	10267	1967
	reb RFSK			1990

SCOTGOLD RESOURSES LTD, CONONISH FARM, near TYNDRUM
Work has ceased; site is on a care and maintenance basis.   Stirling NN 292286

Gauge 2ft 0in

5	4wBE	CE	B2905	1981	+
	reb CE		B3550A	1988	
6	4wBE	CE	B2983	1983	
	reb CE		B3550B	1988	
–	4wBE	WR	(G7125	1967)	
	reb WR		525801	1988	
–	4wBE	WR			
	reb WR		556001	1988	

+   plate reads B2903

SCOTTISH COAL CO, CASTLEBRIDGE COLLIERY, KINCARDINE
Headquarters : Mining (Scotland) Ltd.

Gauge 2ft 6in — Underground   Fife NZ 942928

–	4wBEF	CE	B3325B	1987
–	4wBEF	CE	B3464C	1988
–	4wBEF	CE	B3601	1989

SCOTTISH COAL CO, KILLOCH WASHERY, OCHILTREE
Headquarters : Mining (Scotland) Ltd.

Gauge 4ft 8½in — Surface   East Ayrshire NS 478205

11348/C W.L. No.1	4wDH	RR	10268	1967

SCOTTISH WATER, STORNOWAY WATERWORKS, ISLE OF LEWIS

Gauge 2ft 0in   Western Isles NB 410375

–	4wPM	(MR ?)	Dsm

STRATHCLYDE PASSENGER TRANSPORT EXECUTIVE, BROOMLOAN DEPOT, ROBERT STREET, GOVAN

Glasgow underground railway maintenance locos.   City of Glasgow NS 555655

Gauge 4ft 0in

L2	LOBEY DOSSER	4wBE		CE	B0965B	1977	
L3	RANK BAJIN	4wBE		CE	B0965A	1977	
L4	EL FIDELO	4wBE		CE	B0186	1974	
			reb	CE	B3542	1988	
W5		4wBE		CE	B0186	1974	Dsm +
P89		4wBE		HE	9157	1992	
–		4wBE	R/R	NNM	78101E	1979	
55		4w-4wRER		OldburyC&W		1901	
			reb	Govan		1935	Pvd

+   rebuilt into non-powered permanent way vehicle

WILLIAM SINCLAIR HORTICULTURE LTD   Mid Lothian

Locos are kept at :–   A - Auchencorth Moss, Auchencorth NT 193562
              S - Springfield Moss & Springfield Workshops, Wellington Reformatory, near Leadburn NT 233567
              W - Whim Moss, Lamancha Station, Cowdenburn, near Leadburn NT 206531

Gauge 2ft 0in

T7	DOLLY	4wDH	AB	560	1971	S	OOU
T2	SALLY	4wDH	AK	No.8	1982	W	
T9		4wDM	AK	28	1989	A	
T5		4wDH	AK	47	1994	A	
–		4wDM	MR	5402	1932	S	Dsm
T1	ROLAND	4wDM	MR	8704	1942	A	
T3		4wDM	MR	8738	1942		
	rebuilt as	4wDH			c1998	S	Dsm
T11	ELOUISE	4wDM	MR	21505	1955	A	
T10		4wDM	MR	21520	1955	W	
22128	SYLVIA	4wDM	MR	22128	1961	A	
T6		4wDM	MR	22253	1965	A	
T4	DORIS	4wDM	RH	462365	1960	W	

WILLIAM SINCLAIR HORTICULTURE LTD
Cladance Moss, East Kilbride

Gauge 2ft 6in   South Lanarkshire NS 654490

OLD NICK	4wDH	AB	556	1970	
CHRISTINE	4wDH	Byers		1998	+

+   includes frame of MR 115U094 / 1970

WILLIAM SINCLAIR HORTICULTURE LTD
Ryeflat Moss, Carnwath, near Carstairs
Gauge 2ft 6in   South Lanarkshire NS 953478

05 581		4wDH	AK	18	1985
	JEFFREY	4wDH	AK	19	1985
	RACHEL	4wDH	Byers		1998 a

a   includes frame of AB 562 / 1971

PRESERVATION SITES

ABERDEEN CITY COUNCIL, SEATON PARK, ABERDEEN
Gauge 4ft 8½in   Aberdeenshire NJ 943092

–	0-4-0ST	OC	AB	2239	1947

ALFORD VALLEY RAILWAY CO LTD,
ALFORD STATION, MURRAY PARK, ALFORD
Gauge 2ft 0in   Aberdeenshire NJ 579159

	JAMES GORDON	0-4-0DH	s/o	AK	63	2001
A.V.R. No.1	HAMEWITH	4wDM		L	3198	c1930
	THE BRA'LASS	4wDM	s/o	MR	9381	1948
87022	THE WEE GORDON HIGHLANDER / BYDAND					
		4wDM		MR	22221	1964

ALMOND VALLEY HERITAGE CENTRE, MILLFIELD, LIVINGSTON
Gauge 2ft 6in   West Lothian NT 034667

	YARD No.24	4wDH	AB	557	1970
	ND 10262	4wDH	BD	3752	1980
	"OAKBANK No.2"	4wWE	BLW	20587	1902
20		4wBE	BV	612	1972
38		4wBE	BV	698	1974
42		4wBE	BV	700	1974
18	TAM	4wBE	BV	1143	1976
–		4wBEF	GB	1698	1940
	YARD No.B10	0-4-0DM	HE	2270	1940
7330		4wDM	HE	7330	1973
–		4wDM	SMH	40SPF522	1981

AYRSHIRE RAILWAY PRESERVATION GROUP,
SCOTTISH INDUSTRIAL RAILWAY CENTRE,
MINNIVEY COLLIERY & DUNASKIN SHED,
WATERSIDE RAILWAY, DALMELLINGTON

Gauge 4ft 8½in

East Ayrshire NS 443083, 475073

No.16		0-4-0ST	OC	AB	1116	1910
No.8		0-6-0T	OC	AB	1296	1912
No.19		0-4-0ST	OC	AB	1614	1918
–		0-4-0F	OC	AB	1952	1928
No.10		0-4-0ST	OC	AB	2244	1947
N.C.B.No.23		0-4-0ST	OC	AB	2260	1949
–		0-6-0ST	OC	AB	2358	1954
–		0-4-0ST	OC	AB	2368	1955
No.1		0-4-0DM		AB	347	1941
M3571		0-4-0DM		AB	366	1943
–		0-4-0DM		AB	399	1956
–		4wDMR		Donelli	163	1979
– Yd. No.107		0-4-0DM		HE	3132	1944
–		0-4-0DM		JF	22888	1939
–		0-4-0DM		JF	4200028	1948 Dsm
–		0-4-0DH		NBQ	27644	1959
DY322	YARD No. BE 1116					
	YARD No.AK1	4wDM		RH	224352	1943
M/C 324		4wDM		RH	284839	1950
–		4wDM		RH	417890	1959
–		0-4-0DM		RH	421697	1959
–		4wDH		S	10012	1959
DX 68003	DB 965331	2w-2PMR		Wkm	10179	1968
DX 68002	DB 965330	2w-2PMR		Wkm	10180	1968

Gauge 3ft 0in

–	4wDH		HE	8816	1981
–	4wDM		RH	256273	1948

Gauge 2ft 6in

05/579	4wDH	AB	561	1971
3	4wBE	BV	307	1968
43	4wBE	BV	701	1974
7329	4wDM	HE	7329	1973
3	4wDH	HE	8827	1979
13	4wDH	HE	9082	1984
2	4wDM	RH	183749	1937
No.3	4wDM	RH	210959	1941
No.1	4wDM	RH	211681	1942
1	4wDM	RH	422569	1959

BANFF & BUCHAN DISTRICT COUNCIL LEISURE & RECREATION DEPARTMENT, FRASERBURGH HERITAGE CENTRE
Gauge 2ft 0in   Aberdeenshire NJ 997675

677	KESSOCK KNIGHT		4wDM	s/o	LB	53541	1963	OOU

BARCLAY HOUSE, CALEDONIAN WORKS OFFICE BLOCK SITE, WEST LANGLANDS STREET, KILMARNOCK
Gauge 4ft 8½in   East Ayrshire

	DRAKE	0-4-0ST	OC	AB	2086	1940

CALEDONIAN RAILWAY (BRECHIN) LTD, BRECHIN, near MONTROSE, & BRIDGE OF DUN
Gauge 4ft 8½in   www.caledonianrailway.co.uk   Angus NO 603603, 663587

46464		2-6-0	OC	Crewe		1950
–		0-4-0ST	OC	AB	1863	1926
	HARLAXTON	0-6-0T	OC	AB	2107	1941
–		0-6-0ST	IC	HE	2879	1943
68189	B.A.CO LTD	0-4-0ST	OC	P	1376	1915
	MENELAUS	0-6-0ST	OC	P	1889	1934
–		0-6-0ST	OC	P	2153	1954
–		0-6-0ST	IC	WB	2749	1944
–		0-6-0ST	IC	WB	2759	1944

(D3059 08046)	13059	BRECHIN CITY				
		0-6-0DE		Derby		1954
(D5222)	25072	Bo-BoDE		Derby		1963
(D5233)	25083	Bo-BoDE		Derby		1963
D5314	(26014)	Bo-BoDE		BRCW	DEL59	1959
(D5335)	26035	Bo-BoDE		BRCW	DEL80	1959
(D5370)	27024	Bo-BoDE		BRCW	DEL213	1962
(D6797)	37097	OLD FETTERCAIRN				
		Co-CoDE		_(EE	3226	1962
				(VF	D751	1962
(12052)		0-6-0DE		Derby		1949
12093		0-6-0DE		Derby		1951
–		4wDM		FH	3747	1955
144-6	No.6	0-4-0DM		RH	421700	1959
	DEWAR HIGHLANDER	4wDM		RH	458957	1961

CARNEGIE DUNFERMLINE TRUST, PITTENCRIEFF PARK, DUNFERMLINE
Gauge 4ft 8½in   Fife NT 086872

–		0-4-0ST	OC	AB	1996	1934

COUNTESS OF SUTHERLAND, DUNROBIN STATION, near BRORA

Gauge 2ft 0in   Highland NC 849013

BRORA	0-4-0PM	s/o	Bg	1797	1930
		reb	Bg	2083	1934

JOHN DEWAR & SONS LTD, ABERFELDY DISTILLERY

Gauge 4ft 8½in   Perth & Kinross

–	0-4-0ST	OC	AB	2073	1939

EAST LINKS FAMILY PARK,
JOHN MUIR PARK, BELTONFORD, near DUNBAR

Gauge 2ft 0in   East Lothian NT 648786

–	4wDH		AK	49	1994
–	0-6-0DM	s/o	Bg	3014	1938
rebuilt as	0-6-0DH	s/o	BES		1993

EAST LOTHIAN DISTRICT COUNCIL,
PRESTONGRANGE MINING MUSEUM, PRESTONPANS

Gauge 4ft 8½in   East Lothian NT 374737

N.C.B.No.29	0-4-0ST	OC	AB	1142	1908	
17	0-4-0ST	OC	AB	2219	1946	
No.7 PRESTONGRANGE	0-4-2ST	OC	GR	536	1914	
–	4wDH		EEV	D908	1964	
–	4wDM		MR	9925	1963	
No.33	4wDM		RH	221647	1943	
No.2 IVOR						
GEORGE EDWARDS	4wDM		RH	398613	1956	+
–	4wDM		RH	458960	1962	

+   carries plate 398163 in error

Gauge 2ft 0in

N.C.B. No.10	4wDM	HE	4440	1952

FALKIRK DISTRICT COUNCIL, DEPARTMENT OF LIBRARIES & MUSEUMS,
MUSEUM WORKSHOP, ABBOTSINCH COURT, 7–11 ABBOTSINCH ROAD,
ABBOTSINCH INDUSTRIAL ESTATE, GRANGEMOUTH

Gauge 4ft 8½in   Falkirk NS 936814

No.1	0-4-0DM	JF	22902	1943

FIFE REGIONAL COUNCIL,
LOCHORE MEADOWS COUNTRY PARK, LOCHORE
Gauge 4ft 8½in   Fife NT 172963

| No.30 | | 0-4-0ST | OC | AB | 2259 | 1949 |

THE GARDEN OF COSMIC SPECULATION, PORTRACK HOUSE, HOLYWOOD, DUMFRIES
Gauge 4ft 8½in   Dumfries & Galloway NX 940834

| – | | 0-4-0D | | RH | | |

GLASGOW CITY COUNCIL, CULTURAL AND SPORT GLASGOW
Museum of Transport, Kelvin Hall, Bunhouse Road, Glasgow
Gauge 4ft 8½in   www.glasgowmuseums.com   City of Glasgow NS 565663

103		4-6-0	OC	SS	4022	1894
123		4-2-2	IC	N	3553	1886
(62277)	49 GORDON HIGHLANDER					
		4-4-0	IC	NBH	22563	1920
–		0-4-0VBT	VCG	Chaplin	2368	1885
No.1		0-6-0F	OC	AB	1571	1917
9		0-6-0T	OC	NBH	21521	1917

Gauge 4ft 0in

–		4wBE		_(JF	16559	1925
				(WR	583	1927
	SUBWAY CAR No.1	4w-4wRER		OldburyC&W		1896

Gauge 3ft 6in

| 3007 | | 4-8-2 | OC | NBQ | 25546 | 1945 | a |

a   currently in store

Maryhill Storage Depot, Glasgow
Gauge 4ft 8½in   City of Glasgow

| – | | 2w-2PM | | Albion | | c1916 |

GRAMPIAN TRANSPORT MUSEUM, ALFORD
Gauge 4ft 8½in   Aberdeenshire NJ 577161

| 3 | | 0-4-0ST | OC | AB | 1889 | 1926 |

D. HERBERT, GLASGOW AREA
Locomotives stored at a private location.
Gauge 2ft 6in   City of Glasgow

| 2209 | | 4wDM | | HE | 2209 | 1941 |

No.4	ND 10394		0-4-0DM		HE	2243	1941
R9	ND 6473		4wDM		RH	235727	1944

KEITH & DUFFTOWN RAILWAY ASSOCIATION, DUFFTOWN

Gauge 4ft 8½in   Moray   NJ 323414

KDR 40	THE WEE MAC / THE MACALLAN						
			4wDH		CE	B1844	1979
KDR 41	J&B SPIRIT OF FIFE		0-6-0DH		EEV	D1193	1967
(3052)	CAR No.291		4w-4wRER		MetCam		1932	+
51568	KDR 6 SPIRIT OF BANFFSHIRE						
			2-2w-2w-2DMR		DerbyC&W		1959
52053	KDR 7 SPIRIT OF BANFFSHIRE						
			2-2w-2w-2DMR		DerbyC&W		1960
53628	KDR 4 L213 SPIRIT OF SPEYSIDE						
			2-2w-2w-2DMR		DerbyC&W		1958
55500	140.001		4wDMR		DerbyC&W/		
					Leyland	(R2.001)	1981
55501	140.001		4wDMR		DerbyC&W/		
					Leyland	(R2.002))	1981
CAR 1	C N RAIL 144-5		2-2wPMR		Fairmont 244095		
CAR 2	KDR 43 144-55		2-2wPMR		Fairmont		
CAR 3			2-2wPMR		Fairmont 252180		
PQ 364	45 TMC		4wDH	R/R	NNM	80505	1980

+   now unmotorised

KINGDOM OF FIFE PRESERVATION SOCIETY, KIRKLAND YARD, METHIL

Gauge 4ft 8½in   Fife   NO 373007

10		0-4-0ST	OC	AB	1890	1926	
No.17		0-4-0ST	OC	AB	2292	1951	
(D5340)	26040	Bo-BoDE		BRCW	DEL85	1959	a
400	RIVER EDEN	0-4-0DH		NBQ	27421	1955	
	N.C.B.No.10	0-6-0DH		NBQ	27591	1957	
No.4	NORTH BRITISH	4wDM		RH	421415	1958	
2	THE GARVIE FLYER	0-4-0DE		RH	431764	1960	
1	LARGO LAW	0-4-0DE		RH	449753	1961	

a   currently stored at Barclay Bros Ltd, Transport, Methil West.

THE LEADHILLS & WANLOCKHEAD RAILWAY SOCIETY, LEADHILLS

Gauge 2ft 6in   South Lanarkshire   NS 888145

29		4wBE		WR	(1614 1940)?	

Gauge 2ft 0in

–		0-4-0T	OC	Dec	917	1917
–		0-4-0WT		OK	6335	1913
12		4wDH		CE	B1819D	1978

6 CLYDE	4wDH	HE	6347	1975		
–	4wDH	HE	9348	1994		
21	4wDM	Moes				
8 8564	4wDM	MR	8564	1940	+ Dsm	
K 11129 251	4wDM	MR	8863	1944	a Dsm	
K 11139 253	4wDM	MR	8884	1944	a Dsm	
2 L114 LBC KDL7 ELVAN	4wDM	MR	9792	1955		
QE 102-95 EN81 LITTLE CLYDE	4wDM	RH	7002/0467/2	1966		
QE 102-94 LUCE	4wDM	RH	7002/0467/6	1966		

+   converted into a brake van
a   Converted into a coach.

G. MANN, SAUGHTREE STATION
Gauge 4ft 8½in   Borders   NT 565981

MEG OF SAUGHTREE	4wDM	RH	275882	1949

NATIONAL MUSEUM OF SCOTLAND, CHAMBERS STREET, EDINBURGH
Gauge 5ft 0in   City of Edinburgh   NT 258734

"WYLAM DILLY"	4wG	VC	Hedley	1827-1832 +	

+   incorporates parts of loco of same name built c1814

Gauge 4ft 8½in

"ELLESMERE"	0-4-0WT	OC	H(L)	244	1861

NATIONAL MUSEUM OF SCOTLAND, EDINBURGH WORKSHOPS, GRANTON
Gauge 2ft 0in   City of Edinburgh

5	0-4-0T	OC	AB	988	1903

Gauge 1ft 7in

WYLAM DILLY	4wG	VC	RSM	1885

NORTH EAST FIFE DISTRICT COUNCIL, DEPARTMENT OF RECREATION,
RIO-GRANDE MINIATURE RAILWAY,
CRAIGTOUN COUNTRY PARK, near ST.ANDREWS
Gauge 1ft 3in   Fife   NO 482141

278	2-8-0DH	s/o	SL	R8	1976

NORTH LANARKSHIRE COUNCIL, SUMMERLEE HERITAGE PARK,
WEST CANAL STREET, COATBRIDGE CENTRAL
Gauge 4ft 8½in   North Lanarkshire   NS 728655

No.11	0-4-0ST	OC	GH		1898
No.9	0-6-0T	IC	HC	895	1909
ROBIN	4wVBT	VCG	S	9628	1957

(62174)	(936 103)	977845		4w-4wWER		Cravens		1967
W280				0-4-0DH		AB		1966
		a rebuild of		0-4-0DM		AB	472	1961
–				4wWE		BTH		1908

Gauge 3ft 6in

4112	SPRINGBOK	4-8-2+2-8-4T 4C	_(BP	7827	1957
			(NBH	27770	1957

D. RITCHIE & FRIENDS
Gauge 3ft 0in   City of Edinburgh

–		4wDM	RH	466591	1961

Gauge 2ft 6in

–		4wDM	RH	189992	1938
–		4wDM	RH	242916	1946
–		4wDM	RH	273843	1949
10553		0-4-0DM	RH	338429	1955
P 9303	YARD No.1018	4wBE	VE	7667	

Gauge 2ft 0in

–		4wDM	HE	2654	1942
	TERRAS	4wDM	MR	7189	1937
CCC 51		4wDM	MR	7330	1938
–		4wDM	MR	9982	1954
–		4wDM	RH	179005	1936
–		4wDM	RH	249530	1947

F. ROACH, ROGART STATION, near GOLSPIE
Gauge 4ft 8½in   Highland   NC 725020

8016		4wDM	RH	294263	1950

ROYAL DEESIDE RAILWAY, BANCHORY + MILTON OF CRATHES
Gauge 4ft 8½in   Aberdeenshire   NJ 742962

–			0-4-0ST	OC	AB	807	1897	a
(D2134	03134)	6G1 6G2	0-6-0DM		Sdn		1960	
		rebuilt as	0-6-0DH					
D9551			0-6-0DH		Sdn		1965	
"CASTLE DONINGTON No.1"			0-4-0DM		AB	415	1957	
		rebuilt as	0-4-0DH		AB		1979	
(Sc 79998)	GEMINI	RDB 975003	4w-4wBER		DerbyC&W		1956	
				reb	Cowlairs		1958	
–			2w-2BER		TS&S	NO/1023	1985	
900338	LNER 338		2w-2PMR		Wkm	626	1934	a
	(PWM 2830)		2w-2PMR		Wkm	5008	1949	
A34W			2w-2PMR		Wkm	8501	1960	
A37W			2w-2PMR		Wkm	8502	1960	a

Gauge 600mm

RTT/767162	2w-2PM	Wkm	3235	1943	a

a   currently stored elsewhere

SCAPA FLOW VISITOR CENTRE, LYNESS, HOY

Gauge 1000mm   Orkney Islands ND 310947

–	4wDM	RH	210961	1941

Gauge 2ft 6in

BEV YARD No.4B/9B	4wBE	WR	3805	1948

Gauge 600mm

–	4wDM	RH	229633	1944
–	2w-2PM	Wkm	3030	1941

SCOTRAIL, THORNTON JUNCTION DEPOT

Gauge 4ft 8½in   Falkirk

61994	THE GREAT MARQUESS	2-6-0	3C	Dar	(1761?)	1938

Based here between use on mainline charter trains

SCOTTISH MINING MUSEUM, RAIL & MINING HERITAGE CENTRE, LADY VICTORIA COLLIERY, NEWTONGRANGE

These locos are not on public display.   Mid Lothian NT 332638

Gauge 4ft 8½in

No.21	0-4-0ST	OC	AB	2284	1949

Gauge 3ft 6in

TRAINING LOCO No.2	0-6-0DMF	HE	4074	1955

Gauge 2ft 6in

–	4wBE	CE	5871A	1971
–	4wBEF	CE	B3325A	1986

SCOTTISH RAILWAY PRESERVATION SOCIETY, BO'NESS & KINNEIL RAILWAY, BO'NESS STATION, UNION STREET, BO'NESS

Gauge 4ft 8½in   West Lothian NT 003817

(55189)	419		0-4-4T	IC	StRollox		1907
(62469)	No.256	GLEN DOUGLAS	4-4-0	IC	Cowlairs		1913
(62712)	No.246	MORAYSHIRE	4-4-0	3C	Dar	(1391?)	1928
65243	MAUDE		0-6-0	IC	N	4392	1891
68095	No.42		0-4-0ST	OC	Cowlairs		1887
80105			2-6-4T	OC	Bton		1955
3	LADY VICTORIA		0-6-0ST	OC	AB	1458	1916
No.3			0-4-0ST	OC	AB	1937	1928

LORD ASHFIELD		0-6-0F	OC	AB	1989	1930
No.6		0-4-0ST	OC	AB	2043	1937
B.A.CO.LTD No.3		0-4-0ST	OC	AB	2046	1937
THE WEMYSS COAL CO LTD No.20		0-6-0T	IC	AB	2068	1939
No.6		0-4-0CT	OC	AB	2127	1942
No.24		0-6-0T	OC	AB	2335	1953
17		0-6-0ST	IC	HE	2880	1943
No.19		0-6-0ST	IC	HE	3818	1954
No.5		0-6-0ST	IC	HE	3837	1955
6		0-4-0ST	OC	HL	3640	1926
No.13	N.C.B.13 KELTON FELL	0-4-0ST	OC	N	2203	1876
No.1	LORD ROBERTS	0-6-0T	IC	NR	5710	1902
–		4wVBT	VCG	S	9561	1953
	(RANALD)	4wVBT	VCG	S	9627	1957
	(DENIS)	4wVBT	VCG	S	9631	1958
No.7		0-6-0ST	IC	WB	2777	1945
(D1970)	47643	Co-CoDE		Crewe		1965
D2767		0-4-0DH		NBQ	28020	1960
			reb	AB		1968
(D3558)	08443	0-6-0DE		Derby		1958
(D5304)	26004	Bo-BoDE		BRCW	DEL49	1958
D5310	(26010)	Bo-BoDE		BRCW	DEL55	1960
(D5324)	26024	Bo-BoDE		BRCW	DEL69	1959
(D5347)	27001	Bo-BoDE		BRCW	DEL190	1961
(D5351)	27005	Bo-BoDE		BRCW	DEL194	1961
D5394	(27050)	Bo-BoDE		BRCW	DEL237	1962
(D6725)	37025	Co-CoDE		_(EE	2888	1961
				(VF	D604	1961
(D6875)	37175	Co-CoDE		_(EE	3353	1963
				(EEV	D839	1963
(D7585)	25235	Bo-BoDE		Dar		1964
D8020	(20020)	Bo-BoDE		_(EE	2742	1959
				(RSHD	8052	1959
61503	(303 023)	4w-4wRER		PSteel		1960
No.1		0-6-0DM		AB	343	1941
F.82		4wBE		EEDK	1131	1940
–		0-4-0DH		NBQ	27415	1954
	KILBAGIE	4wDM		RH	262998	1949
–		4wDM		RH	275883	1949
–		0-4-0DE		RH	312984	1951
–		4wDM		RH	321733	1952
–		0-4-0DE		RH	421439	1958
–		0-4-0DE		RH	423658	1958
–		0-4-0DH		RH	457299	1962
Sc51017		2-2w-2w-2DMR		Sdn		1959
Sc51043		2-2w-2w-2DMR		Sdn		1959
(970213)		2w-2PMR		Wkm	6049	1952
–		2w-2PMR		Wkm	10482	1970

Gauge 3ft 0in

–		0-4-0T	OC	AB	840	1899
–		4wDH		MR	110U082	1970

SCOTTISH RAILWAY PRESERVATION SOCIETY,
SHED 47 RAILWAY RESTORATION GROUP,
SCOTTISH VINTAGE BUS MUSEUM,
M90 COMMERCE PARK, LATHALMOND

Gauge 4ft 8½in   Fife NT 093922

No.17		0-4-0ST	OC	AB	2296	1950	
250		0-4-0DH		HE	9045	1980	OOU
			reb	YEC	L135	1994	
251		0-4-0DH		HE	9046	1980	OOU
–		0-4-0DM		JF	4210140	1958	

STRATHSPEY RAILWAY CO LTD

Locos are kept at :–   Aviemore NH 898131
                                                   Boat of Garten NH 943189
                                                      Broomhill NH 997226
Gauge 4ft 8½in   Highland

(45025)	5025	4-6-0	OC	VF	4570	1934	
46512	E.V.COOPER ENGINEER	2-6-0	OC	Sdn		1952	
57566	(828)	0-6-0	IC	StRollox		1899	
–		0-6-0ST	OC	AB	1833	1924	
'17'	BRAERIACH	0-6-0T	IC	AB	2017	1935	
–		0-4-0ST	OC	AB	2020	1936	
75008		0-6-0ST	IC	HE	2857	1943	
48	9103/48	0-6-0ST	IC	HE	2864	1943	
No.60		0-6-0ST	IC	HE	3686	1948	
68030		0-6-0ST	IC	HE	3777	1952	
No.9	CAIRNGORM	0-6-0ST	IC	RSHN	7097	1943	
D2774		0-4-0DH		NBQ	28027	1960	
			reb	AB		1968	
(D3605)	(08490)	0-6-0DE		Hor		1958	
(D5302)	26002	Bo-BoDE		BRCW	DEL47	1958	
D5325	(26025)	Bo-BoDE		BRCW	DEL70	1959	
D5862	31327	A1A-A1ADE		BT	398	1962	
(PWM 651)	97651	0-6-0DE		RH	431758	1959	
–		0-4-0DH		AB	517	1966	
–		4wDM		MR	5763	1957	
14		0-4-0DH		NBQ	27549	1956	
02774		0-4-0DM		RH	260756	1950	
	QUEEN ANNE	4wDM		RH	265618	1948	
–		4wDH		TH	277V	1977	
W51367		2-2w-2w-2DMR		PSteel		1960	
W51402		2-2w-2w-2DMR		PSteel		1960	
(51990	960 932)	977830	2-2w-2w-2DMR	DerbyC&W		1960	
Sc 52008		2-2w-2w-2DMR		DerbyC&W		1961	
(52030	960 932	977831)	2-2w-2w-2DMR	DerbyC&W		1961	
813	CALE	2w-2PMR		Wkm	1288	1933	

VALLEY INTERNATIONAL PARK, CROSSFORD, CARLUKE, near LANARK
Gauge 600mm   NS 831461

1863	4w-4wDH	s/o	Chance		
			64-5031-24	1964	
1	4wDM		RH	243392	1946	OOU

WEST LOTHIAN COUNCIL, POLKEMMET COUNTRY PARK, WHITBURN
Gauge 4ft 8½in   NS 924649

No.8	DARDANELLES	0-6-0ST	OC	AB	1175	1909

WILLIAM WARNOCK, SANDYHOLME GARDEN CENTRE, near ROSEBANK
Gauge 3ft 0in   NS 818483

–	4wDM	JF	3930044	1950

SECTION 3 — WALES

Consequent upon the fragmentation of the County Geography of Wales, due to the creation of a large number of autonomous Unitary Authorities and similar bodies, and in view of the relatively few remaining locations hosting locomotives, this Section of this Handbook is now presented in four Areas of coverage.

Defining Areas in accordance with the 1974-1996 "large counties" era, now provides a direct relationship between this volume and the "Historic Handbook" series which is also published by the Industrial Railway Society. The historic books contain the recorded details of all past and recent locomotives, at all known past and present locations, in the areas they cover, together with extensive texts describing the locations and the businesses they served.

The Areas can, in the main, be summarised as follows:

NORTH WALES
Isle of Anglesey (Ynys Môn), Caernarfonshire, Clwyd, Conwy, Denbighshire, Flintshire, Flintshire Detatched, Gwynedd, Merionethshire and Wrexham.

MID WALES
Breconshire (apart from a narrow strip at its southern boundary which was transferred to Gwent and Mid-Glamorgan – note that Breconshire was also known as Brecknock, and Brecknockshire), Cardiganshire, Ceredigion, Dyfed (north; i.e. Ceredigion), Montgomeryshire, Powys, Radnorshire.

SOUTH-WEST WALES
Carmarthenshire, Dyfed (excluding Ceredigion), Neath Port Talbot, Pembrokeshire, Swansea, and West Glamorgan.

SOUTH-EAST WALES
Blaenau Gwent, Bridgend, Caerphilly, Cardiff, Glamorgan prior to 1974 (but excluding areas now in South-West Wales), Gwent, Merthyr Tydfil, Mid Glamorgan, Monmouthshire, Newport, Torfaen, Rhondda Cynon Taf, South Glamorgan, and Vale of Glamorgan.

The relevant Historic Series Handbooks are as follows:

NORTH WALES
Handbook NW – Industrial Locomotives of North Wales (1992)

MID WALES
Handbook DP – Industrial Locomotives of Dyfed & Powys (1994)

SOUTH-WEST WALES
Handbook DP – Industrial Locomotives of Dyfed & Powys (1994)
Handbook WG – Industrial Locomotives of West Glamorgan (1996)

SOUTH-EAST WALES
Handbook GT – Industrial Locomotives of Gwent (1999)
Handbook GL – Industrial Locomotives of Glamorgan (Mid and South) (2007)

We are preparing update Bulletins, for the published Historic Handbooks, to enable such Bulletins to be downloaded without charge from the Society website at   www.irsociety.co.uk

AREA 1 – NORTH WALES

INDUSTRIAL LOCATIONS

ANGLESEY ALUMINIUM METAL LTD, PENRHOS WORKS, HOLYHEAD

Gauge 4ft 8½in — Isle of Anglesey SH 264807

56-007	0-4-0DH	HE	7183	1970	
–	4wDM	RH	321727	1952	OOU +
–	0-4-0DH	HE	7460	1977	OOU +

+   stored on behalf of Anglesey Railway Traction Ltd

**CASTLE CEMENT (PADESWOOD) LTD,
PADESWOOD HALL CEMENT WORKS, BUCKLEY**

Shunting is performed by EW&SR using a class 08 diesel. — Flintshire SJ 290622

Gauge 4ft 8½in

| No.6 | 4wDH | RR | 10235 | 1965 | OOU |
| No.7 | 4wDH | RR | 10276 | 1967 | OOU |

CORUS, COATED PRODUCTS DIVISION, SHOTTON WORKS

Gauge 4ft 8½in — SJ 302704, 305705

| (D3780) | 08613 | 0-6-0DE | Derby | | 1959 | a |
| (D4166) | 08936 | 0-6-0DE | Dar | | 1962 | a |

a   on hire from RMS Locotec Ltd, Wakefield, West Yorkshire

Gauge 2ft 6in — **Cold Strip Mill**

1	4wDHF	HE	9248	1985	
2	4wDHF	HE	9262	1985	
(5)	4wBE	WR	Q7808	1976	OOU

**GREAVES WELSH SLATE CO LTD
Llechwedd Slate Quarries, Blaenau Ffestiniog**

Gauge 2ft 0in   RTC — Gwynedd SH 702468

| – | 4wDM | RH | 174542 | 1935 | OOU |

Maen Offeren Slate Quarry, Blaenau Ffestiniog

Gauge 2ft 0in — Gwynedd SH 713467, 716465

–	4wBE	CE	5688/2	1969	
–	4wDM	RH	174536	1936	OOU
–	4wDM	RH	175127	1935	OOU
–	4wBE	WR	918	1936	OOU

HANSON QUARRY PRODUCTS EUROPE LTD, HANSON AGGREGATES, PENMAENMAWR GRANITE QUARRIES

No rail operation within quarry.   Conwy   SH 701758

Loco abandoned in a remote location on "Level 2", officially known as "Bottom Bank East Quarry".

Gauge 3ft 0in

1878	PENMAEN	0-4-0VBT	VC	DeW		1878	Dsm

MOSTYN DOCKS LTD, MOSTYN DOCK

(subsidiary of Faber Prest plc)   Flintshire   SJ 156811

Gauge 4ft 8½in

H 003	ROSEDALE	4wDH	S	10070	1961	a
H 057	DL2	4wDH	S	10177	1964	a

a   on hire from R.M.S.Locotec Ltd, Wakefield, West Yorkshire

SPENCER INDUSTRIAL (NW) LTD, SPENCER INDUSTRIAL ESTATE, LIVERPOOL ROAD, BUCKLEY

Gauge 2ft 6in   SJ 289649

51	TOM	0-6-0DH	_(HE	8847	1981	
			(HC	DM1447	1981	OOU

UNITED UTILITIES, MILWR TUNNEL, HALKYN MINE, RHYDMWYN

Gauge 1ft 10½in   (Underground – no public access)   SJ 296536

–		4wDM	RH	182138	1936	OOU
–		4wDM	RH	226309	1943	Dsm a
–		4wDM	RH	354029	1953	OOU
774		4wBE	WR	744	1929	OOU
3		4wBE	WR	773	1930	OOU
–		2-2wDM	EdwardsE&J		2004	b

a   dumped in workshops adjacent to Pen-y-Bryn shaft
b   owned and operated by the Grosvenor Caving Club

PRESERVATION LOCATIONS

BALA LAKE RAILWAY LTD, LLANUWCHLLYN, near BALA

Gauge 1ft 11½in   www.bala-lake-railway.co.uk   Gwynedd   SH 881300

1	GEORGE B	0-4-0ST	OC	HE	680	1898
No.3	HOLY WAR	0-4-0ST	OC	HE	779	1902
	ALICE	0-4-0ST	OC	HE	780	1902
	MAID MARIAN	0-4-0ST	OC	HE	822	1903
	TRIASSIC	0-6-0ST	OC	P	1270	1911
	BOB DAVIES	4wDH		BD	3776	1983
			reb	YEC	L125	1994

CHILMARK	4wDM	RH	194771	1939	
	4wDM	RH	200748	1940	
LADY MADCAP	4wDM	RH	283512	1949	
MEIRIONNYDD	4w-4wDH	SL	22	1973	
(RTT/767156)	2w-2PM	Wkm	3158	c1943	

Gauge 2ft 6in

ND 3051	0-4-0DM	HE	2022	1939	Dsm

BRYNBERW, CORRIS VILLAGE
Gauge 2ft 3in   Gwynedd   SH 768092

–	4wBE	CE	B0457	1974

CAERNARFON AIR MUSEUM, CAERNARFON AIRWORLD, DINAS DINLLS, CAERNARFON
Gauge 2ft 0in   Gwynedd

RTT 767150	2w-2PM	Wkm	(3152 1943)?

CARNARVON SLATE RAILWAY COMPANY, PORTHMADOG
Gauge 2ft 0in   Gwynedd

–	4wBE		WR	M7556	1972
		reb	WR	10114	1984

CONWY VALLEY RAILWAY MUSEUM, BETWS-Y-COED
Gauge 1ft 3in   Conwy   SH 796565

70000	BRITANNIA	4-6-2	OC	TMA	8733	1988	+

+   begun by Longfleet Motor & Engineering Works Ltd, 46 Fernside Road, Poole, Dorset, in 1968; completed by TMA; plate reads 1987

CORRIS RAILWAY COMPANY LTD, MAESPOETH, near CORRIS
Gauge 2ft 3in   www.corris.co.uk   Gwynedd   SH 753069

No.7		0-4-2ST	OC	Winson	17	2005
No.8		4wDM		HE	7274	1973
No.5	ALAN MEADEN	4wDM		MR	22258	1965
	CORRIS RAILWAY No.6	4wDH		RH	518493	1966

DOLGARROG RAILWAY SOCIETY, ALUMINIUM WORKS SIDING, DOLGARROG
Gauge 4ft 8½in   SH 774674

2	TAURUS	0-4-0DM	_(VF	D139	1951
			(DC	2273	1951

FAIRBOURNE RAILWAY LTD, FAIRBOURNE
Gauge 2ft 0in   Gwynedd SH 616128

–	4wDH	HE	9354	1994	a

a   carries worksplate HE 9332 1994

GWYNEDD COUNCIL, BLAENAU FFESTINIOG
The locomotive is on display opposite the railway station.

Gauge 2ft 0in   Gwynedd SH 703458

2207	4wDM	HE	2207	1941	OOU

THE FESTINIOG RAILWAY COMPANY, PORTHMADOG
Locos are kept at :-   Boston Lodge Shed & Works, Gwynedd SH 584379, 585378
Ffestiniog Railway Museum, Porthmadog Goods Shed, Gwynedd SH 571384
Glan-y-Pwll Depot, Blaenau Ffestiniog, Gwynedd SH 693461
Minffordd P.W. Depot, Gwynedd SH 599386
Porthmadog Station, Gwynedd SH 571384

Gauge 2ft 0in

87	2-6-2+2-6-2T 4C	Cockerill	3267	1937	
–	0-6-0WT OC	OK	9239	1921	

Gauge 762mm

4	0-8-0 OC	Harbin	221	1988

Gauge 1ft 11½in

Note: most of the locos have been "rebuilt" by the FRCo many times during their working lives
In this list we detail only those rebuilds which made significant alteration to the loco's appearance.

	MOUNTAINEER	2-6-2T	OC	Alco(C)	57156	1916
			reb	FRCo		c1968
No.10	MERDDIN EMRYS	0-4-4-0T	4C	FRCo		1879
			reb	FRCo		1988
	LIVINGSTON THOMPSON	0-4-4-0T	4C	FRCo		1885 c
			reb	FRCo		1905
	EARL OF MERIONETH /					
	IARLL MEIRIONNYDD	0-4-4-0T	4C	FRCo		1979
	DAFYDD LLOYD GEORGE /					
	DAVID LLOYD GEORGE	0-4-4-0T	4C	FRCo		1992
	TALIESIN	0-4-4T	OC	FRCo		1999
No.2	PRINCE	0-4-0TT	OC	GE	(199?)	1863
	rebuilt as	0-4-0STT		FRCo		1891
			reb	FRCo		1955
			reb	FRCo		1979
No.1	PRINCESS	0-4-0TT	OC	GE	(200?)	1863
	rebuilt as	0-4-0STT		FRCo		1895
No.4	PALMERSTON	0-4-0TT	OC	GE		1864
	rebuilt as	0-4-0STT		FRCo		1888
			reb	FRCo		1910
			reb	FRCo		1933

No.	Name	Type		Builder	No.	Date		
No.5	WELSH PONY/							
	MERLEN GYMREIG	0-4-0STT	OC	GE	234	1867		
			reb	FRCo		1891		
	LILLA	0-4-0ST	OC	HE	554	1891		
	BLANCHE	0-4-0ST	OC	HE	589	1893		
	rebuilt as	2-4-0STT		FRCo		1972		
	LINDA	0-4-0ST	OC	HE	590	1893		
	rebuilt as	2-4-0STT		FRCo		1970		
1	BRITOMART	0-4-0ST	OC	HE	707	1899		
	CASTELL HARLECH/							
	HARLECH CASTLE	0-6-0DH		BD	3767	1983		
	MOELWYN	0-4-0PM		BLW	49604	1918		
	rebuilt as	0-4-0DM		FRCo		1956		
	rebuilt as	2-4-0DM		FRCo		1957		
	CRICCIETH CASTLE /							
	CASTELL CRICIETH	0-6-0DH		FRCo		1995		
	VALE OF FFESTINIOG	4w-4wDH		Funkey		1968		
			reb	FRCo				
	ASHOVER	4wDM		FH	3307	1948		
–		4wDM		FRSociety		1974		
	MOEL HEBOG	0-4-0DM		HE	4113	1955		
	MOEL Y GEST	4wDH		HE	6659	1965		
	HAROLD	4wDM		HE	7195	1974		
8		6wDM		KS	4415	1928		
(MPU 8)		4wDH		Matisa		1956		
	MARY ANN	4wPM		MR		1917	+	
	rebuilt	4wPM		KC		1923		
	rebuilt as	4wDM		FRCo		c1957		
	THE COLONEL	4wDM		MR	8788	1943		
	THE LADY DIANA	4wDM		MR	21579	1957		
MPU9	149	4wDM		MR	22119	1961	a	Dsm
1543		2w-2PMR		Wkm	1543	1934	b	

+   carries incorrect plate 507/1917
a   in use as a winch wagon at Glan-y-Pwll
b   currently away for restoration
c   currently on display at National Railway Museum, York

FLINTSHIRE MUSEUM SERVICE, SHOTTON STORE, UNIT 3, ROWLEY PARK, EVANS WAY, SHOTTON

Gauge 1ft 10½in   SJ 310687

Name	Type	Builder	No.	Date
–	4wDM	RH	331250	1952
–	4wBE	WR	898	1935

GREENFIELD VALLEY TRUST LTD, GREENFIELD VALLEY HERITAGE PARK, HOLYWELL

Gauge 1ft 10½in   Flintshire   SJ 193773

Name	Type	Builder	No.	Date
–	0-4-0BE	WR	(1080 1937?)	

S. HODGSON, HEN EFAIL, GOLAN, DOLBENMAEN

Gauge 2ft 0in   Gwynedd   SH 534421

No.6		4wDM	MR	7403	1939	

I.B. JOLLY, MOLD

Locos are stored at two private locations.   Flintshire

Gauge 4ft 8½in

MRTC 1944		4wDM	MR	1944	1919	

Gauge 2ft 7in

–		4wDM	MR	5025	1929	Dsm

Gauge 600mm

–		0-2-2GasE	HopleyCP		c1982	
(LR 2718) MRTC 997		4wPM	MR	997	1918	Dsm
–		4wDM	MR	4803	1934	Dsm
		4wDM	MR	5852	1933	Dsm
–		4wDM	MR	8723	1941	Dsm
No.9		4wDM	MR	9547	1950	

Gauge 1ft 11½in

–		4wDM	L	30233	1946	
–		4wPM	MR	6013	1931	Dsm

INIGO JONES & CO LTD,
TUDOR SLATE WORKS, GROESLON, near PENYGROES

(subsidiary of Wincilate Ltd)   Gwynedd   SH 471551

Gauge 2ft 3in

–		4wBE	LMM	

LLANGOLLEN RAILWAY plc   www.llangollen-railway.co.uk

Locos are kept at :–

Llangollen Shed, Denbighshire   SJ 212422
Llangollen Station, Denbighshire   SJ 215422
Carrog, Denbighshire   SJ
Glyndyfrdwy, Denbighshire   SJ 150428
Pentrefelin Sidings, Denbighshire   SJ 209432

Gauge 4ft 8½in

2859		2-8-0	OC	Sdn	2765	1918	OOU
3802		2-8-0	OC	Sdn		1938	
5199		2-6-2T	OC	Sdn		1934	
5532		2-6-2T	OC	Sdn		1928	
5539		2-6-2T	OC	Sdn		1928	
6430		0-6-0PT	IC	Sdn		1937	
7754		0-6-0PT	IC	NBQ	24042	1930	
7822	FOXCOTE MANOR	4-6-0	OC	Sdn		1950	
44806	KENNETH ALDCROFT	4-6-0	OC	Derby		1944	
47298		0-6-0T	IC	HE	1463	1924	

48518			2-8-0	OC	Don		1944
80072			2-6-4T	OC	Bton		1953
80136			2-6-4T	OC	Bton		1956
–			0-4-0ST	OC	AE	1498	1906
–			0-6-0T	OC	HC	1731	1942
1			0-6-0ST	IC	HE	1873	1937
		reb	0-6-0T	IC	Llangollen		2007
	AUSTIN 1		0-6-0ST	IC	K	5459	1932
72	2235/72		0-6-0ST	IC	VF	5309	1945
(D147)	46010		1Co-Co1DE		Derby		1961
D1566	(47449)	ORION	Co-CoDE		Crewe		1964
(D2162)	03162		0-6-0DM		Sdn		1960
D3265	(08195 13265)		0-6-0DE		Derby		1956
(D6950)	(37150) 37901		Co-CoDE		_(EE	3325	1963
	MIRLEES PIONEER				(EEV	D824	1963
(D6940)	37240		Co-CoDE		_(EE	3497	1964
					(EEV	D928	1964
(D7663	25213) 25313		Bo-BoDE		Derby		1966
D8142	(20142)		Bo-BoDE		_(EE	3614	1966
					(EEV	D1013	1966
–			0-6-0DE		EEDK	1901	1951
	ELISEG		0-4-0DM		JF	22753	1939
–			0-6-0DE		YE	2630	1956
–			0-6-0DE		YE	2769	1959
D2892			0-4-0DE		YE	2782	1960
–			0-4-0DE		YE	2854	1961
	DR 90005		4wDMR		Matisa	PV6 627	1967
1			2w-2DH	R/R	TH	326V	1988
	Q317 GRN		4wDM	R/R	Unimog	008983	
E50416			2-2w-2w-2DMR		Wkm	7346	1957
M 50447)	M 53447 610		2-2w-2w-2DMR		BRCW		1957
M 50454			2-2w-2w-2DMR		BRCW		1957
M 50528			2-2w-2w-2DMR		BRCW		1958
M 51618			2-2w-2w-2DHR		DerbyC&W		1959
M 51907	LO 262		2-2w-2w-2DMR		DerbyC&W		1960

DAVID MITCHELL, LLANERCWYMEDD, ANGELSEY
Gauge 1ft 3in

–	2w-2PMR	Wkm	4816	1948	Dsm

WREXHAM COUNTY BOROUGH MUSEUM, MINERA LEAD MINES & COUNTRY PARK, VERN ROAD, MINERA, near WREXHAM
Gauge 1ft 10½in   Wrexham   SJ 275510

–	4wDM	RH	183727	1937

Stored on site but not on public display

THE MONORAIL COLLECTION, BLAENAU FFESTINIOG

This collection is in storage at a private location.   Gwynedd

Gauge monorail

1795	HULL	1w1PM	RM	1795	1952		
2910	HAZLEMERE	1w1PM	RM	2910	1953		
3250	HEAP CLOUGH	1w1PM	RM	3250	1953		
3906	WANTAGE	1w1PM	RM	3906	1954		
	BISHOPS SUTTON	1w1PM	RM	3981	1955		
4114	FOLDHILL	1w1PM	RM	4114	1955		
4810	BINFIELD	1w1PM	RM	4810	1955		
4904	SACRISTON	1w1PM	RM	4904	1956		
4989	STEYNING	1w1PM	RM	4989	1956		
–		1w1PM	RM	5013	1956	a	Dsm
	BODMIN	1w1PM	RM	5041	1956		
5074		1w1PM	RM	5074	1956	b	
6560		1w1PM	RM	6560	1957	b	
7050	COOKHAM	1w1PM	RM	7050	1957		
7182	ESHER 'A'	1w1PM	RM	7182	1958		
7493	HENFIELD	1w1PM	RM	7493	1958		
	HASLINGDEN	1w1PM	RM	7498	1958		
8071	CHIPPING NORTON	1w1PM	RM	8071	1959		
	UCKFIELD 'A'	1w1PM	RM	8073	1959		Dsm
8118	GODSTONE	2wPH	RM	8118	1959		
8415		1w1PM	RM	8415	1959		Dsm
–		2wDH	RM	8423	1959	a	
	SHENFIELD	2wPH	RM	8583	1959		
8633	ESHER 'B'	1w1PM	RM	8633	1959		
8638	SLEAFORD	1w1PM	RM	8638	1960		
8653	CHERTSEY	2wPH	RM	8653	1959		
8663	LLANGEFNI	2wPH	RM	8663	1960		
	UCKFIELD 'B'	2wPH	RM	8862	1960		
8992	FAVERSHAM	1w1PM	RM	8992	1960		
	WANSTEAD	2wPH	RM	9391	1960		
	WOODFORD	2wPH	RM	9392	1960		
9536	CREWKERNE	1w1PM	RM	9536	1961		
	KIDLINGTON	1w1PM	RM	9537	1961		
	NAYLAND	2wPH	RM	9795	1960		
	ESHER 'C'	2wPH	RM	9811	1961		
	ESHER 'D'	2wPH	RM	9812	1961		
	TADLEY	2wPH	RM	9852	1961		
	INGRAVE 'A'	2wPH	RM	9853	1961		
9869	UCKFIELD 'C'	2wPH	RM	9869	1961		
9925	LLANGOLLEN	2wPH	RM	9925	1961		
10051	GILLINGHAM	1w1PM	RM	10051	1961		
10067	CAMBERLEY	2wPH	RM	10067	1961		
	LIVERPOOL 'A'	2wPH	RM	10069	1961		
–		2wPH	RM	10070	1961	a	Dsm
	SPALDING 'A'	2wGasH	RM	10248	1961	c	
10258	HESWALL	2wPH	RM	10258	1961		
	EARLEY	2wPH	RM	10260	1961		

	HALE	2wPH	RM	10422	1961	
10593	SPALDING 'B'	2wGasH	RM	10593	1962	c
10782	HARWELL	1w1PH	RM	10782	1962	
	STORRINGTON	1w1PH	RM	10809	1962	OOU
–		1w1PH	RM	10894	1962	Dsm OOU
	BOURNEMOUTH 'A'	1w1PH	RM	10900	1962	OOU
	HAVERHILL	1w1PH	RM	10952	1962	OOU
11097	AYLESFORD	1w1PH	RM	11097	1962	OOU
	OXFORD	1w1PH	RM	11204	1963	OOU
	EYNSHAM	1w1PH	RM	11206	1963	OOU
–		1w1PH	RM	11338	1963	Dsm OOU
–		1w1PH	RM	11451	1963	Dsm OOU
	WEST CALDER	1w1PH	RM	11457	1963	OOU
	TANKERSLEY	1w1PH	RM	11459	1963	OOU
11460	ASHINGTON	1w1PH	RM	11460	1963	OOU
	HECKINGTON	1w1PH	RM	11809	1963	d
11836	BOWBURN	1w1PH	RM	11836	1963	OOU
	WICKHAM	1w1PH	RM	12124	1964	OOU
12126	CHELTENHAM	1w1PH	RM	12126	1964	
12432	HOWDEN	1w1PH	RM	12432	1964	
12438	DURHAM	1w1PH	RM	12438	1964	OOU
–		1w1DH	RM	12625	1964	Dsm OOU
–		1w1DH	RM	12626	1964	Dsm OOU
–		1w1DH	RM	12634	1964	OOU
	MOSTYN	1w1GasH	RM	12649	1964	OOU
12713	ABINGDON	1w1PM	RM	12713	1964	
	SWINDON	1w1PH	RM	12869	1964	OOU
	LONDON 'A'	2wPH	RM	13300	1965	d
	LONDON 'B'	2wPH	RM	13301	1965	d
	SAUNDERSFOOT	2wPH	RM	13313	1965	d
	LIVERPOOL 'B'	2wPH	RM	13318	1965	OOU
	BOURNEMOUTH 'B'	2wPH	RM	13626	1965	OOU
13629	LANCHESTER	2wPH	RM	13629	1965	
	ESHER 'E'	2wPH	RM	13911	1965	OOU
	SWANWICK	2wPH	RM	13913	1965	OOU
	INGRAVE 'B'	2wPH	RM	13929	1965	OOU
	WITTON GILBERT	2wPH	RM	14753	1966	OOU
	WHARNCLIFFE-SIDE	2wPH	RM	14766	1966	
	BANBURY	2wDH	RM	14769	1966	Dsm OOU
	LEESWOOD	2wPH	RM	14789	1966	
	TIPTREE	2wPH	RM	14806	1966	OOU
	WESTBURY	2wDH	RM	15152	1967	OOU
	PENTRE HALKYN	2wPH	RM	15773	1967	d
HOLME UPON SPALDING MOOR		2wPH	RM	15778	1967	
	CONINGSBY	2wDH	RM	15784	1967	g
No.2	MEXBOROUGH	2wDH	Metalair	20002	1968	
	LINCOLN 'A'	2wDH	Metalair	20003	1968	
	BRENTWOOD 'A'	2wPH	Metalair	20004	1968	
	BRENTWOOD 'B'	2wPH	Metalair	20005	1968	
	FARINGDON	1w1DH	Metalair	20007	1968	
17		2wDH	Metalair	20017	1968	

18		2wDH		Metalair	20018	1968	
	LINCOLN 'B'	2wDH		Metalair	20019	1968	
	SKELLINGTHORPE	2wDH		Metalair	20025	1968	
No.39		2wPH		Metalair	20039	1968	Dsm
	CHIRK	2wPH		Metalair	20044	1968	
65		2wDH		Metalair	20065	1968	e
	SHEPSHED	2wDH		Metalair	20067	1968	
–		2wDH		Metalair	20069	1968	f
	PARTINGTON	1w1DH		Metalair	20091	1968	
No.140	RAILCAR A	2wDH		Metalair	20140	1969	g
No.141	RAILCAR B	2wDH		Metalair	20141	1969	g
No.146	"MONOLOCO"	0-2-0ST	OC	CM	11003	1998	h
	WITHERNSEA	2wPH		Metalair	20161	1969	d
No.212	POOLE	2wDH		Metalair	20212	1970	
	TREFNANT	2wPH		Metalair	20222	1971	
–		2wDH		Metalair	20228	1970	
	SALISBURY	2wDH		Metalair	20240	1971	
	DOWNTON	2wDH		Metalair	20242	1971	
265		2wDH		Metalair	20265	1973	i

a   converted to unpowered wagon
b   converted to permanent way manrider
c   horticultural flat power wagon
d   hydraulic tip power wagon
e   converted to passenger carriage
f   converted to stair wagon
g   power wagon
h   built on chassis of trailer wagon Metalair 20146/1969
i   converted to railcar 2002

R.P. MORRIS, BLAENAU FFESTINIOG
These locos are kept at a private location.   Gwynedd

Gauge 3ft 0in

(C13)	2w-2PMR		Wkm	2449	1938	Dsm

Gauge 2ft 0in

14005	STEAM TRAM	4wVBT	G			1969
	rebuilt from	4wDM		L	14005	1940
39005		4wPM		L	39005	1952
(C37)		2w-2PMR		Locospoor		
					B7281E	
	RAIL TAXI	4-2-0PMR		MorrisRP		1967
	"A16W PWM 2788"	2w-2PMR		Wkm	6887	1954
	rebuilt as	2w-2DMR		ENG/GEM		1994
E1	No.3867 CLOGAU	0-4-0BE		WR	(3867	1948)?

Gauge 1ft 11½in

E2	No.7179 GWYNFYNYDD	0-4-0BE		WR	G7179	1967

NARROW GAUGE RAILWAY MUSEUM TRUST,
WHARF STATION, TYWYN
Gauge 2ft 0in   Gwynedd   SH 586004

No.2	0-4-0WT	OC	KS	721	1901

Gauge 1ft 10¾in

GEORGE HENRY	0-4-0VBT	VC	DeW		1877
ROUGH PUP	0-4-0ST	OC	HE	541	1891
JUBILEE 1897	0-4-0ST	OC	MW	1382	1897

Gauge 1ft 10in

13	0-4-0T	IC	Spence	13L	1895

Gauge 1ft 6in

DOT	0-4-0WT	OC	BP	2817	1887

NATIONAL MUSEUM OF WALES
WELSH SLATE MUSEUM, GILFACHDDU, LLANBERIS, LL55 4TY
Gauge 1ft 11½in   Gwynedd   SH 586603

UNA	0-4-0ST	OC	HE	873	1905
–	4wBE		BE		1917
–	4wPMR		WilliamsWJ		+
–	4wDM		RH	175414	1936

+   vintage motorcycle converted for rail use

NATIONAL TRUST, INDUSTRIAL RAILWAY MUSEUM
PENRHYN CASTLE, LLANDYGÁI, near BANGOR
Gauge 4ft 8½in   Gwynedd   SH 603720

HAWARDEN	0-4-0ST	OC	HC	526	1899	
VESTA	0-6-0T	IC	HC	1223	1916	
No.1	0-4-0WT	OC	N	1561	1870	
HAYDOCK	0-6-0T	IC	RS	2309	1876	+

+   works plate reads 1879

Gauge 4ft 0in

FIRE QUEEN	0-4-0	OC	AH		1848

Gauge 3ft 0in

KETTERING FURNACES No.3	0-4-0ST	OC	BH	859	1885
(WATKIN)	0-4-0VBT	VC	DeW		1893

Gauge 2ft 0in

HUGH NAPIER	0-4-0ST	OC	HE	855	1904

Gauge 1ft 11½in

ACORN	4wDM		RH	327904	1951

Gauge 1ft 10¾in

CHARLES	0-4-0ST	OC	HE	283	1882

PENRHYN RAILWAY TRUST
Gauge 3ft 0in

–	4wDMF	RH	375694	1954

Gauge 2ft 0in

1	0-8-0T	OC	Hen	15540	1917
–	4wDMF		RH	353491	1953

All locos are stored at a private location and are not on public view.

A. PILBEAM, LLANRHOS
Gauge 1ft 3in

–	2-2wBER	MossAJ		2000
–	4wBE	Riordan	T6664	1967

Gauge Monorail

–	1w-1PM	RM	8564	1959

QUARRY TOURS LTD,
LLECHWEDD SLATE MINE, BLAENAU FFESTINIOG
Gauge 2ft 0in   Gwynedd SH 699468

–		4wBE		BEV	308	1921	a
–		4wBE		BEV	323	1921	a
(No.4 THE ECLIPSE)		0-4-0WE		Greaves		1927	
	a rebuild of	0-4-0ST	OC	WB	1445	1895	a
THE COALITION		0-4-0WE		Greaves		1930	
	a rebuild of	0-4-0ST	OC	WB	1278	1890	a
–		4wPM		Greaves		c1936	a
MBS 387		4wBE		LMM	1053	1950	a
MBS 236		4wBE		LMM	1066	1950	a
–		4wBE		WR			b
LE/12/65		4wBE		WR			b
–		4wBE		WR			
–		4wBE		WR			
–		4wBE		WR			
–		4wBE		AK	67	2003	

a   on static display (remainder are operational fleet)
b   possibly one of WR C6765 1963 or WR C6766 1963 [see also p.50]

RHEILFFORDD LLYN PADARN CYFYNGEDIG, LLANBERIS LAKE RAILWAY, GILFACHDDU, LLANBERIS, LL55 4TY

Gauge 1ft 11½in   Gwynedd   SH 586603

No.1	ELIDIR	0-4-0ST	OC	HE	493	1889	
No.2	THOMAS BACH	0-4-0ST	OC	HE	849	1904	
No.3	DOLBADARN	0-4-0ST	OC	HE	1430	1922	
–		4wDM		MR	7927	1941	Dsm
No.9	GARRET	4wDM		RH	198286	1940	
No.8	YD No.AD689 TWLL COED	4wDM		RH	268878	1952	
–		4wDM		RH	425796	1958	Dsm
No.7	TOPSY	4wDM		RH	441427	1961	
No.19	LLANELLI	4wDM		RH	451901	1961	

RHYL STEAM PRESERVATION TRUST, RHYL MINIATURE RAILWAY, MARINE LAKE, RHYL

Gauge 1ft 3in   www.rhylminiaturerailway.co.uk   Denbighshire   SJ 003805

44		4-4-0	OC	McGarigle		c1910	
	JOAN	4-4-2	OC	Barnes	101	1920	
	RAILWAY QUEEN	4-4-2	OC	Barnes	102	1921	
105	MICHAEL	4-4-2	OC	Barnes	105	c1928	
106	BILLY	4-4-2	OC	Barnes	106	c1934	
	CLARA	0-4-2DM	s/o	Guest		1961	
–		4wDM		L	10498	1938	
	VINCENT	2w-2-4BER		Hayne		1983	

SNOWDON MOUNTAIN RAILWAY LTD, LLANBERIS

Gauge 800mm   Gwynedd   SH 582597

All locos drive through the rack gear, with the "driving wheels" free to rotate on their axles.

2	ENID	0-4-2T	OC	RACK	SLM	924	1895	
3	WYDDFA	0-4-2T	OC	RACK	SLM	925	1895	
4	SNOWDON	0-4-2T	OC	RACK	SLM	988	1896	
5	MOEL SIABOD	0-4-2T	OC	RACK	SLM	989	1896	
6	PADARN	0-4-2T	OC	RACK	SLM	2838	1922	
7	RALPH	0-4-2T	OC	RACK	SLM	2869	1923	OOU
8	ERYRI	0-4-2T	OC	RACK	SLM	2870	1923	OOU
9	NINIAN	0-4-0DH		RACK	HE	9249	1986	
10	YETI	0-4-0DH		RACK	HE	9250	1986	
11	PERIS	0-4-0DH		RACK	_(HAB	775	1991	
					(HE	9305	1991	
12	GEORGE	0-4-0DH		RACK	HE	9312	1992	
21		2-2w-4DER		RACK	HPET	1074	1995	OOU
22		2-2w-4DER		RACK	HPET	1075	1995	OOU
23		2-2w-4DER		RACK	HPET	1076	1995	OOU

TALYLLYN RAILWAY CO, TYWYN

Loco shed at Tywyn Pendre Station, Gwynedd   SH 590008

Gauge 2ft 6in   www.talyllyn.co.uk

6	T 0006 00 NZ 32	4wDH	BD	3764	1983	d
5		4wDH	BD	3779	1983	d
7	T 0009 00 NZ 35	4wDH	BD	3781	1984	d

Gauge 2ft 3in

No.1	TALYLLYN	0-4-2ST	OC	FJ	42	1865	
No.2	DOLGOCH	0-4-0WT	OC	FJ	63	1866	
No.3	SIR HAYDN	0-4-2ST	OC	HLT	323	1878	
No.4	EDWARD THOMAS	0-4-2ST	OC	KS	4047	1921	
No.6	DOUGLAS	0-4-0WT	OC	AB	1431	1918	
No.7	TOM ROLT	0-4-2T	OC	Pendre		1991	
	built using parts of	0-4-0WT	OC	AB	2263	1949	
–		0-4-0DM		HE	4135	1950	b Dsm
	ALF	0-4-0DM		HE	4136	1950	
6292		4wDH		HE	6292	1967	a Dsm
(19)		2w-2PM		CurwenD		1952	+ Dsm
	TOBY	2w-2PMR		BateJ		1954	
	rebuilt as	2w-2DMR		Pendre		2001	
DIESEL No.5	MIDLANDER	4wDM		RH	200792	1940	
DIESEL No.8	MERSEYSIDER	4wDH		RH	476108	1964	
	"THE FLAIL MOWER"	2-2-0DH		RH	476109	1964	c Dsm
No.10	BRYNEGLWYS	4wDH		SMH	101T023	1985	
	reb			YEC	L145	1995	

+   converted into a flat wagon
a   frames utilised in a hydraulic press
b   stored at Brynglas Station (SH 628031)
c   frames utilised in self-propelled flail mower
d   currently stored elsewhere

UNKNOWN OWNER, BETTISFIELD
Gauge 4ft 8½in   Flintshire

–	4wDM	Bg/DC	2107	1937

R.WATSON-JONES,
WOODLANDS, THE DINGLE, CONSTITUTION HILL, PENMAENMAWR
Gauge 3ft 0in   Conwy SH 720765

–	4wDM	RH	202987	1941

WELSH HIGHLAND LIGHT RAILWAY LTD, DINAS, near CAERNARFON

Public railway operating southwards from terminus in Caernarfon.
Loco shed and workshops at Dinas Station

Gwynedd   SH 477587

Gauge 3ft 0in — Static display at Dinas

LLANFAIR		0-4-0VBT	VC	DeW	1895	OOU

Gauge 1ft 11½in

133		2-8-2	OC	AFB	2683	1952	OOU
134		2-8-2	OC	AFB	2684	1952	
(No.1K)		0-4-0+0-4-0T	4C	BP	5292	1909	
138	MILLENNIUM / MILENIWM	2-6-2+2-6-2	4C	BP	7863	1958	
(140)		2-6-2+2-6-2	4C	BP	7865	1958	
143		2-6-2+2-6-2	4C	BP	7868	1958	
	CASTELL CAERNARFON	4w-4wDH		Funkey		1968	
	CONWAY CASTLE / CASTELL CONWY	4wDM		FH	3831	1958	
	UPNOR CASTLE	4wDM		FH	3687	1954	
	DOLGARROG	4wDM		MR	22154	1962	+

+   currently stabled at or near Rhyd Ddu Station; on track extension works

---

WELSH HIGHLAND RAILWAY LTD, PORTHMADOG

Public railway operating northwards from terminus in Porthmadog.
Loco shed and workshops at Gelert's Farm, Porthmadog.

Gwynedd   SH 571393

Gauge 1ft 11½in

120	NG15 BEDDGELERT		2-8-2	OC	AFB	2667	1951	OOU
	TIGER		4-6-0T	OC	BLW	44699	1917	
No.1	RUSSELL		2-6-2T	OC	HE	901	1906	
	KAREN		0-4-2T	OC	P	2024	1942	
No.3	MOEL TRYFAN		0-4-2T	OC	WB	3023	1953	OOU
	GELERT		0-4-2T	OC	WB	3050	1953	
				reb	Winson		1991	
	(LADY MADCAP)		0-4-0ST	OC	WHR		2006	a
"2"			4wDH		AB	554	1970	
				reb	AB	6613	1987	
1	GOWRIE		4wDH		AB	555	1970	
58	MOEL TRYFAN		0-6-0DH		AUG	23387	1979	
60	ERYRI		0-6-0DH		AUG	23389	1977	
069			0-6-0DH		AUG	24051	1980	
–			4wDM		HE	2024	1940	
59105	VILLAGE IDIOT		0-4-0DMF		HE	3510	1947	
	WEIGHITIN		4wDH		HE	7535	1977	
	EMMA		4wDH		HE	9346	1994	
2			4wDH		HE	9350	1994	
–			4wPM		MR	264	c1916	
36	CNICHT		4wDM		MR	8703	1941	
6			4wDM		MR	11102	1959	
4	ANNE MARIE		4wDM		MR	60S333	1966	
9	KATHERINE		4wDM		MR	60S363	1968	

–		4wDM		RH	203031	1941
1	GLASLYN	4wDM		RH	297030	1952
			reb	WHR(GF)		1981
	KINNERLEY	4wDM		RH	354068	1953
L5	HOVERINGHAM	4wDM		RH	370555	1953
–		4wDMF		RH	481552	1962
	"BUSTA"	2w-2PMR		FRCo		2006

a   under construction. Incorporates some components from HE 652

AREA 2 – MID-WALES

PRESERVATION LOCATIONS

BRECON MOUNTAIN RAILWAY CO LTD, PONTSTICILL STATION & PANT STATION

Pontsticill Station, and the majority of the route of this railway, lies in Powys, and thus in our "Mid Wales Area
The terminus, and principal loco shed and workshops are, however, at Pant, Merthyr Tydfil, which is within ou
"South-East Wales Area". To avoid duplication of data, see the South-East Wales Section for full details.

CRAFT CENTRE, ERWOOD RAILWAY STATION, ERWOOD, near BUILTH WELLS

Gauge 4ft 8½in   Powys SO 089439

600		0-4-0DM	JF	22878	1939

VALE OF RHEIDOL LIGHT RAILWAY, ABERYSTWYTH

Ceredigion SN 587812

Gauge 1000mm (Static display)

–		4wPM	RP	51168	1916	+

+   currently under restoration elsewhere

Gauge 2ft 0in [nominal] (Static display)

–		0-4-0T	OC	Dec	1027	1926	b
	MARGARET	0-4-0ST	OC	HE	605	1894	b
–		0-6-0TT	OC	JF		1905	a
21		0-4-2T	OC	JF	11938	1909	b
23		0-6-2T	OC	JF	15515	1920	b
No.31		0-8-0T	OC	Maffei	4766	1917	b
–		0-4-4T	OC	WB	2228	1924	
D564		4wDM		HC	D564	1930	

Gauge 1ft 11¾in (Operational)

7	OWAIN GLYNDWR	2-6-2T	OC	Sdn		1923	
8		2-6-2T	OC	Sdn		1923	
9	PRINCE OF WALES	2-6-2T	OC	DM	2	1902	d
–		0-4-0ST	OC	KS	3114	1918	b
10		0-6-0DH		BMR	002	1987	c
–		4wDH		HE	7495	1977	e
(68804)	THUNDERBIRD 4 No.5	4wDHR		Perm	005	1985	

Gauge 1ft 10¾in (Static display)

106	1877 KATHLEEN	0-4-0VBT	VC	DeW	1877	

a   either JF 9465 or JF 10249
b   stored at Capel Bangor Station
c   built with parts supplied by BD
d   possibly a new loco built by Sdn in 1924
e   for use as a flail-mower

RHIW VALLEY LIGHT RAILWAY, LOWER HOUSE, MANAFON, near WELSHPOOL

Private railway; has occasional "open days".   Powys   SJ 143028

Gauge 1ft 3in

JACK	0-4-0	OC	_(Rhiw		2003	
			(TMA	25657	2003	a
POWYS	0-6-2T	OC	SL	20	1973	
MONTY	4wPM		_(Jaco		1989	
			(Brunning		1989	

a   construction commenced as an 0-4-2T in 1985, but completed 2003 as listed

TEIFI VALLEY RAILWAY, VALE OF TEIFI NARROW GAUGE RAILWAY, HENLLAN, near LLANDYSUL

Gauge 4ft 8½in   www.teifivr.f9.co.uk   Ceredigion   SN 357406

ROSYTH No.1	0-4-0ST	OC	AB	1385	1914	
SWANSEA VALE No.1	4wVBT	VCG	S	9622	1958	a
7 "SWANSEA JACK"	4wDM	S/O	RH	393302	1955	

a   owned by Y Clwb Rheil Cymru

Gauge 3ft 0in

LM 24	4wDM		RH	244870	1946
C 67	4wPMR		BnM		1972
(C 76)	4wPMR		BnM		1972

Gauge 2ft 6in

	4wDM		RH	(433390 1959?)	OOU

Gauge 2ft 0in

ALAN GEORGE	0-4-0ST	OC	HE	606	1894
–	0-6-0T	OC	KS	2442	1915

WD 3117	SGT MURPHY		0-6-0T	OC	KS	3117	1918	
		rebuilt as	0-6-2T	OC	Winson	9	1991	
–			4wDM		HE	1835	1937	
–			4wDM		HE	2433	1941	
004	SAMMY		4wDM		MR	11111	1959	

JOHN TENNENT & P. SMITH, BRECON

These locos are in store at a private location.   Powys

Gauge 1ft 3in

–		4wDM		AK	6	1981	
–		4wDM		LB	52579	1961	

WELSHPOOL & LLANFAIR LIGHT RAILWAY PRESERVATION CO LTD, LLANFAIR CAEREINION

Gauge 2ft 6in   Powys   SJ 107069

822	THE EARL	0-6-0T	OC	BP	3496	1902	
823	COUNTESS	0-6-0T	OC	BP	3497	1902	
	G.C.G.D. PROVAN WORKS No.1						
8	DOUGAL	0-4-0T	OC	AB	2207	1946	
10	699.01 SIR DREFALDWYN	0-8-0T	OC	AFB	2855	1944	
No.14	SLR 85	2-6-2T	OC	HE	3815	1954	
No.12	JOAN	0-6-2T	OC	KS	4404	1927	OOU
No.6	MONARCH	0-4-4-0T	4C	WB	3024	1953	
764.425		0-8-0T	OC	Resita		1955	
–		0-8-0T	OC	Resita		1955	
No.7	CHATTENDEN						
	YD No.AD690	0-6-0DM		Bg/DC	2263	1949	
No.17	175	6wDM		Diema	4270	1979	
No.11	FERRET YARD No.86	0-4-0DM		HE	2251	1940	
"No.16"	ND 3082						
	SCOOBY / SCWBI	0-4-0DM		HE	2400	1941	
			reb	W&LLR		1992	
–		4wDM		RH	191680	1938	+ Dsm
9150		4wDMR		BD	3746	1976	
–		2w-2PMR		Wkm	2904	1940	

+   frame and wheels used as a carrier

AREA 3 – SOUTH-WEST WALES

INDUSTRIAL LOCATIONS

BP MOBIL OIL LLANDARCY REFINERY LTD, LLANDARCY

Gauge 4ft 8½in   Neath Port Talbot   SS 718960

6	0-6-0DHF	TH	194V	1968
8	0-6-0DHF	TH	246V	1973
	280 - Wales (south-west)			

CELTIC ENERGY LTD, ONLLWYN DISPOSAL POINT, ONLLWYN

Gauge 4ft 8½in   SN 843105

(D3685)	08523	0-6-0DE	Don	1958	a

a   on hire from RMS Locotec Ltd, Wakefield, West Yorkshire

CORUS, STRIP PRODUCTS DIVISION,
PORT TALBOT WORKS, PORT TALBOT

Gauge 4ft 8½in   Neath Port Talbot   SS 771859, 775861, 775876, 775878)

No.	Name	Type		Builder	No.	Year	Notes
1		0-4-0WE	_(BD	3748	1979	
			(GECT	5476	1979	
2		0-4-0WE	_(BD	3749	1979	
			(GECT	5477	1979	
501		0-4-0DE		BBT	3066	1954	
504		0-4-0DE		BBT	3069	1954	
(505)	BT-2	0-4-0DE		BBT	3070	1954	a
506		0-4-0DE		BBT	3071	1954	
509		0-4-0DE		BBT	3099	1956	
(512)	BT-4	0-4-0DE		BBT	3102	1956	+
(513)	BT-3	0-4-0DE		BBT	3103	1957	
			reb	PortTalbotBSC	c1972	a
(514)	BT-1	0-4-0DE		BBT	3120	1957	
			reb	PortTalbotBSC	c1972	a
901		Bo-BoDE		BBT	3063	1955	
902		Bo-BoDE		BBT	3064	1955	
903		Bo-BoDE		BBT	3065	1955	
904		Bo-BoDE	_(BT	92	1957	
			(WB	3137	1957	
905		Bo-BoDE	_(BT	93	1957	
			(WB	3138	1957	
906		Bo-BoDE	_(BT	94	1957	
			(WB	3139	1957	
07		Bo-BoDE	_(BT	95	1957	
			(WB	3140	1957	
			reb	HAB	1993	
08		Bo-BoDE	_(BT	96	1957	
			(WB	3141	1957	
			reb	HAB	1993	
09		Bo-BoDE	_(BT	97	1957	
			(WB	3142	1957	
			reb	HAB	6063	1994	
910		Bo-BoDE	_(BT	98	1957	
			(WB	3143	1957	OOU
953		Bo-BoDE		BBT	3113	1957	
305		0-6-0DH		GECT	5382	1973	
D.E.3		6wDE		GECT	5411	1976	

+   slave unit to BBT 3066
a   converted to a brake tender runner

CORUS, TINPLATE, TROSTRE WORKS, LLANELLI
Gauge 4ft 8½in   Carmarthenshire   SS 531994

(D3789)	08622	H 028	0-6-0DE	Derby	1959	a
	H 015	SYLGWYN	0-6-0DH	HE	7410 1976	a

a   property of RMS Locotec Ltd, Wakefield, West Yorkshire.

CYMRU METALS, CROSS HANDS
Locomotives for resale or for scrap are occasionally present.   Carmarthenshire

SODIFEL GROUP, PAPER MILL, BAGLAN ENERGY PARK, BAGLAN BAY, PORT TALBOT
Gauge 4ft 8½in

(ZZ 44)	0-6-0DH	EEV	D3989	1970

TOTAL OIL, HERBRANDSTON, MILFORD HAVEN
Gauge 4ft 8½in   Pembrokeshire   SM 888085

077	MR 77	0-6-0DH		EEV	D1198	1967
			reb	YEC	L122	1993
078	MR 78	0-6-0DH		HE	6663	1969
			reb	HAB	6586	1999
	EDWARD	4wDH		TH	267V	1976

TRECWN (ETI) LTD, TRECWN VALLEY STORAGE FACILITY, TRECWN
Gauge 2ft 6in   Pembrokeshire   SM 970325

6	OMG 021	4wDH	BD	3782	1984
1		4wDH	BD	3783	1984
2		4wDH	BD	3784	1984

TUNNEL STEELS LTD, RAIL & SLEEPER CENTRE, PRYDWEN ROAD, SWANSEA WEST INDUSTRIAL ESTATE, SWANSEA
Gauge 4ft 8½in   www.tunnelsteel.net   SS 659927

SARA	4wDM	FH	3951	1961	OOU

WELSH WATER plc, SOLVA SEWAGE WORKS, SOLVA HARBOUR
Gauge 600mm   Pembrokeshire   SM 807244

29-32	2-2-0BE		Bradshaw	
		reb	Ash Dale Engineering	2005

PRESERVATION LOCATIONS

AMMAN VALLEY RAILWAY SOCIETY, PANTYFYNNON
Gauge 4ft 8½in

(M50397)	2-2w-2w-2DMR	PRoyal		1958	a

a   currently stored elsewhere

CARMARTHENSHIRE COUNTY COUNCIL
KIDWELLY INDUSTRIAL MUSEUM, LLANGADOG, KIDWELLY
Gauge 4ft 8½in   Carmarthenshire   SN 422078

–	0-4-0ST	OC	AB	1081	1909
–	0-6-0ST	OC	P	2114	1951
No.2	0-4-0DM		AB	393	1954

Gauge 2ft 0in

–	4wDM		RH	398063	1956
		reb	ESCA		1986

GWILI RAILWAY CO LTD, BRONWYDD ARMS
Locos are kept at :-   Bronwydd Arms, Carmarthenshire   SN 417239
Cynwyl Elfed Station, Carmarthenshire   SN 386264
Llwyfan Cerrig, Carmarthenshire   SN 405258

Gauge 4ft 8½in

– VICTORY	0-4-0ST	OC	AB	2201	1945	
1680 SIR JOHN	0-6-0ST	OC	AE	1680	1914	
–	0-4-0ST	OC	RSHN	7058	1942	
71516 WELSH GUARDSMAN / GWARCHODWR CYMREIG	0-6-0ST	IC	RSHN	7170	1944	
HAULWEN	0-6-0ST	IC	VF	5272	1945	
		reb	HE	3879	1961	
(D2178)	0-6-0DM		Sdn		1962	
–	4wDM		RH	394014	1956	
"TRECATTY"	0-6-0DM		RH	421702	1959	
3700-84	2w-2PMR		Woodings	A466	19xx	

LLANELLI & MYNEDD MAWR RAILWAY CO, CYNHEIDRE
Gauge 4ft 8½in   Carmarthenshire   SN 495071

–	4wDH	RR	10222	1965	
Sc52029	2-2w-2w-2DMR	DerbyC&W		1961	
51354	2-2w-2w-2DMR	PSteel		1960	
51396	2-2w-2w-2DMR	PSteel		1960	

NATIONAL TRUST, DOLAUCOTHI GOLD MINES, PUMSAINT

Gauge 1ft 10½in Carmarthenshire SN 666404

–	4wBE	CE	B2944I	1982	
–	4wBE	WR	899	1935	OOU
–	0-4-0BE	WR	5311	1955	

Gauge 400mm Becorit 'Roadrailer' Trapped Rail System

(No. 2 390/2)	2adDHF	BGB 50/400/406	1976
(No. 7 390/7)	2adDHF	BGB100/400/007	1984

NATIONAL WATERFRONT MUSEUM, OYSTERMOUTH ROAD, MARITIME QUARTER, SWANSEA

Gauge 4ft 4in SS 659927

–	4wG	NMW	1981

NEATH PORT TALBOT COUNTY BOROUGH COUNCIL, CEFN COED COLLIERY MUSEUM, CRYNANT, NEATH

Gauge 4ft 8½in Neath Port Talbot SN 786034

–	0-6-0ST	IC	WB	2758	1944

Gauge 2ft 0in

-	4wDH		HE	8812	1978

NEATH PORT TALBOT COUNTY BOROUGH COUNCIL MARGAM COUNTRY PARK, MARGAM

Gauge 2ft 0in

MARGAM CASTLE	0-4-0DH	s/o	AK	65	2001

OAKWOOD ADVENTURE AND LEISURE COMPLEX, CANASTON BRIDGE, NARBERTH

Gauge 600mm — Nutty Jakes Gold Mine Pembrokeshire SN 072124

–	4w-4wRE	s/o	SL	275/1.5.90	1990	
–	4w-4wRE	s/o	SL	275/2.5.90	1990	

Gauge 1ft 3in

LORNA	4-4wDHR		Goold		1989	
LINDY-LOU	0-8-0DH	s/o	SL	7218	1972	
LENKA	4-4wDHR		SL	7322	1973	+
–	0-8-0PH	s/o	SL	R9	1976	

+   4-wheel power unit incorporates the main frames of 4wDM L 7280 / 1936

**PEMBROKESHIRE COUNTY COUNCIL,
SCOLTON MANOR MUSEUM & COUNTRY PARK,
SCOLTON, near HAVERFORDWEST**
Gauge 4ft 8½in   Pembrokeshire SM 991222

No.1378	KIDWELLY					
	GWENDRAETH VALLEY RAILWAY CO No.2					
	MARGARET	0-6-0ST	IC	FW	410	1878
A 123 W)		2w-2PMR		Wkm	3361	1942

**SWANSEA INDUSTRIAL & MARITIME MUSEUM,
LANDORE STORE, SWANSEA**
Gauge 4ft 8½in   Swansea SS 662953

	SIR CHARLES	0-4-0F	OC	AB	1473	1916
1426		0-6-0ST	OC	P	1426	1916
	incorporates parts of			P	1187	
–		0-4-0DM		RSHD/WB	7910	1963

**SWANSEA VALE RAILWAY PRESERVATION SOCIETY,
LLANSAMLET, SWANSEA**
Gauge 4ft 8½in   Swansea SS 670954

	–	0-6-0ST	IC	HE	3829	1955
	M.N.Co.No.1	0-4-0ST	OC	P	1345	1914
2	SAMLET	0-4-0DH		NBQ	27941	1961
312433	ABIGAIL	4wDM		RH	312433	1951
51134		2-2w-2w-2DMR		DerbyC&W		1958
(W51135)		2-2w-2w-2DMR		DerbyC&W		1958
(51147)		2-2w-2w-2DMR		DerbyC&W		1958
(51148)		2-2w-2w-2DMR		DerbyC&W		1958
(55026)	977824	2-2w-2w-2DMR		PSteel		1960

AREA 4 – SOUTH-EAST WALES

INDUSTRIAL LOCATIONS

**CELSA STEEL (UK) LTD,
EAST MOORS ROAD, CARDIFF**
Gauge 4ft 8½in   Cardiff   ST208759
Shunting is carried out by a pool of locomotives hired from EWS.

Gauge 2ft 0in

–	2w-2CE	AS&W	1990	OOU

BEAVOR POWER LTD, GOAT MILL ROAD, DOWLAIS, MERTHYR TYDFIL

Gauge 5ft 3in   Merthyr Tydfil SO 062073

1		0-6-0DH	EEV	(D1266	1969	
				(3954	1969	

CANRON ENERGY, USKMOUTH POWER STATION, USKMOUTH

Gauge 4ft 8½in   (Closed)   Newport

–		0-6-0DH	RH	468046	1963	
	reb		YEC	L106	1992	OOU

COAL PRODUCTS LTD, CWM COKING PLANT, LLANTWIT FARDRE

The Coking Plant is now closed.   Rhondda Cynon Taf ST 066862

Gauge 4ft 8½in

2	0-4-0WE	GB	2180	1948	OOU
3	0-4-0WE	GB	2690	1957	OOU
1	0-4-0WE	GB	2691	1957	OOU

CORUS, STRIP PRODUCTS DIVISION, LLANWERN WORKS, NEWPORT

Gauge 4ft 8½in   Newport ST 385863

302		0-6-0DH	GECT	5379	1972	
304		0-6-0DH	EEV	(D1248	1968	
				(3946	1968	
	reb		LlanwernBSC		1996	OOU
306		0-6-0DH	GECT	5383	1973	
D.E.1		6wDE	GECT	5409	1976	
D.E.2		6wDE	GECT	5410	1976	
D.E.4		6wDE	GECT	5412	1976	
D.E.5		6wDE	GECT	5413	1976	

DOW CORNING LTD, CARDIFF ROAD, BARRY

Gauge 4ft 8½in   Vale of Glamorgan ST 142685

DC 27584	4wDM	R/R	Trackmobile		
			LGN963990492	1992	

FORD MOTOR CO LTD, BRIDGEND FACTORY

Gauge 4ft 8½in   Bridgend SS 931781

–		0-6-0DH	GECT	5391	1973	
	reb	‡		LWO 2108	2002	

‡   rebuilt by R.M.S.Locotec Ltd, Dewsbury, West Yorkshire

HANSON QUARRY PRODUCTS EUROPE LTD, HANSON AGGREGATES, MACHEN QUARRY, near NEWPORT

Gauge 4ft 8½in

Newport ST 221886

(D3366) 08296		0-6-0DE	Derby	1957	

B. HARRIS & SONS, STAR TRADING ESTATE, PONTHIR

Gauge 1000mm

Torfaen ST 333922

–	4wDH	MR	121UA117	1974	OOU

HOCKING RAIL, Specialist Railway Manufacturers & Contractors, CARDIFF DEPOT, YNYSFACH YARD, off HEOL-YR-YNYS, TONGWYNLAIS

Locos for hire or resale are occasionally present in the yard.

Cardiff ST 129824

LAFARGE CEMENT UK, ABERTHAW CEMENT WORKS

Gauge 4ft 8½in   RTC

Vale of Glamorgan ST 033674

125	4wDH	TH	213V	1969	OOU

MINISTRY OF DEFENCE, AIR FORCE DEPARTMENT, CAERWENT

Gauge 4ft 8½in

Monmouthshire ST 480910

See Section 6 for full details.

RWE NPOWER plc, ABERTHAW POWER STATION

Gauge 4ft 8½in

Vale of Glamorgan ST 026664

–	0-6-0DM	P	5014	1959	Pvd
–	2w-2PMR	Geismar	98/28	1998	

ORB STEEL TERMINAL, ORB, NEWPORT
(Operated by English Welsh & Scottish Railway)

Gauge 4ft 8½in

Newport ST 326863

JAMO	4wDH	RR	10198	1965	

PRESERVATION LOCATIONS

BARRY ISLAND RAILWAY
BARRY ISLAND RAIL HERITAGE CENTRE, BARRY ISLAND

Gauge 4ft 8½in

Vale of Glamorgan ST 117667

PAMELA	0-6-0ST	IC	HE	3840	1956
–	0-4-0ST	OC	RSHN	7705	1952
(D3673) 08511	0-6-0DE		Dar		1958

287 - Wales (south-east)

(E6024)	73128		Bo-BoDE/RE		_(EE	3586	1966
					(EEV	E356	1966
(D8128	20228)	2004	Bo-BoDE		_(EE	3599	1965
					(EEV	D998	1965
D9521			0-6-0DH		Sdn		1964
	BILL CADDICK		0-6-0DM		HC	D1186	1959
				reb	HE	8526	
−			0-4-0DH		HE	6688	1968
−			4wDM	R/R	Unilok	2183	1982
51339			2-2w-2w-2DMR		PSteel		1960
51382			2-2w-2w-2DMR		PSteel		1960
51655			2-2w-2w-2DMR		DerbyC&W		1960
51677			2-2w-2w-2DMR		DerbyC&W		1960
(W51919)			2-2w-2w-2DMR		DerbyC&W		1960
W52048			2-2w-2w-2DMR		DerbyC&W		1960

BIG PIT (BLAENAFON) TRUST LTD, BIG PIT MINING MUSEUM, BIG PIT COLLIERY SITE, BLAENAVON
Gauge 4ft 8½in Torfaen SO 236088

6	NORA	0-4-0ST	OC	AB	1680	1920	
	P.D. No.10	0-6-0ST	IC	HC	544	1900	

Gauge 2ft 0in

−		0-4-0DMF		HE	6049	1961	
15/10		4wBEF		_(EE	3147	1961	
				(RSHD	8289	1961	Dsm

COUNTY BOROUGH OF NEWPORT, BLAENAVON WHARF, TOWN REACH, NEWPORT
Gauge 4ft 8½in Newport ST 314880

−	0-4-0ST	OC	AB	1260	1911

BRECON MOUNTAIN RAILWAY CO LTD, PONTSTICILL STATION & PANT STATION
Pontsticill Station, and the majority of the route of this railway, lies in Powys. The terminus, and principal loc shed and workshops are, however, at Pant, Merthyr Tydfil, and thus within our "South East Wales Area".

Gauge 1ft 11¾in Merthyr Tydfil SO 063120

−		2-6-0	OC	BLW	15511	1897	Dsm
2		4-6-2	OC	BLW	61269	1930	
	"PENDYFFRYN"	0-4-0VBT	VC	DeW		1894	
	SYBIL	0-4-0ST	OC	HE	827	1903	
146		2-8-2	OC	Hen	29587	1951	
	GRAF SCHWERIN-LÖWITZ	0-6-2WT	OC	Jung	1261	1908	
−		0-4-0VBT	VC	Redstone		1905	
−		0-6-0DH		BMR	001	1987	+
−		2w-2PMR		Wkm	10943	1976	

+   built from parts supplied by BD

BRIDGEND VALLEYS RAILWAY, PONTYCYMER

Gauge 4ft 8½in   Bridgend SS 904914

| – | 4wDH | FH | 3890 | 1959 |
| – | 4wDH | FH | 4006 | 1963 |

DARE VALLEY COUNTRY PARK, DARE VALLEY RAILWAY, ABERDARE

Gauge 3ft 0in   Rhondda Cynon Taf SN 985026

| – | 0-4-0DMF | HC | DM1314 | 1963 |

ENGLISH WELSH & SCOTTISH RAILWAY, BARRY WAGON REPAIR DEPOT, BARRY

Used for the occasional storage of preserved locomotives

Gauge 4ft 8½in   Vale of Glamorgan ST 107672

| (D1725 47490) 47768 | Co-CoDE | BT | 496 | 1964 |
| (D3596) 08481 | 0-6-0DE | Hor | | 1958 |

NATIONAL MUSEUMS & GALLERIES OF WALES, COLLECTION CENTRE, HEOL CROCHENDY, PARC NANTGARW, NANTGARW

Storage depot, visitors by prior appointment only.   Rhondda Cynon Taf ST 114861

Gauge 4ft 8½in

| 52/001 | 0-4-0F | OC | AB | 1966 | 1929 |
| – | 0-4-0F | OC | AB | 2238 | 1948 |

Gauge 3ft 0in

| – | 4wDM | RH | 187100 | 1937 |

Gauge 2ft 0in

| 4 | 4wBE | GB | | |

D. PARFITT, PORTHCAWL

Gauge 1ft 3in   Bridgend SS

| 1935 SILVER JUBILEE | 4-6-4PE | s/o | SmithP | 1935 |

PONTYPOOL & BLAENAVON RAILWAY COMPANY (1983) LTD, PONTYPOOL & BLAENAVON RAILWAY, BLAENAVON

Gauge 4ft 8½in   Torfaen SO 237093

4253	2-8-0T	OC	Sdn	2640	1917
5668	0-6-2T	IC	Sdn		1926
9629	0-6-0PT	IC	Sdn		1945
1823 HARRY	0-4-0ST	OC	AB	1823	1924

–		0-4-0ST	OC	AB	2015	1935
	LLANTANAM ABBEY	0-6-0ST	OC	AB	2074	1939
2	"PONTYBEREM"	0-6-0ST	OC	AE	1421	1900
No.8		0-6-0ST	IC	RSHN	7139	1944
			reb	HE	3880	1961
(D2141)	03141	0-6-0DM		Sdn		1960
D5627	(31203)	A1A-A1A DE		BT	227	1960
(D6916)	37216	Co-CoDE		_(EE	3394	1963
				(EEV	D860	1963
(E6035)	73128 SILVER JUBILEE/JIWBILI ARIAN					
		Bo-BoDE		_(EE	3597	1965
				(EEV	E367	1965
106		0-6-0DH		EEV	D1226	1967
104	LLANWERN	0-6-0DH		EEV	(D1249	1968
				(	3947	1968
			reb	GECT		1975
170		0-8-0DH		HE	7063	1971
111144		0-6-0DM		HC	D615	1958
DL 16		0-4-0DH		HC	D1387	1967
R.T.No.1	R.T.I.	0-6-0DM		JF	22497	1938
200793	GOWER PRINCESS	4wDM		RH	200793	1940
–		4wDH		S	10083	1961
51351	117 418	2-2w-2w-2DMR		PSteel		1960
51397	117 418	2-2w-2w-2DMR		PSteel		1960
51942	L 233	2-2w-2w-2DMR		DerbyC&W		1961
52044		2-2w-2w-2DMR		DerbyC&W		1960
53632		2-2w-2w-2DMR		DerbyC&W		1958
205018	60117	4-4wDER		Afd/Elh		1957
(1198)	61736	4w-4wRER		Elh		1960
(1198)	61737	4w-4wRER		Elh		1960
(1399)	62385	4w-4wRER		York		1971
	PWM 3962	2w-2PMR		Wkm	6947	1955

PULLMAN RAIL, CANTON TRACTION & ROLLING STOCK DEPOT, CARDIFF
Gauge 4ft 8½in Cardiff ST 173758

(D5338)	26038	Bo-BoDE		BRCW	DEL83	1959
(D3654)	08499	0-6-0DE		Don		1968

RHONDDA HERITAGE PARK,
LEWIS MERTHYR, COED CAE ROAD, TREHAFOD
Gauge 4ft 8½in Rhondda Cynon Taf ST 040912

–	4wDM	RH	441936	1960

Gauge 3ft 0in

–	0-4-0DMF	HE	6696	1966

R. STAPLE, ABERDARE MOTOR REPAIRS,
OLD TRAMWAY, ROBERTSTOWN INDUSTRIAL ESTATE, ABERDARE

Gauge 2ft 0in   Rhondda Cynon Taf   SO 005028

ROBERT	4wDM	s/o	RH	393327	1956

VALE OF GLAMORGAN COUNCIL
BARRY WAGON WORKS

Gauge 4ft 8½in   Vale of Glamorgan   ST 108672

2861	2-8-0	OC	Sdn	2767	1918
4115	2-6-2T	OC	Sdn		1936
5227	2-8-0T	OC	Sdn		1924
6686	0-6-2T	IC	AW	974	1928
44901	4-6-0	OC	Crewe		1945
80150	2-6-4T	OC	Bton		1956
92245	2-10-0	OC	Crewe		1958

SECTION 4 — IRELAND

NORTHERN IRELAND

REPUBLIC OF IRELAND

+   no known locomotives exist

NORTHERN IRELAND

LISTINGS OF LOCATIONS IN NORTHERN IRELAND ARE PRESENTED ON A SINGLE "LAND AREA" BASIS, RATHER THAN A COUNTY BASIS.

The actual county in which a site is located is given in each location title.
We have very few Grid References for any locations in Northern Ireland.

INDUSTRIAL SITES

BULRUSH PEAT CO LTD
Locos are kept at :-

B	-	Newferry Road, Bellaghy, Magherafelt, Co.Derry
G	-	Grove Bog, Carrickmore, Co.Tyrone
GW	-	Glenconway Workshops, Dungiven, Co.Derry
R	-	Randalstown, Co.Antrim

Gauge 750mm

3	4wDM	MR	22220	1964	B		Dsm
2	4wDM	MR	40S307	1967	R		
1	4wDM	MR	40S309	1968	B		OOU
–	4wDH	Schöma	4978	1988	GW		Dsm
–	4wDH	Schöma	4979	1988	B		
–	4wDH	Schöma	4980	1988	B	+	
–	4wDH	Schöma	4992	1989	GW	+	OOU
–	4wDH	Schöma	5601	1999	G		
–	4wDH	Schoma	5602	1999	R		
–	4wDH	Schöma	5603	1999	G	+	

+   slave unit for use with a master unit.

NORTHERN IRELAND RAILWAYS LTD,
York Road Depot, Belfast
Gauge 5ft 3in   Co.Antrim

8097 (97)	4w-4wDER		Derby C&W		1978	a
JXI 2860	4wDMR	R/R	Bruff	531	1986	OOU
–	4wBE		Niteq	01-B177	2001	

a   converted to sandite unit.

Adelaide Yard, Belfast
Gauge 5ft 3in   Co.Antrim

VMT 850	4wDHR		Geismar/Donnelli	1998

SUNSHINE PEAT CO, DERRYHUBBERT ROAD, DUNGANNON

Gauge 2ft 6in   Co.Armagh

			0-4-0DM	HE	(2242	1941?)	Dsm
L3	HENRY ABRAHAM		0-4-0DM	HE	2250	1940	
L4	VICTORIA		0-4-0DM	HE	2252	1940	
L1	ND3053	GAVIN	0-4-0DM	HE	2264	1940	
L2	ND3061	W.P.O'KANE	0-4-0DM	HE	2399	1941	

J. STEVENSON, CLINTY QUARRY, DOURY ROAD, BALLYMENA

Gauge 2ft 0in

–	4wDM	MR	8684	1941	Dsm

PRESERVATION SITES

DEPARTMENT OF THE ENVIRONMENT (N.I.), COUNTRYSIDE AND WILDLIFE BRANCH, BIRCHES PEATLANDS PARK, DERRYHUBBERT ROAD, DUNGANNON

Gauge 3ft 0in   Co.Armagh

		4wDH	AK	44	1993	
1		4wDM	FH	3719	1954	OOU
2	HENRY HEAL	4wDM	Schöma	1727	1955	OOU

DERRY CITY COUNCIL, HERITAGE & MUSEUM SERVICE, FOYLE VALLEY RAILWAY COMPANY, LONDONDERRY

Track laid southwards on route of former GNR(I) broad gauge line, from Londonderry Foyle Road Station.

Gauge 3ft 0in   (open July – September)   Co.Derry

No.4	MEENGLASS	2-6-4T	OC	NW	828	1907
6	COLUMBKILLE	2-6-4T	OC	NW	830	1907
No.2		4wDM	MR	11039	1956	
12		0-4-0+4wDMR		WkB/Dundalk	1934	

DERRY'S LTD, 85 TEAGUY ROAD, ANNAGHMORE

Locomotives occasionally present for resale.   Co.Armagh

DOWNPATRICK & COUNTY DOWN RAILWAY, DOWNPATRICK RAILWAY MUSEUM, DOWNPATRICK STATION, DOWNPATRICK

Gauge 5ft 3in   Co.Down

No.3		0-6-0ST	OC	AE	2021	1928
90		0-6-0T	IC	Inchicore		1875
3		0-4-0T	OC	OK	12662	1935
(RB3)	(RDB 977020)	4wDMR		BRE(D)/Leyland	1981	

G611		4wDH		Dtz	57225	1962
G613		4wDH		Dtz	57226	1962
G617		4wDH		Dtz	57229	1961
E421	W.F.GILLESPIE O.B.E.	6wDH		Inchicore		1961
E432		6wDH		Inchicore		1962
2509		0-4-0+4wDMR		WkB/ELC		1947
(713)		2w-2DMR		Wkm	8916	1962
416A		2w-2PMR		Wkm	8919	1962
	rebuilt as	2w-2DMR		Inchicore		1986
HC1		2w-2DMR		Plasser & Theurer	323	1971

GIANTS CAUSEWAY & BUSHMILLS RAILWAY, BUSHMILLS
Gauge 3ft 0in   Co.Antrim

No.3	SHANE	0-4-0WT	OC	AB	2265	1949
No.1	TYRONE	0-4-0T	OC	P	1026	1904
	RORY	4wDH		SMH	102T016	1976
–		2w-2PMR		Wkm	7441	1956

RAILWAY PRESERVATION SOCIETY OF IRELAND, WHITEHEAD DEPOT
Gauge 5ft 3in   Co.Antrim   J474922

171	SLIEVE GULLION	4-4-0	IC	BP	5629	1913	
		reb		Dundalk	42	1938	+
461		2-6-0	IC	BP	6112	1922	
No.85	MERLIN	4-4-0	3C	BP	6733	1949	
27		0-6-4T	IC	BP	7242	1949	
4		2-6-4T	OC	Derby		1947	
	GUINNESS	0-4-0ST	OC	HC	1152	1919	a
No.184		0-6-0	IC	Inchicore		1880	
131		4-4-0	IC	NR	5757	1901	
–		0-4-0T	OC	OK	12475	1934	
186		0-6-0	IC	SS	2838	1879	
101		Bo-BoDE		_(Don		1970	
				(HE	7197	1970	
102	FALCON	Bo-BoDE		_(Don		1970	
				(HE	7198	1970	
23		4wDM		FH	3509	1951	
–		4w-4wPMR		NCC		1933	
	rebuilt as	4w-4wDMR		NCC		1947	
1		4wDM		RH	382827	1955	
(C18)		2w-2PMR		Wkm	4808	1949	Dsm

Gauge 3ft 0in

5	"DRUMBOE"	2-6-4T	OC	NW	829	1907

+   normally kept at Iarnród Éireann, Dublin Connolly Depot
a   ex works 30/09/1915 but worksplate dated 1919

PETER SCOTT, FINNAGHY, BELFAST

Gauge 1ft 9in   Co.Antrim

–		0-4-0	OC	ScottP		c1969
	reb	2-4-0T	OC	ScottP		1970

+   in store at a private location. No public access

ULSTER FOLK & TRANSPORT MUSEUM, CULTRA, HOLYWOOD

Gauge 5ft 3in   Co.Down   J419806

No.30		4-4-2T	IC	BP	4231	1901
93		2-4-2T	IC	Dundalk	16	1895
800	MAEDHBH	4-6-0	3C	Inchicore		1939
74	DUNLUCE CASTLE	4-4-0	IC	NBQ	23096	1924
No.1		0-6-0ST	OC	RS	2738	1891
–		4wPM	R/R	_(Unilok		1965
				(Jung	A114	1965
1	(8178)	2w-2DMR		AEC		1928
			reb	Dundalk		1933

Gauge 3ft 0in

2		0-4-0Tram	OC	K	T84	1883	
2	BLANCHE	2-6-4T	OC	NW	956	1912	
2		0-4-0T	OC	P	1097	1906	
2		4-4-0T	OC	RS	2613	1887	
(1)	"PUP"	2-2-0PMR		A&O		1907	
11	PHOENIX	4wDM		AtW	114	1928	
			reb	Dundalk		1932	
3		2-4w-2PMR		DC	1519	1926	+
10		0-4-0+4wDMR		WkB		1932	

+   now unmotorised

Gauge 2ft 0in

–		4wDM		FH	3449	1950
–		4wDM		HE	3127	1943
246		4wPM		MR	246	1916
–		4wDM		MR	9202	1946

Gauge 1ft 10in

20		0-4-0T	IC	Spence		1905

REPUBLIC OF IRELAND

LISTINGS OF LOCATIONS IN THE REPUBLIC OF IRELAND ARE PRESENTED
ON A COUNTY BASIS, WITH COUNTIES SORTED ALPHABETICALLY.
BORD NA MONA LOCATIONS ARE LISTED UNDER THIE COUNTY HEADINGS AND LOCOMOTIVES
ARE IN ONE LIST STARTING ON PAGE 316

CARLOW

PRESERVATION SITES

P. BYRNE, GARRETTSTOWN, near RATHVILLY
Gauge 3ft 0in

3	4wDM	RH	314222	1951	Pvd

CAVAN

PRESERVATION SITES

BELTURBET COMMUNITY ASSOCIATION, BELTURBET STATION
Gauge 5ft 3in

−	4wDM	RH	312425	1951

CLARE

PRESERVATION SITES

WEST CLARE RAILWAY, MOYASTA
Gauge 3ft 0in

−	0-6-0DMF	HC	DM719	1950
−	4wDH	RFSD	101L	1989

CORK

PRESERVATION SITES

J. & R. BRADLEY, BALLYNAKILLWEST, NEWTOWNSHANDRUM, near CHARLEVILLE
Gauge 600mm   R 461244

–	4wDM	Struver	60327	c1955	Dsm

IARNRÓD ÉIREANN, CORK (CEANNT / KENT) STATION
Gauge 5ft 3in

36	2-2-2	IC	BuryC&K	1847

TIM NAGLE, GREY GABLES, FEATHERBED LANE, off EASTERN ROAD, KINSALE
Gauge 600mm

–	4wDM	Strüver	60385	c1955

SOUTH COAST RAILWAY PRESERVATION SOCIETY,
c/o HALFWAY VINTAGE CLUB, HALFWAY, near BALLINHASIG
Gauge 5ft 3in

–	4wDM	RH	252843	1948

JOHN TOUIG, LISSAGROOM, UPTON
Gauge 2ft 0in

–	4wDM	RH	264244	1949	OOU

WEST CORK MODEL RAILWAY VILLAGE, CLONAKILTY
Gauge 5ft 3in

90	4wDM	s/o	RH	305322	1951

DONEGAL

INDUSTRIAL SITES

FOREST ENTERPRISES, BELLANAMORE, near FINTOWN
Gauge 2ft 0in

–	4wDM	MR	7944	1943	Dsm

PRESERVATION SITES

COUNTY DONEGAL RAILWAY RESTORATION LTD, THE OLD STATION HOUSE, TYERCONNEL STREET, DONEGAL TOWN
Gauge 3ft 0in

1	4wDM	RH	326051	1952	
LM 104	4wDM	RH	375322	1954	
LM 108	4wDM	RH	379061	1954	
LM 137	4wDM	RH	382817	1955	
(LM 162)	4wDM	RH	402177	1956	Dsm
–	2w-2PMR	RPSI Whitehead		2006	a

a   incorporates parts from Wkm 4808 1948

CUMANN TRAENACH na GAELTACHTA LÁR, FINTOWN STATION
Gauge 3ft 0in

No.6	4wDH	MR	102T007	1974	
		reb AK	78R	2007	
LM 77 H	4wDM	RH	329680	1952	
18	0-4-0+4wDMR	WkB/Dundalk		1940	

Gauge 2ft 0in

–	4wDM	RH	243387	1946	
LM26	4wDM	RH	248458	1946	

DIFFLIN LAKE RAILWAY, OAKFIELD PARK, RAPHOE
Gauge 1ft 3in

THE DUCHESS OF DIFFLIN	0-4-2T	OC	ESR	317	2003
No. 2 THE EARL OF OAKFIELD	0-4-0DH		AK	66	2002

NEIL GALLAGHER.
Gauge 2ft 0in

–	4wDM	RH	371544	1954

currently stored c/o Murphy Plant Hire Co Ltd, Lifford Road, Letterkenny

SAINT CONNELLS MUSEUM, GLENTIES
Gauge 2ft 0in

LM263	4wDM	RH	7002/0600-1	1968	+

+   currently at Bord na Mona, Ballivor Workshops, Co Westmeath for restoration

DUBLIN / BAILE ÁTHA CLIATH

INDUSTRIAL SITES

BREFFNI HIRE PLANT LTD, BALLYHACK FARM, KILSALLAGHAM
Gauge 5ft 3in

RR 11	KT 06 OMV	4wDMR	R/R	Landrover		2006

DUBLIN LUAS, DUBLIN TRAMWAY SYSTEM
Gauge 4ft 8½in

ENG 5873 13 006	4wDM		Richard		1960	pvd
97D 67550	4wDM	R/R	Landrover		1997	
97D 66701	4wDM	R/R	Nissan		1997	
05D 6139	4wDM	R/R	Unimog	205667	2005	

Red Cow Depot, Dublin
Gauge 4ft 8½in

–	4wBE	SET	1007/1	2003
–	4wBH	BBM	156	2002
–	4wDH	Unilok	4013	2004

Sandyford Depot, Dublin
Gauge 4ft 8½in

	4wBH	BBM	155	2002

IARNRÓD ÉIREANN
Departmental Stock

Railcars are based at :–

Athlone, Co.Westmeath
Boyle Station
Connelly Station, Dublin
Ennis, Co.Clare
Heuston Carriage Sidings, Dublin
Inchicore Works, Dublin
Kildare Plant Depot, Co.Kildare
Limerick Junction, Co.Tipperary
Waterford, Co.Waterford

Gauge 5ft 3in

700	4w-4wDMR	Plasser	26	1974	
706	2w-2DMR	Plasser		1974	
707	2w-2DMR	Plasser	281	1976	
711	2w-2PMR	Wkm	8917	1962	OOU
721	2w-2DMR	HPET	1068	1992	
722	4wDMR	MatisaSPA	0214	1994	
723	4wDMR	MatisaSPA	0215	1994	

726		2w-2DM		Plasser	1140	1969	
	reb	2w-2DMR		Inchicore		1998	
728		2w-2DH		Plasser		1974	
	reb	2w-2DHR		Inchicore		1999	
734		2w-2DM		Plasser	1772	1980	
	reb	2w-2DMR		Inchicore		1998	

DART Overhead Maintenance Depot, Connolly
Gauge 5ft 3in

02 D	12723	2w-2DM	R/R	Volvo		2002	
02 D	3124	2w-2DM	R/R	Volvo		2002	
02 D	78046	4wDM	R/R	Unimog	201419	2002	

Inchicore Works, St.Patricks Terrace, Inchicore, Dublin
Gauge 5ft 3in

6111	(2624)	4w-4wDMR	(AEC	8031 046	1953	
			(PRoyal	B35171	1953	a
B113		Bo-BoDE	Inchicore		1950	Pvd	a
015		Co-CoDE	MV	901	1955	Pvd	a
A39		Co-CoDE	MV	925	1955	Pvd	+
A3R		Co-CoDE	MV	889	1955	Pvd	+
C231		Bo-BoDE	MV	977	1956	Pvd	+

+   property of Irish Traction Group
a   owned by CIE Heritage Services

SANLINE SYSTEMS LTD, 12th LOCK, GRAND CANAL, NEWCASTLE ROAD, LUCAN, DUBLIN
Gauge 5ft 3in

–		4wDMR	R/R	Bedford		1981	
92 MH 4823		4wDMR	R/R	Landrover		1992	
06 D 84465		4wDMR		Landrover/Geismar	2006	
–		2w-2PMR		Sanline		199	

PRESERVATION SITES

DEPARTMENT OF MECHANICAL ENGINEERING, PARSONS BUILDING, TRINITY COLLEGE, DUBLIN
Gauge 1ft 9in

| – | | 0-6-0 | IC | Kennan | | 1855 | + |

+   non-working model

**GUINNESS IRELAND GROUP LTD, GUINESS STOREHOUSE MUSEUM, ST JAMES GATE
BREWERY, CRANE STREET, DUBLIN**
(member of Guinness plc)
Gauge 1ft 10in   RTC

17	0-4-0T	IC	Spence		1902	Pvd
47	4wDM	FH	3444		1950	Pvd

GALWAY

INDUSTRIAL SITES

**ATTYMON PEAT CO-OP SOCIETY LTD,
ATTYMON WORKSHOPS & TIP HEAD, LARAGH**   M 586286
and CLONKEEN DEPOT & TIP HEAD, CLONKEEN   M 577309
Sites and locomotives leased from Bord na Mona.
Gauge 3ft 0in

No.3 LM 17E	4wDM	RH	242901	1946	
No.4 (LM34)	4wDM	RH	252239	1947	
No.5 LM38E	4wDM	RH	252246	1947	
No.1 LM 41E	4wDM	RH	252252	1947	
LM164Q	4wDM	RH	392152	1956	
LM 173	4wDM	RH	402985	1957	
LM 346	4wDM	SMH	60SL747	1980	OOU
C 63	4wPMR	BnM		1972	OOU

BORD NA MONA, Derryfadda   M 800432
For loco details see the Bord na Mona fleet list at the end of this Section.

**UNILOKOMOTIVE LTD, INTERNATIONAL DIVISION,
DEERPARK INDUSTRIAL ESTATE, ORANMORE**
New locomotives under construction are usually present.
Gauge 4ft 8½in

–	4wDH	R/R	Unilok	2334	2003	Dsm

PRESERVATION SITES

AUGHRIM SCHOOL HOUSE RESTAURANT, AUGHRIM
Gauge 4ft 8½in   M 789279

–	4wDM	RH	252842	1948

GALWAY MINIATURE RAILWAY (LEISURELAND EXPRESS), SALTHILL, GALWAY
Gauge 2ft 0in

LEISURELAND EXPRESS	4-4-0DH	s/o	SL	2155	2003

M MITCHELL, DUNSANDLE STATION, DUNSANDLE
Gauge 5ft 3in

E428	6wDH	Inchicore	1962

P. SKELTON, near TUAM
Gauge 1ft 10in

21	0-4-0T	OC	Spence	1905

KERRY

PRESERVATION SITES

LARTIGUE MONORAILWAY, JOHN B KEANE ROAD, LISTOWEL
Gauge monorail

L.B.R. 4	0-2-0+2wDH	AK	62	2002

BLENNERVILLE WINDMILL CO LTD, TRALEE&DINGLE STEAM RAILWAY, BLENNERVILLE, near TRALEE
Gauge 3ft 0in

No.5T	2-6-2T	OC	HE	555	1892
LM 92L	4wDM		RH	371967	1954

KILDARE

INDUSTRIAL SITES

COLEMAN TUNNELLING & TECHNOLOGY SERVICES LTD, CLANE
Gauge 2ft 0in

05	4wBE	CE	B1557A	1977
43	4wBE	CE	B2944T	1982
-	4wBE	CE		
DONKEY	4wBE	WR		

BORD NA MONA

Almhain North	N 801211
Ballydermot	N 659216, 656215
Gilltown Landsale	N 796338
Kilberry	S664998
Lullymore	N 711292, 708286, 706286
Prosperous	N 831292
Timahoe	N 781284, 754335
Includes Timahoe North Bog, Drumachon.	335754
Ummeras	N 623147

For all loco details see the Bord na Mona fleet list at the end of this Section.

DEPARTMENT OF DEFENCE, IRISH ARMY,
No.1 MAINTENANCE COMPANY, THE CURRAGH, near KILDARE
Gauge 2ft 0in   RTC

–	4wDM	MR	8970	1945	OOU

KILKENNY

INDUSTRIAL SITES

BORD NA MONA
Templetouthy   S 228677
For loco details see the Bord na Mona fleet list at the end of this section.

LAOIS

INDUSTRIAL SITES

BORD NA MONA, Coolnamóna   S 456947
For loco details see the Bord na Mona fleet list at the end of this Section.

IARNROD EIREANN / IRISH RAIL, ENGINEERING SERVICES DIVISION plc, LAOIS TRAIN-CARE FACILITY, near PORTLAOISE
Gauge 5ft 3in

TOM LYNAM	4wBE	Scul		621	2008

PRESERVATION SITES

IRISH STEAM PRESERVATION SOCIETY, STRADBALLY HALL, STRADBALLY
Gauge 3ft 0in   S 568966

No.2	0-4-0WT	OC	AB	2264	1949	
NIPPY	4wDM		FH	2014	1936	
–	4wDM		HE	2280	1941	Dsm
4	4wDM		RH	326052	1952	

STRADBALLY STEAM MUSEUM, STRADBALLY
Gauge 1ft 10in   S 575961

15	0-4-0T	IC	Spence		1912	+

+   carries incorrect plate dated 1895

LEITRIM

PRESERVATION SITES

IRISH NARROW GAUGE TRUST and the CAVAN & LEITRIM RAILWAY CO LTD, DROMOD STATION, DROMOD

Gauge 5ft 3in

720		2w-2DMR	BRE	1984
JZA 979		2-2wDM	‡	1959

‡   conversion of a Scammell road lorry by Cold Chon Ltd, Oranmore, Co. Galway /1963

Gauge 3ft 0in

1	DROMAD		0-4-2ST	OC	KS	3024	1916
		rebuilt as	0-4-2T	OC	AK		1993
(LM 180)			0-4-0DM		Dtz	57122	1960
(LM 186)			0-4-0DM		Dtz	57132	1960
LM 196			0-4-0DM		Dtz	57138	1960
LM 258			0-4-0DM		Dtz	57839	1965
LM 260			0-4-0DM		Dtz	57841	1965
LM 262			0-4-0DM		Dtz	57843	1965
–			4wDM		HE	6075	1961	Dsm
F511	DINMOR		4wDM		JF	3900011	1947
9			4wDH		MR	115U093	1970
LM 49			4wDM		RH	259189	1948
(LM 87)			4wDM		RH	329696	1952	Dsm
LM 91			4wDM		RH	371962	1954
LM 101			4wDM		RH	379059	1954
LM 106			4wDM		RH	375345	1954
LM 114			4wDM		RH	379070	1954
(LM 131)			4wDM		RH	379086	1955	Dsm
LM 138			4wDM		RH	382819	1955
212			4wDM		RH	394022	1956
213	L2		4wDM		RH		
LM 161			4wDM		RH	402175	1956
LM 174			4wDM		RH	402986	1957
LM 175			0-4-0DM		RH	420042	1958
LM 11			0-4-0DM		Ruhrthaler	1348	1934
(LM 316)			4wDM		SMH	60SL741	1980	Dsm
(LM 349)			4wDM		SMH	60SL743	1980	Dsm
(LM 351)			4wDM		SMH	60SL745	1980	Dsm
LM 350			4wDM		SMH	60SL748	1980
LM 345			4wDM		SMH	60SL749	1980	Dsm
LM 361			4wDH		DunEW	LM361	1984
LM 362			4wDH		DunEW	G4464	1984
LM 369			4wDH		DunEW	S4484	1984
(C 11)			2w-2PHR		*		1934
		reb	2w-2PMR		BnM(Cs)		c1963

5		2w-2PMR	DC	1495	1927	
	rebuilt as	2w-2DHR	AK		1995	
(C 42)		2w-2PMR	Wkm	7129	1955	DsmT
C 47		4wPMR	BnM	3	1958	
C 51		4wPMR	BnM	7	1958	
C 56		2w-2PMR	Wkm	7681	1957	DsmT
C 66		4wDMR	BnM		1972	
C 70		4wPMR	BnM		1972	
C 74		4wPMR	BnM		1972	
W6/11-4		2w-2PMR	Wkm	9673	1964	

* unknown German builder

Gauge 2ft 0in

No.1		4wDM	HE	2239	1940	
	reb	HE		7340	1972	
No.3		4wDM	HE	2304	1940	
	reb	HE		7341	1972	
–		4wDM	HE	2659	1942	
No.2		4wDM	HE	2763	1943	
	reb	HE		7342	1972	
LM 16 B		4wDM	RH	200075	1940	
LM 42 C		4wDM	RH	252849	1947	
LM198		4wDM	RH	398076	1956	OOU

Gauge 1ft 10in

–	0-4-0T	IC	Spence		1912	Dsm
–	4wDM		FH	3068	1947	
–	4wDM		FH	3446	1950	
–	4wDM		FH	3447	1950	Dsm

ANDREW MARSHALL, STRACARNE, MOHILL

Gauge 3ft 0in

LM 141	4wDM	RH	392142	1955	
LM 178	0-4-0DM	Dtz	57120	1960	
LM 187	0-4-0DM	Dtz	57133	1960	

LONGFORD

INDUSTRIAL SITES

BORD NA MONA, Mountdillon   N 048688
Locos are also outstationed at Lanesborough Power Station.
For loco details see the Bord na Mona fleet list at the end of this Section.

LOUTH

PRESERVATION SITES

RIVERSTOWN MILL RAILWAY,
RISTORANTE BELLA SERRA, RIVERSTOWN, DUNDALK
Gauge 4ft 8½in

No.4	ROBERT NELSON No.4	0-6-0ST	IC	HE	1800	1936
	BREL 75	4wDMR		BRE/Leyland		
				RB002/001	c1984	

MAYO

INDUSTRIAL SITES

BORD NA MONA
Oweninny-Bellacorick ("T.A.E.")   R.T.C   F 990196
Serves B.S.L. (E.S.B.) Bellacorick Power Station.
For loco details see the Bord na Mona fleet list at the end of this Section.

PRESERVATION SITES

NORTH MAYO HERITAGE CENTRE, ENNISCRONE HOUSE, near CROSSMALINA
Gauge 3ft 0in

LM 129	X	4wDM	RH	383264	1955

WESTPORT HOUSE & CHILDRENS ZOO,
WESTPORT HOUSE COUNTRY ESTATE, WESTPORT
Gauge 1ft 3in

WESTPORT HOUSE EXPRESS					
	2-6-0DH	s/o	SL	80.10.89	1989

MEATH

INDUSTRIAL SITES

BORD na MONA, Kinnegad   N 600441
For loco details see the Bord na Mona fleet list at the end of this Section.

DIXON BROS. LTD, AGRICULTURAL & PLANT CONTRACTORS, CULLENTRA
RATHMORE, ENFIELD
Gauge 5ft 3in

90 MH 4885	4wDM	R/R	Fiat		
98 MH 6417	4wDH	R/R	Mortimer	1996	a
M948 NCF	4wDM	R/R	Unimog		
			427115 1W 164948	1994	OOU
R648 JFE	4wDMR	R/R	Landrover 136483	1998	
R904 WBC	4wDMR	R/R	Landrover 136517	1998	
–	2w-2PMR		Bance		
			SD1/2NPAC/086	2000	

a   first registered 1998, upon conversion to rail use

OLIVER DIXON PLANT HIRE LTD, ST OLIVER'S ROAD, LONGWOOD
Gauge 5ft 3in

94 MH 585	4wDM	R/R	Ford	1994
89 MH 3147	4wDM	R/R	Ford	1989

NEW BOLIDEN GROUP, TARA MINES, NAVAN
Gauge 5ft 3in

148010 10 280 GZM	4wDM	R/R	Unilok	3028	1987

PRESERVATION SITES

BRIAN DARLINGTON, BEREA, CAULSTOWN, DUNBOYNE
Gauge 2ft 0in

–	4wDM	LB	54183	1964

OFFALY

INDUSTRIAL SITES

BORD NA MONA

Bellair N 190329

Blackwater N 002251
Also includes Cloonberrun Depot & Workshops (M 293962), and Cornaveagh Bog, Cloonshask (M 263946)
The site serves B.S.L. (E.S.B.) Shannonbridge Power Station (M 976243).

Boora N 181196
The site serves B.S.L. (E.S.B.) Shannonbridge Power Atation (M 976243) and Derrinlough Briquetting Plant (N 083148).

Clonsast N 535165

Derrygreenagh N 495382, 495384
The site serves Croghan Briquetting Plant (N 276516), Gorteenkeel Tip Head (N 233483), and Trogher Siding (N 319509). Also serves a gravel quarry a mile west of Ballycon, and Edenderry Euro Power Station.

Edenderry N 613273

Killaun N 094079

Lemanaghan

Monettia N 347165
For loco details see the Bord na Mona fleet list at the end of this Section.

CLONMACNOIS & WEST OFFALY RAILWAY, BORD NA MONA - THE IRISH TURF BOARD, BLACKWATER WORKS, SHANNONBRIDGE
Gauge 3ft 0in

| LM 323 | 0-4-0DM | HE | 8924 | 1979 | |

TOM O'GRADY TRANSPORT LTD, QUARRY, near EDENDERRY
Gauge 3ft 0in

1	4wDM	RH	249526	1947	OOU
4	4wDM	RH	300518	1950	OOU
2	4wDM	RH	314223	1951	OOU

PRESERVATION SITES

BORD NA MONA VINTAGE MACHINERY MUSEUM,
BLACKWATER WORKS, SHANNONBRIDGE
Gauge 3ft 0in   N 002252

LM 254		0-4-0DM	Dtz	57835	1965
LM 368		4wDH	DunEW	LM368	c1984
LM 105	U	4wDM	RH	375344	1954
LM 111		4wDM	RH	379079	1954
–		4wDM	RH	422567	1958
LM 343		4wDM	SMH	60SL746	1980
C 55		2w-2PMR	Wkm	7680	1957

T. BRADY, WALSH ISLAND, GEASHILL
Gauge 3ft 0in

C45	2w-2PMR	Wkm	7132	1955

D. BRADY, WALSH ISLAND, GEASHILL
Gauge 3ft 0in

LM 78	4wDM	RH	329682	1952
LM 136	4wDM	RH	382815	1955
LM 197	0-4-0DM	Dtz	57139	1960

SEAN KELLY, MUCKLAGH, TULLAMORE
Gauge 3ft 0in   Private Site

C 69	4wPMR	BnM		1972

LOUGH BOORA PARKLANDS, BOORA SCULPTURE PARK
Gauge 3ft 0in

(LM171)	4wDM	RH	402983	1956

WALSH ISLAND HERITAGE COMMITTEE, WALSH ISLAND
Gauge 3ft 0in   N 516197

LM 28 G 12	4wDM	RH	249543	1947

ROSCOMMON

PRESERVATION SITES

ARIGNA MINES EXPERIENCE, ARIGNA
Gauge 2ft 0in

ARIGNA MINES	ST.ELBA	4wDM	L	8023	1936	
–		4wDM	MR	5861	1934	a
2563	41	4wPM	OK	2563	1929	a

a   not on public display

HELLS KITCHEN PUBLIC HOUSE, MAIN STREET, CASTLEREA
Gauge 5ft 3in

A55	Co-CoDE	MV	941	1956

TIPPERARY

INDUSTRIAL SITES

BORD NA MONA
Littleton (Ballydeath)   S 207535
For loco details see the Bord na Mona fleet list at the end of this Section.

PRESERVATION SITES

IRISH TRACTION GROUP, CARRICK-ON-SUIR
Gauge 5ft 3in

B103	A1A-A1ADE	BRCW	DEL22	1956
G601	4wDH	Dtz	56118	1956
G616	4wDH	Dtz	57227	1961
226	Bo-BoDE	MV	972	1956

WATERFORD

INDUSTRIAL SITES

FAS KILCHORN ESTATE, c/o ALL STORE COMMERCIAL CENTRE, BALLYTRUCKLE ROAD, WATERFORD
Gauge 3ft 0in

LM 183		0-4-0DM	Dtz	57127	1960	Dsm

PRESERVATION SITES

PERKS FUNFAIR, ARDMORE PARK, WATERFORD
Gauge 1ft 3in   Site Closed

–		2-8-0DH	s/o	SL	73 35	1973	
	reb	2-6-0					OOU

TRAMORE MINIATURE RAILWAY, TRAMORE
Gauge 1ft 3in

–		2-8-0PH	s/o	SL	22	1973

GARRY WALSH, BILBERRY STATION SITE, LANGFORD
Gauge 5ft 3in

C202 (C227 106)	Bo-BoDE	MV	973	1957

carries running number C202 but locomotive is C227

WATERFORD & SUIR VALLEY RAILWAY, KILMEADON
Gauge 3ft 0in

LM 179		0-4-0DM	Dtz	57121	1960	
LM 193		0-4-0DM	Dtz	57135	1960	
LM 257		0-4-0DM	Dtz	57836	1965	a
(LM 256)		0-4-0DM	Dtz	57837	1965	
LM 259		0-4-0DM	Dtz	57840	1965	
LM 314		0-4-0DM	HE	8548	1977	
LM 356		4wDH	DunEW			
No.3 ENTERPRISE		4wDM	MR	60S382	1969	
	reb	4wDH	AK		2004	
LM 18 G		4wDM	RH	242902	1946	
LM 96 L		4wDM	RH	375314	1954	a
LM 125 O		4wDM	RH	379084	1954	a
LM 348		4wDM	SMH	60SL744	1980	
C 78		4wPMR	BnM		1972	

a   stored at Iarnrod Eireann/Irish Rail, Sally Park Goods Yard, Waterford

WESTMEATH

INDUSTRIAL SITES

BORD NA MONA, Ballivor   N 644541

BORD NA MONA, Coolnagan   N 384702
For loco details see the Bord na Mona fleet list at the end of this Section.

JOHN DIXON PLANT HIRE LTD, SARSFIELDTOWN, KILLUCAN
Gauge 5ft 3in

06 WH 4510	4wDMR	R/R	Landrover	c2006
99 WH 4717	4wDMR	R/R	Landrover/Harsco	c1999
90 MH 3006	4wDMR	R/R	Ford	1990

MIDLAND IRISH PEAT MOSS LTD, KILLINAGH, RATHOWEN

All locos are kept at :-

    Mill & Packing Factory, Rathaspick to Crossea Road.   N 279662

Gauge 2ft 0in

1		4wDM	Diema	2639	1963
2	GHOST	4wDM	R&R	84	1938
3		4wDM	MR	7304	1938
4		4wDM	Diema	2242	1959
5	74/6383	4wDM	Diema	2872	1966
6		4wDM	MR	9543	1950
7		4wDH	AK	No.9	1983

WEXFORD

INDUSTRIAL SITES

ARNRÓD ÉIREANN, ENNISCORTHY STATION
Gauge 5ft 3in

710	2w-2DMR	Wkm	8918	1962	a	Dsm
714	2w-2DMR	Wkm	8920	1962		OOU

a   stored for private owner

PRESERVATION SITES

OFFICES OF PUBLIC WORKS, J.F.KENNEDY ARBORETUM, NEW ROSS
Gauge 2ft 0in

–	4wDM	RH	371538	1954	OOU

BORD NA MONA

BORD NA MONA — IRISH TURF BOARD

The Bord operates rail systems on peat bogs throughout the country, and locomotives are kept at the locations listed below.

Al	(N 801211)	Almhain North, Co.Kildare
Bd	(N 659216, 656215)	Ballydermot, Co.Kildare
Be	(N 190329)	Bellair, Co.Offaly
Bi	(N 644541)	Ballivor, Co.Westmeath
Bl	(N 002251)	Blackwater, Co.Offaly
Bo	(N 181196)	Boora, Co.Offaly
Cg	(N 384702)	Coolnagan, Co.West Meath
Cm	(S 456947)	Coolnamona, Co.Laois
Cs	(N 535165)	Clonsast, Co.Offaly. R.T.C.
De	(M 800432)	Derryfadda, Co.Galway
Dg	(N 495382, 495384)	Derrygreenagh, Co.Offaly
Ed	(n 613273)	Edenderry, Co.Offaly
Gi	(N 796338)	Gilltown Landsale, Co.Kildare.
K	(S 664998)	Kilberry, Co.Kildare
Kd	(N 600441)	Kinnegad, Co.Meath
Kn	(N 094079)	Killaun, Co. Offaly
Le	( )	Lemanaghan
Li	(S 207535)	Littleton, Co.Tipperary
Lu	(N 711292, 708286, 706286)	Lullymore, Co.Kildare
M	(N 048688)	Mountdillon, Co.Longford
Mo	(N 347165)	Monettia, Co.Offaly.
Pr	(N 831292)	Prosperous, Co. Kildare
TAE	(F 990196)	Oweninny-Bellacorick, Co.Mayo R.T.C.
Te	(S 228677)	Templetouhy, Co.Kilkenny
Ti	(N 781284, 754335)	Timahoe, Co.Kildare R.T.C.
U	(N 623147)	Ummeras, Co. Kildare.

LOCO FLEET LIST

Gauge 3ft 0in

18			4wDM	RH	211687	1941	Dsm	Lu
LM 14	CW		4wDM	RH	198290	1940	OOU	Cs
LM 23	E		4wDM	RH	244788	1946	OOU	Dg
LM 25	E	7	4wDM	RH	244871	1946	OOU	Cs
LM 30	G		4wDM	RH	249545	1947		Gi
LM 35			4wDM	RH	252240	1947		Al
LM 36	E	2	4wDM	RH	252241	1947	OOU	M
		rebuilt as	4wDH	BnM				
LM 37	E		4wDM	RH	252245	1947		M
LM 39	E		4wDM	RH	252247	1947		M
		rebuilt as	4wDH	BnM				
LM 40	E		4wDM	RH	252251	1947		M
		rebuilt as	4wDH	BnM(M)		2008		

LM 46			4wDM	RH	259184	1948	OOU	Dg
		rebuilt as	4wDH	BnM				
LM 47	F		4wDM	RH	259185	1948		Al
		rebuilt as	4wDH	BnM				
LM 48	F		4wDM	RH	259186	1948		Lu
LM 50			4wDM	RH	259190	1948	OOU	Cg
LM 51			4wDM	RH	259191	1948	OOU	Cg
LM 52	F	15	4wDM	RH	259196	1948		U
		rebuilt as	4wDH	BnM(K)				
LM 54	F		4wDM	RH	259198	1948	Dsm	K
LM 55			4wDM	RH	259205	1948	OOU	Dg
LM 56	F	7	4wDM	RH	259204	1948	Dsm	Gi
(LM 57	F)		4wDM	RH	259203	1948		Pr
		rebuilt as	4wDH	BnM(Dg)				
(LM 58	F)		4wDM	RH	259206	1948	Dsm	Li
LM 59			4wDM	RH	259737	1948	OOU	Cs
LM 60	F		4wDM	RH	259738	1948	OOU	Dg
(LM 62	F)		4wDM	RH	259743	1948		
		rebuilt as	4wDH	BnM(U)				Kd
LM 63	F		4wDM	RH	259744	1948		Bi
LM 64	F		4wDM	RH	259745	1948	OOU	Cs
(LM 65)			4wDM	RH	259749	1948	OOU	Li
LM 66	5		4wDM	RH	259750	1948		M
LM 67			4wDM	RH	259751	1948	Dsm	Cg
(LM 68)			4wDM	RH	259752	1948		Te
LM 69	F		4wDM	RH	259755	1948		Kd
LM 70			4wDM	RH	259756	1948		Cg
LM 71	F		4wDM	RH	259757	1948		M
LM 72	F		4wDM	RH	259758	1948	Dsm	M
LM 73	8		4wDM	RH	259759	1948	OOU	M
LM 74	F	6	4wDM	RH	259760	1948	OOU	Bd
LM 75	R		4wDM	RH	326047	1952	Dsm	Lu
LM 80	H	13	4wDM	RH	329685	1952	OOU	Dg
LM 81	H		4wDM	RH	329686	1952		Dg
LM 82			4wDM	RH	329688	1952	OOU	Ti
LM 83			4wDM	RH	329690	1952		U
		rebuilt as	4wDH	BnM				
LM 85			4wDM	RH	329693	1952		M
LM 86	J		4wDM	RH	329695	1952	OOU	M
LM 93	T		4wDM	RH	373376	1954		Bd
LM 94	T		4wDM	RH	373377	1954		Bd
LM 95	T		4wDM	RH	373379	1954	OOU	
LM 97	T		4wDM	RH	375332	1954	Dsm	Lu
LM 98	T		4wDM	RH	375335	1954	OOU	Cs
(LM 99)			4wDM	RH	375336	1954		K
		rebuilt as	4wDH	BnM(Be)		1988		
LM 100			4wDM	RH	375341	1954		Bd
LM 102			4wDM	RH	379076	1954	OOU	Be
LM 107			4wDM	RH	379055	1954	OOU	K
LM 109			4wDM	RH	379064	1954	OOU	Bo
LM 110			4wDM	RH	379066	1954	OOU	Bo

LM 113	U			4wDM	RH	379068	1954			Dg
(LM 115)	U			4wDM	RH	379073	1954			K
			rebuilt as	4wDH	BnM					
LM 116	M	15		4wDM	RH	379077	1954	Dsm		TAE
LM 117	U			4wDM	RH	379910	1954	OOU		Bo
LM 118				4wDM	RH	379913	1954			Cm
LM 119	V			4wDM	RH	379916	1954	Dsm		Gi
LM 121				4wDM	RH	379922	1954			
			rebuilt as	4wDH	BnM					Lu
LM 123				4wDM	RH	379925	1954			
			rebuilt as	4wDH	BnM		1996			Gi
LM 124	N			4wDM	RH	379081	1954	Dsm		Cs
LM 126				4wDM	RH	379927	1954	OOU		Bo
LM 127				4wDM	RH	379928	1954	OOU		Bo
LM 128	X			4wDM	RH	383260	1955			Bl
LM 130	P			4wDM	RH	382812	1955			K
			rebuilt as	4wDH	BnM(K)		2002			
LM 132	P			4wDM	RH	382809	1955	OOU		Kd
LM 133	P			4wDM	RH	379090	1955	OOU		Dg
LM 134	Q			4wDM	RH	382811	1955			Ti
LM 135	Q			4wDM	RH	382814	1955	OOU	a	Dg
LM 139	Q			4wDM	RH	392137	1955	OOU		Li
LM 140	Q			4wDM	RH	392139	1955			Bi
LM 143				4wDM	RH	392148	1956			K
LM 144	Q			4wDM	RH	392149	1956	Dsm		Dg
(LM 145)				4wDM	RH	394023	1956			Dg
LM 146				4wDM	RH	394024	1956	OOU		Dg
LM 147	X			4wDM	RH	394025	1956	OOU		Dg
LM 148	X			4wDM	RH	394026	1956			Gi
			rebuilt as	4wDH	BnM					
LM 149	X			4wDM	RH	394028	1956	OOU		Dg
			rebuilt as	4wDH	BnM(Dg)					
LM 150	X			4wDM	RH	394027	1956			Dg
			rebuilt as	4wDH	BnM(Dg)					
LM 151				4wDM	RH	392150	1956			K
			rebuilt as	4wDH	BnM					
(LM 152)	Q			4wDM	RH	392151	1956	Dsm		Bi
LM 153	Q			4wDM	RH	394029	1956			Bd
			rebuilt as	4wDH	BnM					
LM 154	X			4wDM	RH	394030	1956			Bl
			rebuilt as	4wDH	BnM(Bl)		2003			
LM 155	X			4wDM	RH	394031	1956	OOU		M
LM 156	X			4wDM	RH	394032	1956			
			rebuilt as	4wDH	BnM(Dg)					Dg
LM 157	X			4wDM	RH	394033	1956			Dg
			rebuilt as	4wDH	BnM(Dg)					
LM 158				4wDM	RH	394034	1956			Dg
LM 159	X			4wDM	RH	402174	1956			Al
			rebuilt as	4wDH	BnM		2001			
LM 160				4wDM	RH	402176	1956			U
			rebuilt as	4wDH	BnM		1995			

LM 163	X		4wDM	RH	402178	1956		Pr
LM 165			4wDM	RH	402179	1956	OOU	Dg
		rebuilt as	4wDH	BnM(Dg)				
(LM 166)	Q		4wDM	RH	402977	1956		Bi
LM 167			4wDM	RH	402978	1956	OOU	Cm
LM 168	Q		4wDM	RH	402980	1956	OOU	Dg
LM 169	Q		4wDM	RH	402981	1956		Dg
LM 170			4wDM	RH	402982	1956	Dsm	Te
LM 176			0-4-0DM	BnM		1961		
		rebuilt as	4wDH	BnM(Dg)		1999		Ed
LM 181			0-4-0DM	Dtz	57123	1960		Bo
LM 184			0-4-0DM	Dtz	57130	1960	OOU	Bl
LM 185			0-4-0DM	Dtz	57131	1960	OOU	Bo
(LM 189)			0-4-0DM	Dtz	57125	1960	OOU	Dg
LM 190			0-4-0DM	Dtz	57128	1960	OOU	Dg
LM 191			0-4-0DM	Dtz	57134	1960	OOU	Dg
LM 192			0-4-0DM	Dtz	57129	1960	OOU	Dg
LM 194			0-4-0DM	Dtz	57136	1960		Bl
LM 199			0-4-0DM	HE	6232	1962		
		rebuilt as	4wDH	BnM(Dg)		1995		Dg
LM 200			0-4-0DM	HE	6233	1962		Bo
LM 201			0-4-0DM	HE	6234	1962		Dg
LM 202			0-4-0DM	HE	6235	1962	OOU	Dg
(LM 203)	LM 240		0-4-0DM	HE	6236	1962		
		rebuilt as	0-4-0DH	BnM(Bo)		2008	e	Bi
LM 204			0-4-0DM	HE	6237	1963		
		rebuilt as	4wDH	BnM(Dg)		1993		M
LM 205			0-4-0DM	HE	6238	1963		Bl
(LM 206)	LM 335		0-4-0DM	HE	6239	1963		
		rebuilt as	0-4-0DH	BnM(Bo)		2008	e	Al
LM 207			0-4-0DM	HE	6240	1963		Bi
LM 208			0-4-0DM	HE	6241	1963		
		rebuilt as	4wDH	BnM(Dg)	19932	1995		Dg
LM 209			0-4-0DM	HE	6242	1963		Bn
LM 210			0-4-0DM	HE	6243	1963		
		rebuilt as	4wDH	BnM(Dg)		1992		Dg
LM 211			0-4-0DM	HE	6244	1963	OOU	Bl
LM 212			0-4-0DM	HE	6245	1963		Bi
LM 213			0-4-0DM	HE	6246	1963		Dg
(LM 214)			0-4-0DM	HE	6247	1963		M
LM 215			0-4-0DM	HE	6248	1963		Ed
LM 216			0-4-0DM	HE	6249	1963		Gi
LM 217			0-4-0DM	HE	6250	1963		Bl
LM 218			0-4-0DM	HE	6251	1963		
		rebuilt as	4wDH	BnM(Dg)		1994		Bl
LM 219			0-4-0DM	HE	6252	1963		Le
LM 220			0-4-0DM	HE	6253	1963		Dg
LM 221			0-4-0DM	HE	6254	1963		Dg
LM 222			0-4-0DM	HE	6255	1963		Bl
LM 223			0-4-0DM	HE	6256	1963		
		rebuilt as	4wDH	BnM(Dg)		1993		Bl

LM 225			0-4-0DM	HE	6304	1964		
		rebuilt as	4wDH	BnM(Dg)		1994		Dg
LM 226			0-4-0DM	HE	6305	1964		
		rebuilt as	4wDH	BnM(M)		1994		Be
LM 227			0-4-0DM	HE	6306	1964		Bo
LM 228			0-4-0DM	HE	6307	1964		Bo
LM 229	(LM 294)		0-4-0DM	HE	8531	1977		Bl
LM 230			0-4-0DM	HE	6309	1964		Bl
LM 231			0-4-0DM	HE	6310	1964	OOU	Bl
LM 232			0-4-0DM	HE	6311	1964		Dg
LM 233			0-4-0DM	HE	6312	1965		Mo
LM 234			0-4-0DM	HE	6313	1965		Bl
LM 235			0-4-0DM	HE	6314	1965		Bo
LM 236			0-4-0DM	HE	6315	1965		Bl
LM 237			0-4-0DM	HE	6316	1965		Be
LM 238			0-4-0DM	HE	6318	1965		
		rebuilt as	4wDH	BnM(Dg)		2000		Ed
LM 239			0-4-0DM	HE	6317	1965		Al
(LM 240)	LM 203		0-4-0DM	HE	6319	1965		
		rebuilt as	0-4-0DH	BnM(Bo)		2008	e	Gi
LM 242			0-4-0DM	HE	6321	1965		M
LM 243			0-4-0DM	HE	6322	1965		Kn
LM 244			0-4-0DM	HE	6323	1965		Bo
LM 245			0-4-0DM	HE	6324	1965		Bo
LM 246			0-4-0DM	HE	6325	1965		Be
LM 247			0-4-0DM	HE	6326	1965		M
LM 248			0-4-0DM	HE	6328	1965	OOU	M
LM 249			0-4-0DM	HE	6327	1965	OOU	M
LM 250			0-4-0DM	HE	6329	1965		M
LM 251			0-4-0DM	HE	6330	1965		M
LM 252			0-4-0DM	HE	6331	1965		
		rebuilt as	4wDH	BnM		2000		M
LM 253			0-4-0DM	Dtz	57834	1965	OOU	Bl
LM 255			0-4-0DM	Dtz	57838	1965	OOU	Cg
LM 261			0-4-0DM	Dtz	57842	1965	OOU	Bl
LM 266			0-4-0DM	HE	7232	1971		Bo
LM 267			0-4-0DM	HE	7233	1971		M
LM 268			0-4-0DM	HE	7234	1971		Li
LM 269			0-4-0DM	HE	7235	1971		Bo
LM 270			0-4-0DM	HE	7237	1971		
		rebuilt as	4wDH	BnM		2000		M
LM 271			0-4-0DM	HE	7236	1971		Li
LM 272			0-4-0DM	HE	7239	1971		Cg
LM 273			0-4-0DM	HE	7246	1972		Be
LM 274			0-4-0DM	HE	7238	1971		M
LM 275			0-4-0DM	HE	7240	1972		Cm
LM 276			0-4-0DM	HE	7241	1972	OOU	Li
LM 277			0-4-0DM	HE	7242	1972		Bo
LM 278			0-4-0DM	HE	7243	1972		Be
LM 280			0-4-0DM	HE	7245	1972		Bl
LM 281			0-4-0DM	HE	7247	1972		Bl
LM 282			0-4-0DM	HE	7248	1972		Bl

LM 283		0-4-0DM	HE	7250	1972		Bo
(LM 284)		0-4-0DM	HE	7249	1972		Bo
LM 285		0-4-0DM	HE	7253	1972		Dg
LM 286		0-4-0DM	HE	7254	1972		Bl
LM 287		0-4-0DM	HE	7255	1972		Dg
LM 288		0-4-0DM	HE	7256	1972		Bl
LM 289		0-4-0DM	HE	7252	1972		Dg
LM 290		0-4-0DM	HE	7251	1972		Dg
LM 292		0-4-0DM	HE	8529	1977		Bl
LM 293		0-4-0DM	HE	8530	1977		Bl
LM 294	(LM 229)	0-4-0DM	HE	6308	1964		Bl
LM 295		0-4-0DM	HE	8532	1977		
	rebuilt as	4wDH	BnM(Bl)		1993		Bl
LM 296		0-4-0DM	HE	8534	1977		Bl
LM 297		0-4-0DM	HE	8533	1977		Kn
LM 298		0-4-0DM	HE	8538	1977	Dsm	Bo
LM 299		0-4-0DM	HE	8537	1977		Dg
LM 300		0-4-0DM	HE	8535	1977		
LM 301		0-4-0DM	HE	8536	1977		Bo
LM 302		0-4-0DM	HE	8539	1977		M
LM 303		0-4-0DM	HE	8540	1977		
	rebuilt as	4wDH	BnM(Dg)		2000		Bd
LM 304		0-4-0DM	HE	8543	1977		Bo
LM 305		0-4-0DM	HE	8544	1977		Dg
LM 306		0-4-0DM	HE	8541	1977		Cm
LM 307		0-4-0DM	HE	8542	1977		Bo
LM 308		0-4-0DM	HE	8546	1977		Bo
LM 309		0-4-0DM	HE	8545	1977		Te
LM 310		0-4-0DM	HE	8547	1977		Bd
LM 311		0-4-0DM	HE	8551	1977		Li
LM 311	(LM 332)	0-4-0DM	HE	8930	1980		Bl
LM 312		0-4-0DM	HE	8550	1977		Pr
LM 313		0-4-0DM	HE	8549	1977		Bl
LM 315		0-4-0DM	HE	8922	1979		Bl
(LM 317)		4wDM	SMH	60SL742	1980		Cm
LM 318		0-4-0DM	HE	8925	1979		M
LM 319		0-4-0DM	HE	8926	1979		Bo
LM 320		0-4-0DM	HE	8939	1980		Df
LM 321		0-4-0DM	HE	8927	1980		Li
LM 322		0-4-0DM	HE	8923	1979		
LM 324		0-4-0DM	HE	8931	1980		Dg
LM 325		0-4-0DM	HE	8942	1981	OOU	Li
LM 326		0-4-0DM	HE	8932	1980		Bl
LM 327		0-4-0DM	HE	8933	1980		Cm
LM 328		0-4-0DM	HE	8935	1980		Li
LM 329		0-4-0DM	HE	8936	1980	OOU	Li
LM 330		0-4-0DM	HE	8937	1980	OOU	M
LM 331		0-4-0DM	HE	8934	1980		De
LM 333		0-4-0DM	HE	8940	1980		Li
LM 334		0-4-0DM	HE	8941	1981		Bl
LM 335		0-4-0DM	HE	8938	1980		Bl

LM 336	0-4-0DM	HE	8943	1981		Bo
LM 337	0-4-0DM	HE	8944	1981		Dg
LM 338	0-4-0DM	HE	8945	1981		Li
LM 339	0-4-0DM	HE	8946	1981		Gl
LM 340	0-4-0DM	HE	8928	1980		Bl
LM 342	0-4-0DM	HE	8929	1980		Bl
LM 354	4wDH	DunEW			OOU	Bl
LM 355	4wDH	DunEW			OOU	M
LM 357	4wDH	DunEW			OOU	Bl
LM 358	4wDH	DunEW				Bi
LM 359	4wDH	DunEW			OOU	M
LM 360	4wDH	DunEW			OOU	Bi
LM 363	4wDH	DunEW	LM363	c1984	OOU	Mo
LM 364	4wDH	DunEW		1984		Bl
LM 365	4wDH	DunEW	LM365	c1984	OOU	De
LM 367	4wDH	DunEW	LM367	1984	OOU	Bl
LM 370	4wDH	DunEW			OOU	Mo
LM 371	4wDH	DunEW			OOU	Bi
LM 372	4wDH	DunEW				Bl
LM 374	4wDH	HE	9239	1984		Cg
LM 375	4wDH	HE	9240	1984		M
LM 376	4wDH	HE	9241	1984		M
LM 377	4wDH	HE	9243	1984		M
LM 378	4wDH	HE	9242	1984		De
LM 379	4wDH	HE	9251	1985		Li
LM 380	4wDH	HE	9252	1985		Li
LM 381	4wDH	HE	9253	1985		De
LM 382	4wDH	HE	9254	1986		Dg
LM 383	4wDH	HE	9255	1986		Dg
LM 384	4wDH	HE	9256	1986		Bo
LM 385	4wDH	HE	9257	1986		M
LM 386	4wDH	HE	9258	1986		De
LM 387	4wDH	HE	9259	1986		K
LM 388	4wDH	HE	9272	1986		Te
LM 389	4wDH	BnM(Bl)		1994		Bl
LM 390	4wDH	BnM(Bl)		1994		Bl
LM 391	4wDH	BnM(Bo)		1994		Be
LM 392	4wDH	BnM(Bo)		1995		Bo
LM 393	4wDH	BnM(Bo)		1995		Bo
LM 394	4wDH	BnM(Bo)		1996		Bo
LM 395	4wDH	BnM(Bl)		1995		Bl
LM 396	4wDH	BnM(Bl)		1995		Bl
LM 397	4wDH	BnM(Bo)		2005		Li
LM 398	4wDH	BnM(Bo)		2005		Bl
LM 399	4wDH	BnM(Bo)		2004		Bl
LM 400	4wDH	BnM(Bo)		2004		Bl
LM 401	4wDH	BnM(M)		1996		M
LM 402	4wDH	BnM(M)		1996		M
LM 403	4wDH	BnM(De)		2000		Bl
LM 404	4wDH	BnM(De)		2000		M
LM 405	4wDH	BnM(Bl)		2000		Bl

Loco	Type	Builder	No	Date	Status	Note	Location
LM 406	4wDH	BnM(Bl)		2000			Bl
LM 407	4wDH	BnM(Li)		2002			Bo
LM 408	4wDH	BnM(Bl)		2001			Bl
LM 409	4wDH	BnM(Bl)		2001			Bl
LM 410	4wDH	BnM(Bo)		1998			Bl
LM 411	4wDH	BnM(Bo)		1999			Bl
LM 412	4wDH	BnM(Dg)		2000			Ed
LM 413	4wDH	BnM(Dg)		2000			Ed
LM 414	4wDH	BnM(Dg)		2000			Ed
LM 415	4wDH	BnM(Dg)		2000			Ed
LM 416	4wDH	BnM(Bo)		2000			Ed
LM 417	4wDH	BnM(Bo)		2000			Ed
LM 418	4wDH	BnM(Bo)		2000			Ed
LM 419	4wDH	BnM(Bo)		2000			Ed
LM 420	4wDH	BnM(Bo)		2000			Ed
LM 421	4wDH	BnM(Bo)		2000			Ed
LM 422	4wDH	BnM(De)		2000			Ed
LM 423	4wDH	BnM(De)		2000			Ed
LM 424	4wDH	BnM(De)		2000			Ed
LM 425	4wDH	BnM(Bl)		2002			Bl
LM 426	4wDH	BnM(Bl)		2002			Bl
LM 427	4wDH	BnM(M)		2002			M
LM 428	4wDH	BnM(M)		2001			M
LM 429	4wDH	BnM(Bo)		2004			Bl
LM 430	4wDH	BnM(Bo)		2004			Bl
LM 431	4wDH	BnM(Dg)		2004			Bo
LM 432	4wDH	BnM(Dg)		2004			Bl
LM 433	4wDH	BnM(Dg)		2004			Bl
LM 434	4wDH	BnM(Dg)		2004			Li
LM 435	4wDH	BnM(Bo)		2005			Bl
LM 436	4wDH	BnM(Bo)		2005			Bl
LM 437	4wDH	BnM(Bo)		2006			Te
LM 438	4wDH	BnM(Bo)		2006			M
LM 439	4wDH	BnM(Bo)		2006			Bo
LM.440	4wDH	BnM(Bo)		2006			Bo
LM 441	4wDH	BnM(Bo)		2007			M
C 49	4wPMR	BnM	5	1958	OOU	b	M
C 53	4wPMR	BnM	9	1958	OOU		Dg
C 54	4wPMR	BnM	10	1958	DsmT		Bl
(C 60)	4wDMR	BnM		c1960	OOU		M
C 64	4wPMR	BnM		1972	DsmT		Li
C 65	4wPMR	BnM		1972	DsmT		M
C 71	4wPMR	BnM		1972	DsmT	c	M
C 72	4wPMR	BnM		1972	DsmT		Bi
C 77	2w-2PMR	BnM		1972	OOU		Cg
C 80	4wPMR	BnM		1972		d	
F (210)	4wDM	BnM			OOU		Li
F 222	4wDM	BnM		1983	OOU		Bl

323 - Bord na Mona

F 230	CIR 862	4wDM	BnM		OOU	BI
F 308		4wDM	BnM			Bo
F 836		4wDM	BnM(BI)	2008		BI
F 353		4wDM	BnM	1983		BI
F 630	341 NRI	4wDM	BnM		OOU	BI
F 842	CIR 861	4wDM	BnM			BI
F 866		4wDM	BnM	c1975		BI
F 878		4wDM	BnM	c1975		BI
RM 1		4wDM	BnM(BI)			BI
RL 1		4wDM	BnM(M)		OOU	M
(RL 2)		4wDM	BnM(TAE/M)	2003		Bo
RM 3		4wDH	BnM(M)	2004		M
RM 4		4wDH	BnM(M)	2004		Dg
RM 5		4wDH	BnM(M)	2004		Cg
RM 6		4wDH	BnM(M)	2004		BI

a   carries plate 382841
b   Dumped near loading point at Derryounce Bog
c   rebuilt as Ambulance car
d   Ambulance car – stables in Machinery Museum compound when not required
e   incorrectly numbered following rebuilding

SECTION 5 – OFFSHORE ISLANDS

CHANNEL ISLANDS

PRESERVATION SITES

ALDERNEY RAILWAY SOCIETY, MANNEZ QUARRY, ALDERNEY

Gauge **4ft 8½in**   601087

(6 ALD 40)	4wVBT	VCG	S	6909	1927	Dsm	
ALD 7 MOLLY 2	4wDM		RH	425481	1958		
D100 ELIZABETH	0-4-0DM		_(VF	D100	1949		
			(DC	2271	1949		
1044	2-2w-2w-2RER		MetCam		1960		
1045	2-2w-2w-2RER		MetCam		1960		
(PWM 3776)	2w-2PMR		Wkm	6655	1953	DsmT	
PWM 3954 MARY LOU	2w-2PMR		Wkm	6939	1955	+	
1 GEORGE RLC/009025	2w-2PMR		Wkm	7091	1955		
(8 9028) SHIRLEY	2w-2PMR		Wkm	7094	1955		
7 (9022)	2w-2PMR		Wkm	8086	1958		
(9)	2w-2PMR		Wkm	9359	1963		

+   currently in store c/o Nick Best, National Westminster Bank Ltd, Victoria Street, St.Annes

STEAM MOTOR & GENERAL MUSEUM, RUE DE BECHET, TRINITY, JERSEY

Gauge **4ft 8½in**   652532

LA MEUSE	0-6-0T	OC	LaMeuse	3442	1933
–	0-4-0ST	OC	P	2085	1948
–	0-4-0ST	OC	P	2129	1952
J.T.DALY	0-4-0ST	OC	WB	2450	1931
(D1)	0-4-0DH		NBQ	27734	1958

Gauge **2ft 0in**

–	4wDM	s/o	MR	11143	1960	
–	4wDM		MR	60S383	1969	Dsm +

+   in use as a brake van

ISLE OF MAN

INDUSTRIAL SITES

ISLE OF MAN TRANSPORT, MANX ELECTRIC RAILWAY CONTRACT
Gauge 3ft 0in

H 048		0-6-0DM	RH	281290	1949	a
LM 344		4wDM	SMH	60SL751	1980	
LM 366		4wDH	DunEW		1984	
LM 373		4wDH	DunEW		1984	

a   on hire from RMS Locotec Ltd, Wakefield, West Yorkshire

NATIONAL AIR TRAFFIC SERVICES LTD, LAXEY
Gauge 3ft 6in   SC 432847

| – | | 4wDMR | Wkm | 10956 | 1976 |

PRESERVATION SITES

J. EDWARDS, BALLAKILLINGAN HOUSE, CHURCHTOWN, near RAMSEY
The loco is stored at a private site and is not available for viewing.   SC 425945

Gauge 3ft 0in

| No.14 | THORNHILL | 2-4-0T | OC | BP | 2028 | 1880 |

GROUDLE GLEN RAILWAY LTD, LHEN COAN, GROUDLE GLEN
Gauge 2ft 0in   SC 418786

	ANNIE	0-4-2T	OC	BoothR		1997	
	SEA LION	2-4-0T	OC	WB	1484	1896	
		reb		‡		1987	
	PARRACOMBE	0-4-0DM	s/o	Bg	3232	1947	
No.1	DOLPHIN	4wDM		HE	4394	1952	
No.2	WALRUS	4wDM		HE	4395	1952	
	POLAR BEAR	4wBE		WR	556801	1988	
		reb		AK	72R	2004	*

‡   rebuilt by British Nuclear Fuels Ltd, Windscale Factory, Sellafield, Cumbria
*   carries worksplate BEV 313

ISLE OF MAN TRANSPORT, DEPARTMENT OF TOURISM & TRANSPORT

Isle of Man Steam Railway

Locos are kept at :
Douglas SC 374754, 375755
Port Erin SC 198689

Gauge 3ft 0in

No.1	SUTHERLAND	2-4-0T	OC	BP	1253	1873	
	CALEDONIA No.15	0-6-0T	OC	D	2178	1885	
No.4	LOCH	2-4-0T	OC	BP	1416	1874	
No.5	(MONA)	2-4-0T	OC	BP	1417	1874	OOU +
No.8	(FENELLA)	2-4-0T	OC	BP	3610	1894	
No.9	DOUGLAS	2-4-0T	OC	BP	3815	1896	OOU +
No.10	G.H. WOOD	2-4-0T	OC	BP	4662	1905	
No.11	MAITLAND	2-4-0T	OC	BP	4663	1905	
No.12	HUTCHINSON	2-4-0T	OC	BP	5126	1908	
No.13	KISSACK	2-4-0T	OC	BP	5382	1910	
No.17	VIKING	4wDH		Schöma	2086	1958	
18	AILSA	4wDH		_(HAB	770	1990	
				(HE	9446	1990	
		reb	HE		9342	1995	
19		0-4-0+4DMR		WkB/Dundalk		1950	
20		0-4-0+4DMR		WkB/Dundalk		1951	
–		4wDM		MR	22021	1959	
–		4wDM		MR	40S280	1966	
(23)		2w-2PMR		Wkm	5763	1950	
No.2		2w-2PMR		Wkm	7442	1956	OOU

+   in store for Isle of Man Railway & Tramway Preservation Society

Port Erin Railway Museum, Railway Station, Port Erin

Gauge 3ft 0in
SC 198689

No.6	PEVERIL	2-4-0T	OC	BP	1524	1875
16	MANNIN	2-4-0T	OC	BP	6296	1926

Homefield Depot, Salisbury Street, Douglas

Gauge 3ft 0in
SC 378766

No.7	TYNWALD	2-4-0T	OC	BP	2038	1880	
–		4wPM	s/o	FH	2027	1937	
No.23	DR.R.PRESTON HENDRY	4w-4wWE		MER		1900	+

+   stored on un-motorised bogies, property of Isle of Man Railway & Tramway Presevation Society

LAXEY & LONAN HERITAGE TRUST, GREAT LAXEY MINE RAILWAY

Gauge 1ft7in
SC 433847

ANT	0-4-0T	OC	GNS	20	2004
BEE	0-4-0T	OC	GNS	21	2004

SECTION 6
MINISTRY OF DEFENCE

DEPOT TYPES :

DM	Defence Munitions
DRCS	Defence Rail & Container Services
DSDC	Defence Storage & Distribution Centre
DERA	Defence Evaluation & Research Agency
79 Sqn	79 Railway Squadron RLC
275 Sqn	275 Squadron RLC(V)

LOCATIONS :

ASH	(SO 932338)	DSDC Ashchurch, Gloucestershire
BIS	(SP 581203)	DSDC Bicester, Oxfordshire
CD	(SU 014455)	Copehill Down Battle Training Area, Salisbury Plain, Wiltshire
CWT	(ST 480910)	DRCS, Caerwent, Monmouthshire
DH	(SU 276266)	DM Dean Hill, Hampshire
ER	(NY 246656)	DM Eastriggs, Dumfries & Galloway
ERN	(SX 45x60x)	RNAD, Ernesettle, Devon.
GD	( )	DM Glen Douglas, near Arrochar, Argyll & Bute
KIN	(SP 373523, 374524)	DM Kineton, Warwickshire
LON	(NY 363682)	DM Longtown, Cumbria
LUD	(SU 261507)	Ludgershall Railhead, Wiltshire
LUL	(SY 863822)	Lulworth Ranges, East Lulworth, Dorset
LYD	(TR 033198)	Cinque Ports Training Area, Lydd, Romney Marsh, Kent. (n.g. only)
MCH	(SU 395103)	Marchwood Sea Mounting Centre (Marchwood Military Port), Hampshire
SHO	(TM 946856)	DERA Shoeburyness, Southend-on-Sea, Essex
SHO(PA)	(TM)	DERA Shoeburyness (Project Avocet), Essex

LOCOMOTIVES

Gauge 4ft 8½in

The following list conforms to the renumbering scheme recently introduced, although in some cases the new numbers are not yet carried. The former number is shown in brackets.

01501 (627)	0-6-0DH	AB	664	1984	OOU	MCH
01502 (628)	0-6-0DH	AB	665	1984	OOU	MCH
01503 (629)	0-6-0DH	AB	666	1984	OOU	MCH
01504 (630)	0-6-0DH	AB	667	1984	OOU	MCH
01505 (626)	0-6-0DH	AB	663	1984	OOU	MCH
01506 (631)	0-6-0DH	AB	668	1984	OOU	MCH
01510 (272)	4wDH	TH	320V	1987		ER
01511 (275)	4wDH	TH	323V	1988		BIS
01512 (301)	4wDH	TH	319V	1988		
	rep LH Group		76699	2002		BIS
01513 (302)	4wDH	TH	318V	1987		
	rep LH Group		76638	2002		BIS

No.	Name	Type	R/R	Builder	Works No.	Date		Location
01514 (303)		4wDH		TH	V332	1988		
		rep LH Group			76634	2002		GD
01515 (304)		4wDH		TH	321V	1987		
		rep LH Group			76629	2002		GD
01520 (274)		4wDH		TH	322V	1987		ERN
01521 (278)		4wDH		TH	V333	1988		LUD
01522 (254)		4wDH		TH	272V	1977		LUD
01523 (259)		4wDH		TH	299V	1981		ASH
01524 (261)		4wDH		TH	301V	1982		SHO
01525 (264)		4wDH		TH	306V	1983		SHO
01526 (265)		4wDH		TH	307V	1983		KIN
01527 (256)		4wDH		TH	274V	1977		MCH
01528 (267)		4wDH		TH	309V	1984		ER
01529 (268)		4wDH		TH	310V	1984		MCH
01530 (269)		4wDH		TH	311V	1984		LON
01541 (260)		4wDH		TH	300V	1982		MCH
01542 (262)		4wDH		TH	302V	1982		ASH
01543 (263)		4wDH		TH	303V	1982		KIN
01544 (252)		4wDH		TH	270V	1977		LUD
01545 (253)		4wDH		TH	271V	1977		LON
01546 (255)		4wDH		TH	273V	1977		KIN
01547 (266)		4wDH		TH	308V	1983		KIN
01548 (257)		4wDH		TH	275V	1978		MCH
01549 (258)		4wDH		TH	298V	1981		CWT
01550 (271)		4wDH		TH	324V	1987		BIS
430		0-6-0DH		RH	466621	1961	OOU	CD
	ANNA	4wRE		Wkm	11547	1987		LUL
	FIONA	4wRE		Wkm	11548	1987		LUL
	BELLA	4wRE		Wkm	11549	1987		LUL
	DEBBIE	4wRE		Wkm	11550	1987		LUL
	ENID	4wRE		Wkm	11551	1987		LUL
	CLAIRE	4wRE		Wkm	11552	1987		LUL
–		4wDMR		Wkm	11621	1986		LUL
9121		4wDMR		BD	3710	1975		KIN
(9123)		4wDMR		BD	3712	1975	DsmT	KIN
9128	THE HORNET	4wDMR		BD	3744	1976		LON
9129		4wDMR		BD	3745	1976	275Rly	BIS
TNS 101		2w-2DMR		Robel 56.27-10-AF32		1983		ASH
TNS 102		2w-2DMR		Robel 56.27-3.AF33		1983		ER
RBGT 1		2w-2DMR		Robel 56.27-10-AG39		1983		SHO
AD 06		2w-2DMR		Robel 56.27-10-AG40		1983		CWT
08 CP 05		4wDM	R/R	Ford/Wkm	11618	1986		BIS
52 RN 36		4wDM	R/R	Unimog	2660.10	1978		GD
–		4wDM	R/R	Unimog 406121 10 029450				GD

(DRC 730J) KAR 536V	4wDM	R/R	Unimog 416123 10 004971		1970	KIN
01 RN 17	4wDM	R/R	Unimog 472100 2W 152685		1989	

Gauge 2ft 6in

	RAMBO	4wBEF	CE	B0483	1976	SHO(PA)
	TERMINATOR	4wBEF	CE	B0483	1976	SHO(PA)
DH 888	ND 10392	4wDH	BD	3755	1981	DH
DH 887	T 0005 ND 10393	4wDH	BD	3756	1981	DH

Gauge 600mm

50		4wDH	AB	719	1987	
		reb	HAB		1996	ER
51	RIVER SARK	4wDH	AB	720	1987	
		reb	HAB		1996	ER
52		4wDH	AB	721	1987	
		reb	HAB		1996	ER
53		4wDH	AB	764	1988	
		reb	HAB		1996	ER
54		4wDH	AB	765	1988	
		reb	HAB		1995	ER

SECTION 7

NETWORK RAIL

and CONTRACTORS

All vehicles listed within this section have a gauge of 4ft 8½in unless otherwise indicated.

The following abbreviations are used :-

CMD	Central Materials Depot
C&WMD	Carriage and Wagon Maintenance Depot
EMU	Electric Multiple Unit
OHLM	Overhead Line Maintenance
OTPD	On Track Plant Depot
PW	Permanent Way
RCE	Regional Civil Engineer
RSD	Rolling Stock Development
S&T	Signal & Telegraph
TMD	Traction Maintenance Depot
T&RSD	Traction and Rolling Stock Depot
T&RSED	Traction and Rolling Stock Electric Depot
T&RSMD	Traction and Rolling Stock Maintenance Depot

DEPOTS, STABLING POINTS AND ALLOCATIONS

AD	Ashford Plant SouthEast Depot, Kent	TR 021415
AL	Aylesbury TMD, Buckinghamshire	SU 818134
AT	Ashford T&RSD, Kent	TR 015420
AV	Andover Station, Hampshire	
BN	Bounds Green, London	
BS	Bescot TMD	
CF	Cardiff Canton T&RSMD	ST 172758
CH	Chester Plant Depot, Cheshire	
CL	Carlisle Upperby C&WMD, Cumbria	NY 412545
CTRL	Channel Tunnel Rail Link, Kent	
DA	Dalmeny Forth Bridge CE Workshops, Edinburgh	NT 139778
DM	Doncaster Marshgate Plant Depot, South Yorkshire	SE 573038
DP	Darlington Park Lane Plant Depot, Co.Durham	NZ 294138
DT	Railway Technical Centre, Derby, Derbyshire	SK 365350
DY	Derby Etches Park T&RSMD	SK 368349
EA	Eastleigh Area S&T Works, Hampshire	SU 458192
EP	Eastleigh South West Area Plant Depot, Hampshire	SU 458194
GB	Guide Bridge Plant Depot, Greater Manchester	SJ 928976
HB	Halkirk Ballast Tip, Highland	ND 126581
HG	Hither Green Plant South-East Depot, Greater London	TQ 393743
KN	Kings Norton Plant Depot, West Midlands	
LNWR	LNWR Ltd, Crewe Carriage Works, Cheshire	ST 714537
LO	Longsight TMD's, Greater Manchester	SJ 867963
ML	Motherwell TMD, North Lanarkshire	NS 749581
OO	Old Oak Common TMD, Greater London	SU 217824
RB	Rugby Plant Depot, Warwickshire	SP 514761
RD	Reading Plant Depot, Berkshire	SU 704738
RE	Ramsgate T&RSMD, Kent	TR 372657
RY	Royston, South Yorkshire	SE 369128
SD	Stafford OHLM Depot, Staffordshire	SJ 922225
SH	Shettleston CCE Plant Depot West, Glasgow	NS 654644
SP	Slateford Plant Depot, Edinburgh	NT 228714
SPK	Stonebridge Park Carriage Repair Shop	
SPM	St Philips Marsh, T7RSMD, Bristol	
SU	Selhurst TMD, Greater London	TQ 333678
SY	Stanningley Plant Depot, West Yorkshire	SE 222344
TB	Three Bridges Central Plant Depot, West Sussex	TQ 287364
TE	Thornaby TMD, North Yorkshire	NZ 462185
TM	Temple Mills TMD, Greater London	
TO	Toton TMD, Nottingham, Nottinghamshire	SK 484354
WB	Whitby, North Yorkshire	NZ 898107
WG	Wigan OHLM Depot, Greater Manchester	SD 593038
WK	Woking Plant Depot, Surrey	
YP	York Plant Workshops, North Yorkshire	SE 590518

LOCOMOTIVES

–		4wBE		Niteq	B155	2000		SU
–		4wBE		Niteq	B188	2002		SPM
–		4wBE		Niteq	B200	2005		OO
–		4wBE		Niteq	B246	2007		BN
–		4wDH	R/R	Unilok	4009	2002		LO
–		4wDH	R/R	Unilok	4010	2002		SPK
31105		A1A-A1ADE		BT	122	1959	a	DT
31233		A1A-A1ADE		BT	260	1960	a	DT
31285		A1A-A1ADE		BT	318	1961	a	DT
43013		Bo-BoDE		Crewe		1976	b	DT
43014		Bo-BoDE		Crewe		1976	b	DT
43062		Bo-BoDE		Crewe		1977	b	DT
43089		Bo-BoDE		Crewe		1978	b	DT
86901	(E3136 86253) CHIEF ENGINEER							
		Bo-BoWE		Don		1965	c	LNWR
86902	(E3190 86210) RAIL VEHICLE ENGINEERING							
		Bo-BoWE		_(EE	3482	1965		
				(EEV	E328	1965	c	LNWR
97301	(D6800 37100)	Co-CoDE		_(EE	3229	1962		
				(VF	D754	1962		
97303	(D6878 37178)	Co-CoDE		_(EE	3356	1963		
				(EEV	D842	1963		
–		4wBE	R/R	Zephir	2111	2007		RE

a owned by Network Rail
b Network Rail Measurement Train
c used as load bank test, one bogie is now de-motorised (Bo-4WE)

MULTIPLE UNITS

DE-ICING AND SANDITE

Some de-icing vehicles may be temporarily reallocated for sandite duties during the autumn months.

Converted Electrical Multiple Unit Stock

930 010	ADB975600	(S10988S)	4w-4RER		Lancing/Elh	1941			
				reb	Selhurst	1980	OOU		DY
930 010	ADB975601	(S10843S)	4w-4RER		Lancing/Elh	1948			
				reb	Selhurst	1980	OOU		DY
930 012	ADB975605	(S10940S)	4w-4RER		Lancing/Elh	1947			
				reb	Selhurst	1981	OOU		AT
930 101	ADB977207	(S61658)	4w-4RER		Afd/Elh	1958			
				reb	Elh	1990			AT
930 101	ADB977609	(65414)	4w-4RER		Afd/Elh	1957			
				reb	Elh	1990			AT
930 204	977874	(65302)	4w-4RER		Afd/Elh	1954			SU
930 204	977875	(65304)	4w-4RER		Afd/Elh	1954			SU
930 206	977925	(65379)	4w-4RER		Afd/Elh	1954			SU
930 206	977924	(65382)	4w-4RER		Afd/Elh	1954			SU
999606		(62356)	4w-4wRER		York	1971			

Converted Diesel Multiple Unit Stock

960.010	L124 977858	(55024)	2-2w-2w-2DMR	PSteel	1960	+		AL
960.011	L125 BEN 977859	(55025)	2-2w-2w-2DMR	PSteel	1960	+		LO
960.013	L130 BILL 977866	(55030)	2-2w-2w-2DMR	PSteel	1960	+		AL
960.012	L122 977873	(55022)	2-2w-2w-2DMR	PSteel	1960	+		DT
960 015	975042	(M55019)	2-2w-2w-2DMR	GRC&W	1958			AL
960.021	L121 ADB977723	(55021)	2-2w-2w-2DMR	PSteel	1960	+		AL
	(55029)	GB 977968	EURAILSCOUT					
			2-2w-2w-2DMR	PSteel	1960			RB

+   these vehicles are also used for route learning duties

RESEARCH AND DEVELOPMENT

These units can be seen at work throughout the rail network.

960 101	977963	(61937)	4w-4wWER	York		1962	a	
960 102	977966	(61928)	4w-4wWER	York		1962	a	
950 001	DB 999600		4w-4wDHR	York(BRE)		1987		DT
950 001	DB 999601		4w-4wDHR	York(BRE)		1987		DT
999 605	(S62482)		4w-4wRER	York(BRE)		1974		SU
999 700	EURAILSCOUT		4w-4wDER	Plasser	138	2002	b c	DT
999 701	EURAILSCOUT		4w-4wDER	Plasser	138	2002	b c	DT
999 800			4w-4wDER	Plasser	152	2004	b	
999 801			4w-4wDER	Plasser	153	2004	b	
–			2w-2FER	Parry	12			

a   stored at MOD Shoeburyness, Essex.
b   Survey car.
c   Work in tandem as 125mph track Assessment Unit.

MISCELLANEOUS

960 301	977987	(51371)	2-2w-2w-2DMR	PSteel	1960	b		AL
960 301	977988	(51413)	2-2w-2w-2DMR	PSteel	1960	b		AL
960 302	977975	(55027)	2-2w-2w-2DMR	Psteel	1960			CF
960 303	977976	(55031)	2-2w-2w-2DMR	PSteel	1960			CF
901.001	DB999602 (S62483)		4w-4wRER	York(BRE)	1974	a		RE
55012			2-2w-2w-2DMR	GRC&W	1959	c	OOU	TE
977992	(51375)		2-2w-2w-2DMR	PSteel	1960	c		AL

a   ultrasonic test units.
b   liquid delivery unit.
c   route learning unit and inspection saloon.

PLANT

GENERAL PURPOSE MAINTENANCE

98202	4wDMR	Plasser	52530A	1983		RD
DR 98204A	4wDMR	Plasser	52759A	1984		SP
DR 98209A	4wDMR	Plasser	52764A	1985		AD
DR 98210A	4wDMR	Plasser	52765A	1985		RD
DR 98215	4wDMR	Plasser	53192A	1988		HG
DR 98216	4wDMR	Plasser	53193A	1988		WK
DR 98217	4wDMR	Plasser	53194A	1988		HG
DR 98218	4wDMR	Plasser	53195A	1988		HG
DR 98219	4wDMR	Plasser	53196A	1988		EP
DR 98220	4wDMR	Plasser	53197A	1988		EA
DR 98221	4wDMR	Plasser	53198A	1988		RD
DR 98300A	4wDMR	Geismar	G.780.001	1985		GB
DR 98302A	4wDMR	Geismar	G.780.003	1985		YP
DR 98305	4w-4wDHR	Geismar	799	1997		AT
DR 98306	4w-4wDHR	Geismar	800	1997		AT
DR 98307	4w-4wDHR	Geismar	825	1998		TB
DR 98308	4w-4wDHR	Geismar	826	1998		EP
DX 98505	4wDHR	Plasser	52793	1985		SP
DX 98704	4wDHR	Perm	002	1986	OOU	SH
DX 98710	4wDHR	Perm	011	1986		AV
DR 97001	4w-4wDHR	Eiv de Brieve 001URS		2003		CTRL

DR 97011	4w-4wDHR	Windhoff	2625	2004	CTRL
DR 97012	4w-4wDHR	Windhoff	2626	2004	CTRL
DR 97013	4w-4wDHR	Windhoff	2627	2004	CTRL
DR 97014	4w-4wDHR	Windhoff	2628	2004	CTRL
DR 98001	4w-4wDHR	Windhoff	2516	2000	SD
DR 98002	4w-4wDHR	Windhoff	2517	2000	SD
DR 98003	4w-4wDHR	Windhoff	2506	2000	SD
DR 98004	4w-4wDHR	Windhoff	2507	2000	SD
DR 98005	4w-4wDHR	Windhoff	2518	2000	SD
DR 98006	4w-4wDHR	Windhoff	2519	2000	WG
DR 98007	4w-4wDHR	Windhoff	2520	2000	KN
DR 98008	4w-4wDHR	Windhoff	2521	2000	SD
DR 98009	4w-4wDHR	Windhoff	2508	2000	SD
DR 98010	4w-4wDHR	Windhoff	2509	2000	SD
DR 98011	4w-4wDHR	Windhoff	2510	2000	RB
DR 98012	4w-4wDHR	Windhoff	2511	2000	RB
DR 98013	4w-4wDHR	Windhoff	2512	2000	RB
DR 98014	4w-4wDHR	Windhoff	2513	2000	RB
DR 98901	4w-4wDHR	Windhoff	2492	1998	TM
DR 98902	4w-4wDHR	Windhoff	2494	1998	TM
DR 98903	4w-4wDHR	Windhoff	2522	1999	WG
DR 98904	4w-4wDHR	Windhoff	2524	1999	WG
DR 98905	4w-4wDHR	Windhoff	2526	1999	TM
DR 98906	4w-4wDHR	Windhoff	2528	1999	TO
DR 98907	4w-4wDHR	Windhoff	2530	1999	TM
DR 98908	4w-4wDHR	Windhoff	2532	1999	DT
DR 98909	4w-4wDHR	Windhoff	2534	1999	CL
DR 98910	4w-4wDHR	Windhoff	2536	1999	BS
DR 98911	4w-4wDHR	Windhoff	2538	1999	CF
DR 98912	4w-4wDHR	Windhoff	2540	2000	TM
DR 98913	4w-4wDHR	Windhoff	2542	2000	TM
DR 98914	4w-4wDHR	Windhoff	2544	2000	S
DR 98915	4w-4wDHR	Windhoff	2546	2000	ML
DR 98916	4w-4wDHR	Windhoff	2548	2000	ML
DR 98917	4w-4wDHR	Windhoff	2550	2000	BS
DR 98918	4w-4wDHR	Windhoff	2552	2000	DT
DR 98919	4w-4wDHR	Windhoff	2554	2000	EP
DR 98920	4w-4wDHR	Windhoff	2556	2000	WK
DR 98921	4w-4wDHR	Windhoff	2558	2000	EP
DR 98922	4w-4wDHR	Windhoff	2560	2000	WK
DR 98923	4w-4wDHR	Windhoff	2562	2000	WK
DR 98924	4w-4wDHR	Windhoff	2564	2000	EP
DR 98925	4w-4wDHR	Windhoff	2566	2000	TB
DR 98926	4w-4wDHR	Windhoff	2579	2001	EP
DR 98976	4w-4wDHR	Windhoff	2580	2001	EP
DR 98927	4w-4wDHR	Windhoff	2581	2001	WK
DR 98977	4w-4wDHR	Windhoff	2582	2001	WK
DR 98928	4w-4wDHR	Windhoff	2583	2001	AD
DR 98978	4w-4wDHR	Windhoff	2584	2001	AD
DR 98929	4w-4wDHR	Windhoff	2585	2001	AD
DR 98979	4w-4wDHR	Windhoff	2586	2001	AD

DR 98930	4w-4wDHR	Windhoff	2587	2001		EA
DR 98980	4w-4wDHR	Windhoff	2588	2001		EA
DR 98931	4w-4wDHR	Windhoff	2589	2001		EA
DR 98981	4w-4wDHR	Windhoff	2590	2001		EA
DR 98932	4w-4wDHR	Windhoff	2591	2001		EA
DR 98982	4w-4wDHR	Windhoff	2592	2001		EA

PERSONNEL CARRIERS & RESPONSE

	–		2w-2PMR	Wkm			DsmT	HB
	–		2w-2PMR	Wkm			DsmT	RY
(DX 68003)	68/007	DB965951	2w-2PMR	Wkm	10647	1972	OOU	DP
	68/043		2w-2DMR	Wkm				
			reb	DonM		1983	+	DM

+   converted to tunnel inspection units

A

Entry	Page	Entry	Page	Entry	Page
A&O [PUP]	296	AB 1876	110	AB 2260	251
AB 699	31	AB 1889	254	AB 2261	115
AB 776	172	AB 1890	255	AB 2262	247
AB 782	174	AB 1927	147	AB 2263	276
AB 807	257	AB 1931	172	AB 2264	305
AB 840	259	AB 1937	258	AB 2265	295
AB 880	188	AB 1944	176	AB 2268	116
AB 885	173	AB 1950	115	AB 2274	75
AB 929	88	AB 1952	251	AB 2284	258
AB 945	112	AB 1964	170	AB 2292	255
AB 946	247	AB 1966	289	AB 2296	260
AB 984	109	AB 1969	115	AB 2315	112
AB 988	256	AB 1984	187	AB 2320	223
AB 1015	78	AB 1989	259	AB 2323	159
AB 1047	84	AB 1995	202	AB 2333	47
AB 1069	247	AB 1996	252	AB 2335	259
AB 1081	283	AB 2008	57	AB 2343	185
AB 1116	251	AB 2015	290	AB 2350	172
AB 1142	253	AB 2017	260	AB 2352	215
AB 1147	115	AB 2020	260	AB 2354	215
AB 1175	261	AB 2043	259	AB 2358	251
AB 1193	78	AB 2046	259	AB 2360	62
AB 1219	33	AB 2047	179	AB 2361	75
AB 1223	185	AB 2068	259	AB 2368	251
AB 1245	47	AB 2069	194	AB 2369	225
AB 1260	288	AB 2073	253	AB 2373	77
AB 1296	251	AB 2074	290	AB 333	84
AB 1338	78	AB 2086	252	AB 343	259
AB 1385	279	AB 2088	172	AB 347	251
AB 1398	179	AB 2107	252	AB 349	83
AB 1431	276	AB 2126	91	AB 352	172
AB 1458	258	AB 2127	259	AB 354	200
AB 1472	152	AB 2134	116	AB 357	112
AB 1473	285	AB 2138	215	AB 358	88
AB 1477	31	AB 2139	215	AB 359	136
AB 1550	47	AB 2157	85	AB 362	209
AB 1571	254	AB 2168	159, 212	AB 363	160
AB 1572	116	AB 2183	34	AB 366	251
AB 1578	68	AB 2199	83	AB 371	103
AB 1598	115	AB 2201	283	AB 372	245
AB 1605	103	AB 2207	280	AB 376	112
AB 1614	251	AB 2212	106	AB 385	245
AB 1619	85	AB 2215	111	AB 388	141
AB 1641	25	AB 2217	62	AB 393	283
AB 1659	78	AB 2219	253	AB 395	61
AB 1680	288	AB 2220	112	AB 398	147
AB 1719	179	AB 2221	88	AB 399	251
AB 1807	247	AB 2226	36	AB 400	122
AB 1815	122	AB 2230	116	AB 401	116
AB 1823	289	AB 2238	289	AB 415	257
AB 1833	260	AB 2239	250	AB 416	58
AB 1863	252	AB 2243	31	AB 422	120
AB 1865	115	AB 2244	251	AB 435	61
AB 1871	28	AB 2248	67, 70	AB 440	224
AB 1875	57	AB 2258	239	AB 441	58
		AB 2259	254	AB 446	88

AB 472	257	AB 740	81	AE 2071	27
AB 473	237	AB 741	80	AEC [1]	296
AB 478	190	AB 758	83	AEC [No.1]	141
AB 482	246	AB 759	83	AEC 8031 046	301
AB 486	187	AB 760	59	AEC 852004?	215
AB 491	210	AB 761	59	AEG 1565	79
AB 499	172	AB 764	330	AEI/MV 1029	55
AB 506/1	81	AB 765	330	AFB 2667	277
AB 506/2	81	AB 5997	110	AFB 2668	197
AB 509	105	AB 6004	52	AFB 2683	277
AB 510	105	AB 6140	51	AFB 2684	277
AB 511	106	AB 6526	49	AFB 2685	66
AB 512	106	AB 6613	277	AFB 2855	280
AB 515	247	AB 6719	115	Afd [15224]	112
AB 516	247	AB 6930	32	Afd [31027]	199
AB 517	260	ABG 646	231	Afd [31065]	199
AB 552	79	ABG 659	184, 219	Afd [31178]	199
AB 554	277	ABG 660	184, 219	Afd [31263]	199
AB 555	277	ACCars [11]	86	Afd [31323]	199
AB 556	249	ACCars [21]	85	Afd [31556]	111
AB 557	250	ACCars [22]	86	Afd [31625]	95
AB 558	74	ACCars [79976]	122	Afd [31638]	199
AB 560	249	ACCars [79978]	83	Afd [31737]	226
AB 561	251	AE 1386	170	Afd [48624]	60
AB 578	181	AE 1421	290	Afd/Elh [60000]	201
AB 579	181	AE 1465	151	Afd/Elh [60001]	201
AB 594	120	AE 1498	269	Afd/Elh [60016]	201
AB 600	246	AE 1547	97	Afd/Elh [60019]	201
AB 612	55	AE 1563	187	Afd/Elh [60108]	46
AB 613	55	AE 1568	115	Afd/Elh [60110]	229
AB 614	221	AE 1572	77	Afd/Elh [60117]	290
AB 615	115	AE 1600	145	Afd/Elh [60118]	201
AB 616	51	AE 1680	283	Afd/Elh [60122]	200
AB 618	223	AE 1720	29	Afd/Elh [60124]	96
AB 621	149	AE 1738	25	Afd/Elh [60127]	215
AB 622	149	AE 1748	86	Afd/Elh [60130]	148
AB 630	127	AE 1764	29	Afd/Elh [60138]	141
AB 637	223	AE 1772	47	Afd/Elh [60142]	112
AB 646	231	AE 1798	88	Afd/Elh [60145]	201
AB 647	148	AE 1810	115	Afd/Elh [60146]	65
AB 649	247	AE 1865	37	Afd/Elh [60149]	201
AB 651	75	AE 1875	83	Afd/Elh [60150]	65
AB 658	127	AE 1883	115	Afd/Elh [60151]	200
AB 659	184, 219	AE 1913	60	Afd/Elh [60154]	108
AB 660	184, 219	AE 1917	235	Afd/Elh [61229]	108
AB 663	328	AE 1919	187	Afd/Elh [61230]	108
AB 664	328	AE 1928	29	Afd/Elh [61275]	227
AB 665	328	AE 1945	235	Afd/Elh [61287]	208
AB 666	328	AE 1971	107	Afd/Elh [61658]	334
AB 667	328	AE 1972	130	Afd/Elh [61743]	65
AB 668	328	AE 1973	172	Afd/Elh [61798]	46
AB 719	330	AE 1977	212	Afd/Elh [61799]	46
AB 720	330	AE 2004	108	Afd/Elh [61804]	46
AB 721	330	AE 2021	294	Afd/Elh [61805]	46
AB 738	81	AE 2057	197	Afd/Elh [65302]	334
AB 739	81	AE 2068	84	Afd/Elh [65304]	334

BD 3698	93	BEV 308	274	BGB 916/6/004	223
BD 3699	179	BEV 323	274	BH 266	78
BD 3701	109	BEV 551	62	BH 305	226
BD 3702	143	BEV 640	117	BH 748	79
BD 3703	59	Bg 680	78	BH 859	273
BD 3704	49	Bg 774	192	BH 897	77
BD 3706	141	Bg 800	212	BH 912	78
BD 3707	58	Bg 1695	192	BL [No.1]	48
BD 3708	90	Bg 1769	196	BL 10	227
BD 3709	56	Bg 1797	253	BL 11	211
BD 3710	329	Bg 2042	160	BL 15	118
BD 3712	329	Bg 2043	160	BL 22	56
BD 3713	208	Bg 2083	253	BL 30	47
BD 3730	209	Bg 2085	192	BL 32	216
BD 3732	209	Bg 2095	92	BLW 15511	288
BD 3733	156	Bg 3002	117	BLW 20587	250
BD 3734	125	Bg 3014	253	BLW 44656	25
BD 3735	125	Bg 3024	192	BLW 44699	277
BD 3736	125	Bg 3027	185	BLW 49604	267
BD 3737	125	Bg 3217	148	BLW 61269	288
BD 3738	125	Bg 3232	326	BLW 69496	228
BD 3739	125	Bg 3235	41	BLW 69621	115
BD 3740	125	Bg 3236	45	BLW 72080	186
BD 3743	90	Bg 3357	65	BM [No.3]	152
BD 3744	329	Bg 3406	99	BMR 001	288
BD 3745	329	Bg 3410	185	BMR 002	279
BD 3746	280	Bg 3434	123	BnM 3	307
BD 3748	281	Bg 3435	165	BnM 5	323
BD 3749	281	Bg 3436	123	BnM 7	307
BD 3751	203	Bg 3437	165	BnM 9	323
BD 3752	250	Bg 3500	49	BnM 10	323
BD 3753	59	Bg 3538	32	BnM [C 60]	323
BD 3755	330	Bg 3539	25	BnM [C 63]	302
BD 3756	330	Bg 3555	186	BnM [C 64]	323
BD 3764	276	Bg 3565	79	BnM [C 65]	323
BD 3767	267	Bg 3578	186	BnM [C 66]	307
BD 3775	107	Bg 3590	212	BnM [C 67]	279
BD 3776	264	BgC 646	52	BnM [C 69]	311
BD 3779	276	BgC 736	242	BnM [C 70]	307
BD 3780	28	BgC 760	242	BnM [C 71]	323
BD 3781	276	BgC 2007	25	BnM [C 72]	323
BD 3782	282	Bg/DC 1097	188	BnM [C 74]	307
BD 3783	282	Bg/DC 1647	103	BnM [C 76]	279
BD 3784	282	Bg/DC 2107	276	BnM [C 77]	323
BE 314	123	Bg/DC 2136	224	BnM [C 78]	313
BE 16302	94	Bg/DC 2263	280	BnM [C 80]	323
BE 16303	204	Bg/DC 2268	242	BnM [F 210]	323
BE 16306	204	Bg/DC 2393	66	BnM [F 222]	323
BE 16307	94	Bg/DC 2395	66	BnM [F 230]	324
BE [26500]	77	Bg/DC 2724	134	BnM [F 308]	324
BE [4wBE]	273	Bg/DC 2725	220	BnM [F 353]	324
BE [6]	86	BGB 50/400/406	284	BnM [F 630]	324
BE [8]	86	BGB 100/400/007	284	BnM(Bl) [F 836]	324
BE [9]	201	BGB 916/6/001	223	BnM [F 842]	324
Bedford 4wDMR R/R]	301	BGB 916/6/002	223	BnM [F 866]	324
Berwyn [No.2]	40	BGB 916/6/003	223	BnM [F 878]	324

BnM [LM 176]	319	BnM(Bl) [RL 2]	324	BP 7827	257
BnM(Bl) [LM 389]	322	BnM(Bl) [RM 1]	324	BP 7856	242
BnM(Bl) [LM 390]	322	BnM(Bl) [RM 3]	324	BP 7863	277
BnM(Bo) [LM 391]	322	BnM(Bl) [RM 4]	324	BP 7865	277
BnM(Bo) [LM 392]	322	BnM(Bl) [RM 5]	324	BP 7868	277
BnM(Bo) [LM 393]	322	BnM(Bl) [RM 6]	324	BP 7892	55
BnM(Bo) [LM 394]	322	Bonnymount [CLARA]	178	BP 8038	228
BnM(Bl) [LM 395]	322	BoothE [DOUGAL]	40	BP 8039	167
BnM(Bl) [LM 396]	322	BoothR [ANNIE]	326	BP 8043	89
BnM(Bo) [LM 397]	322	Borsig 5913	197	BP 8069	116
BnM(Bo) [LM 398]	322	Borsig 6022	197	BPH 7911	181
BnM(Bo) [LM 399]	322	Bow [58850]	199	BPH 7912	181
BnM(Bo) [LM 400]	322	Bowman [2w-2BER]	41	BPH 7923	175
BnM(M) [LM 401]	322	Bowman [4w-4DER]	41	BPH 7980	147
BnM(M) [LM 402]	322	Bowman [4wDER]	41	Bradshaw [2-2-0BE]	282
BnM(De) [LM 403]	322	Bowman [4wPER]	41	BRCW DEL22	312
BnM(De) [LM 404]	322	Bowman [4wVBT]	41	BRCW DEL45	54
BnM(Bl) [LM 405]	322	BP 710	142	BRCW DEL46	48
BnM(Bl) [LM 406]	323	BP 1253	327	BRCW DEL47	260
BnM(Li) [LM 407]	323	BP 1255	148	BRCW DEL49	259
BnM(Bl) [LM 408]	323	BP 1412	39	BRCW DEL55	259
BnM(Bl) [LM 409]	323	BP 1414	39	BRCW DEL56	54
BnM(Bo) [LM 410]	323	BP 1416	327	BRCW DEL59	252
BnM(Bo) [LM 411]	323	BP 1417	327	BRCW DEL69	259
BnM(Dg) [LM 412]	323	BP 1524	327	BRCW DEL70	260
BnM(Dg) [LM 413]	323	BP 1827	187	BRCW DEL80	252
BnM(Dg) [LM 414]	323	BP 1989	240	BRCW DEL83	290
BnM(Dg) [LM 415]	323	BP 2028	326	BRCW DEL85	255
BnM(Bo) [LM 416]	323	BP 2038	327	BRCW DEL88	90
BnM(Bo) [LM 417]	323	BP 2464	55	BRCW DEL93	68
BnM(Bo) [LM 418]	323	BP 2605	151	BRCW DEL100	120
BnM(Bo) [LM 419]	323	BP 2734	55	BRCW DEL105	186
BnM(Bo) [LM 420]	323	BP 2817	273	BRCW DEL107	72
BnM(Bo) [LM 421]	323	BP 2825	227	BRCW DEL113	54
BnM(De) [LM 422]	323	BP 2840	239	BRCW DEL117	147
BnM(De) [LM 423]	323	BP 3496	280	BRCW DEL119	39
BnM(De) [LM 424]	323	BP 3497	280	BRCW DEL120	72
BnM(Bl) [LM 425]	323	BP 3610	327	BRCW DEL122	58
BnM(Bl) [LM 426]	323	BP 3815	327	BRCW DEL126	120
BnM(M) [LM 427]	323	BP 4231	296	BRCW DEL127	122
BnM(M) [LM 428]	323	BP 4662	327	BRCW DEL128	147
BnM(Bo) [LM 429]	323	BP 4663	327	BRCW DEL144	72
BnM(Bo) [LM 430]	323	BP 5126	327	BRCW DEL145	54
BnM(Dg) [LM 431]	323	BP 5292	277	BRCW DEL156	58
BnM(Dg) [LM 432]	323	BP 5382	327	BRCW DEL157	58
BnM(Dg) [LM 433]	323	BP 5629	295	BRCW DEL164	96
BnM(Dg) [LM 434]	323	BP 6112	295	BRCW DEL170	181
BnM(Bo) [LM 435]	323	BP 6296	327	BRCW DEL174	111
BnM(Bo) [LM 436]	323	BP 6488	155	BRCW DEL175	96
BnM(Bo) [LM 437]	323	BP 6639	148	BRCW DEL179	181
BnM(Bo) [LM 438]	323	BP 6733	295	BRCW DEL187	112
BnM(Bo) [LM 439]	323	BP 6841	152	BRCW DEL189	112
BnM(Bo) [LM 440]	323	BP 6919	66	BRCW DEL190	259
BnM(Bo) [LM441]	323	BP 6925	66	BRCW DEL194	259
BnM(Cs) [ex Germany]	306	BP 7242	295	BRCW DEL196	96
BnM(Bl) [RL 1]	324	BP 7431	66	BRCW DEL213	252

BRCW DEL229	89	BT 98	281	BT 875	55
BRCW DEL237	259	BT 121	58	BTH 1085	55
BRCW DEL244	159	BT 122	333	BTH 1131	147
BRCW DEL253	175	BT 125	68	BTH [4wWE]	257
BRCW [E3003]	55	BT 132	89	Bton [31618]	199
BRCW [ESL107}	142	BT 136	224	Bton [31806]	95
BRCW [249]	112	BT 146	120	Bton [32110]	179
BRCW [4416]	142	BT 147	120	Bton [32473]	199
BRCW [50437]	186	BT 156	154	Bton [32636]	199
BRCW [50447]	269	BT 161	144	Bton [32640]	103
BRCW [50454]	269	BT 180	90	Bton [32646]	103
BRCW [50455]	186	BT 181	169	Bton [32650]	111
BRCW [50479]	176	BT 184	229	Bton [32655]	199
BRCW [50494]	187	BT 200	224	Bton [32662]	152
BRCW [50517]	186	BT 227	290	Bton [32670]	111
BRCW [50528]	269	BT 230	159	Bton [32678]	111
BRCW [50531]	176	BT 231	155	Bton [33001]	226
BRCW [50556]	176	BT 234	89	Bton [34007]	95
BRCW [51321]	120	BT 260	333	Bton [34010]	71
BRCW [51813]	230	BT 262	154	Bton [34016]	95
BRCW [51842]	230	BT 269	49	Bton [34023]	199
BRCW [52071]	48	BT 284	83	Bton [34027]	175
BRCW [52077]	48	BT 296	154	Bton [34028]	71
BRCW [53028]	31	BT 301	61	Bton [34039]	121
BRCW [54256]	141	BT 302	34	Bton [34046]	181
BRE [720]	306	BT 315	62	Bton [34051]	226
BRE(D)/Leyland [55513]	59	BT 318	333	Bton [34053]	106
BRE(D)/Leyland [55533]	59	BT 322	159	Bton [34058]	88
BRE(D)/Leyland [RB3]	294	BT 324	144, 147	Bton [34059]	199
BRE(D)/Leyland [55508]	83	BT 342	58	Bton [34067]	140
BRE(D)/Leyland [55510]	81	BT 343	147	Bton [34070]	71
BRE(D)/Leyland [55530]	81	BT 358	58	Bton [34072]	71
BRE(D)/Leyland [55503]	80	BT 366	122	Bton [34073]	146
BRE(D)/Leyland [55528]	83	BT 398	260	Bton [34081]	155
BRE(D)/Leyland [[55523]	81	BT 419	224	Bton [34092]	239
BRE/Leyland RB002/001	308	BT 455	90	Bton [34105]	95
BRE(S) [SANS PAREIL]	76	BT 467	122	Bton [42073]	47
Bredbury	50	BT 482	205	Bton [42085]	121
BrownGM [0-4-0DM]	78	BT 483	212	Bton [80064]	199
BrownJ [D5902]	57	BT 494	225	Bton [80072]	269
BrownJ [D6353]	153	BT 496	289	Bton [80078]	71
Bruff 502	67	BT 524	212	Bton [80079]	175
Bruff 516	230	BT 532	36	Bton [80080]	57
Bruff 517	104	BT 540	85	Bton [80097]	147
Bruff 519	120	BT 549	39	Bton [80098]	186
Bruff 531	293	BT 648	155	Bton [80100]	199
Brunning	279	BT 657	90	Bton [80104]	71
BT 71	226	BT 671	49	Bton [80105]	258
BT 89	120	BT 683	120	Bton [80135]	228
BT 91	243	BT 694	90	Bton [80136]	269
BT 92	281	BT 695	154	Bton [80150]	291
BT 93	281	BT 705	212	Bton [80151]	199
BT 94	281	BT 707	229	Bton [BOXHILL]	226
BT 95	281	BT 708	83	Bton [GLADSTONE]	226
BT 96	281	BT 803	61	BuryC&K [36]	298
BT 97	281	BT 804	154	BuryC&K [No.3]	226

CE B1886B	79	CE B3162A	244	CE B3467	165		
CE B2200A	231	CE B3167	52	CE B3477A	166		
CE B2205A	166	CE B3168	222	CE B3477B	166		
CE B2205B	166	CE B3193A	165	CE B3478	166		
CE B2238A	232	CE B3198A	222	CE B3480/1A	182		
CE B2238B	232	CE B3198B	222	CE B3480/1B	183		
CE B2247A	24	CE B3198C?	165	CE B3482A	86		
CE B2259	233	CE B3201A	207	CE B3501	166		
CE B2273A	166	CE B3201B	207	CE B3502A	164		
CE B2273B	166	CE B3204A	101	CE B3502B	164		
CE B2274A	166	CE B3214A	24	CE B3517	207		
CE B2274B	166	CE B3214B	183	CE B3518	233		
CE B2293	74	CE B3224A	222	CE B3530A	222		
CE B2905	248	CE B3224B	166	CE B3530B	222		
CE B2926	52	CE B3224C	166	CE B3532	164		
CE B2935A	165	CE B3234	166	CE B3538	244		
CE B2935B	165	CE B3239	166	CE B3542	249		
CE B2944I	284	CE B3245	232	CE B3550A	248		
CE B2944T	304	CE B3246	166	CE B3550B	248		
CE B2964A	232	CE B3249B	164	CE B3555	165		
CE B2964B	232	CE B3259A	230	CE B3565	166		
CE B2972B	234	CE B3259B	230	CE B3570	164		
CE B2983	248	CE B3259C	230	CE B3591	166		
CE B2986A	166	CE B3262	222	CE B3601	248		
CE B2986B	166	CE B3266	222	CE B3602A	222		
CE B3034A	166	CE B3270A	166	CE B3602B	222		
CE B3034B	166	CE B3270B	166	CE B3603	233		
CE B3040A	207	CE B3270C	166	CE B3606A	40		
CE B3040B	207	CE B3270D	167	CE B3606B	41		
CE B3043A	234	CE B3270E	167	CE B3606C	40		
CE B3045A	166	CE B3289B	232	CE B3606D	40		
CE B3045B	166	CE B3290	164	CE B3611	53		
CE B3060	75	CE B3322A	164	CE B3615	233		
CE B3070A	133	CE B3322B	164	CE B3634A	164		
CE B3070B	133	CE B3322C	164	CE B3634B	164		
CE B3070C	133	CE B3325A	258	CE B3635	165		
CE B3070D	133	CE B3325B	248	CE B3642A	183		
CE B3077A	24	CE B3329A	133	CE B3642B	183		
CE B3084	45	CE B3329B	133	CE B3644	222		
CE B3086	238	CE B3332A	165	CE B3645A	234		
CE B3100A	230	CE B3335	234	CE B3645B	234		
CE B3100B	230	CE B3340	165	CE B3649A	222		
CE B3101A	233	CE B3352A	166	CE B3649B	222		
CE B3102	166	CE B3352B	166	CE B3656	222		
CE B3118B	165	CE B3362B	232	CE B3672 [JM93]	133		
CE B3118C	165	CE B3363A	167	CE B3672 [JM94]	133		
CE B3132A	39	CE B3363B	167	CE B3672 [JM95]	133		
CE B3132B	43	CE B3410	164	CE B3686A	24		
CE B3135B	101	CE B3411	164	CE B3686B	24		
CE B3141B	79	CE B3417	233	CE B3686C	24		
CE B3142B	232	CE B3433	165	CE B3686D	24		
CE B3155A	164	CE B3434A	232	CE B3689B	165		
CE B3156	166	CE B3434B	232	CE B3689C	165		
CE B3157A	164	CE B3439	165	CE B3707	166		
CE B3157B	164	CE B3445	167	CE B3723	232		
CE B3161	166	CE B3464C	248	CE B3732	234		

CE B3766A	183	CE B4427A	131, 132	Cockerill 1626	34
CE B3766B	183	CE B4427B	131, 132	Cockerill 2525	154
CE B3766C	183	CE B4427C	131, 132	Cockerill 2945	119
CE B3766D	183	CE B4427D	131, 132	Cockerill 3083	188
CE B3773A	222	CE B4444	233	Cockerill 3267	266
CE B3782 [LM13]	133	CE B4447	233	ColebySim [WENDY]	81
CE B3782 [LM15]	133	CE [4wDH]	24	Consett [10]	163
CE B3786A	133	CE [4wBE]	24	Corpet 493	158
CE B3786B	133	CE [4wBE]	24	Couillet 1140	197
CE B3787	182	CE [4wBE]	42	Couillet 1209	197
CE B3791	133	CE [4wBE]	75	Couillet 1318	197
CE B3794	234	CE [4wBE]	121	Cowlairs [62469]	258
CE B3797	232	CE [4wBE]	145	Cowlairs [68095]	258
CE B3799	133	CE [4wBE]	145	CPM 1731.01	157
CE B3800A	165	CE [4wBE]	145	CPM 1731.02UK	146
CE B3800B	165	CE [4wBE]	145	CravenEA [111]	128
CE B3800C	165	CE [4wBE]	146	CravenJ	189
CE B3804 [LM10]	133	CE [4wBE]	304	Cravens [3906]	140
CE B3804 [LM12]	133	CE [4wBEF]	113	Cravens [3907]	140
CE B3804 [LM14]	133	CE [4w-4wBEF]	222	Cravens [51485]	148
CE B3825	24	CE [4w-4wBEF]	234	Cravens [62174]	257
CE B3830B	232	CE [4]	165	Cravens [L 132]	138
CE B3832A	222	CE [5]	183	Cravens [L 133]	138
CE B3850	165	CE [6]	183	Crewe [HARDWICKE]	226
CE B3864A	222	CE [P7]	165	Crewe [PET]	227
CE B3864B	234	CE [PL 1]	165	Crewe [1439]	76
CE B3875	222	CE [PL 2]	165	Crewe [1868]	143
CE B3903	24	CE [SP03]	24	Crewe [3020]	77
CE B3906/2	234	CE [SP36]	24	Crewe [41241]	239
CE B3942	234	CE [SP86]	24	Crewe [41298]	31
CE B3963	222	CE [T/E 300]	230	Crewe [41312]	95
CE B4000	234	Chance 64-5031-24	261	Crewe [41313]	103
CE B4010A	24	Chance 73 5097-24	225	Crewe [42765]	147
CE B4010B	24	Chance 76 50141 24	225	Crewe [42859]	127
CE B4023	223	Chance 76-50145-24	85	Crewe [42968]	175
CE B4057B	24	Chance 78-50157-24	124	Crewe [43013]	333
CE B4066RF	101	Chance 79 50166 24	90	Crewe [43014]	333
CE B4071.4	134	Chance 79.50167.24	194	Crewe [43062]	333
CE B4075.1	24	Chaplin 2368	254	Crewe [43089]	333
CE B4075.2	24	Chrz 2871	112	Crewe [44123]	88
CE B4162	223	Chrz 2944	112	Crewe [44767]	161
CE B4174A	134	Chrz 2959	62	Crewe [44871]	147
CE B4174B	134	Chrz 3135	112	Crewe [44901]	291
CE B4246A	113	Chrz 3138	128	Crewe [45000]	226
CE B4246B	113	Chrz 3459	48	Crewe [45690]	147
CE B4299	233	Chrz 3506	117	Crewe [45699]	116
CE B4308	207	Chrz 4015	88	Crewe [46201]	147
CE B4314A	63	Chrz 5374	158	Crewe [46203]	57
CE B4314B	63	Chrz 5485	34	Crewe [46229]	226
CE B4338	207	Civil No.1	59	Crewe [46233]	57
CE B4349	223	Clarkson 4669	48	Crewe [46235]	212
CE B4355	166	ClayCross [4wDM]	129	Crewe [46428]	147
CE B4381A	113	ClayCross [LIZZIE]	62	Crewe [46441]	115
CE B4381B	113	CM 11003	272	Crewe [46443]	175
CE B4388	222	Coalbrookdale [0-4-0ST]	174	Crewe [46447]	31
CE B4423	166	Cockerill 1625	242	Crewe [46464]	252

Crewe [48151]	116	Crewe [D3904]	205	Dar [D3699]	237
Crewe [48173]	186	Crewe [D3911]	221	Dar [D3723]	228
Crewe [48305]	121	Crewe [D3918]	237	Dar [D4036]	37
Crewe [49395]	228	Crewe [D5032]	228	Dar [D4037]	205
Crewe [58926]	239	Crewe [D5054]	147	Dar [D4038]	171, 237
Crewe [70000]	36	Crewe [D5061]	228	Dar [D4039]	237
Crewe [70013]	121	Crewe [D5081]	90	Dar [D4041]	183
Crewe [71000]	147	Crewe [41001]	227	Dar [D4042]	237
Crewe [92134]	36	Crewe [43013]	333	Dar [D4067]	122
Crewe [92240]	199	Crewe [43014]	333	Dar [D4092]	54
Crewe [92245]	291	Crewe [43062]	333	Dar [D4158]	205
Crewe [D 53]	57	Crewe [43089]	333	Dar [D4166]	237, 263
Crewe [D 67]	158	Crewe [87001]	227	Dar [D4167]	63
Crewe [D 86]	54	Crewe [87031]	212	Dar [D4173]	36
Crewe [D 99]	147	Crewe [87035]	37	Dar [D4174]	144, 147
Crewe [D 100]	54	Crewe [89001]	55	Dar [D4177]	177
Crewe [D 120]	57	CurwenD [19]	276	Dar [D5185]	122
Crewe [D 123]	122	CurwenD [4-4-2]	128	Dar [D7585]	259
Crewe [D 135]	90			Dar [D7594]	111
Crewe [D1041]	147			Dar [12131]	155
Crewe [D1048]	58	**D**		Darlington 2195	75
Crewe [D1062]	175	D 708	226	DB 2	47
Crewe [D1107]	186	D 2178	327	DB 3	48
Crewe [D1566]	269	D 2890	97	DB 4	48
Crewe [D1606]	60	D 3704	49	DC 1495	307
Crewe [D1619]	58	D 4101	187	DC 1519	296
Crewe [D1643]	167	Dar [1463]	76	DC 1895	84
Crewe [D1656]	116	Dar [43106]	175	DC 2047	227
Crewe [D1661]	181	Dar [61994]	258	DC 2157	187
Crewe [D1662]	206	Dar [62712]	258	DC 2164	228
Crewe [D1842]	186	Dar [63395]	228	DC 2176	200
Crewe [D1855]	159	Dar [63460]	76	DC 2177	209
Crewe [D1969]	54	Dar [65894]	77	DC 2180	85
Crewe [D1970]	259	Dar [68088]	155	DC 2181	47
Crewe [D1971]	34	Dar [69023]	77	DC 2184	236
Crewe [D1994]	167	Dar [78018]	76	DC 2251	201
Crewe [D3429]	176	Dar [78019]	121	DC 2252	85
Crewe [D3575]	83	Dar [78022]	239	DC 2269	64
Crewe [D3586]	175	Dar [78059]	199	DC 2271	325
Crewe [D3587]	234	Dar [D3067]	224	DC 2273	265
Crewe [D3588]	89	Dar [D3074]	170	DC 2274	201
Crewe [D3591]	71	Dar [D3079]	226	DC 2400	224
Crewe [D3735]	245	Dar [D3232]	147	DC 2482	228
Crewe [D3738]	234	Dar [D3236]	52, 199	DC 2486	181
Crewe [D3739]	177	Dar [D3308]	89	DC 2503	112
Crewe [D3740]	131, 237	Dar [D3336]	240	DC 2552	60
Crewe [D3755]	221, 237	Dar [D3452]	39	DC 2566	84
Crewe [D3757]	58	Dar [D3460]	210, 237	DC 2567	205
Crewe [D3759]	144	Dar [D3462]	181	DC 2568	173
Crewe [D3761]	144	Dar [D3476]	83	DC 2573	99
Crewe [D3835]	205	Dar [D3489]	112	DC 2574	90
Crewe [D3836]	234	Dar [D3666]	68	DC 2577	120
Crewe [D3892]	235	Dar [D3668]	112	DC 2578	68
Crewe [D3896]	205	Dar [D3673]	287	DC 2583	156
Crewe [D3898]	245	Dar [D3679]	205	DC 2589	55
Crewe [D3902]	89	Dar [D3689]	232	DC 2591	112

DC 2592	76	Derby [D3059]	252	Derby [D3998]	36
DC 2615	181	Derby [D3101]	122	Derby [D4002]	235
DC 2616	60	Derby [D3167]	129	Derby [D5207]	155
DC 2656	84	Derby [D3174]	111	Derby [D5209]	240
DC 2657	155	Derby [D3180]	167	Derby [D5217]	80
DC 2661	60	Derby [D3190]	170	Derby [D5222]	252
DC 2679	31	Derby [D3201]	175	Derby [D5233]	252
DC 2683	54	Derby [D3255]	83	Derby [D7523]	181
DC 2691	120	Derby [D3261]	215	Derby [D7535]	67
DC 2705	54	Derby [D3265]	269	Derby [D7541]	228
DC 2706	85	Derby [D3272]	151	Derby [D7612]	68
DC 2715	186	Derby [D3290]	37	Derby [D7615]	122
DC 2718	61	Derby [D3358]	96	Derby [D7663]	269
DDak 521	96	Derby [D3366]	287	Derby [D7671]	58
DDak 669	179	Derby [D3378]	237	Derby [D7672]	186
Dec 246	107	Derby [D3390]	38	Derby [7120]	48
Dec 917	255	Derby [D3401]	58, 234	Derby [12049]	96
Dec 1027	278	Derby [D3415]	205	Derby [12052[	252
Dec 1126	203	Derby [D3503]	144	Derby [12061]	61
Dec 1735	25	Derby [D3513]	38	Derby [12077]	58
DeDietrich 89134	119	Derby [D3526]	83	Derby [12082]	246
Derby [4]	295	Derby [D3538]	221, 237	Derby [12083]	120
Derby [158A]	57	Derby [D3551]	71	Derby [12088]	162
Derby [673]	226	Derby [D3556]	83	Derby [12093]	252
Derby [41000]	226	Derby [D3558]	259	Derby [12099]	175
Derby [41708]	54	Derby [D3559]	39	Derby [49002]	37
Derby [42500]	226	Derby [D3560]	144	Derby [49006]	77
Derby [43924]	239	Derby [D3562]	246	Derby [APT-E]	77
Derby [44027]	57	Derby [D3763]	177, 234	DerbyC&W [8097]	293
Derby [44422]	181	Derby [D3765]	151	DerbyC&W [99]	146
Derby [44806]	268	Derby [D3767]	220	DerbyC&W [3335]	51
Derby [45491]	57	Derby [D3769]	51	DerbyC&W [28361]	227
Derby [46100]	140	Derby [D3771]	171	DerbyC&W [28690]	208
Derby [73050]	34	Derby [D3780]	237, 263	DerbyC&W [50019]	58
Derby [73082]	199	Derby [D3782]	234	DerbyC&W [50599]	84
Derby [73096]	95	Derby [D3789]	237, 282	DerbyC&W [50619]	89
Derby [73129]	57	Derby [D3795]	149	DerbyC&W [50628]	255
Derby [80002]	239	Derby [D3796]	30	DerbyC&W [50632]	290
Derby [D 4]	57	Derby [D3798]	154	DerbyC&W [50645]	168
Derby [D 8]	60	Derby [D3802]	175	DerbyC&W [50926]	168
Derby [D 14]	120	Derby [D3937]	175	DerbyC&W [50928]	240
Derby [D 22]	96	Derby [D3940]	155	DerbyC&W [50933]	175
Derby [D 40]	57	Derby [D3941]	224	DerbyC&W [50971]	111
Derby [D147]	269	Derby [D3942]	220	DerbyC&W [50980]	39
Derby [D172]	36	Derby [D3948]	141	DerbyC&W [51131]	120
Derby [D182]	57	Derby [D3953]	145, 235	DerbyC&W [51134]	285
Derby [D3000]	128	Derby [D3956]	237	DerbyC&W [51135]	285
Derby [D3002]	67	Derby [D3975]	220	DerbyC&W [51138]	167
Derby [D3014]	67	Derby [D3977]	237	DerbyC&W [51147]	285
Derby [D3018]	169	Derby [D3978]	37	DerbyC&W [51148]	285
Derby [D3019]	173	Derby [D3981]	205	DerbyC&W [51151]	167
Derby [D3022]	175	Derby [D3986]	126	DerbyC&W [51562]	227
Derby [D3023]	61	Derby [D3991]	145	DerbyC&W [51565]	240
Derby [D3029]	212	Derby [D3993]	120	DerbyC&W [51566]	89
Derby [D3030]	170	Derby [D3994]	177	DerbyC&W [51567]	58
Derby [D3044]	177	Derby [D3995]	205	DerbyC&W [51568]	255

DerbyC&W [51571]	111	(R2.001)	255	Don [D3662]	183
DerbyC&W [51572]	230	DerbyC&W/Leyland		Don [D3685]	237, 281
DerbyC&W [51592]	68	(R2.002)	255	Don [56040]	154
DerbyC&W [51604]	68	DerbyC&W/Leyland		Don [56097]	167
DerbyC&W [51610]	58	RB004	177	Don [56098]	120
DerbyC&W [51616]	122	Derby C&W[5]	171	Don [58001]	54
DerbyC&W [51618]	269	DeW [CHALONER]	25	Don [E3061]	55
DerbyC&W [51622]	122	DeW [GELLI]	28	Don [E3136]	333
DerbyC&W [51655]	288	DeW [G HENRY]	273	Don [E3137]	212
DerbyC&W [51663]	181	DeW [KATHLEEN]	279	Don [E5001]	77
DerbyC&W [51669]	112	DeW [LLANFAIR]	277	Don [HE 7197]	295
DerbyC&W [51677]	288	DeW [PENMAEN]	264	Don [HE 7198]	296
DerbyC&W [51849]	112	DeW [PENYFFRYN]	288	Don L44	138
DerbyC&W [51852]	181	DeW [WATKIN]	273	Don L45	138
DerbyC&W [51859]	181	Diema 1600	27	Don L46	138
DerbyC&W [51880]	181	Diema 2242	314	Don L47	138
DerbyC&W [51886]	31	Diema 2639	314	Don L48	138
DerbyC&W [51887]	181	Diema 2872	314	Don L49	138
DerbyC&W [51899]	31	Diema 3543	102	Don L50	138
DerbyC&W [51907]	269	Diema 4270	280	Don L51	138
DerbyC&W [51909]	88	DK [4wDE]	198	Don L52	138
DerbyC&W [51914]	89	DM 2	279	Don L53	138
DerbyC&W [51919]	288	Dodman [GAZELLE]	107	Don L54	138
DerbyC&W [51922]	227	Don [No.1]	226	Donelli 163	251
DerbyC&W [51933]	72	Don [251]	152	Donelli 190/80	126
DerbyC&W [51935]	176	Don [990]	152	Donelli [VMT850]	293
DerbyC&W [51937]	58	Don [48518]	269	Dorothea [ELEPHANT]	77
DerbyC&W [51941]	176	Don [60007]	228	Dotto [4-6wRE]	217
DerbyC&W [51942]	290	Don [60009]	36	Dowty [4wPM]	99
DerbyC&W [51947]	39	Don [60019]	95	DP 21104	48
DerbyC&W [51950]	90	Don [60022]	226	DP 21499	110
DerbyC&W [51990]	260	Don [60103]	226	DP 21500	110
DerbyC&W [51993]	224	Don [60532]	54	DP 22070	110
DerbyC&W [52005]	224	Don [60800]	77	DP 22071	110
DerbyC&W [52006]	88	Don [73156]	121	DP 22072	110
DerbyC&W [52008]	260	Don [D2046]	67	DP 22073	110
DerbyC&W [52012]	224	Don [D2051]	155	DP 22074	110
DerbyC&W [52025]	88	Don [D2059]	103	Dtz 10050	192
DerbyC&W [52029]	283	Don [D2062]	147	Dtz 10248	59
DerbyC&W [52030]	260	Don [D2063]	155	Dtz 19531	195
DerbyC&W [52031]	224	Don [D2066]	54	Dtz 56118	312
DerbyC&W [52044]	290	Don [D2069]	90	Dtz 57120	307
DerbyC&W [52048]	288	Don [D2072}	48	Dtz 57121	313
DerbyC&W [52053]	255	Don [D2073]	36	Dtz 57122	306
DerbyC&W [52054]	39	Don [D2078]	163	Dtz 57123	319
DerbyC&W [52060]	168	Don [D2079]	225	Dtz 57125	319
DerbyC&W [52062]	90	Don [D2081]	85	Dtz 57127	313
DerbyC&W [53064]	176	Don [D2084]	62	Dtz 57128	319
DerbyC&W [55929]	58	Don [D2089]	85	Dtz 57129	319
DerbyC&W [55966]	58	Don [D2090]	77	Dtz 57130	319
DerbyC&W [55976]	58	Don [D2094]	173	Dtz 57131	319
DerbyC&W [79018]	58	Don [D2099]	60	Dtz 57132	306
DerbyC&W [79900]	63	Don [D2112]	127	Dtz 57133	307
DerbyC&W [79998]	257	Don [D2113]	60	Dtz 57134	319
DerbyC&W [No.4]	51	Don [D2399]	85	Dtz 57135	313
DerbyC&W/Leyland		Don [D3654]	290	Dtz 57136	319

Dtz 57138	306	EE 2150	237	EE 3003	122
Dtz 57139	311	EE 2160	77	EE 3007	55
Dtz 57225	295	EE 2300	123	EE 3011	55
Dtz 57226	295	EE 2301	165	EE 3013	55
Dtz 57227	312	EE 2345	240	EE 3016	68
Dtz 57229	295	EE 2347	77	EE 3024	68
Dtz 57834	320	EE 2348	58, 62	EE 3025	55
Dtz 57835	311	EE 2354	167	EE 3027	55
Dtz 57836	313	EE 2363	205	EE 3067	186
Dtz 57837	313	EE 2367	228	EE 3068	34
Dtz 57838	320	EE 2416	123	EE 3081	147
Dtz 57839	306	EE 2417	149	EE 3091	147
Dtz 57840	313	EE 2474	53	EE 3147	288
Dtz 57841	306	EE 2476	75	EE 3223	186
Dtz 57842	320	EE 2519	49	EE 3226	252
Dtz 57843	306	EE 2521	165	EE 3228	90
Dundalk 16	296	EE 2522	165	EE 3229	333
Dundalk 42	295	EE 2527	53	EE 3237	116
DunEW G4464	306	EE 2668	57	EE 3238	147
DunEW LM361	306	EE 2669	54	EE 3245	169
DunEW LM363	322	EE 2726	34	EE 3268	159
DunEW LM365	322	EE 2742	259	EE 3281	120
DunEW LM367	322	EE 2753	240	EE 3317	39
DunEW LM368	311	EE 2754	205	EE 3321	49
DunEW [LM 354]	322	EE 2757	206	EE 3325	269
DunEW [LM 355]	322	EE 2763	54	EE 3327	61
DunEW [LM 356]	313	EE 2770	167	EE 3335	134
DunEW [LM 357]	322	EE 2848	79	EE 3337	54
DunEW [LM 358]	322	EE 2853	212	EE 3343	116
DunEW [LM 359]	322	EE 2863	228	EE 3347	49
DunEW [LM 360]	322	EE 2866	77	EE 3353	259
DunEW [LM 364]	322	EE 2872	167	EE 3356	333
DunEW [LM 366]	326	EE 2888	259	EE 3366	61
DunEW [LM 370]	322	EE 2895	155	EE 3368	58
DunEW [LM 371]	322	EE 2900	68	EE 3376	122
DunEW [LM 372]	322	EE 2905	56	EE 3379	54
DunEW [LM 373]	326	EE 2907	227	EE 3384	175
DunEW S4484	306	EE 2914	56	EE 3385	67
		EE 2920	56	EE 3392	116
E		EE 2921	61	EE 3393	90
EB 37	78	EE 2924	56	EE 3394	290
EB 48?	115	EE 2941	55	EE 3395	54
EB 53	242	EE 2962	124	EE 3405	169
EBW [GWR 262]	240	EE 2963	205	EE 3408	116
Eclipse [4wDM]	225	EE 2965	212	EE 3413	120
Eddy Knowell [4wDM]	216	EE 2966	205	EE 3482	333
Eddy Knowell [4wDMR]	216	EE 2969	206	EE 3491	206
EdwardsE&J	264	EE 2972	124	EE 3497	269
EE 1188	187	EE 2975	154	EE 3505	116
EE 1378	148	EE 2978	206	EE 3507	46
EE 2083	165	EE 2987	206	EE 3511	112
EE 2086	123	EE 2989	206	EE 3512	122
EE 2122	221, 237	EE 2993	147	EE 3523	89
EE 2124	207	EE 2994	206	EE 3524	212
EE 2129	221, 237	EE 2998	54	EE 3531	147
EE 2146	206, 237	EE 3002	54	EE 3535	54

EE 3539	186	EEDK 652	134	EEDK 2007	77
EE 3547	80	EEDK 702	134	EEDK 2098	115
EE 3565	186	EEDK 703	134	EES 8199	221
EE 3569	89	EEDK 704	134	EES 8314	134
EE 3573	120	EEDK 717	55	EES 8390	54
EE 3578	167	EEDK 752	135	EES 8396	116
EE 3582	120	EEDK 753	135	EES 8409	61
EE 3584	154	EEDK 755	135	EES 8411	58
EE 3586	288	EEDK 756	135	EES 8419	122
EE 3595	87	EEDK 759	136	EEV D 816	39
EE 3597	290	EEDK 760	169	EEV D 820	49
EE 3598	90	EEDK 761	41	EEV D 824	269
EE 3599	288	EEDK 762	136	EEV D 826	61
EE 3603	55	EEDK 763	136	EEV D 833	49
EE 3608	90	EEDK 788	115	EEV D 839	259
EE 3610	207	EEDK 793	136	EEV D 842	333
EE 3614	269	EEDK 795	136	EEV D 845	54
EE 3625	167	EEDK 797	136	EEV D 850	175
EE 3637	120	EEDK 799	136	EEV D 851	67
EE 3639	51	EEDK 802	136	EEV D 858	116
EE 3640	49	EEDK 803	32	EEV D 859	90
EE 3648	212	EEDK 804	136	EEV D 860	290
EE 3669	72	EEDK 805	136	EEV D 861	54
EE 3670	235	EEDK 806	41	EEV D 863	169
EE 3678	39	EEDK 807	82, 215	EEV D 866	116
EE 3685	58	EEDK 808	203	EEV D 871	120
EE 3686	58	EEDK 809	82	EEV D 908	253
EE 3695	48	EEDK 810	136	EEV D 917	247
EE 3696	206	EEDK 811	136	EEV D 928	269
EE 3706	55	EEDK 812	169	EEV D 936	116
EE 3713	80	EEDK 813	136	EEV D 938	46
EE 3715	143	EEDK 814	136	EEV D 942	112
EE 3717	206	EEDK 815	136	EEV D 943	122
EE 3718	80	EEDK 816	136	EEV D 952	89
EE 3719	112	EEDK 817	136	EEV D 953	212
EE 3770	182	EEDK 818	136	EEV D 960	147
EE 3771	68	EEDK 819	136	EEV D 964	54
EE 3777	57	EEDK 820	136	EEV D 968	186
EE 3778	37	EEDK 821	136	EEV D 976	80
EE 3785	147	EEDK 822	136	EEV D 994	186
EE 3787	212	EEDK 824	136	EEV D 998	288
EE 3789	154	EEDK 826	136	EEV D1002	55
EE 3791	212	EEDK 827	136	EEV D1009	207
EE 3796	171	EEDK 830	136	EEV D1007	90
EE 3797	228	EEDK 874	227	EEV D1013	269
EE 3799	60	EEDK 905	208	EEV D1024	167
EE 3800	60	EEDK 925	136	EEV D1036	120
EE 3801	37	EEDK 928	136	EEV D1038	51
EE 3803	212	EEDK 931	136	EEV D1039	49
EE 3805	175	EEDK 932	136	EEV D1047	212
EE 3812	39	EEDK 1130	188	EEV D1049	121
EE 3814	175	EEDK 1131	259	EEV D1064	72
EE 3819	212	EEDK 1151	142	EEV D1065	235
EE/Elh [11179]	227	EEDK 1195	228	EEV D1073	39
EE/Elh [S11187]	142	EEDK 1553	228	EEV D1080	58
EEDK 601	134	EEDK 1901	269	EEV D1081	58

EEV D1090	48	EEV E375	143	Elh [14573]	208
EEV D1091	206	EEV E377	206	Elh [61736]	290
EEV D1101	55	EEV E378	80	Elh [61737]	290
EEV D1120	180	EEV E379	112	Elh [65321]	208
EEV D1122	146	EEV 3768	165	Elh [65373]	108
EEV D1123	34	EEV 3870	80	Emmeln [PERCY}	187
EEV D1124	132	EEV 3946	286	Emmeln 081309	187
EEV D1137	184, 231	EEV 3947	290	ESR 295	92
EEV D1141	182	EEV 3954	286	ESR 300	57
EEV D1142	68	EEV 3987	144	ESR 301	32
EEV D1148	57	EEV 3989	282	ESR 311	118
EEV D1149	37	EEV 3994	219, 238	ESR 312	216
EEV D1156	147	EEV 3998	231	ESR 317	299
EEV D1158	212	EEV 4003	74	ESR 323	214
EEV D1160	154	EEV 5352	206	EVM [32521]	108
EEV D1162	212	Eiv de Brieve 001URS	333	EVRA [2w-2DER]	63
EEV D1167	171	EK [1212]	80		
EEV D1168	228	Electro [56022]	80	**F**	
EEV D1170	60	Electro [56006]	54		
EEV D1171	60	Electro [56009]	119	Fairbourne No.4	128
EEV D1172	37	Elh [30499]	147	Fairmont 252180	255
EEV D1174	212	Elh [30506]	95	Fairmont [CAR No.2]	255
EEV D1176	175	Elh [30541]	198	Fairmont 244095	255
EEV D1183	39	Elh [30825]	228	FE 265	197
EEV D1185	175	Elh [30828]	95	FE 266	197
EEV D1190	212	Elh [30830]	228	Ferndale 21	52
EEV D1193	255	Elh [30841]	228	FFP [FIRE FLY]	170
EEV D1194	231	Elh [30847]	198	FH 1568	26
EEV D1197	108	Elh [30850]	226	FH 1747	65
EEV D1198	282	Elh [30925]	226	FH 1767	27
EEV D1199	104	Elh [30926]	228	FH 1776?	189
EEV D1200	104	Elh [30928]	198	FH 1777	117
EEV D1201	62	Elh [34101]	228	FH 1830	180
EEV D1202	237	Elh [35005]	95	FH 1881	62
EEV D1226	290	Elh [35006]	89	FH 1887	117
EEV D1227	106	Elh [35009]	146	FH 1891	185
EEV D1228	55	Elh [35010]	83	FH 1896	41
EEV D1230	63	Elh [35011]	181	FH 1980	203
EEV D1231	206	Elh [35018]	70	FH 2014	305
EEV D1232	247	Elh [35022]	140	FH 2025	65
EEV D1233	206	Elh [35025]	106	FH 2027	327
EEV D1248	286	Elh [35027]	140	FH 2054	72
EEV D1249	290	Elh [35028]	143	FH 2102	31
EEV D1266	286	Elh [35029]	226	FH 2163	29
EEV E328	333	Elh [E6001]	89	FH 2196	191
EEV E337	206	Elh [E6002]	89	FH 2201	65
EEV E339	89	Elh [E6003]	122	FH 2306	192
EEV E343	120	Elh [E6005]	175	FH 2325	144
EEV E348	167	Elh [E6006]	175	FH 2514	26
EEV E352	120	Elh [10656]	77	FH 2528	196
EEV E354	154	Elh [11161]	108	FH 2544	196
EEV E356	288	Elh [11201]	108	FH 2555	117
EEV E365	87	Elh [12795]	208	FH 2586	192
EEV E367	290	Elh [12796]	208	FH 2631	27
EEV E368	90	Elh [13003]	106	FH 2834	27
EEV E373	80	Elh [13004]	159	FH 2893	69

FH 2895	208	FJ 63	276	GB 2543	241
FH 2896	34	FJ 158	199	GB 2690	286
FH 3057	173	FJ 172L	203	GB 2691	286
FH 3068	307	FJ 173L	196	GB 2782	48
FH 3116	108	Flor 16626	34	GB 2848	242
FH 3147	83	FMB 001	128	GB 2920	213
FH 3270	170	FMB 002	71	GB 2960	41
FH 3271	31	Ford [89MH3147]	309	GB 3545	211
FH 3281	67	Ford [90MH3006]	314	GB 3546	101
FH 3294?	86	Ford [94MH585]	309	GB 3547	97
FH 3307	267	FosterRastrick]	226	GB 3825	101
FH 3317	91	FoxA [AMOS]	93	GB 6061	62
FH 3424	62	FRCo [BUSTA]	278	GB 6081	223
FH 3438	148	FRCo [CRICCIETH]	267	GB 6082	223
FH 3444	302	FRCo [DAVID]	266	GB 6083	223
FH 3446	307	FRCo [EARL OF]	266	GB 6099	86
FH 3447	307	FRCo [LIVINGSTONE	266	GB 6121	222
FH 3449	296	FRCo [No.10]	266	GB 6132	153
FH 3465	50	FRCo [TALIESIN]	266	GB 6135	223
FH 3509	295	Frenze [IVOR]	153	GB 6136	223
FH 3541	173	Freud 73	25	GB 420099	223
FH 3582	26	FRgroup4 [ROCKET]	85	GB 420172	41
FH 3627?	203	Frichs 397	100	GB 420253	189
FH 3658	200	Frichs 360	34	GB 420355/1	219
FH 3687	277	Frichs 403	127	GB 420355/2	219
FH 3716	79	Frichs 415	35	GB 420383/1	125
FH 3719	294	FRSociety	267	GB 420383/2	125
FH 3738	112	Funkey [CASTELL]	277	GB 420408	219
FH 3747	252	Funkey [D4]	189	GB 420435	223
FH 3756	46	Funkey [D5]	189	GB 420452	243
FH 3765	31	Funkey [VALE OF -]	267	GB 420461/ 2	134
FH 3776	41	FW 242	29	GB 420461/ 3	134
FH 3777	112	FW 358	85	GB 420461/ 4	134
FH 3787	94	FW 410	285	GB 420461/ 5	134
FH 3817	32			GB 420461/ 6	134
FH 3831	277	**G**		GB 420461/ 7	134
FH 3832	64	G&S [5751]	216	GB 420461/ 8	135
FH 3890	289	G&S [BROGAN]	150	GB 420461/ 9	135
FH 3892	208	G&S [No.4]	129	GB 420461/10	135
FH 3894	32	Gartell 1001	96	GB 420461/11	135
FH 3906	99	Gartell [AMANDA]	179	GB 420461/12	135
FH 3916	117	Gartell [AXE]	179	GB 420461/13	135
FH 3922	75	GB 1210	241	GB 420461/14	135
FH 3947	89	GB 1325	241	GB 420461/15	135
FH 3951	282	GB 1326	241	GB 420461/16	135
FH 3953	173	GB 1445	60	GB 420461/17	135
FH 3958	49	GB 1570	158	GB 420461/18	135
FH 3967	159	GB 1698	250	GB 420461/19	135
FH 3982	156	GB 1840	117	GB 420461/20	135
FH 3983	96	GB 2000	115	GB 420461/21	82
FH 4006	289	GB 2180	286	GB 420461/23	135
FH 4008	62	GB 2345	41	GB 420461/24	135
FH [BLUEBELL]	26	GB 2382	43	GB 420461/25	135
Fiat [90 MH 4885]	309	GB 2493	62	GB 420461/26	135
Fisons [No.05]	102	GB 2508	79	GB 420461/27	135
FJ 42	276	GB 2509	79	GB 420461/28	135

HAB 6063	281	HC 1309	242	HC DM 647	149
HAB 6385	132	HC 1334	31	HC DM 655	244
HAB 6432	184	HC 1366	78	HC DM 664	241
HAB 6459	51	HC 1369	242	HC DM 686	203
HAB 6478	44	HC 1435	239	HC D 697	159
HAB 6479	44	HC 1450	224	HC D 707	156
HAB 6480	44	HC 1464	88	HC DM 717	233
HAB 6578	193	HC 1539	34	HC DM 719	297
HAB 6586	282	HC 1544	215	HC DM 724	165
HAB 6694	247	HC 1604	194	HC DM 725	165
HAB 6767	231	HC 1631	225	HC DM 726	165
HAB 6768	184, 219	HC 1632	64	HC DM 727	165
HAB 6769	184, 219	HC 1643	66	HC DM 729	165
HAB 6941	197	HC 1661	114	HC DM 733	241
Hackworth [BRADYLL]	76	HC 1672	78	HC DM 739	92
Hackworth [SANS PAREIL]	76	HC 1682	167	HC DM 746	244
HallT 1859401	129	HC 1689	236	HC DM 749	241
Hano 8282	97	HC 1700	154	HC DM 750	117
Hano 8310	94	HC 1704	240	HC DM 752	50
Hano 10629	66	HC 1709	224	HC D 761	240
Hano 10634	197	HC 1731	269	HC DM 771	167
Harbin 221	266	HC 1742	31	HC DM 772	167
HardyK 01	168	HC 1752	121	HC DM 773	167
HardyK 02	168	HC 1776	224	HC DM 781	149
HardyK E1	127	HC 1782	240	HC DM 786	233
HardyK E3	168	HC 1800	34	HC DM 797	233
Hart 2110	242	HC 1821	224	HC DM 798	233
HartlepoolBSC [1]	219	HC 1822	185	HC DM 799	233
HartlepoolBSC [2]	219	HC 1823	78	HC DM 801	92
Haydock C	187	HC 1857	180	HC DM 803	241
HaylockJ [0-4-2T]	71	HC 1864	65	HC DM 804	149
Hayne [4w-4BE]	118	HC 1882	242	HC DM 819	49
Hayne [GORAM]	118	HC 1884	62	HC DM 840	150
Hayne [VINCENT]	275	HC 1885	114	HC DM 841	92
HB D1418	189	HC 1888	240	HC DM 842	75
HB D1419	37	HC [DS 75]	243	HC D 843	173
HC 402	240	HC D 557	241	HC DM 924	92
HC 431	185	HC D 558	192	HC DM 929	150
HC 526	273	HC D 564	278	HC DM 932	233
HC 544	288	HC D 565	227	HC DM 933	150
HC 555	175	HC D 570	227	HC DM 936	234
HC 573	227	HC D 571	241	HC DM 970	149
HC 633	241	HC D 573	227	HC DM 971	167
HC 639	198	HC D 577	242	HC DM 980	233
HC 640	198	HC D 578	115	HC DM 981	233
HC 679	240	HC D 579	115	HC DM 986	233
HC 680	147	HC D 582	227	HC DM1002	189
HC 750	119	HC D 586	115	HC DM1011	167
HC 895	256	HC D 611	59	HC D1012	211
HC 1026	32	HC D 612	59	HC D1031	116
HC 1152	295	HC D 615	290	HC D1037	224
HC 1208	223	HC D 625	241	HC DM1058	149
HC 1223	273	HC D 628	115	HC DM1067	79
HC 1238	191	HC D 629	116	HC DM1108	234
HC 1243	162	HC D 631	243	HC D1075	117
HC 1308	34	HC DM 634	241	HC D1076	148

HC DM1108	233	HE 317	40	HE 1954	115
HC D1114	58	HE 409	40	HE 1963	117
HC DM1117	59	HE 469	85	HE 1974	191
HC DM1119	80	HE 493	275	HE 1982	155
HC DM1120	149	HE 541	273	HE 2008	241
HC D1121	58	HE 542	141	HE 2017	178
HC D1153	85	HE 554	267	HE 2019	189
HC DM1164	150	HE 555	303	HE 2022	265
HC DM1169	49	HE 589	267	HE 2024	277
HC DM1170	80	HE 590	267	HE 2067	31
HC D1171	88	HE 605	278	HE 2075	91
HC DM1173	149	HE 606	279	HE 2087	159
HC D1171	88	HE 638	202	HE 2145	89
HC D1186	288	HE 652	278	HE 2176	27
HC D1199	61	HE 671	153	HE 2198	114
HC D1202	240	HE 678	114	HE 2207	266
HC DM1238	123	HE 679	40	HE 2208	203
HC DM1247	49	HE 680	264	HE 2209	254
HC DM1270	149	HE 684	241	HE 2239	307
HC DM1274	77	HE 686	175	HE 2242?	294
HC DM1287	167	HE 705	156	HE 2243	255
HC DM1309	165	HE 707	267	HE 2248	49
HC DM1314	289	HE 763	41	HE 2250	294
HC DM1332	167	HE 779	264	HE 2251	280
HC D1341	119	HE 780	264	HE 2252	294
HC D1344	128	HE 822	264	HE 2254	49
HC D1345	243	HE 823	117	HE 2263	98
HC DM1352	149	HE 827	288	HE 2264	294
HC DM1356	244	HE 849	275	HE 2265	98
HC DM1366	107	HE 855	273	HE 2266	178
HC DM1368	241	HE 873	273	HE 2267	49
HC D1373	179	HE 901	277	HE 2270	250
HC D1377	213	HE 920	196	HE 2280	305
HC D1387	290	HE 921	123	HE 2290	64
HC D1388	63	HE 994	153	HE 2304	307
HC DM1393	117	HE 996	243	HE 2387	242
HC D1396	132	HE 1215	191	HE 2389	47
HC DM1413	149	HE 1429	107	HE 2390	241
HC DM1414	149	HE 1430	275	HE 2398	178
HC DM1426	223	HE 1440	224	HE 2399	294
HC DM1433	244	HE 1463	268	HE 2400	280
HC DM1434	223	HE 1493	242	HE 2402	98
HC DM1435	92	HE 1529	57	HE 2409	84
HC DM1439	149	HE 1540	242	HE 2411	172
HC DM1441	223	HE 1580	57	HE 2413	215
HC DM1442	92	HE 1684	242	HE 2414	224
HC DM1443	150	HE 1690	70	HE 2419	158
HC DM1444	233	HE 1697	243	HE 2433	280
HC DM1447	264	HE 1786	243	HE 2463	242
HC DM1448	165	HE 1800	308	HE 2536	26
HC DM1449	165	HE 1835	280	HE 2577	80
HC DM1450	165	HE 1842	94	HE 2607	80
HE 283	274	HE 1859	48	HE 2641	239
HE 287	159	HE 1873	269	HE 2642	66
HE 299	240	HE 1944	197	HE 2654	257
HE 316	152	HE 1953	34	HE 2659	307

HE 2666	156	HE 3798	103	HE 5340	241
HE 2699	240	HE 3800	111	HE 5460	98
HE 2705	224	HE 3806	88	HE 5511	90
HE 2763	307	HE 3809	237	HE 5596	239
HE 2820	144	HE 3810	68	HE 5622	89
HE 2855	34	HE 3815	280	HE 5636	61
HE 2857	260	HE 3818	259	HE 5644	115
HE 2864	260	HE 3823	88	HE 6007	191
HE 2868	188	HE 3825	116	HE 6008	26
HE 2879	252	HE 3829	285	HE 6012	144
HE 2880	259	HE 3837	259	HE 6013	53
HE 2890	96	HE 3839	187	HE 6018	191
HE 2959	241	HE 3840	287	HE 6048	150
HE 3097	203	HE 3846	128	HE 6049	288
HE 3127	296	HE 3850	31	HE 6075	306
HE 3132	251	HE 3851	123	HE 6232	319
HE 3133	66	HE 3855	115	HE 6233	319
HE 3149	50	HE 3879	283	HE 6234	319
HE 3155	115	HE 3880	290	HE 6235	319
HE 3163	68	HE 3882	96	HE 6236	319
HE 3168	224	HE 3883	188	HE 6237	319
HE 3180	228	HE 3885	68	HE 6238	319
HE 3183	77	HE 3887	200	HE 6239	319
HE 3192	60, 237	HE 3888	60, 237	HE 6240	319
HE 3193	200	HE 3889	172	HE 6241	319
HE 3200	241	HE 3890	31, 70	HE 6242	319
HE 3395	66	HE 3892	60	HE 6243	319
HE 3411	149	HE 3902	189	HE 6244	319
HE 3496	43	HE 3903	189	HE 6245	319
HE 3510	277	HE 3904	189	HE 6246	319
HE 3526	173	HE 3905	192	HE 6247	319
HE 3595	50	HE 4019	241	HE 6248	319
HE 3614	244	HE 4057	241	HE 6249	319
HE 3621	189	HE 4074	258	HE 6250	319
HE 3646	26	HE 4109	49	HE 6251	319
HE 3653	203	HE 4110	49	HE 6252	319
HE 3686	260	HE 4113	267	HE 6253	319
HE 3694	187	HE 4135	276	HE 6254	319
HE 3696	115	HE 4136	276	HE 6255	319
HE 3698	47	HE 4182	110	HE 6256	319
HE 3715	224	HE 4351	26	HE 6263	75
HE 3770	173	HE 4394	326	HE 6273	243
HE 3776	224	HE 4395	326	HE 6285	189
HE 3777	260	HE 4440	253	HE 6289	123
HE 3781	96	HE 4478	117	HE 6292	276
HE 3782	31	HE 4524	86	HE 6294	238
HE 3783	224	HE 4556	153	HE 6295	238
HE 3785	224	HE 4569	43	HE 6298	208
HE 3788	224	HE 4756	241	HE 6299	191
HE 3790	83	HE 4758	27	HE 6304	320
HE 3791	111	HE 4816	149	HE 6305	320
HE 3792	103	HE 4870	103	HE 6306	320
HE 3793	115	HE 4991	43	HE 6307	320
HE 3794	47	HE 5222	43	HE 6308	321
HE 3796	68	HE 5238	171	HE 6309	320
HE 3797	111	HE 5308	129	HE 6310	320

HE		HE		HE	
HE 6311	320	HE 7120	129	HE 7341	307
HE 6312	320	HE 7159	236	HE 7342	307
HE 6313	320	HE 7161	206	HE 7366	102
HE 6314	320	HE 7178	59	HE 7367	102
HE 6315	320	HE 7179	115	HE 7375	150
HE 6316	320	HE 7180	61	HE 7381	223
HE 6317	320	HE 7181	206	HE 7383	223
HE 6318	320	HE 7183	263	HE 7384	101
HE 6319	320	HE 7189	36	HE 7385	186
HE 6321	320	HE 7195	267	HE 7386	92
HE 6322	320	HE 7197	295	HE 7396	53, 124
HE 6323	320	HE 7198	295	HE 7406	44
HE 6324	320	HE 7232	320	HE 7409	125
HE 6325	320	HE 7233	320	HE 7410	238, 282
HE 6326	320	HE 7234	320	HE 7425	73
HE 6327	320	HE 7235	320	HE 7426	44
HE 6328	320	HE 7236	320	HE 7427	44
HE 6329	320	HE 7237	320	HE 7446	92
HE 6330	320	HE 7238	320	HE 7447	178
HE 6331	320	HE 7239	320	HE 7448	186
HE 6347	256	HE 7240	320	HE 7450	178
HE 6348	163	HE 7241	320	HE 7451	178
HE 6612	79	HE 7242	320	HE 7455	232
HE 6614	206	HE 7243	320	HE 7456	232
HE 6619	26	HE 7245	320	HE 7460	263
HE 6644	67	HE 7246	320	HE 7474	125
HE 6646	49	HE 7247	320	HE 7486	223
HE 6647	91	HE 7248	320	HE 7490	223
HE 6651	111	HE 7249	321	HE 7495	279
HE 6652	66	HE 7250	321	HE 7519	150
HE 6659	267	HE 7251	321	HE 7521	223
HE 6660	66	HE 7252	321	HE 7530	244
HE 6662	218	HE 7253	321	HE 7535	277
HE 6663	282	HE 7254	321	HE 7541	238
HE 6678	185	HE 7255	321	HE 7543	44
HE 6684	244	HE 7256	321	HE 8505	243
HE 6688	288	HE 7259	210	HE 8507	232
HE 6696	290	HE 7274	265	HE 8515	75
HE 6706	44	HE 7276	206	HE 8526	288
HE 6707	44	HE 7279	206	HE 8529	321
HE 6950	235	HE 7281	125	HE 8530	321
HE 6971	127, 184	HE 7282	125	HE 8531	320
HE 6973	55	HE 7283	125	HE 8532	321
HE 6975	44	HE 7284	125	HE 8533	321
HE 6981	124	HE 7285	125	HE 8534	321
HE 6999	98	HE 7286	125	HE 8535	321
HE 7003	206	HE 7287	125	HE 8536	321
HE 7009	59	HE 7288	125	HE 8537	321
HE 7010	197	HE 7289	125	HE 8538	321
HE 7011	197	HE 7290	125	HE 8539	321
HE 7012	197	HE 7304	184	HE 8540	321
HE 7013	197	HE 7307	244	HE 8541	321
HE 7017	126	HE 7329	251	HE 8542	321
HE 7018	193	HE 7330	250	HE 8543	321
HE 7041	245	HE 7332	80	HE 8544	321
HE 7063	290	HE 7340	307	HE 8545	321

HE 8546	321	HE 8937	321	HE 9123	135
HE 8547	321	HE 8938	321	HE 9124	135
HE 8548	313	HE 8939	321	HE 9125	135
HE 8549	321	HE 8940	321	HE 9126	135
HE 8550	321	HE 8941	321	HE 9127	135
HE 8551	321	HE 8942	321	HE 9128	135
HE 8561	192	HE 8943	322	HE 9129	135
HE 8566	223	HE 8944	322	HE 9130	135
HE 8567	149	HE 8945	322	HE 9131	135
HE 8568	149	HE 8946	322	HE 9132	135
HE 8575	149	HE 8953	223	HE 9133	135
HE 8577	149	HE 8966	50	HE 9134	134
HE 8581	244	HE 8968	50	HE 9146	241
HE 8582	223	HE 8969	203	HE 9155	152
HE 8583	92	HE 8973	123	HE 9157	249
HE 8802	223	HE 8975	149	HE 9174	161
HE 8805	127	HE 8976	44	HE 9175	161
HE 8812	284	HE 8977	44	HE 9176	161
HE 8816	251	HE 8978	44	HE 9200	44
HE 8819	189	HE 8979	184	HE 9212	244
HE 8821	149	HE 8985	91	HE 9222	173
HE 8825	152	HE 8986	92	HE 9225	150
HE 8827	251	HE 8990	223	HE 9227	77
HE 8828	86	HE 8998	93	HE 9239	322
HE 8829	84	HE 8999	93	HE 9240	322
HE 8830	50	HE 9000	44	HE 9241	322
HE 8832	244	HE 9036	213	HE 9242	322
HE 8833	223	HE 9045	260	HE 9243	322
HE 8834	150	HE 9046	260	HE 9248	263
HE 8841	223	HE 9053	91	HE 9249	275
HE 8842	92	HE 9056	191	HE 9250	275
HE 8843	150	HE 9057	178	HE 9251	322
HE 8844	233	HE 9079	84	HE 9252	322
HE 8847	264	HE 9080	84	HE 9253	322
HE 8848	165	HE 9081	186	HE 9254	322
HE 8849	165	HE 9082	251	HE 9255	322
HE 8850	165	HE 9092	246	HE 9256	322
HE 8902	206	HE 9103	134	HE 9257	322
HE 8909	150	HE 9104	134	HE 9258	322
HE 8911	189	HE 9105	134	HE 9259	322
HE 8917	61	HE 9106	134	HE 9262	263
HE 8922	321	HE 9107	135	HE 9271	244
HE 8923	321	HE 9108	135	HE 9272	322
HE 8924	310	HE 9109	135	HE 9282	97
HE 8925	321	HE 9110	135	HE 9283	107
HE 8926	321	HE 9111	135	HE 9286	210
HE 8927	321	HE 9112	135	HE 9288	44
HE 8928	322	HE 9113	135	HE 9294	189
HE 8929	322	HE 9114	135	HE 9305	275
HE 8930	321	HE 9115	135	HE 9306	44
HE 8931	321	HE 9116	135	HE 9307	44
HE 8932	321	HE 9117	135	HE 9310	207
HE 8933	321	HE 9118	135	HE 9311	207
HE 8934	321	HE 9119	135	HE 9312	275
HE 8935	321	HE 9120	82	HE 9332	266
HE 8936	321	HE 9122	135	HE 9333	66

Jesty [VITACRESS]	70	JF 4210094	159	Kitching [DERWENT]	76
JF 11938	278	JF 4210108	114	KraussS 4045	34
JF 13355	49	JF 4210127	89	Krauss 5742	109
JF 13573	107	JF 4210130	90	Krauss 8378	110
JF 15513	117	JF 4210131	129	Krupp 1308	34
JF 15515	278	JF 4210132	72	Krupp 1662	153
JF 15991	241	JF 4210137	215	Krupp 1663	153
JF 16038	58	JF 4210138	248	Krupp 1664	110
JF 16559	254	JF 4210140	260	KS 720	118
JF 18800	107	JF 4210141	69	KS 721	273
JF 18892	149	JF 4210145	129	KS 886	110
JF 20067	31	JF 4220001	159	KS 926	110
JF 20337	194	JF 4220007	172	KS 1049	28
JF 20685	241	JF 4220015	185	KS 1158	97
JF 21294	241	JF 4220016	63	KS 1269	82
JF 21295	203	JF 4220022	209	KS 2395	191
JF 21442	215	JF 4220031	215	KS 2405	117
JF 21999	48	JF 4220033	243	KS 2442	279
JF 22060	241	JF 4220038	221	KS 3010	154
JF 22497	290	JF 4220039	84	KS 3014	52
JF 22503	96	JF 4220045	46	KS 3024	306
JF 22753	269	JF 4240010	79	KS 3063	91
JF 22871	70	JF 4240012	172	KS 3114	279
JF 22878	278	JF 4240015	172	KS 3117	280
JF 22888	251	JF 4240017	217	KS 4034	28
JF 22889	96	JF[0-6-0TT]	278	KS 4047	276
JF 22893	241	JMR [LONDON]	118	KS 4167	187
JF 22898	182	Jung 939	91	KS 4219	110
JF 22900	182	Jung 1261	288	KS 4250	192
JF 22902	253	Jung 3175	30	KS 4256	25
JF 22928	39	Jung 2279	189	KS 4260	25
JF 22971	47	Jung 3872	107	KS 4388	187
JF 22982	172	Jung 4878	189	KS 4404	280
JF 3900002	243	Jung 5869	192	KS 4408	197
JF 3900011	306	Jung 7509	156	KS 4415	267
JF 3930044	261	Jung 11787	195	KS 4421	187
JF 3930048	178	Jung A114	296	KS 4428	31
JF 4000001	69			KS 4449	175
JF 4000007	182	**K**		KS 4450	70
JF 4100003	224				
JF 4100005	225	K 2509	163	**L**	
JF 4100013	185	K 2551 T56	218		
JF 4110006	76	K 3799	170	L 962	188
JF 4160001	116	K 4263	228	L 1626	185
JF 4160002	108	K 5459	269	L 3198	250
JF 4160004	28	K 5469	242	L 3742	59
JF 4160005	28	K 5470	158	L 3834	191
JF 4200003	224	K 5474	68	L 3916	96
JF 4200018	76	K T84	296	L 4088	122
JF 4200019	61	KC 1612	185	L 4228	26
JF 4200022	225	KC [8]	50	L 4404	48
JF 4200028	251	KC [20]	185	L 6299	65
JF 4210018	159	Kennan [0-6-0]	301	L 6502	118
JF 4210074	174	Kershaw 45.121A	155	L 7280	284
JF 4210079	122	Kew [0-4-0ST]	141	L 7954	229
JF 4210082	215	Kierstead/AK	177	L 8022	89

L 8023	312	
L 9256	72	
L 9993	114	
L 10180	41	
L 10225	224	
L 10498	275	
L 10805	117	
L 10994	56	
L 11221	26	
L 11410	41	
L 14005	272	
L 14006	160	
L 18557	72	
L 20449	242	
L 20698	40	
L 20886	118	
L 26288	63	
L 26366	129	
L 28039	71	
L 29890	117	
L 30233	268	
L 32801	156	
L 33650	89	
L 33651	207	
L 33937	203	
L 34025	65	
L 34521	203	
L 34523	91	
L 34652	102	
L 34758	182	
L 35811	129	
L 36743	160	
L 37170	26	
L 37366	62	
L 37658	110	
L 37911	27	
L 38296	178	
L 39005	272	
L 39419	190	
L 40009	48	
L 40011	156	
L 40407	98	
L 41545	216	
L 41803	203	
L 42319	180	
L 42494	97	
L 44052	141	
L 50191	229	
L 52031	52	
Lake&Elliot [HENRY]	83	
LaMeuse 3243	189	
LaMeuse 3442	325	
Lancing/Elh [10656]	77	
Lancing/Elh [12795]	208	
Lancing/Elh [12796]	208	
Lancing/Elh [14351]	159	
Lancing/Elh [14352]	159	
Lancing/Elh [14573]	208	
Lancing/Elh [S10843S]	334	
Lancing/Elh [S10940S]	334	
Lancing/Elh [S10988S]	334	
LancTan [4wPM]	151	
Landrover 136483	309	
Landrover [06WH4510]	314	
Landrover [4wDMR]	139	
Landrover [92.MH.4823]	301	
Landrover [97D 67550]	300	
Landrover [K678 KHH]	104	
Landrover [KT06OMV]	300	
Landrover 136517	309	
Landrover/Geismar [06D84465]	301	
Landrover/Harsco [99WH4717]	314	
Lawson 2	102	
Lawson 3	102	
Lawson 4	102	
Lawson 5	102	
Lawson 6	102	
LB 50888	36	
LB 51651	45	
LB 51721	48	
LB 51917	72	
LB 51989	153	
LB 52528	36	
LB 52579	280	
LB 52610	192	
LB 52726	186	
LB 52885	50	
LB 52886	99	
LB 53162	80	
LB 53225	52	
LB 53541	252	
LB 53726	59	
LB 53976	102	
LB 53977	102, 235	
LB 54181	98	
LB 54183	309	
LB 54684	35	
LB 54781	80	
LB 55070	96	
LB 55413	126	
LB 55730	28	
LB 55870	101	
LB 56371	89	
LBNGRS 1	26	
Leake [0-4-0BE]	71	
Leake [0-4-0DM]	71	
Leake [4w-4BER]	71	
LemonB [2-6-2]	171	
LemonB [JACK]	107	
Lewin [0-4-0T]	78	
Leyland [55503]	80	
Leyland [55508]	83	
Leyland [55513]	59	
Leyland [55528]	83	
Leyland [55533]	59	
Leyland [LEV 1]	155	
Leyland/DerbyC&W RB002/001	308	
Leyland/DerbyC&W RB004	177	
LH Group 76629	329	
LH Group 76634	329	
LH Group 76638	328	
LH Group 76699	328	
Lima 8758	240	
Lima 8856	186	
LJ [3]	109	
Llangollen [1]	269	
LMM 1053	274	
LMM 1066	274	
LMM [4wBE]	268	
LO 141	42	
LO 157	84	
LO 172	84	
LocoEnt No.1	76	
LocoEnt No.2	226	
Locospoor B7281E	272	
Longhedge [31592]	199	
Longleat [CEAWLIN]	214	
Longleat [LENKA]	214	

M

M&P/BP [No.13]	142	
Mace [PAM]	112	
Mace [SIMON]	112	
Maffei 4127	66	
Maffei 4766	278	
MaK 1000.867	105	
MaK 1000.868	105	
MaK 1000.869	105	
MaK 1000.870	105	
MaK 1000.871	105	
Massey [2w-2PM]	66	
Massey [4wBER]	66	
Matisa 2655	201	
Matisa D8.005	162	
Matisa PV5 570	77	
Matisa PV6 627	269	
Matisa PV620	64	
Matisa [MPU 8]	267	
MatisaSPA 0214	300	
MatisaSPA 0215	300	
Maxitrack [INVICTA]	37	
McGarigle [44]	275	
McGarigle [4-4-0]	110	
McGarigle [CAGNEY]	156	

MER [No.23]	327	MetCam [L 65]	138	MetCam [9441]	139
Mercedes [NR05VRE]	161	MetCam [L 66]	138	MetCam [9459]	139
Mercia [1009]	30	MetCam [L 67]	138	MetCam [9507]	140
Mercury 5337	58	MetCam [L 130]	138	MetCam [9533]	139
Meridian [1]	37	MetCam [L 131]	142	MetCam [9561]	139
Metalair 20002	271	MetCam [L 135]	138	MetCam [9577]	139
Metalair 20003	271	MetCam [L 150]	138	MetCam [9691]	139
Metalair 20004	271	MetCam [L 151]	138	MetCam [10012]	142
Metalair 20005	271	MetCam [TCC 1]	138	MetCam [11012]	142
Metalair 20007	271	MetCam [TCC 5]	138	MetCam [11182]	142
Metalair 20017	271	MetCam [16]	142	MetCam [12048]	142
Metalair 20018	272	MetCam [1018]	71	MetCam [21147]	140
Metalair 20019	272	MetCam [1030]	85	MetCam [22679]	142
Metalair 20025	272	MetCam [1031]	131	MetCam [50160]	185
Metalair 20039	272	MetCam [1044]	325	MetCam [50164]	58
Metalair 20044	272	MetCam [1045]	325	MetCam [50167]	187
Metalair 20065	272	MetCam [1304]	71	MetCam [50170]	58
Metalair 20067	272	MetCam [1305]	86	MetCam [50193]	122
Metalair 20069	272	MetCam [1306]	106	MetCam [50203]	122
Metalair 20091	272	MetCam [1406]	138	MetCam [50204]	229
Metalair 20140	272	MetCam [1407]	138	MetCam [50222]	181
Metalair 20141	272	MetCam [1441]	138	MetCam [50253]	58
Metalair 20161	272	MetCam [1481]	138	MetCam [50256]	108
Metalair 20212	272	MetCam [1506]	140	MetCam [50266]	122
Metalair 20222	272	Metcam [1507]	140	MetCam [50269]	240
Metalair 20228	272	MetCam [1515]	138	MetCam [50321]	122
Metalair 20240	272	MetCam [1677]	168	MetCam [50338]	181
Metalair 20242	272	MetCam [1532]	138	MetCam [50746]	230
Metalair 20265	272	MetCam [1560]	138	MetCam [51187]	173
MetallbauE 0-6-0DH	199	MetCam [1561]	138	MetCam [51188]	63
MetAmal/BRCW		MetCam [1570]	139	MetCam [51189]	240
[ESL107]	142	MetCam [1576]	139	MetCam [51192]	148
MetC&W [1293]	227	MetCam [1577]	139	MetCam [51205]	173
MetC&W [L134]	142	MetCam [1672]	139	MetCam [51210]	229
MetCam [L11]	83	MetCam [1673]	139	MetCam [51213]	84
MetCam [L 15]	137	MetCam [1677]	168	MetCam [51226]	154
MetCam [L 16]	137	MetCam [1680]	139	MetCam [51228]	155
MetCam [L 17]	137	MetCam [1681]	139	MetCam [51247]	229
MetCam [L 18]	137	MetCam [1682]	139	MetCam [51427]	122
MetCam [L 19]	137	MetCam [1690]	139	MetCam [51433]	187
MetCam [L 20]	137	MetCam [1691]	139	MetCam [51434]	155
MetCam [L 21]	137	MetCam [3016]	141	MetCam [51499]	155
MetCam [L 22]	137	MetCam [3209]	138	MetCam [51503]	155
MetCam [L 23]	137	MetCam [3215]	139	MetCam [51505]	63
MetCam [L 24]	138	MetCam [3229]	139	MetCam [51511]	229
MetCam [L 25]	138	MetCam [3315]	139	MetCam [51512]	173
MetCam [L 26]	138	MetCam [3327]	142	MetCam [51803]	240
MetCam [L 27]	138	MetCam [3329]	139	MetCam [65217]	205
MetCam [L 28]	138	MetCam [3530]	142	MetCam [CAR No.88]	143
MetCam [L 29]	138	MetCam [3634]	141	MetCam [CAR No.92]	143
MetCam [L 30]	138	MetCam [3662]	143	MetCam [CAR No.93]	143
MetCam [L 31]	138	MetCam [3706]	138	MetCam [289]	56
MetCam [L 32]	138	MetCam [3721]	74	MetCam [291]	255
MetCam [L 62]	138	MetCam [3733]	143	MH 2	48
MetCam [L 63]	138	MetCam [3734]	142	MH A110	242
MetCam [L 64]	138	MetCam [9125]	139	MH NG39A	48

Minilok 158	44	MR 2098	48	MR 7053	91
Minilok 160	206	MR 2171	247	MR 7059	110
Minilok [4wDH]	206	MR 2197	192	MR 7066	97
Minirail [3]	40	MR 2262	187	MR 7105	26
Minirail [JOHN]	129	MR 3663	61	MR 7108	26
Mkm 109	57	MR 3720	203	MR 7126	41
Moes [4]	84	MR 3739	42	MR 7128	27
Moes [10]	35	MR 3797	158	MR 7129	26
Moes [11]	84	MR 3849	33	MR 7153	156
Moes [12]	35	MR 3995	130	MR 7188	45
Moes [13]	84	MR 4023	95	MR 7189	257
Moes [17]	84	MR 4217	77	MR 7190	45
Moes [21]	256	MR 4565	50	MR 7191	50
Moes [27]	84	MR 4570	26	MR 7192	156
Moës [TU 20]	107	MR 4572	61	MR 7199	95
Moors Valley 20	192	MR 4709	195	MR 7214	26
MorrisRP [RAIL TAXI]	272	MR 4724	95	MR 7215	45
Morse [712]	216	MR 4803	268	MR 7304	314
Morse [4-4-0PM]	216	MR 4805	26	MR 7330	257
Mortimer [98 MH 6417]	309	MR 5025	268	MR 7333	225
MossA [5305]	118	MR 5038	192	MR 7371	117
MossAJ [2-2wBER]	274	MR 5213	224	MR 7374	97
MossAJ [2-2wPMR]	118	MR 5226	95	MR 7403	268
MossAJ [2-6-2DM]	151	MR 5260	122	MR 7463	43, 47
MossAJ [MOROG]	129	MR 5297	197	MR 7469	200
MossAJ [R-DRAGON]	118	MR 5355	97	MR 7471	192
Motala 516	34	MR 5402	249	MR 7474	156
Motala 586	163	MR 5603	26	MR 7481	130
Moyse 1364	73	MR 5608	25	MR 7493	129
Moyse 1365	73	MR 5609	186	MR 7494	225
Moyse 1464	73	MR 5612	26	MR 7498	45
MR 246	296	MR 5613	26	MR 7512	29
MR 264	277	MR 5646	41	MR 7522	50
MR 435	61	MR 5713	197	MR 7710	191
MR 460	58	MR 5763	260	MR 7902	28
MR 461	26	MR 5821	191	MR 7927	275
MR 872	203	MR 5852	268	MR 7933	26
MR 997	268	MR 5853	61	MR 7944	298
MR 1111	191	MR 5859	242	MR 7955	117
MR 1320	192	MR 5861	312	MR 7956	25
MR 1363	158	MR 5863	203	MR 8540	195
MR 1364	33	MR 5875	25	MR 8564	256
MR 1369	191	MR 5877	27	MR 8565	33
MR 1377	26	MR 5879	180	MR 8600	217
MR 1381	203	MR 5880	49	MR 8606	107
MR 1757	29	MR 5881	124	MR 8614	70
MR 1930	78	MR 5902	193	MR 8622	130
MR 1934	174	MR 5906	117	MR 8627	50
MR 1935	130	MR 5912	193	MR 8640	189
MR 1944	268	MR 6012	26	MR 8641	26
MR 2014	246	MR 6013	268	MR 8644	242
MR 2024	58	MR 6031	99	MR 8655	45
MR 2026	167	MR 6035	192	MR 8663	191
MR 2029	84	MR 7033	191	MR 8667	59
MR 2059	35	MR 7036	26	MR 8669	191
MR 2097	247	MR 7037	45	MR 8678	124

MR	8684	294	MR	9543	314	MR	22224	160
MR	8687	200	MR	9547	268	MR	22235	196
MR	8694	95	MR	9655	27	MR	22238	46
MR	8695	26	MR	9676	99	MR	22253	249
MR	8696	46	MR	9677	99	MR	22258	265
MR	8698	50	MR	9711	109	MR	26007	71
MR	8700	247	MR	9774	195	MR	26014	92
MR	8703	277	MR	9778	190	MR	102G038	99
MR	8704	249	MR	9792	256	MR	102T007	299
MR	8720	214	MR	9846	50	MR	105H006	65
MR	8723	268	MR	9869	108	MR	110U082	259
MR	8727	179	MR	9921	121	MR	115U093	306
MR	8729	66	MR	9925	253	MR	121UA117	287
MR	8730	108	MR	9932	214	MR	40S273	65
MR	8731	27	MR	9976	189	MR	40S280	327
MR	8738	249	MR	9978	178	MR	40S307	293
MR	8739	59	MR	9982	257	MR	40S309	293
MR	8745	26	MR	10161	203	MR	40S310	182
MR	8748	191	MR	10409	26	MR	40S383	50
MR	8756	61	MR	11001	204	MR	40S412	46
MR	8788	267	MR	11003	26	MR	40SD501	192
MR	8813	190	MR	11039	294	MR	40SD502	97
MR	8820	190	MR	11102	277	MR	60S317	26
MR	8825	46	MR	11111	280	MR	60S318	178
MR	8826	129	MR	11142	191	MR	60S333	277
MR	8855	59	MR	11143	325	MR	60S363	277
MR	8856	66	MR	11177	59	MR	60S364	59
MR	8860	50	MR	11218	150	MR	60S382	313
MR	8863	256	MR	11223	117	MR	60S383	325
MR	8874	130	MR	11246	59	MR	[4wDM]	27
MR	8875	97	MR	11258	117	MR	[4wDM]	200
MR	8877	65	MR	11264	29	MR	[4wPM] ?	249
MR	8878	191	MR	11297	26	MR	[MARY ANN]	267
MR	8882	97	MR	11298	26	MSI	[PLANET]	148
MR	8884	256	MR	20058	46	MV	889	301
MR	8885	43	MR	20073	65	MV	901	301
MR	8886	42	MR	20082	99	MV	925	301
MR	8887	197	MR	21282	92	MV	941	312
MR	8905	43	MR	21505	249	MV	972	312
MR	8934	41	MR	21520	249	MV	973	313
MR	8937	50	MR	21579	267	MV	977	301
MR	8970	304	MR	21615	26	MV/BP	989	150
MR	8979	224	MR	21619	169	MV	[1]	111
MR	8981	197	MR	22021	327	MV	[1293]	227
MR	8992	117	MR	22031	144	MV	[D5705]	147
MR	8994	202	MR	22045	191	MW	437	174
MR	8995	189	MR	22070	61	MW	641	199
MR	9009	148	MR	22119	267	MW	865	240
MR	9019	203	MR	22128	249	MW	1207	54
MR	9104	191	MR	22144	158	MW	1210	242
MR	9202	296	MR	22154	277	MW	1317	106
MR	9231	43, 47	MR	22209	193	MW	1382	273
MR	9264	130	MR	22210	153	MW	1472	235
MR	9381	250	MR	22211	193	MW	1532	33
MR	9382	99	MR	22220	293	MW	1601	242
MR	9409	199	MR	22221	250	MW	1675	123

MW 1762	167
MW 1795	242
MW 1877	92
MW 1955	111
MW 2009	167
MW 2010	154
MW 2015	167
MW 2018	88
MW 2025	211
MW 2047	175

N

N 1561	273
N 2119	91
N 2203	259
N 2937	185
N 3209	198
N 3553	254
N 4004	114
N 4392	258
N 4444	152
N 5087	152
NB 17111	197
NBH 18386	114
NBH 21521	254
NBH 22563	254
NBH 22600	121
NBQ 23096	296
NBH 23223	121
NBH 23403	147
NBH 23406	57
NBQ 23436	57
NBQ 23610	116
NBQ 24040	212
NBQ 24042	268
NBQ 24048	212
NBQ 24151	54
NBQ 24154	239
NBH 24564	31
NBH 24607	175
NBH 24648	90
NBH 25437	175
NBH 25438	155
NBH 25458	228
NBQ 25546	254
NBQ 26165	54
NBQ 26207	34
NBQ 26609	228
NBQ 27097	235
NBH 27291	31
NBQ 27414	176
NBQ 27415	259
NBQ 27421	255
NBQ 27426	194
NBQ 27549	260

NBQ 27591	255
NBQ 27644	251
NBQ 27645	32
NBQ 27648	209
NBQ 27653	116
NBQ 27656	172
NBQ 27732	247
NBQ 27734	325
NBH 27770	257
NB 27793	55
NBQ 27876	185
NBQ 27932	61
NBQ 27941	285
NBQ 28020	259
NBQ 28027	260
NCC [1]	295
NDLW 698	179
Neasden 3	31
Nissan [97D 66701]	300
Niteq B155	333
Niteq B168	139
Niteq B177	293
Niteq B183	164
Niteq B184	139
Niteq B188	333
Niteq B193	94
Niteq B200	333
Niteq B217	139
Niteq B222	139
Niteq B246	333
NMW [4wG]	284
NNM 75511	246
NNM 77501	36
NNM 78101E	249
NNM 80505	255
NNM 81504	246
NNM 82503	221
NNM 83501	221
NNM 83503	221
NNM 83504	222
NNM 83506	127
Nohab 1163	111
Nohab 1164	152
Nohab 2082	34
Nohab 2229	112
NR 5408	240
NR 5710	259
NR 5757	295
NR 5907	185
NW 454	57
NW 828	294
NW 829	295
NW 830	294
NW 956	296

O

Oerlikon [28249]	227
OK 614	189
OK 1473	189
OK 2343	189
OK 2378	117
OK 2544	25
OK 5102	97
OK 5662	158
OK 5668	107
OK 5744	65
OK 5834	25
OK 6335	255
OK 6641	117
OK 7122	108, 109
OK 7529	59
OK 8356	97
OK 9239	196, 266
OK 9998	196
OK 10750	189
OK 10808	25
OK 10956	109
OK 10957	109
OK 11309	109
OK 11784	200
OK 12470	109
OK 12475	295
OK 12662	294
OK 12722	107
OK 12740	25
OK 13101	109
OK 2563	312
OK 3444?	192
OK 3685	27
OK 4013	94
OK 4470	191
OK 4588	192
OK 5125	59
OK 5926	242
OK 6193	204
OK 6501?	156
OK 6504	27
OK 6703	27
OK 6931	128
OK 7269	203
OK 7595	178
OK 7600	25
OK 7728	27
OK 7734	128
OK 7741	204
OK 8986	25
OK 20777	94
OK 21160	192
OK [4wDM]	129
OldburyC&W [55]	249

OldburyC&W [No.1]	254	P 1970	163	Perm 005 [68804]	279
		P 1976	90	Perm 006 [68805]	162
P		P 1990	176	Perm 007 [68702]	162
		P 1999	115	Perm 007 [68806]	162
P 614	110	P 2000	54	Perm 008 [68807]	168
P 737	115	P 2003	242	Perm 010 [68706]	162
P 783	42	P 2004	212	Perm 010 [68809]	103
P 784	69	P 2012	200	Perm 011 [68710]	335
P 917	185	P 2024	277	Perm 011 [68810]	103
P 933	187	P 2027	116	Perm 012 [98707]	162
P 1008	130	P 2029	158	Perm MTU 001	116
P 1026	295	P 2031	68	Perm T002	84
P 1097	296	P 2039	84	Perm T003	170
P 1159	224	P 2050	189	Perm/Landrover	
P 1163	57	P 2081	187	[N338CNE]	145
P 1187	285	P 2084	49	Perm/Landrover	
P 1257	172	P 2085	325	[N337CNE]	239
P 1270	264	P 2087	31	Perm/Landrover	
P 1316	203	P 2100	141	[P580 JVC]	164
P 1327	99	P 2103	242	Perm/Landrover	
P 1345	285	P 2104	158	[P71 HAO]	239
P 1351	129	P 2105	31	Perm/Volkswagen	
P 1370	147	P 2110	172	[L253HKK]	146
P 1376	252	P 2111	57	Perm/Volkswagen	
P 1378	158	P 2114	283	[M992 NNB]	234
P 1426	285	P 2129	325	Plasser 26	300
P 1430	173	P 2130	119	Plasser 138 [999700]	334
P 1438	147	P 2131	173	Plasser 138 [999701]	334
P 1530	188	P 2142	76	Plasser 152	334
P 1547	57	P 2147	88	Plasser 153	334
P 1555	170	P 2150	235	Plasser 281	300
P 1567	244	P 2153	252	Plasser 419	67
P 1579	182	P 2155	150	Plasser 1140	301
P 1611	71	P 5003	243	Plasser 52530A	335
P 1631	111	P 5014	287	Plasser 52759A	335
P 1636	112	Parry 8	210	Plasser 52760A	173
P 1690	200	Parry 12	334	Plasser 52764A	335
P 1722	176	Pendre [TOM ROLT]	276	Plasser 52765A	335
P 1738	173	Perm [E669 JOU]	29	Plasser 52766A	111
P 1749	129	Perm [F511 LRR]	163	Plasser 52788	34
P 1756	28	Perm [G276 NAU]	163	Plasser 52792	215
P 1759	172	Perm [L263 MNU]	63	Plasser 52793	335
P 1788	180	Perm [L975 MNU]	163	Plasser 53192A	335
P 1803	187	Perm [M491 PTV]	164	Plasser 53193A	335
P 1859	119	Perm [N517 YAU]	164	Plasser 53194A	335
P 1870	158	Perm [N798 XRA]	164	Plasser 53195A	335
P 1871	158	Perm [P161 FAU]	164	Plasser 53196A	335
P 1889	252	Perm [P758 GNN]	164	Plasser 53197A	335
P 1893	90	Perm [R447 XRA]	164	Plasser 53198A	335
P 1900	31	Perm [R913 MAU]	164	Plasser [706]	300
P 1903	112	Perm [S292 NAU]	164	Plasser [728]	301
P 1925	116	Perm 001 [68800]	168	Plasser [734]	301
P 1935	115	Perm 001 [98401]	85	Plasser & Theurer [323]	295
P 1940	29	Perm 002 [68704]	335	Potter [No.1]	156
P 1963	66	Perm 002 [68801]	59	Powell [2-4wPM]	155
P 1967	77	Perm 004 [68803]	59	Prestige [3205]	69

Pritchard [46]	56	PWR BO.598W.01	106	RH 182138	264
PRoyal [2624]	301			RH 183062	176
PRoyal [50397]	283	**R**		RH 183727	269
PRoyal [50413]	40	R&R 80	204	RH 183744	200
PRoyal [W4W]	215	R&R 84	314	RH 183749	251
PSteel [51339]	288	RangeRover [AXI 1400]	104	RH 183773	129
PSteel [51341]	58	Ravenglass 5	48	RH 186318	41
PSteel [51342]	84	Ravenglass 10	48	RH 187081	204
PSteel [51346]	72	Ravenglass [ICLNo1]	48	RH 187100	289
PSteel [51347]	34	Ravenglass [PERKINS]	48	RH 187101	100
PSteel [51351]	290	Ravenglass [SCOOTER]	47	RH 187105	27
PSteel [51352]	206	Ravenglass [W-FIELD	48	RH 189972	191
PSteel [51353]	58	Red(F) [2w-2BE]	105	RH 189992	257
PSteel [51354]	286	Red(T) [TAMAR]	150	RH 191646	59
PSteel [51356]	81	Redstone	288	RH 191679	174
PSteel [51359]	159	RegentSt [4-2-2]	65	RH 191680	280
PSteel [51360]	63	Renault [N842 HFB]	29	RH 192888	130
PSteel [51363]	96	Resco L105	201	RH 193974	209
PSteel [51365]	67	Resco L106	122	RH 193984	179
PSteel [51367]	260	Resco L107	129	RH 194771	265
PSteel [51370]	99	Resco L112	200	RH 194784	143
PSteel [51371]	335	Resco [IRON DUKE]	226	RH 195846	191
PSteel [51372]	185	Resco [RH 425477]	31	RH 195849	100
PSteel [51375]	335	Resita [0-8-0T]	280	RH 198228	191
PSteel [51376]	206	Resita [764.425]	280	RH 198241	100
PSteel [51381]	85	RFSD 067/GA/57000/001	222	RH 198286	275
PSteel [51382]	288	RFSD L101	297	RH 198287	242
PSteel [51384]	84	RFSD L106	97	RH 198290	316
PSteel [51388]	72	RFSK V336	124	RH 198297	191
PSteel [51392]	81	RFSK V337	146	RH 200069	102
PSteel [51395]	58	RFSK V339	131	RH 200075	307
PSteel [51396]	283	RH 164346	26	RH 200478	117
PSteel [51397]	290	RH 164350	191	RH 200512	169
PSteel [51398]	58	RH 166010	91	RH 200513	27
PSteel [51400]	96	RH 166024	204	RH 200516	26
PSteel [51401]	34	RH 166045	102	RH 200744	129
PSteel [51402]	260	RH 170200	101	RH 200748	265
PSteel [51405]	96	RH 170369	156	RH 200761	144
PSteel [51407]	67	RH 170374	188	RH 200792	276
PSteel [51412]	99	RH 171901	190	RH 200793	290
PSteel [51413]	335	RH 172892	26	RH 201970	95
PSteel [55021]	334	RH 172901	26	RH 202000	41
PSteel [55022]	334	RH 174535	186	RH 202036	117
PSteel [55023]	169	RH 174536	263	RH 202967	156
PSteel [55024]	334	RH 174542	263	RH 202969	230
PSteel [55025]	334	RH 175127	263	RH 202987	276
PSteel [55026]	285	RH 175414	273	RH 203016	202
PSteel [55027]	335	RH 175418	225	RH 203026	26
PSteel [55029]	334	RH 177604	193	RH 203031	278
PSteel [55030]	334	RH 177638	200	RH 207103	85
PSteel [55031]	335	RH 177639	197	RH 209429	143
PSteel [55033]	83	RH 179005	257	RH 209430	26
PSteel [55034]	212	RH 179009	213	RH 210479	180
PSteel [61503]	259	RH 179870	191	RH 210481	209
PWR AO.296V.03	45	RH 179880	68	RH 210959	251
PWR B0366	192	RH 181820	197	RH 210961	258

RH 211609	109	RH 242902	313	RH 259755	317
RH 211679	158	RH 242915	187	RH 259756	317
RH 211681	251	RH 242916	257	RH 259757	317
RH 211687	316	RH 242918	50	RH 259758	317
RH 213834	178	RH 243387	299	RH 259759	317
RH 213839	64	RH 243392	261	RH 259760	317
RH 213840	200	RH 244487	80	RH 260712	208
RH 213848	100	RH 244558	42	RH 260716	190
RH 213853	85	RH 244559	102	RH 260719	191
RH 215755	211	RH 244580	149	RH 260754	199
RH 217967	65	RH 244788	316	RH 260755	199
RH 217973	85	RH 244870	279	RH 260756	260
RH 217993	50	RH 244871	316	RH 262998	259
RH 217999	25	RH 246793	100	RH 263001	120
RH 218016	27	RH 247178	102	RH 264244	298
RH 221561	87	RH 247182	101	RH 264251	117
RH 221623	192	RH 248458	299	RH 264252	52
RH 221625	189	RH 249526	310	RH 265617	162
RH 221626	50	RH 249530	257	RH 265618	260
RH 221639	83	RH 249543	311	RH 268878	275
RH 221647	253	RH 249545	316	RH 268881	208
RH 222068	59	RH 252239	302	RH 273525	46
RH 222074	117	RH 252240	316	RH 273843	257
RH 222100	156	RH 252241	316	RH 275882	256
RH 222101	177	RH 252245	316	RH 275883	259
RH 223667	191	RH 252246	302	RH 275886	159
RH 223692	26	RH 252247	316	RH 277265	29
RH 223700	122	RH 252251	316	RH 277273	48
RH 223741	55	RH 252252	302	RH 279591	76
RH 223744	50	RH 252823	88	RH 279597	185
RH 223749	191	RH 252842	303	RH 280865	191
RH 224315	102	RH 252843	298	RH 280866	101
RH 224337	243	RH 252849	307	RH 281266	83
RH 224347	151	RH 256273	251	RH 281269	175
RH 224352	251	RH 256314	192	RH 281271	120
RH 226276	113	RH 259184	317	RH 281290	158, 238, 326
RH 226302	200	RH 259185	317	RH 283507	26
RH 226309	264	RH 259186	317	RH 283512	265
RH 229633	258	RH 259189	306	RH 283513	46
RH 229647	41	RH 259190	317	RH 283871	72
RH 229648	100	RH 259191	317	RH 284838	236
RH 229655	100	RH 259196	317	RH 284839	251
RH 229656	100	RH 259198	317	RH 294263	257
RH 229657	102	RH 259203	317	RH 294266	32
RH 235513	120	RH 259204	317	RH 294268	109
RH 235519	209	RH 259205	317	RH 294269	101
RH 235624	86	RH 259206	317	RH 296091	29
RH 235654	242	RH 259737	317	RH 297030	278
RH 235711	65	RH 259738	317	RH 297054	117
RH 235725	191	RH 259743	317	RH 297066	102
RH 235727	255	RH 259744	317	RH 299099	212
RH 235729	186	RH 259745	317	RH 300518	310
RH 236364	167	RH 259749	317	RH 304469	34
RH 237914	191	RH 259750	317	RH 304470	194
RH 242868	159	RH 259751	317	RH 305302	188
RH 242901	302	RH 259752	317	RH 305306	185

RH 305315	194	RH 371535	101	RH 382811	318
RH 305322	298	RH 371538	315	RH 382812	318
RH 306092	172	RH 371544	299	RH 382814	318
RH 312425	297	RH 371937	129	RH 382815	311
RH 312433	285	RH 371962	306	RH 382817	299
RH 312984	259	RH 371967	303	RH 382819	306
RH 312988	76	RH 371971	167	RH 382820	200
RH 312989	162	RH 373359	27	RH 382824	176
RH 312990	129	RH 373376	317	RH 382827	295
RH 313390	245	RH 373377	317	RH 383260	318
RH 313394	62	RH 373379	317	RH 383264	308
RH 314222	297	RH 375314	313	RH 384139	58
RH 314223	310	RH 375315	27	RH 390772	141
RH 319284	63	RH 375316	27	RH 392117	197
RH 319286	159	RH 375322	299	RH 392137	318
RH 319290	175	RH 375332	317	RH 392139	318
RH 319294	159	RH 375335	317	RH 392142	307
RH 320573	49	RH 375336	317	RH 392148	318
RH 321727	263	RH 375341	317	RH 392149	318
RH 321732	51	RH 375344	311	RH 392150	318
RH 321733	259	RH 375345	306	RH 392151	318
RH 321734	159	RH 375347	244	RH 392152	302
RH 323587	80	RH 375360	76	RH 392157	78
RH 326047	317	RH 375693	84	RH 393302	279
RH 326051	299	RH 375694	274	RH 393303	157
RH 326052	305	RH 375696	101	RH 393304	123
RH 326058	55	RH 375699	101	RH 393325	61
RH 327904	274	RH 375701	129	RH 393327	291
RH 327964	225	RH 375713	129	RH 394009	224
RH 327974	40	RH 379055	317	RH 394014	283
RH 329680	299	RH 379059	306	RH 394022	306
RH 329682	311	RH 379061	299	RH 394023	318
RH 329685	317	RH 379064	317	RH 394024	318
RH 329686	317	RH 379066	317	RH 394025	318
RH 329688	317	RH 379068	318	RH 394026	318
RH 329690	317	RH 379070	306	RH 394027	318
RH 329693	317	RH 379073	318	RH 394028	318
RH 329695	317	RH 379076	317	RH 394029	318
RH 329696	306	RH 379077	318	RH 394030	318
RH 331250	267	RH 379079	311	RH 394031	318
RH 338416	208	RH 379081	318	RH 394032	318
RH 338429	257	RH 379084	313	RH 394033	318
RH 338438	84	RH 379086	306	RH 394034	318
RH 338439	158	RH 379090	318	RH 395294	74
RH 339105	117	RH 379659	244	RH 395305	40
RH 339209	174	RH 379910	318	RH 398063	283
RH 347747	212	RH 379913	318	RH 398076	307
RH 349041	38	RH 379916	318	RH 398101	178
RH 349061	108	RH 379922	318	RH 398102	178
RH 353491	274	RH 379925	318	RH 398611	154
RH 354013	76	RH 379927	318	RH 398613	253
RH 354028	91	RH 379928	318	RH 398616	84
RH 354029	264	RH 381704	101	RH 402174	318
RH 354068	278	RH 381705	117	RH 402175	306
RH 359169	216	RH 382808	236	RH 402176	318
RH 370555	278	RH 382809	318	RH 402177	299

RH 402178	319	RH 424841	187	RH 466618	88
RH 402179	319	RH 425477	31	RH 466621	329
RH 402439	102	RH 425481	325	RH 466625	132
RH 402803	63	RH 425483	236	RH 466629	71
RH 402977	319	RH 425796	275	RH 466630	225
RH 402978	319	RH 425798	27	RH 468043	94, 132
RH 402980	319	RH 431758	260	RH 468046	286
RH 402981	319	RH 431760	209	RH 468048	32
RH 402982	319	RH 431761	61	RH 476106	186
RH 402983	311	RH 431763	240	RH 476108	276
RH 402985	302	RH 431764	255	RH 476109	276
RH 402986	306	RH 432648	90	RH 476112	188
RH 404967	61	RH 432654	102	RH 476124	76
RH 408430	26	RH 432661	102	RH 476133	101
RH 408496	187	RH 432665	103	RH 476140	78
RH 411319	172	RH 433388	158	RH 476141	229
RH 411320	245	RH 433390?	279	RH 480678	59
RH 411321	245	RH 435398	65	RH 480679	244
RH 411322	158	RH 435403	111	RH 480680	101
RH 412427	173	RH 437367	100	RH 480686	144
RH 412431	61	RH 441424	186	RH 480690	122
RH 414300	87	RH 441427	275	RH 480692	93
RH 414303	129	RH 441934	77	RH 480695	88
RH 416210	74	RH 441936	290	RH 480696	201
RH 416214	62	RH 441944	103	RH 480697	54
RH 416568	94	RH 441945	101	RH 480698	61
RH 417889	131	RH 441948	188	RH 481552	278
RH 417890	251	RH 441951	27	RH 487963	61
RH 417892	225	RH 443642	39	RH 496038	173
RH 418596	175	RH 444193	108	RH 496039	173
RH 418600	79	RH 444200	100	RH 497542	192
RH 418764	159	RH 444207	27	RH 497547	150
RH 418770	65	RH 444208	50	RH 497753	152
RH 418792	29	RH 449753	255	RH 497760	50
RH 418793	69	RH 449754	167	RH 499435	185
RH 418803	83	RH 451901	275	RH 504546	92
RH 420042	306	RH 452280	217	RH 504565	94
RH 420137	63	RH 452294	208	RH 506415	101
RH 421415	255	RH 457299	259	RH 506491	192
RH 421418	129	RH 458641	99	RH 512463	103
RH 421419	229	RH 458957	252	RH 512572	84
RH 421432	130	RH 458959	182	RH 512842	154
RH 421433	129	RH 458960	253	RH 513139	248
RH 421435	231	RH 458961	99	RH 518190	51
RH 421436	172	RH 459515	169	RH 518493	265
RH 421439	259	RH 459517	94, 132	RH 518494	72
RH 421697	251	RH 459518	167	RH 525947	176
RH 421700	252	RH 459519	93, 132	RH 544996	235
RH 421702	283	RH 462365	249	RH 544997	172
RH 422567	311	RH 463150	98	RH 544998	185
RH 422569	251	RH 463153	31	RH 7002/0467/2	256
RH 422573	154	RH 463154	130	RH 7002/0467/6	256
RH 423657	187	RH 466591	257	RH 7002/0567/6	59
RH 423658	259	RH 466594	103	RH 7002/0600-1	299
RH 423661	111	RH 466616	108	RH 7002/0767/6	101
RH 424839	163	RH 466617	94	RH 7002/0867/3	101

Entry	Page	Entry	Page	Entry	Page
RH 7002/0967/6	50	RM 9925	270	Roanoke	42
RH 7002/1067/2	185	RM 10051	270	Robel 21 11 RK1	132
RH 7002-0967-5	95	RM 10067	270	Robel 21.12 RN5	126
RH [0-4-0D]	254	RM 10069	270	Robel 21.12RK3	232
RH [213]	306	RM 10070	270	Robel 54.12-107 AD183	220
RH [LM 39]	26	RM 10248	270	Robel 54.12-107 AD184	220
RH [M.W.11026]	213	RM 10258	270	Robel 54.12-56-AA169	126
RH [Y.W.A. L2]	225	RM 10260	270	Robel 54.12-56-RT1	126
RHDR [PW2]	110	RM 10422	271	Robel 54.12-56-RW3	126
Rhiw [JACK]	279	RM 10593	271	Robel 54-12-(65?)-RR1	126
Rhiwbach [2w-2PM]	179	RM 10782	271	Robel 56.27-10-AG32	329
Richard [13006]	300	RM 10809	271	Robel 56.27-10-AG35	206
Riordan T6664	274	RM 10894	271	Robel 56.27-10-AG36	238
RM 1795	270	RM 10900	271	Robel 56.27-10-AG37	238
RM 2910	270	RM 10952	271	Robel 56.27-10-AG38	64, 238
RM 3250	270	RM 11097	271	Robel 56.27-10-AG39	329
RM 3906	270	RM 11204	271	Robel 56.27-10-AG40	329
RM 3981	270	RM 11206	271	Robel 56.27-3.AF33	329
RM 4114	270	RM 11338	194	Robel [4wDM]	224
RM 4810	270	RM 11345	271	Robel [CE 9604]	126
RM 4904	270	RM 11451	271	Rosewall [1]	168
RM 4989	270	RM 11457	271	RP 51168	278
RM 5013	270	RM 11459	271	RP 52124	130
RM 5041	270	RM 11460	271	RPSI Whitehead	299
RM 5074	270	RM 11809	271	RR 10187	80
RM 6560	270	RM 11836	271	RR 10188	238
RM 7050	270	RM 12124	271	RR 10194	63
RM 7182	270	RM 12126	271	RR 10197	80
RM 7493	270	RM 12432	272	RR 10198	287
RM 7498	270	RM 12438	271	RR 10199	179
RM 8071	270	RM 12625	271	RR 10201	172
RM 8073	270	RM 12626	271	RR 10202	34
RM 8111	102	RM 12634	271	RR 10204	206
RM 8118	270	RM 12649	271	RR 10207	172
RM 8253	123	RM 12713	271	RR 10212	119
RM 8415	270	RM 12869	271	RR 10213	55
RM 8423	270	RM 13300	271	RR 10214	221
RM 8564	274	RM 13301	271	RR 10215	221
RM 8583	270	RM 13313	271	RR 10217	246
RM 8633	270	RM 13318	271	RR 10218	179
RM 8638	270	RM 13626	271	RR 10220	221
RM 8653	270	RM 13629	271	RR 10221	179
RM 8663	270	RM 13911	271	RR 10222	283
RM 8862	270	RM 13913	271	RR 10226	116
RM 8992	270	RM 13929	271	RR 10229	73
RM 9391	270	RM 14753	271	RR 10232	80
RM 9392	270	RM 14766	271	RR 10235	263
RM 9514	204	RM 14769	271	RR 10236	125
RM 9536	270	RM 14789	271	RR 10238	125
RM 9537	270	RM 14806	271	RR 10239	221
RM 9795	270	RM 15152	271	RR 10240	144
RM 9811	270	RM 15773	271	RR 10241	94
RM 9812	270	RM 15778	271	RR 10242	209
RM 9852	270	RM 15784	271	RR 10247	247
RM 9853	270	RMS LWO2108	286	RR 10248	247
RM 9869	270	RMS LWO2918	119	RR 10249	247

RR 10251	206	RSHN 7170	283	RSHN 7942	53
RR 10252	70	RSHN 7214	57	RSHN 7944	79
RR 10253	74	RSHN 7284	113	RSHN 7963	165
RR 10255	212	RSHN 7289	212	RSHN 7964	165
RR 10256	119	RSHN 7298	79	RSHN 7980	75
RR 10262	126, 238	RSHN 7386	141	RSHN 8046	53
RR 10266	247	RSHN 7409	79	RSHD 8052	259
RR 10267	248	RSHN 7412	80	RSHD 8063	240
RR 10268	248	RSHN 7416	209	RSHD 8064	205
RR 10269	184	RSHD 7430	79	RSHD 8097	84
RR 10271	34	RSHN 7485	115	RSHD 8098	155
RR 10272	154	RSHN 7493	123	RSHD 8102	60
RR 10273	118	RSHN 7537	119	RSHD 8136	34
RR 10275	51	RSHN 7544	171	RSHD 8148	212
RR 10276	263	RSHN 7597	60	RSHD 8157	31
RR 10277	125	RSHN 7609	88	RSHD 8161	54
RR 10279	55	RSHN 7617	31	RSHN 8169	120
RR 10280	73, 238	RSHN 7661	224	RSHD 8183	54
RR 10282	116	RSHN 7667	167	RSHD 8184	85
RR 10283	116	RSHN 7668	112	RSHD 8193	186
RR 10284	52	RSHN 7671	83	RSHD 8196	61
RR 10286	219, 238	RSHN 7673	112	RSHN 8201	79
RR 10289	219, 238	RSHN 7680	128	RSHD 8214	124
RS 1	76	RSHN 7681	215	RSHD 8215	205
RS 19	143	RSHN 7683	163	RSHD 8217	212
RS 24	109	RSHN 7684	187	RSHD 8218	205
RS 150	215	RSHN 7697	79	RSHD 8221	206
RS 2309	273	RSHN 7705	287	RSHD 8224	124
RS 2613	296	RSHN 7746	79	RSHD 8227	154
RS 2730	79	RSHN 7760	79	RSHD 8230	205
RS 2738	296	RSHN 7761	57	RSHD 8239	206
RS 3367	152	RSHN 7763	79	RSHD 8241	206
RS 3377	228	RSHN 7765	80	RSHD 8245	147
RS 3894	181	RSHN 7796	79	RSHD 8246	206
RS 3895	57	RSHN 7800	79	RSHD 8250	54
RS 4089	226	RSHN 7803	194	RSHD 8254	54
RS A4	163	RSHN 7816	112	RSHD 8255	122
RSHD 6947	76	RSHN 7817	57	RSHD 8259	55
RSHN 6980	79	RSHN 7818	154	RSHD 8263	55
RSHN 7006	187	RSHN 7845	230	RSHD 8265	55
RSHN 7007	79	RSHN 7846	112	RSHD 8268	68
RSHN 7031	84	RSHN 7849	237	RSHD 8276	68
RSHD 7035	79	RSHN 7859	99	RSHD 8277	55
RSHN 7042	112	RSHN 7860	90	RSHD 8279	55
RSHN 7058	283	RSHN 7864	120	RSHD 8289	288
RSHN 7063	226	RSHN 7865	68	RSHD 8321	186
RSHN 7069	240	RSHN 7900	220	RSHD 8322	34
RSHN 7070	152	RSHN 7901	79	RSH/WB 8343	46
RSHN 7078	79	RSHD/WB 7910	285	RSHD 8344	186
RSHN 7086	106	RSHD 7913	181	RSHD 8364	119
RSHN 7097	260	RSHD 7914	60	RSHD 8365	246
RSHN 7098	79	RSHN 7922	55	RSHD 8366	188
RSHN 7136	60	RSHN 7924	112	RSHD 8368	154
RSHN 7139	290	RSHN 7925	76	RSHD 8383	159
RSHN 7151	88	RSHN 7935	123	RSHD 8419	122
RSHN 7169	224	RSHN 7936	149	RSM [WYLAM DILLY]	256

RT&Co(C) [4wPM]	180	S 10037	113, 238	Schöma 5131	233
Ruhrthaler 1348	306	S 10040	33	Schöma 5132	233
Ruhrthaler 3909	191	S 10048	184, 220	Schöma 5220	233
Ruhrthaler 3920	86	S 10070	238, 264	Schöma 5221	234
RVR [PX 205]	201	S 10072	144	Schöma 5239	204
RWH 2009	79	S 10077	80	Schöma 5240	163
		S 10083	290	Schöma 5262	105
S		S 10087	51	Schöma 5263	105
		S 10089	105	Schöma 5264	105
S 6155	174	S 10107	51	Schöma 5266	105
S 6185	174	S 10108	213	Schöma 5268	105
S 6515	31	S 10111	44	Schöma 5269	105
S 6807	235	S 10118	236	Schöma 5366	105
S 6909	325	S 10119	206	Schöma 5367	105
S 7109	180	S 10127	132	Schöma 5401	105
S 7232	224	S 10128	119	Schöma 5402	105
S 7492	87	S 10137	206	Schöma 5403	137
S 7701	35	S 10140	164	Schöma 5404	137
S 8024	115	S 10143	88	Schöma 5405	137
S 8837	242	S 10144	220	Schöma 5406	137
S 9365	159	S 10147	218	Schöma 5407	137
S 9366	31	S 10150	210	Schöma 5408	137
S 9369	159	S 10151	184	Schöma 5409	137
S 9370	57	S 10156	52	Schöma 5410	137
S 9373	115	S 10157	144	Schöma 5411	137
S 9374	181	S 10159	160	Schöma 5412	137
S 9376	172	S 10161	221	Schöma 5413	137
S 9387	87	S 10164	238	Schöma 5414	137
S 9390	186	S 10165	179	Schöma 5415	137
S 9401	53,176	S 10166	129	Schöma 5416	137
S 9418	31	S 10175	181	Schöma 5464	105
S 9535	187	S 10177	238, 264	Schöma 5465	105
S 9536	233	S 10180	172	Schöma 5571	183
S 9537	31	S 10186	51	Schöma 5572	183
S 9559	79	S&H 7501	218	Schöma 5573	183
S 9561	259	S&H 7502	85	Schöma 5574	183
S 9578	34	S&H 7512	126	Schöma 5575	183
S 9584	243	Sabero [LA HERRERA]	198	Schöma 5576	183
S 9596	235	Sanline [2w-2PMR]	301	Schöma 5601	293
S 9597	188	Sara [TINY]	68	Schoma 5602	293
S 9599	235	Saxby 1943	198	Schöma 5603	293
S 9622	279	Scarrott [DRAKE]	65	Schöma 5610	131
S 9627	259	Schalke 10-310-0054	124	Schöma 5611	131
S 9628	256	Schalke 10-310-0055	124	Schöma 5694	133
S 9629	226	Schalke 10-310-8070	124	Schöma 5695	133
S 9631	259	Schichau 4216	152	Schöma 5696	133
S 9632	185	Schöma 1676	197	Schöma 5697	133
S 10003	77	Schöma 1727	294	Schöma 5698	133
S 10006	247	Schöma 2086	327	Schöma 5699	133
S 10007	106	Schöma 4017	87	Schöma 5700	133
S 10012	251	Schöma 4978	293	Schöma 5701	133
S 10021	247	Schöma 4979	293	Schöma 5702	133
S 10022	247	Schöma 4980	293	Schöma 5712	132
S 10023	236	Schöma 4992	293	Schöma 5713	132
S 10029	38	Schöma 5129	233	Schöma 5714	132
S 10033	247	Schöma 5130	233	Schw 6728	97

Schw 9124	107	Sdn [4566]	175	Sdn [7029]	211
ScienceMus [NOVELTY]	148	Sdn [4588]	67	Sdn [7200]	31
ScottP	296	Sdn [4612]	39	Sdn [7202]	170
Scul [4wBE]	105	Sdn [4920]	68	Sdn [7229]	146
Scul [6wBE]	132	Sdn [4930]	175	Sdn [7325]	175
Scul 621	305	Sdn [4936]	211	Sdn [7802]	175
SCW [0-4-0DH]	60	Sdn [4953]	211	Sdn [7808]	170
Sdn [7]	279	Sdn [4965]	211	Sdn [7812]	175
Sdn [8]	279	Sdn [4979]	46	Sdn [7819]	214
Sdn [1363]	170	Sdn [4942]	170	Sdn [7820]	181
Sdn [1369]	68	Sdn [5029]	211	Sdn [7821]	186
Sdn [1420]	68	Sdn [5043]	211	Sdn [7822]	268
Sdn [1442]	69	Sdn [5051]	170	Sdn [7827]	67
Sdn [1450]	88	Sdn [5080]	30	Sdn [7828]	181
Sdn [1466]	170	Sdn [5164]	175	Sdn [7903]	89
Sdn [1501]	175	Sdn [5193]	181	Sdn [7927]	170
Sdn [1638]	111	Sdn [5199]	268	Sdn [9400]	215
Sdn [2516]	215	Sdn [5224]	181	Sdn [9600]	212
Sdn [2807]	89	Sdn [5227]	291	Sdn [9629]	289
Sdn [2818]	226	Sdn [5239]	67	Sdn [9642]	89
Sdn [2857]	175	Sdn [5322]	170	Sdn [9681]	88
Sdn [2859]	268	Sdn [5526]	68	Sdn [9682]	169
Sdn [2861]	291	Sdn [5532]	268	Sdn [46512]	260
Sdn [2873]	68	Sdn [5538]	88	Sdn [46521]	121
Sdn [2874]	181	Sdn [5539]	268	Sdn [48431]	239
Sdn [2885]	211	Sdn [5541]	88	Sdn [75014]	67
Sdn [3205]	68	Sdn [5542]	89	Sdn [75027]	199
Sdn [3217]	198	Sdn [5552]	39	Sdn [75029]	228
Sdn [3440]	226	Sdn [5553]	36	Sdn [75069]	175
Sdn [3650]	170	Sdn [5572]	170	Sdn [75078]	239
Sdn [3738]	170	Sdn [5619]	176	Sdn [75079]	95
Sdn [3802]	266	Sdn [5637]	179	Sdn [92203]	90
Sdn [3803]	68	Sdn [5643]	47	Sdn [92207]	71
Sdn [3814]	228	Sdn [5668]	289	Sdn [92212]	96
Sdn [3822]	170	Sdn [5764]	175	Sdn [92214]	147
Sdn [3845]	206	Sdn [5775]	239	Sdn [92219]	57
Sdn [3850]	181	Sdn [5786]	71	Sdn [92220]	215
Sdn [3855]	146	Sdn [5900]	170	Sdn [D 821]	175
Sdn [3862]	158	Sdn [5952]	173	Sdn [D 832]	181
Sdn [4003]	226	Sdn [5967]	158	Sdn [D1010]	181
Sdn [4073]	215	Sdn [5972]	116	Sdn [D1013]	175
Sdn [4079]	170	Sdn [6000]	215	Sdn [D1015]	143
Sdn [4110]	211	Sdn [6023]	170	Sdn [D1023]	226
Sdn [4115]	291	Sdn [6024]	211	Sdn [D2018]	85
Sdn [4121]	211	Sdn [6106]	170	Sdn [D2020]	200
Sdn [4141]	121	Sdn [6412]	181	Sdn [D2022]	215
Sdn [4144]	170	Sdn [6430]	268	Sdn [D2023]	111
Sdn [4150]	175	Sdn [6435]	39	Sdn [D2024]	111
Sdn [4160]	181	Sdn [6619]	228	Sdn [D2027]	60
Sdn [4247]	39	Sdn [6634]	36	Sdn [D2037]	60
Sdn [4248]	215	Sdn [6960]	91	Sdn [D2041]	83
Sdn [4253]	289	Sdn [6984]	89	Sdn [D2117]	48
Sdn [4270]	89	Sdn [6989]	30	Sdn [D2118]	60
Sdn [4277]	67	Sdn [6990]	121	Sdn [D2119]	181
Sdn [4555]	67	Sdn [6998]	170	Sdn [D2120]	32
Sdn [4561]	181	Sdn [7027]	36	Sdn [D2128]	128

Sdn [D2133]	181	ShuttC	218	SLM 2838	275
Sdn [D2134]	257	Siemens 6	243	SLM 2869	275
Sdn [D2138]	58	Siemens 455	78	SLM 2870	275
Sdn [D2139]	60	Siemens 457	163	SLM 3977	55
Sdn [D2141]	290	Siemens 862	79	SMH 101T018	26
Sdn [D2144]	229	SkinnerD [4wPM]	190	SMH 101T020	59
Sdn [D2145]	98	SL 663	28	SMH 101T023	276
Sdn [D2148]	115	SL 1/84	225	SMH 102T016	295
Sdn [D2152]	215	SL 139/1.2.89	198	SMH 103GA078	30
Sdn [D2158]	62	SL 139/2.1.89	198	SMH 104G063	191
Sdn [D2162]	269	SL 15.5.78	118	SMH 40SD515	122
Sdn [D2170]	120	SL 15/2/79	217	SMH 40SD516	191
Sdn [D2178]	283	SL 17/6/79	225	SMH 40SPF522	250
Sdn [D2180]	120	SL 20	279	SMH 40SD529	59
Sdn [D2182]	90	SL 2121	121	SMH 60SD754	224
Sdn [D2184]	83	SL 2151	187	SMH 60SD755	225
Sdn [D2189]	115	SL 2155	303	SMH 60SL741	306
Sdn [D2192]	67	SL 22 [4w-4wDH]	265	SMH 60SL742	321
Sdn [D2196]	116	SL 22 [2-8-0PH]	313	SMH 60SL743	306
Sdn [D2197]	200	SL 23	66	SMH 60SL744	313
Sdn [D2199]	60, 237	SL 275/1.5.90	284	SMH 60SL745	306
Sdn [D2371]	100	SL 275/2.5.90	284	SMH 60SL746	311
Sdn [D2381]	116	SL 321.11.90	80	SMH 60SL747	302
Sdn [D9500]	61	SL 343.2.91	151	SMH 60SL748	306
Sdn [D9502]	61	SL 365.3.91	217	SMH 60SL749	306
Sdn [D9504]	34, 118	SL 495.10.92	130	SMH 60SL751	326
Sdn [D9513]	224	SL 546.4.93	168	SmithEL [BLACK S-]	118
Sdn [D9516]	34	SL 606.3.94	198	SmithN [CLIVE]	162
Sdn [D9518]	34	SL 70.5.87	65	SmithP	289
Sdn [D9520]	34	SL 7217	118	SMR [OUTHWAITE]	229
Sdn [D9521]	288	SL 7218	284	SouthCrofty [60]	42
Sdn [D9523]	34	SL 7219	114	SouthCrofty [66]	42
Sdn [D9524]	235	SL 73 35	313	Spence [13L]	273
Sdn [D9525]	61	SL 7322	284	Spence [15]	305
Sdn [D9526]	181	SL 7434	40	Spence [17]	302
Sdn [D9529]	111	SL 75 356	214	Spence [20]	296
Sdn [D9531]	147	SL 75.3.87	95	Spence [21]	303
Sdn [D9537]	130	SL 76.3.88	123	Spence 29L	204
Sdn [D9539]	115	SL 80.10.89	308	Spence [0-4-0T]	307
Sdn [D9551]	257	SL R8	256	SPL No.1	142
Sdn [D9553]	90	SL R9	284	Spondon [4wBE]	62
Sdn [D9555]	89	SL RG.11.86	96	SRS [T597 OKK]	161
Sdn [51017]	259	SL RG11-86	123	SS 1448	47
Sdn [51043]	259	SL SE4 [A]	86	SS 1585	116
Sdn [NORTH STAR]	215	SL SE4 [B]	86	SS 2838	295
Sdn [W20W]	111	SL [ANNE]	151	SS 3518	169
Sdn [W22W]	171	SL [Bo-BoDH]	179	SS 4022	254
Sdn Col [NORTH STAR]	216	SL [BUSY BASIL]	108	SS 4150	207
SDSI(S) [0-4-0ST]	78	SL [DOUGAL]	216	SS 4492	77
SET [4wBE]	139	SL [SHELAGH]	48	StanhopeT [4wDM]	229
SET 1007/1	300	SL/UK LOCO		StanhopeT [4wVBT]	128
SGLR [2]	62	[2-2w etc BER]	152	Statfold [2-2wPMR]	169
Sharon [HILLARY]	56	SLM 924	275	Steamtown [3041]	29
ShepherdFG [0-4-0BE]	46	SLM 925	275	StewartWP [4472]	153
ShepherdFG [No.1]	46	SLM 988	275	Stoke [BEL 2]	227
SherwoodForest 4wPM	168	SLM 989	275	Stoke [No.2]	76

Unimog 004971	330	VF 4674	226	VF D 754	333
Unimog 008983	269	VF 5200	240	VF D 762	116
Unimog 025642	184	VF 5257	200	VF D 763	147
Unimog 027869	155	VF 5258	209	VF D 770	169
Unimog 029065	113	VF 5261	85	VF D 810	120
Unimog 029450	329	VF 5262	47	VF E 277	55
Unimog 072555	119	VF 5265	236	VIW 4432	198
Unimog 083216	33	VF 5272	283	VIW 4433	111
Unimog 092692	81	VF 5309	269	VIW 4441	111
Unimog 099195	145	VF D 77	201	VIW 4446	239
Unimog 101335	139	VF D 78	85	VL [HAMPTON]	142
Unimog 107518	104	VF D 98	64	VL [SIDDONS]	139
Unimog 114455	157	VF D 100	325	Volkswagen/Harsco	
Unimog 126262	139	VF D 139	265	[YM02 DJY]	234
Unimog 126899	161	VF D 140	201	Vollert [DAISY]	126
Unimog 140729	161	VF D 145	224	Vollert [HIGH PEAK]	53
Unimog 152685	330	VF D 208	228	Volvo [12723]	301
Unimog 160572	45	VF D 212	181	Volvo [13124]	301
Unimog 164948	309	VF D 226	240	Van der Heiden	
Unimog 166200	210	VF D 278	60	[MOUNTAINEER]	128
Unimog 166990	157	VF D 293	84		
Unimog 172544	113	VF D 294	205	**W**	
Unimog 184641	157	VF D 295	173		
Unimog 185674	168	VF D 297	156	WalkerG [14]	118
Unimog 187252	168	VF D 312	221, 237	WalkerG [RED DRAGON]	118
Unimog 195421	126	VF D 314	207	Waterfield [No.3]	92
Unimog 197493	104	VF D 319	221, 237	WB 1278	274
Unimog 197505	104	VF D 336	206, 237	WB 1425	109
Unimog 199146	207	VF D 340	237	WB 1445	274
Unimog 199635	164	VF D 350	77	WB 1484	326
Unimog 200083	161	VF D 375	77	WB 1491	192
Unimog 200405	104	VF D 376	58, 62	WB 1568	190
Unimog 201419	301	VF D 382	167	WB 1760	40
Unimog 205667	300	VF D 391	205	WB 1781	203
Unimog 207425	184	VF D 395	228	WB 1889	192
Unimog [NK54SDY]	161	VF D 429	57	WB 2029	197
Unimog [NK54SDZ]	161	VF D 430	54	WB 2043	156
		VF D 482	206	WB 2067	203
		VF D 488	54	WB 2087	122
V		VF D 495	167	WB 2088	107
VE 7667	257	VF D 557	56	WB 2090	202
VER [3]	201	VF D 559	227	WB 2091	203
VER [4]	201	VF D 566	56	WB 2133	97
VER [6]	201	VF D 572	56	WB 2135	50
VER [7]	201	VF D 573	61	WB 2192	197
VER [8]	201	VF D 576	56	WB 2193	112
VER [9]	201	VF D 579	228	WB 2216	110
VER[10]	201	VF D 582	77	WB 2221	187
VF 2759	148	VF D 588	167	WB 2228	278
VF 3272	60	VF D 604	259	WB 2287	229
VF 3736	239	VF D 611	155	WB 2370	123
VF 3954	175	VF D 616	68	WB 2450	325
VF 3977	121	VF D 631	147	WB 2457	197
VF 4195	111	VF D 641	147	WB 2460	197
VF 4570	260	VF D 751	252	WB 2469	31
VF 4653	175	VF D 753	90	WB 2472	110

WB 2473	170	WB 3213	154	Windhoff 2585	336		
WB 2511	110	Wbton 2	192	Windhoff 2586	336		
WB 2542	84	WCI [LINDSEY]	116	Windhoff 2587	337		
WB 2545	198	WeaverP [0-4-0VBT]	216	Windhoff 2588	337		
WB 2565	159	Werk 868	104	Windhoff 2589	337		
WB 2572	39	WHR [LADY MADCAP]	277	Windhoff 2590	337		
WB 2613	85	WilliamsWJ	273	Windhoff 2591	337		
WB 2623	187	WilsonAJ [THE WASP]	243	Windhoff 2592	337		
WB 2624	110	WiltonICI [0-4-0VBT]	77	Windhoff 2625	337		
WB 2627	229	WiltonICI [RH 476140]	78	Windhoff 2626	337		
WB 2648	185	WiltonICI[OUTHWAITE]	229	Windhoff 2627	337		
WB 2654	159	Windhoff 2492	336	Windhoff 2628	337		
WB 2655	67	Windhoff 2494	336	Winson 9	280		
WB 2668	172	Windhoff 2506	336	Winson 12	153		
WB 2670	119	Windhoff 2507	336	Winson 14	153		
WB 2680	194	Windhoff 2508	336	Winson 17	265		
WB 2682	47	Windhoff 2509	336	Winson 20	153		
WB 2702	242	Windhoff 2510	336	Winson/BVR 16	153		
WB 2746	60	Windhoff 2511	336	WkB [10]	296		
WB 2749	252	Windhoff 2512	336	WkB/Dundalk [12]	294		
WB 2758	284	Windhoff 2513	336	WkB/Dundalk [18]	299		
WB 2759	252	Windhoff 2516	336	WkB/Dundalk [19]	327		
WB 2766	39	Windhoff 2517	336	WkB/Dundalk [20]	327		
WB 2777	259	Windhoff 2518	336	WkB/ELC [2509]	295		
WB 2779	79	Windhoff 2519	336	Wkm 417	229		
WB 2819	229	Windhoff 2520	336	Wkm 497	193		
WB 2820	189	Windhoff 2521	336	Wkm 590	240		
WB 2842	187	Windhoff 2522	336	Wkm 626	257		
WB 2895	198	Windhoff 2524	336	Wkm 673	111		
WB 2898	76	Windhoff 2526	336	Wkm 730	46		
WB 2962	39	Windhoff 2528	336	Wkm 899	77		
WB 2994	163	Windhoff 2530	336	Wkm 946	69		
WB 2996	47	Windhoff 2532	336	Wkm 1288	260		
WB 3019	176	Windhoff 2534	336	Wkm 1305	229		
WB 3023	277	Windhoff 2536	336	Wkm 1308	155		
WB 3024	280	Windhoff 2538	336	Wkm 1519	33		
WB 3050	277	Windhoff 2540	336	Wkm 1521	155		
WB 3058	39	Windhoff 2542	336	Wkm 1522	155		
WB 3059	187	Windhoff 2544	336	Wkm 1543	267		
WB 3061	85	Windhoff 2546	336	Wkm 1548	169		
WB 3119	185	Windhoff 2548	336	Wkm 1580	176		
WB 3121	39	Windhoff 2550	336	Wkm 1946	83		
WB 3137	281	Windhoff 2552	336	Wkm 1949	194		
WB 3138	281	Windhoff 2554	336	Wkm 2449	272		
WB 3139	281	Windhoff 2556	336	Wkm 2522	27		
WB 3140	281	Windhoff 2558	336	Wkm 2555	104		
WB 3141	281	Windhoff 2560	336	Wkm 2558	29		
WB 3142	281	Windhoff 2562	336	Wkm 2559	27		
WB 3143	281	Windhoff 2564	336	Wkm 2904	280		
WB 3150	188	Windhoff 2566	336	Wkm 2981	196		
WB 3151	128	Windhoff 2579	336	Wkm 3030	258		
WB 3207	188	Windhoff 2580	336	Wkm 3031	197		
WB 3208	207	Windhoff 2581	336	Wkm 3032	196		
WB 3209	119	Windhoff 2582	336	Wkm 3033	27		
WB 3210	246	Windhoff 2583	336	Wkm 3034	100		
WB 3211	188	Windhoff 2584	336	Wkm 3151	63		

Wkm		Wkm		Wkm	
Wkm 3152	265	Wkm 6885	177	Wkm 7612	79
Wkm 3158	265	Wkm 6887	272	Wkm 7623	229
Wkm 3161	204	Wkm 6892	171	Wkm 7680	311
Wkm 3164	225	Wkm 6896	84	Wkm 7681	307
Wkm 3170	33	Wkm 6901	61	Wkm 7690	176
Wkm 3174	178	Wkm 6934	59	Wkm 7824	96
Wkm 3175	103	Wkm 6936	200	Wkm 8025	243
Wkm 3235	258	Wkm 6939	325	Wkm 8085	176
Wkm 3236	63	Wkm 6941	100	Wkm 8086	325
Wkm 3238	190	Wkm 6944	199	Wkm 8087	194
Wkm 3245	161	Wkm 6947	290	Wkm 8089	215
Wkm 3282	25	Wkm 6948	171	Wkm 8195	110
Wkm 3284	63	Wkm 6952	202	Wkm 8196	145, 148
Wkm 3287	197	Wkm 6963	31	Wkm 8197	31
Wkm 3361	285	Wkm 6965	111	Wkm 8198	69
Wkm 3366	67	Wkm 6967	200	Wkm 8263	31
Wkm 3403	204	Wkm 7031	238	Wkm 8267	180
Wkm 3414	33	Wkm 7073	230	Wkm 8272	59
Wkm 3431	103	Wkm 7090	169	Wkm 8501	257
Wkm 3578	103	Wkm 7091	325	Wkm 8502	257
Wkm 4091	213	Wkm 7094	325	Wkm 8505	215
Wkm 4092	127	Wkm 7129	307	Wkm 8774	170
Wkm 4131	191	Wkm 7132	311	Wkm 8916	295
Wkm 4139	194	Wkm 7139	188	Wkm 8917	300
Wkm 4146	69	Wkm 7346	269	Wkm 8918	315
Wkm 4149	69	Wkm 7438	111	Wkm 8919	295
Wkm 4153	171	Wkm 7441	295	Wkm 8920	315
Wkm 4154	67	Wkm 7442	327	Wkm 9359	325
Wkm 4165	179	Wkm 7445	200	Wkm 9523	33
Wkm 4166	90	Wkm 7504	209	Wkm 9673	307
Wkm 4168	100	Wkm 7505	209	Wkm 9688	61
Wkm 4171	98	Wkm 7506	171	Wkm 10179	251
Wkm 4254	89	Wkm 7508	171	Wkm 10180	251
Wkm 4808	295	Wkm 7509	199	Wkm 10343	81
Wkm 4816	269	Wkm 7513	171	Wkm 10482	259
Wkm 4985	162	Wkm 7514	130	Wkm 10645	236
Wkm 4992	67	Wkm 7515	96	Wkm 10646	81
Wkm 5002	67	Wkm 7516	90	Wkm 10647	337
Wkm 5008	257	Wkm 7517	99	Wkm 10648	162
Wkm 5009	64	Wkm 7519	169	Wkm 10705	199
Wkm 5019	176	Wkm 7564	243	Wkm 10706	81
Wkm 5864	189	Wkm 7565	46	Wkm 10707	96
Wkm 5763	327	Wkm 7574	145	Wkm 10708	199
Wkm 6049	259	Wkm 7576	161	Wkm 10731	230
Wkm 6603	111	Wkm 7577	176	Wkm 10839	96
Wkm 6607	208	Wkm 7580	89	Wkm 10841	64, 238
Wkm 6643	173	Wkm 7581	199, 200	Wkm 10842	64, 238
Wkm 6645	103	Wkm 7586	161	Wkm 10843	81
Wkm 6646	69	Wkm 7591	222	Wkm 10943	288
Wkm 6648	88	Wkm 7594	79	Wkm 10956	326
Wkm 6652	69	Wkm 7595	75	Wkm 11547	329
Wkm 6655	325	Wkm 7597	49	Wkm 11548	329
Wkm 6857	81	Wkm 7598	89	Wkm 11549	329
Wkm 6872	111	Wkm 7603	222	Wkm 11550	329
Wkm 6878	91	Wkm 7610	224	Wkm 11551	329
Wkm 6884	100	Wkm 7611	76	Wkm 11552	329

Wkm 11618	329	WR 5034?	204	WR S7950	176
Wkm 11621	329	WR 5035	200	WR 7964	121
Wkm 11622	132	WR 5311	284	WR 7967	52
Wkm 11677	104	WR 5655	176	WR T8033	204
Wkm 11678	104	WR 5665	67	WR 8079	78
Wkm 11679	104	WR 5931?	47	WR 10102	133
Wkm 11680	104	WR 6092	189	WR 10104	133
Wkm 11681	104	WR 6133	43	WR 10105	133
Wkm 11682	245	WR 6218	45	WR 10106	133
Wkm 11683	245	WR 6297	43	WR 10114	265
Wkm 11684	104	WR 6298	67	WR 10142	102
Wkm 11685	104	WR 6502	133	WR 525801	248
Wkm 11686	161	WR 6503	133	WR 544901	102
Wkm 11687	161	WR 6504	133	WR 546001	102
Wkm 11688	161	WR 6505	133	WR 546601	102
Wkm 11689	161	WR 6593	43	WR 556001	248
Wkm 11717	69	WR 6595	43	WR 556801	326
Wkm [2-2wPMR]	64	WR C6694	45	WR L 800	102
Wkm [2w-2PMR]	200	WR C6710	43	WR L 801	102
Wkm [2w-2PMR]	199	WR C6716	191	WR L1009	92
Wkm [2w-2PMR]	229	WR C6717	191	WR L1021	41
Wkm [2w-2PMR]	240	WR D6754	43	WR [1300]	65
Wkm [2w-2PMR]	337	WR C6765	50, 274	WR [1514]	27
Wkm [2w-2PMR]	337	WR C6766	50, 274	WR [19]	59
Wkm [68/043]	337	WR 6769	67	WR [2]	50
Wkm [900312]	111	WR C6770	67	WR [3]	74
Wkm [NVR 1612]	34	WR D6800	67	WR [5]	48
WkmR 11730	184	WR E6807	43	WR [7]	50
WMD 1265	155	WR D6886	64	WR [8] Dsm	67
WMD 1267	240	WR D6905	93	WR [LLECHWEDD]	50
WMD 1268	85	WR D6912	192	WR [DONKEY]	304
WMD 1269	240	WR K7070	191	WR [1580]	102
Wolverton [65451]	148	WR F7117	102	WR [PV 7]	45
Woodings A466	283	WR G7124	67	WR [0-4-0BE]	42
Woolwich [31874]	95	WR G7125	248	WR [0-4-0BE]	45
WR 583	254	WR G7174	38	WR [0-4-0BE]	64
WR 744	264	WR G7179	272	WR [0-4-0BE]	74
WR 773	264	WR H7197	67	WR [0-4-0BE]	76
WR 887	195	WR M7534	200	WR [0-4-0BE]	76
WR 892	188	WR M7535	200	WR [0-4-0BE]	80
WR 898	267	WR M7544	101	WR [0-4-0BE]	80
WR 899	284	WR M7548	193	WR [0-4-0BE]	162
WR 918	263	WR M7550	132	WR [4wBE]	40
WR 1080?	267	WR M7556	265	WR [4wBE]	50
WR 1298	41	WR N7605	132	WR [4wBE]	274
WR 1393	97	WR N7606	132	WR [4wBE]	274
WR 1614?	255	WR N7607	132	WR [4wBE]	274
WR 2489	29	WR N7608	230	WR [4wBE]	274
WR 3492	60	WR 7617	133	WSR [9351]	181
WR 3557	35	WR N7620	133		
WR 3805	258	WR N7621	133		
WR 3867?	272	WR P7624?	47	**Y**	
WR 4149?	46	WR N7639	101	YE 2294	110
WR 4998	204	WR 7654	218	YE 2295	110
WR 5031	204	WR N7661	29	YE 2474	224
WR 5033	200	WR Q7808	263	YE 2480	61

YE 2481	236	YE 2906	232	**9E**		
YE 2498	31	YE 2908	125			
YE 2521	54	YE 2909	124	9E [30053]	71	
YE 2594	232	YE 2935	231	9E [30096]	198	
YE 2628	44	YE 2938	124	9E [30102]	152	
YE 2630	269	YE 2940	61	9E [30120]	39	
YE 2635	231	YE 2943	125	9E [30245]	226	
YE 2641	178	YE 2944	231	9E [No.563]	76	
YE 2654	34	YE 2945	125	9E [W24]	103	
YE 2661	128	YE 2952	49			
YE 2670	34	YEC L105	44			
YE 2672	186	YEC L106	286			
YE 2675	173	YEC L112	222			
YE 2676	36	YEC L116	70			
YE 2677	115	YEC L117	44			
YE 2679	202	YEC L120	236			
YE 2684	44	YEC L121	209			
YE 2687	177	YEC L122	282			
YE 2690	125	YEC L123	245			
YE 2709	125	YEC L124	213			
YE 2714	231	YEC L125	264			
YE 2718	116	YEC L127	104			
YE 2732	87	YEC L135	260			
YE 2736	232	YEC L142	119			
YE 2740	232	YEC L145	276			
YE 2745	69	YEC L149	104			
YE 2748	186	YEC L168	127			
YE 2750	232	YEC L173	150			
YE 2756	53, 177	YEC L180	219, 238			
YE 2760	90	YEC L186	213			
YE 2768	125	York [3267]	163			
YE 2769	269	York [61928]	334			
YE 2782	269	York [61937]	334			
YE 2788	125	York [62043]	194			
YE 2791	172	York [62287]	129			
YE 2793	125	York [62351]	186			
YE 2798	232	York [62356]	334			
YE 2812	128	York [62364]	89			
YE 2813	61	York [62378]	89			
YE 2817	58	York [62384]	122			
YE 2825	220	York [62385]	290			
YE 2832	220	York(BRE) [62482]	334			
YE 2843	226	York(BRE) [62483]	335			
YE 2849	61	York(BRE) [DB 999600]	334			
YE 2850	120	York(BRE) [DB 999601]	334			
YE 2851	61	York(BRE) [S62482]	336			
YE 2854	269	Young&Co [2-4-0]	227			
YE 2856	209					
YE 2868	188					
YE 2872	172					
YE 2877	124					
YE 2878	231					
YE 2889	231	**Z**				
YE 2890	232					
YE 2895	236	Zephir 1928	119			
YE 2902	125	Zephir 2111	333			
YE 2903	124	Zephir 2136	119			
YE 2904	231					
YE 2905	232					

Andrew Barclay 1927 of 1927 at East Lancashire Light Railway, Bury, Greater Manchester.

Andrew Barclay 2043 of 1937, previously National Coal Board, Scottish Area. Now at East Lothian District Council, Prestongrange Mining Museum, Prestonpans.

Andrew Barclay 2260 of 1949 at National Coal Board, Scottish Area, Cardowan Colliery, Strathclyde. Now at Ayrshire Railway Preservation Group, Dalmellington, East Ayrshire.

Andrew Barclay 401 of 1956 at Lever Bros Port Sunlight Ltd, Port Sunlight, Merseyside. Now at The West Coast Railway Company, Carnforth, Lancashire.

Andrew Barclay 506/1 and AB 506/2 of 1969 at Mobil Oil Co Ltd (now BP Oil Co Ltd),
Coryton Bulk Terminal, Stanford-le-Hope, Essex.

Andrew Barclay 600 of 1976 at B.P. Oil Grangemouth Refinery Ltd, (now INEOS)
Grangemouth Refinery, Falkirk.

Andrew Barclay 649 of 1980 at B. P. Oil Grangemouth Refinery Ltd, (now INEOS) Grangemouth Refinery, Falkirk.

Associated Equipment Co Ltd of 1938 at G.W.R. Preservation Group, Southall, Greater London.

Ashford built 1910, 323 (ex BR 31323), at Bluebell Railway Co Ltd, East Sussex.

Alan Keef/Kierstead of 1979 seen at Telford Development Corporation, Telford and now at the Telford Horsehay Steam Trust, Shropshire.

Alan Keef 6 of 1981 at Richardsons Moss Litter Co Ltd, Solway Moss, Longtown, Cumbria. Now at John Tennent & P Smith, Brecon.

Baguley 3232 of 1947 at L.J. Smith, Battlesbridge, Essex. Now at Groudle Glen Railway Ltd, Isle of Man.

Beyer Peacock 4663 of 1905 at Isle of Man Steam Railway.

Clayton 4365U/69 of 1963, former BR D8568, at Ribblesdale Cement Ltd, Clitheroe, Lancashire. Now at Chinnor & Princes Risborough Railway Association, Chinnor,Oxfordshire.

Clayton B0457 of 1974 at Aberllefenni Slate Quarries, Aberllefenni, Gwynedd. Now preserved in Corris village.

Darlington built 1957 (ex BR D3476) at E.C.C. Ports Ltd Fowey Jetties, Cornwall. Now at Colne Valley Railway Preservation Society Ltd, Castle Hedingham, Essex.

English Electric 1188/ Drewry 2157 of 1941 in the Ministry of Defence, Army Department fleet. Now at Foxfield Light Railway Society, Blythe Bridge, Staffordshire.

F.C. Hibberd 1891 of 1934 at Tarmac Roadstone Holdings Ltd, Wirksworth Limestone Quarries, Derbyshire. Now at Chasewater Railway, Brownhills, Staffordshire.

Built in 1928 by General Electric Co, photographed at Chemical & Insulation Co Ltd, Faverdale, Darlington. Now at Darlington Railway Preservation Society, Hopetown, Darlington, County Durham.

Greenwood & Batley 2508 or 2509 of 1955 at National Smokeless Fuels Ltd, Avenue Carbonisation Plant, Wingerworth, Derbyshire. The chassis of both of these locos survive at Tanfield Railway, Durham.

Greenwood & Batley 420383/1 or 420383/2 at the then British Steel Corporation (now Corus), Dawes Lane Coke Ovens, Scunthorpe, Lincolnshire.

G.E.C. Traction 5473 of 1978 at the then British Steel Corporation (now Corus), Teesside Works.

G.E.C. Traction 5578 of 1980 at Imperial Chemical Industries Ltd, Mond Division, Winnington Works, Northwich, Cheshire. Now at Barrington Cement Works, Cambridgeshire.

Hudswell Clarke 555 of 1900 at Severn Valley Railway Co Ltd, Shropshire.

Hudswell Clarke 680 of 1903 at East Lancashire Light Railway Co Ltd, Bury, Greater Manchester.

Hudswell Clarke 1632 of 1929 at Falmouth Shiprepair Ltd, Falmouth Docks, Cornwall. Now at "Bygones" Victorian Exhibition Street & Railway Museum, Torquay, Devon.

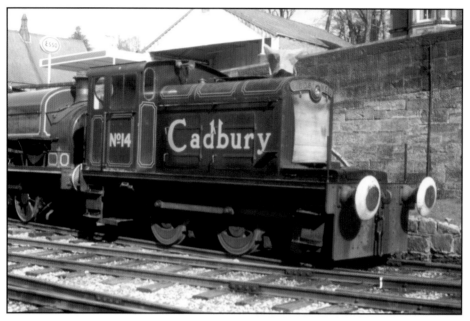

Hudswell Clarke D1012 of 1956 at Llangollen Steam Railway Society, Llangollen, Clwyd. Now at Cadbury World, Bourneville, West Midlands.

Hudswell Clarke D1153 of 1959 at Central Electricity Generating Board, Elland Power Station, West Yorkshire. Now at Mangapps Farm Railway Museum, Burnham-on-Crouch, Essex.

Hudswell Clarke D1387 of 1967 at National Coal Board, Renishaw Park Colliery, Derbyshire. Now at Pontypool & Blaenavon Railway, Blaenavon, South-East Wales.

Hunslet 1430 of 1922 at Llanberis Lake Railway, Gilfachddu, Llanberis, Gwynedd.

Hunslet 2209 of 1941 at Dolwyddelan, Gwynedd. Now preserved in the Glasgow area.

Hunslet 3698 of 1950 at the Lakeside & Haverthwaite Railway Co Ltd, Haverthwaite, Cumbria.

Hunslet 4113 of 1955 at The Festiniog Railway Co Ltd, Porthmadog, Gwynedd.

Hunslet 6013 of 1961 at Central Electricity Generating Board, Uskmouth Power Station, Gwent. Now at Sam Ward, Killamarsh, Derbyshire.

Hunslet 7161 at Ministry of Defence, Royal Ordnance Factory, Chorley, Lancashire. Now owned by Harry Needle Railroad Co Ltd at Long Marston, Warwickshire.

Hunslet 8977 of 1980 at Central Electricity Generating Board, Carrington Power Station, Greater Manchester. Now at Cumbria County Council, Port of Workingtom, Cumbria.

Hunslet 9249 of 1986 at the Snowdon Mountain Railway Ltd, Llanberis, Gwynedd.

Henschel 28035 of 1948 at Llanberis Lake Railway, Gilfachddu, Llanberis, Gwynedd.
Now at South Tynedale Railway Preservation Society, Alston, Cumbria.

Hawthorn Leslie 3597 at Falmouth Shiprepair Ltd, Falmouth Dock, Cornwall. Now at Statfold Barn Railway, Staffordshire.

Head, Wrightson 21 of 1870 at Cleveland County Council, Preston Park & Museum, Eaglescliffe, Cleveland. Now at Stockton-on-Tees Borough Council. Bridge Road Roundabout, Stockton-on-Tees.

JF 4220022 of 1962 at Ministry of Defence, Royal Ordnance Factory, Chorley, Lancashire. Now at The Stratford & Broadway Railway Society, Long Marston, Warwickshire.

Kerr Stuart 4404 of 1927 at Welshpool & Llanfair Light Railway, Llanfair Caereinion, Powys.

Metropolitan-Cammell of 1965, L23 at London Transport Executive, Ealing Common Depot.

Moyse 1364 and 1465 at Shell (UK) Ltd, Teesport Refinery, Grangetown, Cleveland. Now both locos are at Ed Murray & Sons Ltd, Hartlepool, County Durham.

Motor Rail 8695 of 1941 at Bedfordshire County Council, Dovery Down County Primary School, Leighton Buzzard. Now at Leighton Buzzard Narrow Gauge Railway Society, Bedfordshire.

Motor Rail 22045 of 1959 at London Brick Co Ltd, Warboys Works, Cambridgeshire. Now at Moseley Railway Trust, Apedale Country Park, Chesterton, Staffordshire.

Manning Wardle 1601 of 1903 at Kent & East Sussex Railway, Kent. Now at Middleton Railway Trust, Hunslet, Leeds, West Yorkshire.

MW 2025 of 1923 at L.C.P. Fuels Ltd, Pensnett Trading Estate, Shut End, West Midlands.

Nord Nederlandsche Machinefabriek 73511 of 1979 at Carless Capel & Leonard Ltd (now Carless Solvents Ltd), Harwich Refinery, Parkeston, Essex.

Peckett 1376 of 1915 at Lochty Private Railway Co, Anstruther, Fife. Now at Caledonian Railway (Brechin) Ltd, Angus & Dundee City.

Peckett 1631 of 1923 at Kent & East Sussex Railway, Kent.

Peckett 2027 of 1942 at British Nuclear Fuels Ltd, Windscale Factory, Sellafield. Now at The West Coast Railway Company, Carnforth, Lancashire.

Peckett 2100 of British Gas Corporation, Portsmouth Works, Hampshire. Now at G.W.R. Preservation Group Ltd, Southall, Greater London.

Peckett 5014 of Central Elecricity Board, Aberthaw Power Station, South Glamorgan. Now RWE NPower.

An unidentified 3ft 0in gauge Ruston & Hornsby at Caledonian Peat Products Ltd, Gardrum Moss, Sheildhall, near Falkirk. Now at Irish Narrow Gauge Trust, Dromod, Leitrim, ROI.

Ruston & Hornsby 275882 of 1950 at B.P. Chemicals International Ltd, Salt End Refinery, Hull, Humberside. Now at G. Mann, Saughtree Station, Borders, Scotland.

Ruston & Hornsby 381705 of 1956 at Imperial Chemical Industries Ltd, Nobels Roburite Works, Shevington, Greater Manchester. Now at West Lancashire Light Railway, Hesketh Bank, Lancashire .

Ruston & Hornsby 395294 of 1956 at Port of Sunderland Authority, South Docks, Sunderland.

Ruston & Hornsby 414300 of 1957 at Ministry of Defence, Royal Naval Armament Depot, Bedenham, Hampshire. Now at John Golding Heavy Haulage Ltd, Wootton-under-Edge, Gloucestershire.

Ruston & Hornsby 432479 of 1959 at Rowntree-Mackintosh Ltd, York. Was at Wyvernrail plc, Ecclesbourne Valley Railway, Wirksworth, Derbyshire.

Ruston & Hornsby 458957 of 1961 at John Dewar & Sons Ltd, Whiskey Blenders, Inveralmond, Perth. Now at Caledonian Railway (Brechin) Ltd, Angus & Dundee City.

Ruston & Hornsby 463153 of 1961 at British Gas Corporation, Portsmouth Works, Hampshire. Now at Quainton Railway Society Ltd, Quainton Road Station, Buckinghamshire.

Ruston & Hornsby 487963 of 1963 at Alan Keef Ltd, Cote Farm, Cote, Oxfordshire.
Now at Derbyshire Dales Narrow Gauge Railway, Rowsley South, Derbyshire.

Ruston & Hornsby 544996 of 1968 at Central Electricity Generating Board, Hartlepool
Power Station, Seaton Carew, Cleveland. Now at Elsecar Steam Railway, Elsecar,
Barnsley, South Yorkshire.

Built by Robel, Manchster Ship Canal Co Ltd, CE 9604, at Ellesmere Port, Cheshire.
Now at Grant Rail Ltd, Frodingham. Scunthorpe, Lincolnshire.

Rolls Royce 10199 of 1964 at Esso Petroleum Co Ltd, Bowling, near Dumbarton,
Strathclyde. Now at East Somerset Railway Co Ltd, West Cranmore Railway Station,
Shepton Mallet, Somerset.

Rolls Royce 10217 of 1965 at Clyde Cement Co Ltd, Gartsherrie Works, Strathclyde. Now at Caledonian Paper plc, Shewalton, Irvine, North Ayrshire after rebuilding at Hunslet Engine Co, 9371 of 2006.

Rolls Royce 10275 of 1969 at British Steel Corporation, Corby Ironstone Quarries, Gretton Brook Shed, Corby, Northamptonshire. Now at Bombardier, Litchurch Lane, Derby.

Robert Stephenson & Hawthorn 7681 of 1951 at Central Electricity Generating Board, Agecroft power Station, Greater Manchester. Now at Steam, Swindon Heritage Centre, Swindon, Wiltshire.

Robert Stephenson & Hawthorn 7697 of 1953 at Bardon Hill Quarries (Ellis & Everard) Ltd, Bardon Hill Granite Quarry, Leicestershire. Now at Tanfield Railway Preservation Society, Marley Hill, County Durham.

Robert Stephenson & Hawthorn 7817 of 1954 at Central Electricity Generating Board, Castle Donington Power Station, Leicestershire. Now at Midland Railway, Butterley, Derbyshire.

Robert Stephenson & Hawthorn 7900 of 1958 at Vulcan Materials Company (UK) Ltd, Hartlepool Tinplate Works, Hartlepool, Cleveland. Now at A.V. Dawson Ltd, Middlesbrough, North Yorkshire.

Ruhrthaler 1348 of 1934 at The Narrow Gauge Railway Centre of North Wales, Gloddfa Ganol, Gwynedd. Now at Irish Narrow Gauge Trust, Dromod, Leitrim, ROI.

Sentinel 9628 of 1957 at R.B. Tennent Ltd, Whifflet Foundry, Coatbridge. Now at Monklands District Council, Summerlee Heritage Park, Coatbridge Central, North Lanarkshire.

Sentinel 10137 of 1962 at Tees & Hartlepool Port Authority, Grangetown, Cleveland. Now at Harry Needle Railroad Co Ltd, Long Marston, Warwickshire.

Swindon built 1958, ex BR D2024, at Tees & Hartlepool Port Authority, Grangetown, Cleveland. Now at Kent & East Sussex Railway, Kent.

Swindon built 1964, ex BR D9524, at B.P. Refinery (Grangemouth) Ltd, Grangemouth Refinery, Central Scotland. Now at Elsecar Steam Railway, Elsecar, Barnsley, South Yorkshire.

Siemens 455 of 1908 at National Coal Board, Westoe Colliery, County Durham. Now at North of England Open Air Museum, Beamish Hall, County Durham.

Swiss Locomotive & Machinefabrik, 924 of 1895 at Snowdon Mountain Railway Ltd, Llanberis, Gwynedd.

Swiss Locomotive & Machinefabrik 3977/Brown Boverie 4559. Now at Barrow Hill Roundhouse Railway Centre, Barrow Hill, Staveley, Derbyshire.

Stratford built 1924, 69621 at Stour Valley Railway Preservation Society, Chappel & Wakes Colne, Essex. Now at the North Norfolk Railway, Sheringham.

Thomas Hill 278V of 1978 at Blue Circle Industries Ltd, Westbury Cement Works, Wiltshire. Now Lafarge Cement.

Thomas Hill 291V of 1980 at Mobil Oil Co Ltd, Coryton BulkTerminal, Essex. Now B.P. Oil Co Ltd.

Thomas Hill 307V of 1983, Ministry of Defence, Army Department. Now renumbered to 01526.

Thomas Hill 312V of 1984 at Conoco Ltd, Humber Refinery, South Killingholme, Lincolnshire.

W.G. Bagnall 1278 of 1890 rebuilt by Greaves to 0-4-0WE in 1930 at Quarry Tours Ltd, Llechwedd Slate Mine, Blaenau Ffestiniog, Gwynedd.

W.G. Bagnall 2759 of 1944 at Lochty Private Railway Co, Ansthruther, Fife. Now at Caledonian Railway (Brechin) Ltd, Angus & Dundee City.

W.G. Bagnall 3121 of 1957 at Cornish Steam Locomotive Society Ltd, Imperial Kiln, Bugle, near St Austell. Now at Bodmin & Wenford Railway plc, Cornwall.

W.G.Bagnall 3208 of 1961 at Ley's George Fisher (Lincoln) Ltd, North Hykeham,
Lincolnshire. Now at Moveright International, c/o John Watts Farm, Wishaw,
Warwickshire.

Wickham 8197 of 1958 at Quainton Railway Society Ltd, Buckingham Railway Centre,
Quainton Road Station, near Aylesbury, Buckinghamshire.

Built by Wigan Coal & Iron Co in 1887. Now at The West Coast Railway Company, Carnforth, Lancashire.

Wingrove & Rogers 583 of 1927/J.Fowler 16559 of 1925 at Strathclyde Passenger Transport Executive, Govan Depot, Glasgow. Now preserved at Museum of Transport, Kelvin Hall, Glasgow.

An unidentified Wingrove & Rogers at French Kier Construction Ltd, Plant Depot, Setchey, Norfolk before it moved to its current location at Quarry Tours Ltd, Llechwedd Slate Mine, Gwynedd,

Yorkshire 2641 of 1957 at B.P. Oil Ltd, Purfleet Terminal, Essex. Now at Blachford Light Railway, Emborough Quarry, Somerset.

Yorkshire 2895 of 1964 at Pimbrook Ltd, Tutbury, Derbyshire. Now at Elsecar Steem Railway, Elsecar Heritage Workshops, Elsecar, Barnsley, South Yorkshire.

YE 2905 of 1963 at British Steel Corporation (now Corus), Aldwarke Works, Rotherham